MONITORING EARTH'S OCEAN, LAND, AND ATMOSPHERE FROM SPACE—
Sensors, Systems, and Applications

Edited by
Abraham Schnapf
Aerospace Consultant
Aerospace Systems Engineering
Willingboro, New Jersey

Volume 97
PROGRESS IN
ASTRONAUTICS AND AERONAUTICS

Martin Summerfield, Series Editor-in-Chief
Princeton Combustion Research Laboratories, Inc.
Monmouth Junction, New Jersey

Published by the American Institute of Aeronautics and Astronautics, Inc.
1633 Broadway, New York, NY 10019

American Institute of Aeronautics and Astronautics, Inc.
New York, New York

Library of Congress Cataloging in Publication Data
Main entry under title:

Monitoring earth's ocean, land, and atmosphere—sensors, systems,
and applications.

(Progress in astronautics and aeronautics; v. 97)
Includes index.
1. Artificial satellites. 2. Remote sensing—Equipment and supplies.
I. Schnapf, Abraham. II. Series.
TL507.P75   vol. 97   [TL796]   629.1s [551'.028]   85-13509
ISBN 0-915928-98-1

Second Printing

Table of Contents

The Economic Benefits of Operational Environmental Satellites...........216
W.J. Hussey

Earth Radiation Budget Satellite...261
J.A. Dezio and C.A. Jensen

The Upper Atmosphere Research Satellite.....................................293
P.T. Burr and C.A. Reber

**Some Possibilities on an Observing System for the World
Climate Program...305**
V.E. Suomi

Chapter III.   Remote Sensing of the Land Resources................347

Landsat-D and -D′—The Operational Phase of Land Remote Sensing from Space..349

E.W. Mowle

Spaceborne Lidar Sensors: Opportunity and Challenge......................746
D.B. Hogan and A. Rosenberg

The Earth Observing System: A Multidisciplinary System for the Long-Term Acquisition of Earth Science Data from Space...............797
D.R. Broome Jr.

Authors

Earthview—Remote Sensing of the Earth from Space
John H. McElroy
National Oceanic and Atmospheric Administration, Washington, D.C.

**The TIROS Meteorological Satellites—Twenty-five Years:
1960-1985**
Abraham Schnapf
Aerospace Systems Engineering, Willingboro, New Jersey

**The Nimbus Satellite System: Remote Sensing R&D Platform
of the 1970s**
I.S. Haas
General Electric Co., Philadelphia, Pennsylvania
R. Shapiro
NASA Goddard Space Flight Center, Greenbelt, Maryland

**Remote Sensing of the Earth with the Defense Meteorological
Satellite**
Louis Gomberg
RCA Corporation, Princeton, New Jersey
S.M. McElroy
U.S. Air Force System Command, Los Angeles, California

**The Defense Meteorological Satellite Program:
A Review of Its Impact**
Walter D. Meyer
Control Data Corporation, Englewood, Colorado

The Development of the Geosynchronous Weather Satellite System
J.R. Greaves
NASA Headquarters, Washington, D.C.
W.E. Shenk
NASA Goddard Space Flight Center, Greenbelt, Maryland

The GOES-G and -H Spacecraft Design
Louis R. Fermelia
Hughes Aircraft Company, Los Angeles, California

Preface

When the first U.S. satellite was launched in January 1958, there were many skeptics as to the practical value of the space program. On April 1, 1960, in a little over two years, the world's first Earth observation satellite—TIROS—was successfully orbited, demonstrating for the first time the potential of remote sensing from space to provide direct benefits to mankind.

A quarter of a century has passed since the launching of TIROS-I and the initiation of systematic observations of this planet for useful applications from the vantage point of space. Over 135 Earth observation satellites have been launched on this 25th anniversary of TIROS-I.

The impact of remote sensing from space is already apparent in the form of a whole body of successful applications from meteorological, environmental, land, and ocean observation satellites.

Remote sensing programs in the U.S. expanded from research and development weather satellites to operational systems, experimental programs for observing the land, oceans, and the atmosphere. Foreign programs evolved in the Soviet Union, France, Japan, the European Space Agency, West Germany, India, Canada, China, Brazil, and Argentina. Many other countries are contributing hardware and software to the principal space programs. Over 140 countries are participating in the acquisition of meteorological and Landsat data in real time.

Today weather satellite systems are capable of providing global cloud cover images day and night, measurements of the vertical temperature and moisture profiles of the atmosphere, sea surface and land temperatures, cloud top temperatures, rainfall and moisture patterns, wind direction and intensity, solar radiation, the planet's heat balance, mapping the sea ice and snow cover, measurement of the solar energetic particles, as well as mapping ozone and other weather and climate related data. The remote sensing meteorological and environmental satellites are also providing a cost-effective means of collecting data on a global scale from fixed and moving platforms. An international search and rescue program has been implemented to locate downed aircraft and ships in distress. The capability of providing timely and routine remote observations on a global basis has already improved the accuracy of short term as well as longer term weather forecasts that have resulted in the saving of countless lives and millions of dollars in property. The improved and timely forecasts have provided cost benefits to the transportation, construction, maritime, agriculture, and fishing industries. No major storm has gone undetected since the introduction of the TIROS Operational System in 1966.

The data products utilized in weather forecasts are derived from sophisticated digitally processed radiance values and are used in short-range tornado and hurricane predictions, frost warnings, flash flood warnings, spring thaw alerts, and global analysis of conditions critical to transportation, fishing, and the health of crops and forests.

The operational and technology satellites have provided researchers with a vast data bank to better understand the complex weather systems and apply the data along with the conventionally observed data for the improvement in the global numerical weather prediction model. The weather satellite has been an important input to the data set that was generated for the Global Atmospheric Research Program that culminated in 1979 with the Global Weather Experiment, perhaps the largest and most complex international experiment ever conducted by nations of the world.

Land remote sensing from space evolved with the successful launch of Landsat-1 in 1972. The Landsat Program, despite the fact that five satellites have been launched to date, has not reached an operational status, although it is being used on a semi-operational basis. The Government's decision to commercialize Landsat has been the principal reason for its delay in becoming an operational system.

The land observation system has produced a body of experimental results which has clearly established the potential for future operational applications. The Landsat data span a wide range of Earth science disciplines and the results point to great expectations in the future operational systems. An important achievement in the land remote sensing system is the capability of keeping current an inventory of this planet's resources. The Landsat satellite has been able to observe with great precision the Earth's renewable and nonrenewable resources. The multispectral imaging sensors from Landsat have demonstrated the capability of providing scenes from space that can be processed to extract a wide variety of useful information that is beneficial to agriculture for crop classification and forecasting the state of health of crops and trees, forest inventory, urban land use, mapping surface features, data for water management, flood damage assessment, monitoring the coastline and estuaries, rangeland management, and observation of geologic formations to locate and define faults or hint at mineral, oil, and gas fields. As in weather satellites, there is world-wide interest in the potential economic and environmental benefits from land remote sensing. Besides the U.S., the Soviet Union, ESA, West Germany, France, Canada, Japan, and India have active land resources space programs. A number of countries have installed sophisticated Earth stations and data processing systems to receive and process the data from Landsat.

The Ocean Observation Remote Sensing Program has gotten off to a slower start than the atmosphere and land space systems. However, despite the short mission life of Seasat-I, launched in 1978, sufficient data have been derived from this proof-of-concept that space observation of the oceans has the potential of yielding economic benefits as well as a better understanding of oceanographic phenomena. Seasat results demonstrated the ability to derive wind speed and direction from sea surface roughness observations. Additionally, Seasat data produced information for determining ocean swells, currents, eddies, sea slope, ocean geoids, ocean temperature, internal waves, and sea ice extent. These ocean data sets have been useful to the maritime, fishing, and weather forecasters.

A number of future programs in the U.S., the Soviet Union, Japan, ESA, and Canada will provide dedicated satellites for ocean observations on a global scale.

Numerous experimental satellites have been launched with specific mission objectives to observe and to monitor the atmosphere for chemical composition, pollutants, and radiation flux; to measure the topography of the ocean surface and sea state; to provide geophysical and geodetic data; to measure the Earth's magnetic fields; to observe the Earth's day and night thermal imagery; and by laser techniques, to measure the minute movements of the large tectonic plates.

Remote sensing from space has been an important mission for many of the U.S. manned space programs. The space transportation system has provided the means to carry out large, complex Earth observation experiments through very sophisticated instruments, such as the SIR-A and -B shuttle imaging radar, the large-format camera, and the MOMS remote free flyer.

The Space Shuttle will provide the capability of placing the space station and its companion space platforms in orbit to perform complex multidisciplinary experiments that will be capable of making simultaneous observations of the Earth's atmosphere, land, and oceans. With this future broad-based remote sensing program, it is expected that a better understanding of the interactive and dynamic processes that take place between the atmosphere, land, and oceans will lead to greater benefits to all of mankind.

This book has been organized into seven chapters that cover the principal activities of remote sensing of the atmosphere, the land, and the oceans from space. The first chapter by Dr. John McElroy is an extensive introduction to the remote sensing of this planet from space. This comprehensive overview covers the key programs as well as the political and international activities in remote sensing.

The second chapter deals with the remote sensing of the atmosphere from low-Earth orbit and geostationary orbit by meteorological and environmental satellites. It includes papers that describe the development of the TIROS/NOAA and the SMS/GOES satellites all the way from a research to an operational system. A description and the operation of the Defense Meteorological Satellite Program is included in this chapter along with its impact. The technology satellite systems such as Nimbus, ATS, ERBE, and UARS are described in individual papers. This chapter also includes articles that depict processing of the satellite data and the products of the operational systems, as well as the economic benefits of the environmental satellites. Finally, a paper describes the Climate Program and its future requirements.

The third chapter consists of two papers on the Land Remote Sensing Program. The first paper covers the Landsat system and the second summarizes its principal applications.

The fourth chapter deals with the remote sensing of the oceans. Included within are four papers covering the Seasat Program, the Seasat applications for the ocean industries, the forthcoming Geosat mission, and the TOPEX Program.

The fifth chapter includes nine papers on the important international remote sensing programs. There are papers from ESA's Meteosat geostationary meteorological system; the French SPOT land remote sensing program; the West Germany MOMS-1 mission with the Space Shuttle; the ESA ERS-1 experimental ocean remote sensing satellite; Canada's Radarsat; the Japanese GMS geostationary meteorological system; the MOS-1, Japan's marine observation system; studies on the future JERS-1, the Earth remote system for Japan; and finally, a paper from India providing an overview of the remote sensing activities in India's past, present, and future programs.

The sixth chapter includes two papers on the remote sensing activities from the Space Shuttle. One paper discusses the SIR-A and -B shuttle imaging radar system and its results; the other deals with the recent flight of the large-format camera.

The seventh chapter covers some of the future activities in remote sensing. The first paper looks at the future operational weather satellites; the second paper covers some future concepts of sophisticated spaceborne active laser sensors; and the final paper describes the Earth Observing System conceived for the space platform to carry out multidisciplinary and long-term acquisition of Earth science data from space.

I want to extend my gratitude to all the authors for their fine contributions and would like to thank the AIAA editorial staff, especially Mrs. Jeanne Godette for her assistance and effort in pulling this book together. I want to express my appreciation to Dr. M. Summerfield and Dr. B. Edelson for their guidance and suggestions for this book. I especially want to acknowledge Mr. Charles Schmidt, Division Vice President and General Manager, and Mr. A. Manna, Division Vice President, Marketing and Advanced Planning for RCA Astro-Electronics Division, for providing the support and services needed for the logistics support in making this book a reality.

Abraham Schnapf
Volume Editor
June 1985

Chapter I.   Earthview—Remote Sensing of the Earth from Space

Earthview—Remote Sensing of the Earth from Space

John H. McElroy*
National Oceanic and Atmospheric Administration, Washington, D.C.

Abstract

The multidimensional view of the Earth and its immediate environment that is provided by spaceborne sensors,
operating at many wavelengths and directed at many different phenomena, has revolutionized man's understanding of
his planet and the surrounding space environment. This
achievement, carried out largely with automated, unmanned
spacecraft, ranks with the finest contributions made by the
space program. Academic, industrial, and government contributors from many countries have created a new discipline
based on the view from space and have forced a sweeping
revision of the fields of meteorology, hydrology, ocean-
ology, geology, geography, forestry, agriculture, geodynamics, solar-terrestrial interactions, and many others. It
is not feasible to ignore space-derived data in any of
those fields. As with any new discipline, remote sensing
from space has not avoided controversy. In spite of that
controversy, space remote sensing systems continue to
progress and to contribute stunning new insights. Notably,
space remote sensing systems are not only interdisciplinary, but are also becoming one of the most international
of technologies. The world is ringed with satellites from
a number of nations already and many more are to come
before the end of the decade. The remote sensing program,
born in the openness of the U.S. civil space program, is in
the forefront of establishing that space is indeed to be
explored "for the benefit of all mankind." In the years to
come, it is inevitable that new international programs will
emerge that are modeled on the International Geophysical
Year or the Global Weather Experiment, and, whether they
are called the International Geosphere-Biosphere Program or
Global Habitability or another title, they will be based on

This paper is declared a work of the U.S. Government and
therefore is in the public domain.
*Assistant Administrator for Environmental Satellite, Data,
and Information Services.

3

and lead to the further advancement of the world view provided by space remote sensing systems.

I. Introduction

The technologies of remote sensing, high-speed computation and wideband communication have created a new
capability to examine the planet Earth as never before
possible. These advances have made it possible to begin
the study of the Earth as a total entity. The Earth's
space radiation environment, atmosphere, hydrosphere,
lithosphere, biosphere, and their interactions can now be
treated as a total coupled system.

This paper will outline some of the many contributions that have resulted from Earth observation systems,
which are the subject of this book. But an effort will
also be made to incorporate them into an overall framework,
indeed into an "Earthview."

There is a growing awareness that the component parts
of the Earth system cannot be analyzed in isolation from
one another. Further, it is also recognized that man can
and is altering the Earth system on a global scale. NASA's
Global Habitability Program is one response to the need for
expanded understanding of the planet Earth and of the ways
that man may perturb the Earth's environment.[1]

Recently, the Commission on Physical Sciences, Mathematics, and Resources of the National Research Council,
National Academy of Sciences, published a report proposing
an International Geosphere-Biosphere Program (IGBP).[2] The
report states:

"If, however, we could launch a cooperative interdisciplinary program in the earth sciences, on an international scale, we might hope to take a major step toward
revealing the physical, chemical, and biological workings
of the Sun-Earth system and the mysteries of the origins
and survival of life in the biosphere."

This report will probably lead to a formal proposal to the
International Council of Scientific Unions (ICSU) General
Assembly in 1985.

As still a further indication of the strong scientific
interest in a "holistic" effort in understanding the Earth,
the NASA Advisory Council has formed an Earth Systems
Science Committee to assist in the planning of NASA's
research on fundamental questions on the Earth's ecosystem.
All of the above proposals and observations rely upon the
advances mentioned earlier in remote sensing, which provide
the capability to create global synoptic analyses of a wide
variety of parameters.

It is important to place the above physical analyses and experiments into a still larger framework, that of anticipating the conditions, problems, and opportunities that will confront world society in the next century. A thorough scientific groundwork must underlie any substantive projection of the future of the world. One attempt, the so-called "Global 2000" study,[3] was subject to some criticism because of both methodology and its scientific underpinnings, although it should be noted that the authors were among those forthrightly declaring the limitations of the study.[4] The advances in remote sensing technology provide a powerful approach to the strengthening of the scientific basis for long-range prescriptive forecasts and models of events or trends, either desired or undesired, and allow the evaluation of alternative strategies to reach the desired outcome. Certainly, physical, ecological, economic, and sociological models will play an increasingly important role in government policy analysis and aiding in decision making[5] and must, therefore, be on the soundest possible footing.

The first six sections of this paper will address the achievements in a number of discipline areas in the Earth sciences: solar-terrestrial interactions, the dynamic atmosphere, the dynamic oceans and coastal regions, the solid Earth, the biosphere, and the Earth's climate. These sections will be followed by five sections that address the wider issues associated with remote sensing and its inevitably international context, namely: the difficulties in categorizing remote sensing programs, a review of international concerns about remote sensing and its future development, commercial opportunities in remote sensing, remote sensing and the space station, and future directions and opportunities for international cooperation in remote sensing.

There is no doubt that remote sensing is one of the most exciting and controversial fields in the entire space program. It is also true that the assessment of the total Earth environment is one of the most challenging and important tasks of that program and that it is not a task for a single nation or even a few nations, but one requiring and deserving the best talents of the entire globe. One prefatory comment needs to be made: the following discussions largely neglect the numerous and significant contributions of the Soviet Union to Earth observations. The lack of ready availability of programmatic information and observational data has denied wider recognition to many highly skilled Soviet scientists and engineers. It is hoped that future cooperative efforts will eliminate some of the barriers that prevent the easy exchange of information.

II. Solar-Terrestrial Interactions

Not all accounts of advances in spaceborne Earth
observation systems would begin with a section on solar-
terrestrial interactions, yet it is this interaction that
transfers energy at essentially all wavelengths and in many
different forms from the sun to the Earth. Directly and
indirectly, it is this energy that a remote sensing system
detects. Indeed, a report written only 3 years ago said,[6]
"This study deliberately excludes classical meteorology,
a discipline so broad and complex and with such a long
historical independent development of its own that it
has traditionally been treated separately from solar-
terrestrial research. The dividing line between the
effects of solar-energy input to the troposphere and the
rest of the atmosphere, however, is logically hard to
maintain and is in fact becoming blurred. Perhaps some
day both fields will be unified as a single discipline."
The IGBP effort discussed above is one step toward
that unification. Certainly, the connections of solar-
terrestrial events to a variety of human activities are
well known indeed. Geomagnetic storms disrupt cable communication systems, electrical power distribution grids,
and even oil pipelines. Solar events perturb the ionosphere and adversely affect long-distance radio communications. Other solar events pose a danger to astronauts
working outside their spacecraft or in some instances even
inside their spacecraft. It is, therefore, not surprising
that such powerful events are suspected of producing other
effects as well. A connection currently being pondered is
the link between solar variability and weather and climate,
e.g., "Why does the 22-year magnetic cycle of the sun
correlate so well with a pattern of droughts in the United
States?"[2]
The solar-terrestrial research program is one of the
most distinguished in the space sciences. From the first
discovery of the Van Allen belts, to the most recent discoveries by the two Dynamics Explorer satellites, the program has produced unexpected discoveries and new insights
into both the sun and the immediate space environment that
surrounds the Earth. No effort will be made to trace the
early discoveries here, because they are well covered elsewhere, and in a particularly readable way in Newell's outstanding book.[7] Two recent research missions do, however,
deserve mention, as do the more routine measurements
carried out by the civil and military weather satellites.
The Solar Maximum Mission (SMM) was launched on
Feb. 14, 1980. This satellite is involved in two notable

activities, the set of scientific measurements for which it was designed and the first satellite repair mission of the Space Shuttle, for which SMM was also designed, but which no one hoped would be necessary. In addition, the latter activity will be relevant to the space station discussion that comes later in this paper. Among the most important measurements made by this satellite is that using the active cavity radiometer (ACRIM), which provides data on the energy output of the sun. Obviously, even the slightest variations of the solar "constant" have great importance to the total Earth system. The results obtained to date show that the total energy fluctuates up to 0.3%, the maximum peak-to-peak excursion around the mean output energy, and the fluctuations last for periods of days to months.[8] This measurement, clearly in the "applications" category, is complemented by equally important measurements aimed at understanding solar flares and, in particular, answering the questions:

1) Where in the solar atmosphere do the flares originate?

2) How is the energy of a flare stored before release?

3) What triggers the release of energy that propagates outward and eventually reaches the Earth?

Although such questions and measurements have traditionally been the domain of the scientist seeking greater understanding of astrophysics, any examination of the Earth as a total system must consider these energetic perturbations.

The second research mission that will be discussed briefly is the Dynamics Explorer (DE). This mission is reviewed in great depth in two recent special issues in the scientific literature.[9,10] As is SSM, the mission is a major contribution to viewing the total environment surrounding the Earth and to studying carefully the couplings among the magnetosphere, ionosphere, and atmosphere. The list of discoveries and accomplishments by this comparatively low-cost mission, which follows in the best traditions of the NASA "Explorer" program, is too long to give here, but several that particularly fit the mold of developing a total Earth-system view are:

1) Produced first truly global images of the auroral oval and the evolution of auroral substorms.

2) Found strong coupling between convectively driven ions and the neutral atmosphere.

3) Discovered evidence of electric field acceleration of atmospheric oxygen.

4) Discovered global neutral winds in the thermosphere with speeds up to 800 m/s (1800 mph).

The principal measurements of the DE program have provided new insights into the transfer of energy, carried by
both the solar wind and solar ultraviolet radiation, into
the magnetosphere, ionosphere, and thermosphere and how
energy is eventually coupled to the lower atmosphere. This
coupling produces changes in global atmospheric circulation
and in the temperature structure of the thermosphere.
Again, the importance of global scale examinations of the
Earth is evident, as the attempt is made to develop the
total system view.
     In addition to the research satellites, the opera-
tional weather satellites, both civil and defense, provide
continuing measurements of the space environment. The
geostationary satellites carry a whole-sun x-ray sensor,
energetic particle sensors (high-energy protons, electrons,
and alpha particles), and a magnetometer. The polar-
orbiting NOAA satellites carry energetic particle sensors
and measure the total energy deposited by electrons and
ions from the magnetosphere into the atmosphere, where
heating is produced. The Defense Meteorological Satellite
Program (DMSP) satellites carry energetic particle sensors,
precipitating particle sensors, and an auroral imager. The
satellite measurements are incorporated into a complex
terrestrial observation network that provides support to
both operating agencies and the research community.[11]
     The above activities represent the present, but an
ambitious future research program is under study, the
International Solar-Terrestrial Physics (ISTP) Program. In
keeping with the general theme of this paper, this program
is proposed as a cooperative program among NASA, the
European Space Agency (ESA), and the Japanese Institute of
Space and Astronautical Sciences (ISAS). The program
involves five satellites, called SOHO, Tail, Wind, Equator,
and Polar, and a satellite cluster called Multipoint. SOHO
is an acronym for Solar and Heliospheric Observer. As can
be deduced from the names of the spacecraft, they either
orbit or are stationed at critical points in space to
measure "the cause and effect in the sun-Earth interaction
chain from the solar interior, solar surface, and solar
corona through the solar wind throughout the Earth's magnetosphere and into the Earth's atmosphere."[12]
     Improvements are also being sought in the instruments
being carried on the geostationary weather satellites. The
Space Environment Laboratory of NOAA's Environmental
Research Laboratories has identified a solar x-ray imager
as the highest priority addition to the instrument complement. The photosphere obscures the observation of the
corona and solar activity at many wavelengths, but the pho-

tosphere does not radiate in the soft x-ray and far ultraviolet portions of the spectrum, while many important solar
events do. Thus, a sensor operating at these wavelengths
"can observe and monitor coronal holes, solar flares,
erupting filaments, erupting filament ejecta in the corona,
and active region loop systems." All of these phenomena
affect geomagnetic activity or can be used in the forecast
of solar activity and its consequences on Earth.[13]
  From the above discussion, it can be seen that a wide
range of instrumentation is either in place or planned that
will provide a detailed analysis of the energy entering the
Earth system and will also provide an accurate analysis of
the flow of energy among the various elements of the
Earth's atmosphere and surrounding radiation fields. This
is clearly a vital definition of the boundary between space
and the next subject to be discussed in this paper--remote
sensing and the atmosphere.

III. The Dynamic Atmosphere

  The preceding section provided the solar inputs to the
terrestrial system. The next step is to move downward into
the atmosphere to the region having the most direct and
obvious effects on our daily activities, the lower atmosphere. Along the way, however, an observer would have to
pass through an extraordinarily complex and dynamic region,
often termed the "middle atmosphere," that occupies the
region between the top of the troposphere and the bottom of
the thermosphere.[67] Space does not permit a treatment of
the many experiments that addressed this region, but the
Solar Backscatter Ultraviolet (SBUV) instrument and Upper
Atmosphere Research Satellites(UARS) mentioned in Sec. VII
will provide valuable new insights. They will continue a
series of measurements that extend back to the beginnings
of the space program and include the successful U.K./U.S.
cooperative ventures with the Ariel series of satellites in
the early 1960s.
  Suppose it were proposed that 150 nations join
together for a period of coordinated observations of the
Earth. Suppose further that the proposal includes the
launching of four satellites into polar orbit and of five
satellites into geostationary orbit and that these satellites be provided by several countries. Also suppose that
an extensive, and international, "ground-truth" network of
ships, aircraft, balloons, buoys, and terrestrial stations
be prepared to participate in the program as well. How
many people would today predict international, or even
U.S., acceptance of such a proposal? Probably not many.

Yet just such a proposal was accepted and the observations
were carried out during the Global Weather Experiment.
Most of the coordinated measurements were carried out in
1979, but the research and analyses continue today.[14,15]
     One of the heritages of the Global Weather Experiment
is the continuing observation provided by the international
ring of geostationary weather satellites that monitor the
Earth within a latitude band somewhat beyond 50 deg north
and south of the equator. Although coordinated only infor-
mally by an international group of meteorologists and engineers, it is a de facto international Earth observation
satellite system. It currently comprises observations provided by Europe, India, Japan, and the United States, with
the USSR planning to provide a satellite later in the
decade.
     The U.S. civil polar-orbiting TIROS/NOAA weather
satellites are also quite international in character.
France provides the Argos platform location and data collection system. The United Kingdom is presently providing
a stratospheric sounding unit (SSU) and is examining providing a substantial new instrument for the next generation
satellites. The United States, Canada, and France are providing subsystems for the search and rescue satellite-aided
tracking (SARSAT) program. Thus, three nations are contributing hardware for the satellite. In each instance,
that hardware is fully funded by the responsible country.
     The objective of recalling the above information is to
observe that nations have and continue to collaborate in
sophisticated satellite observations systems and, while
the satellites are provided by a limited group of nations,
all nations benefit. But even though only a small number
provide the satellites, many nations, no matter how small,
contribute daily conventional measurements to the global
weather observations.
     As in other places in this paper, it is evident that a
global system must be continuously observed in a variety of
ways and that the atmospheric system is coupled between the
magnetosphere, ionosphere, and thermosphere above the lower
atmosphere and the land and ocean at the base of the atmosphere. The overall value of these observations has been
so widely and well documented that only a few further comments will be made here.[16-18]
     A significant advantage of the operational weather
satellites is their relative permanence, continuity of systematic observations, frequent observations of the entire
Earth, and standardized data formats. This will be shown
to be quite significant for measurements of the biosphere
and the detection of climate change.

Weather satellites will soon have been a part of the space program for 25 years, the launch of TIROS-1 having taken place on April 1, 1960, less than 3 years after the launch of the first Earth satellite. The Soviet Union has been operating the Meteor series of polar-orbiting weather satellites since 1969.

The current U.S. polar-orbiting satellites are named simply NOAA-1, NOAA-2, etc., as successive satellites in the series are launched. The program has evolved from one in which simple black-and-white images of cloud patterns were transmitted to one of enormous sophistication in which 16,000 atmospheric temperature profiles or "soundings" are produced daily for incorporation into global forecasting models. The early images have changed in spatial resolution, but, even more importantly, in spectral resolution and calibration. The imager now flown on the U.S. polar-orbiting satellites is the advanced very-high-resolution radiometer (AVHRR). The last word in the title is most significant, because it states that a precise, radiometric measurement is made of upcoming radiation. This radiometric precision permits not only extended meteorological applications of the instrument, but also other applications such as sea surface temperature measurements and ice and vegetation mapping. The latter three applications properly fall in other sections of this paper, but because of their close association with the weather satellites, a few comments will be made here.

The AVHRR, with channels extending well into the thermal infrared, detects sea surface temperature gradients that are indicative of ocean surface currents, nutrient-rich cool upwelling waters, and ocean eddy structures. Major ocean currents, such as the Gulf Stream, are now routinely measured and the data provided to the maritime community. Data taken on successive days are used to eliminate the effects of clouds. Similarly, sea and lake ice are routinely monitored using the AVHRR. This contributes to the maximizing of the period of navigability on the Great Lakes. It also allows, when cloud conditions permit, the monitoring of the main ice edge, individual ice floes and large icebergs, and the identification of "leads"--navigable passageways--for such critical regions as the Alaskan north slope.

In addition to these maritime applications, the AVHRR can be used for some of the same functions that the multi-spectral scanner (MSS) on Landsat performs. Although the spatial resolution is less (approximately 1 km for the AVHRR instead of the 80 m for the MSS), the spectral coverage is wider and the swath width of the sensor, combined

with the orbital altitude, allows a given spot on the Earth
to be revisited twice a day--once during daylight hours and
once at night. As will be noted below, Landsat data can be
used to map vegetation and, through an analytical product
called the "vegetation index," can map vegetation condition. This can also be done with coarser spatial resolution, but is more frequently done using the AVHRR on the
polar-orbiting weather satellites.

In the meteorological area, the satellite data are
continuously broadcast to anyone who cares to build a
receiving station. Low-resolution data can be received by
very inexpensive stations. Nearly a thousand such stations
have been deployed in more than 120 countries. Higher-
quality data can also be received, including images at both
higher spatial resolution and soundings, but with a more
expensive ground station. A few dozen such stations are in
place around the world. It is difficult to think of a more
responsible and humanitarian act within the space program
than the continued provision of these data to all people.

The satellite soundings are now having a major impact
on numerical weather forecasting. Before the availability
of satellite soundings, barely 20% of the Earth was
included in routine weather observations using rawinsondes.
The remainder of the Earth, largely ocean areas, was
covered by sporadic aircraft and ship measurements and by a
very few number of systematic weather ship observations.
These observations were nonuniformly distributed, concentrated near major flight and shipping paths, particularly
absent in the tropics and the Southern Hemisphere, and
largely--if sensibly--absent in the area of severe storms.
The TIROS operational vertical sounder (TOVS), flown on
each of the two polar-orbiting weather satellites, blankets
the Earth with temperature and humidity soundings. It is
the only consistent source of data for the 80% of the globe
that is not observed using rawinsondes and is a vital input
to the numerical forecasts. As efforts are made to extend
the useful weather forecasts to 5 days and beyond, ocean
data become critical and the satellite is the only source
of that data.

The geostationary weather satellites have a shorter,
but no less, distinguished history. They also have progressed from providing simple image data to producing both
enhanced imagery on an operational basis and atmospheric
soundings on an experimental basis. The satellite imagery
is also used to derive wind vectors through the displacement of clouds on successive images. Now familiar to
millions of people from their television weather news, the
satellites have become a major tool in tracking and analyz-

ing severe weather events. As noted previously, a number of countries have deployed geostationary weather satellites. Europe's Meteosat, poised over Africa at 0° longitude, was the first to provide routine water vapor imagery. Japan's Geostationary Meteorological Satellite (GMS) complements the U.S. coverage of the Pacific Ocean. India's Indian National Satellite (INSAT) monitors the Indian Ocean and provides national communications services as well.

The two U.S. geostationary satellites that observe the eastern and western segments of the Western Hemisphere are called GOES-East and GOES-West, where GOES is an acronym for Geostationary Operational Environmental Satellite. GOES-East regularly follows the evolution and path of hurricanes as they proceed from near West Africa to landfall in the Caribbean and North America. GOES-West tracks the large comma-shaped Pacific storms as they sweep from west to east toward the California coast. The program is currently moving from one employing a pure imaging device as the operational sensor, the visible-infrared spin-scan radiometer (VISSR), to a new sensor that combines the operational function with an atmospheric sounding function, the VISSR atmospheric sounder (VAS). The VAS provides soundings over a narrower latitude band than the polar orbiter; but, within the confines of that band, nominally 50°N and 50°S of the equator and a similar band of longitudes, it offers more frequent soundings over a given area. This capability will enhance the ability of forecasters to follow the development of rapidly changing severe storm conditions. Because VAS operates in the infrared, it cannot derive soundings in cloudy areas. However, the ability of a geostationary satellite to observe an area continuously frequently allows this disadvantage to be overcome. VAS can make soundings through the holes in cloud cover that come and go over a period of time, so the ability to maintain observation eventually allows sufficient measurements to be made. The next several years will see this capability incorporated into operational use by U.S. weather forecasters. Unfortunately, none of the other geostationary weather satellite systems have yet included this capability, so it currently exists only in the Western Hemisphere.

Both the polar-orbiting and geostationary weather satellites carry data collection systems for the readout of in situ environmental data. In addition to providing standard meteorological readings in remote locations, the data collection systems allow the monitoring of sea conditions through measurements on ocean buoys, readout of data from aircraft and balloons, and the relay of hydrological data on river levels, snow thickness, etc.

Over the next 15 years or so, NOAA will be bringing two new generations of weather satellites into operation. They are presently called, logically if unimaginatively, GOES-Next and NOAA-Next. In addition to maintaining current capabilities, the geostationary satellites will bring the atmospheric sounding system to full operational utility. This will dramatically improve the use of the satellite in mesoscale severe storm forecasting. For the first time, the satellite will have the flexibility to carry out soundings without interrupting the imaging operations. Further, additional channels will be provided in the multi-spectral imaging mode and some improvements in spatial resolution will be made. In the polar-orbiting system, the principal near-term change for NOAA-K through -M (the last of the current series) is the addition of an advanced microwave sounding unit (AMSU) that is proposed for joint development with the United Kingdom. This unit will greatly expand the utility of the atmospheric soundings by permitting them to be made through cloud cover and thereby greatly improving global synoptic measurements. A modest change will also be made in the satellite's imaging system to enhance its capability to map vegetation.

No nation can forecast its weather from data taken exclusively within its own boundaries. The global character of weather forecasting has led to the formation of extensive international ties and, indeed, extensive moral obligations, even if they are not codified into the diplomatic machinery of diplomatic notes or treaties. The nature of these ties and the complex, interdependent set of measurements necessary for weather forecasting are described in two recent papers.[19,20]

An indication of the strength and value of these ties became evident during the recent abortive efforts to transfer the civil weather satellites to private industry. Before Congress acted to block the action altogether, the Reagan Administration conducted an intensive study of continued U.S. participation in the current international exchange of weather data. At present, all data are made freely available to all countries at no cost. While this is clearly in the best humanitarian tradition, it also represented a serious obstacle to converting weather satellites from a governmental function to a profit-making activity. After an extensive evaluation, it was concluded that U.S. interests in continuing the exchange of weather data were more important than the desire to place the minimum obstacles in the path of a private firm on its way to profitability. For this reason, the policy decision made was that, in the event the satellites were transferred, the

chosen private firm would be required to continue the
international free-of-cost exchange of weather data.

In keeping with the theme of treating the Earth as a
coupled physical system, the transfer of energy to and from
the atmosphere to the oceans and land is certainly an
important element in determining system behavior--i.e., the
albedo of the sea or of a large snow field can "lock-in"
the atmosphere or the energy of surface winds is coupled to
the sea. In either case, a total system view is necessary.

IV. The Dynamic Oceans and Coastal Regions

In meteorology, a major contribution of the weather
satellite has been the provision of measurements from the
traditionally data-sparse regions, particularly the oceans.
Prior to the advent of satellites, this lack of data was
obviously most acute in the Southern Hemisphere. Probably
the most striking illustration is in the prediction of the
landfall of hurricanes and typhoons. The entire growth
cycle of the storm occurs over water, where observations
are few. Further, the path of the storm is affected by
synoptic scale disturbances that are also occurring over
water. This is clearly a case where data taken only over
land are inadequate to predict the weather over land.
Similarly, if adequate data are unavailable to forecast
what will happen over land, because of the lack of data
over the oceans, then it is clearly not possible to forecast what will happen over the sea either. Therefore, the
contribution of the weather satellites to maritime weather
forecasts has proved to be a major one.

Although the contribution of the weather satellites to
the maritime community was large, it was also obvious that
these measurements do not meet all requirements. This led
to a series of pioneering instruments and missions aimed at
meeting the needs of ocean research and operations.[21]

Among the passive instruments were the electrically
scanning microwave radiometer (ESMR) on Nimbus-5 and the
scanning multifrequency microwave radiometer (SMMR) on
Nimbus-7. Within the limitations inherent in a 25 km spatial resolution, these instruments allowed maps to be made
showing the extent and type of ice in both polar regions.[22]
Active systems have also been flown, notably the radar
altimeters on GEOS-3 and Seasat and the scatterometer and
synthetic aperture radar on Seasat. These active systems
demonstrated the capabilities of spaceborne sensors to
measure the various dynamic features of the ocean and even
the subsurface topography.

The success of the above missions has created a demand
in the maritime community for operational data that can be
used in a near-real-time mode to guide shipping, fishing,
and oil drilling and exploration activities. The research
community also desires data from such systems to address
the fundamental oceanographic and climatological questions
involved in understanding the dynamics of the Earth on many
different time scales. A few of these issues will be
addressed below.

There are no current systematic measurements of wind
stress on the oceans, which is a major contributor to
oceanic circulation. The surface wind field is also an
essential factor in forecasting storm surge and surface
waves, where the wind field used in the predictive model
may be the dominant error source.[23,24] The experience with
the Seasat scatterometer shows that surface wind speed and
direction can be measured to an adequate precision to make
a major contribution to marine operations and maritime
weather forecasts.

There is no current systematic measurement of sea-
surface topography, although very useful data have been
gained from GEOS-3 and Seasat and the U.S. Navy will fly a
single follow-up mission called Geosat. Altimetric measurements from space can monitor major current systems and
their related eddy and ring structures. Such measurements
also map the bottom topography through mean sea height
changes produced by gravity anomalies, which are in turn
produced by large features on the sea floor. Altimetric
data also provide information on wind and wave speed, significant wave heights, and the statistics of ocean waves,
as well as the topography of the great polar ice sheets.[25]

The use of passive microwave radiometers to map the
sea surface temperature through clouds allows the dynamic
features of the upper ocean to be tracked. These include
such features as upwelling zones, eddies, fronts, and
currents. Moderate spatial resolution radiometers also
allow ice-edge analyses to be made, which are so vital to
Arctic and Antarctic resupply and oil tanker operations.
All of the above applications are discussed, as well as
others, in two recent review papers.[26,27] The extensive,
and higher spatial resolution, infrared sea surface
temperature measurements now conducted operationally will
continue.

In addition to the above measurements, which can be
accomplished with radiometers, altimeters, and scatterometers, even more sophisticated measurements can be made
using synthetic aperture radar techniques. In this
instance, radar maps can be produced with spatial resolu-

tions approaching that of high-quality imaging sensors. This opens an entirely new set of possibilities in ocean measurements. The many discoveries and results produced by the synthetic aperture radar on Seasat are too numerous to list here, but are thoroughly discussed elsewhere.[28-31] They include, for example, unique global marine wind measurements, altimeter wave height measurements, and the production of high-resolution images of arctic ice floes.

It is scarcely surprising that the wealth of results produced by the above missions has not gone unnoticed in other countries. For example, the Soviet Union has launched a number of highly successful ocean satellites. Europe, Japan, and Canada have all announced plans for missions that will capitalize on these discoveries. The United States is also examining two new major missions, called Topex and the Navy Remote Ocean Sensing Satellite (N-ROSS), and some smaller scale efforts involving sensors that will fly on the Space Shuttle or on free-flying satellites when the opportunity is available. In the recurring theme of this paper, it will be evident that the "coordinated sum" of these missions vastly exceeds the arithmetic sum. A summary of these foreign and U.S. missions will now be given.

Japan is preparing the Marine Observation Satellite-1 (MOS-1) for flight in 1986. The satellite will carry three sensors and a data collection system. The first sensor is the multispectral electronic self-scanning radiometer (MESSR), which will provide 50 m spatial resolution over a 200 km swath width in the visible and near-infrared spectra. The second sensor is the visible and thermal infrared radiometer (VTIR), which will sweep a 1-3 mrad instantaneous field of view along a 1500 km swath width and provide data farther into the infrared spectrum than the MESSR. The last instrument is the microwave scanning radiometer (MSR), which will use two circularly scanned Dicke radiometers operating at 24 and 31 GHz. This set of instruments will permit the measurement of marine pollution, red tide, currents, and sea surface temperature.[32] Japan is also planning the development of a Japanese Earth Resources Satellite (JERS-1) that is planned to carry a synthetic aperture radar providing 25 m spatial resolution over a 75 km swath width.

The first European Remote Sensing Satellite, known as ERS-1, is a more extensive use of the microwave spectrum than MOS-1.[33] It employs a sophisticated advanced microwave instrument (AMI) that combines the functions of a synthetic aperture radar (providing 30 m spatial resolution over an 80 km swath width) with those of a wind and wave

scatterometer to provide the speed and direction of wind
fields and the direction and length of wave fields. A 2 m
absolute and 10 cm relative accuracy microwave altimeter
will provide data on major ocean currents and significant
wave heights, while sea surface temperature will be derived
from an along-track scanning radiometer (ATSR) that operates in the infrared spectrum. Finally, water vapor will
be measured using a microwave sounder. This satellite will
be a major step toward the use of remotely sensed data in
coastal and ocean applications, particularly with respect
to sea ice and related ice formations on land. The satellite will also make major contributions to scientific
understanding of the coastal zones and global-scale ocean
processes, especially in support of the World Climate
Research Program (WCRP) which will be discussed below. The
mission is scheduled for flight in 1989.

Canada is currently evaluating a mission termed
Radarsat.[34] This mission is targeted at four sets of
applications for a synthetic aperture radar: operations in
sea-ice-covered waters, basic oceanography (as in understanding the short ocean surface gravity waves that are
detected by a radar system), agricultural crop identification for renewable resources, and topographical feature
detection and identification for nonrenewable resources.
This last capability also contributes to renewable resource
applications through land-form mapping and providing information to map soil types--both of which are important for
forestry, rangeland, and agricultural applications.

The major U.S. missions planned for the oceans and
coasts mentioned above, N-ROSS and Topex, will now be
reviewed briefly. N-ROSS has been proposed as a joint
Navy, NASA, and NOAA mission and, while it has great utility to the Navy, it also has equally great utility to the
civil maritime community. The mission is planned to capitalize on the experience gained with Seasat and GEOS-3 and
will provide both operational data and new research
results. The N-ROSS will carry four microwave instruments,
providing essentially all-weather capability. The instruments include a scatterometer (provided by NASA) that is an
improved version of what was flown on Seasat, an altimeter
identical to that to be flown on Geosat, a microwave imager
identical to that to be flown on the DMSP, and a low-
frequency radiometer of a new design. The scatterometer
will provide wind speed and direction, the altimeter will
supply significant wave height, the microwave imager will
add ice edge analyses and precipitation, and the radiometer
will provide high-spatial-resolution sea surface temperature measurements.[35]

NASA is planning an ocean topographic satellite,
Topex, which will have the capability to make high-
precision (2 cm) altimetric measurements. This extraordinary accuracy will permit substantial improvements in the
understanding of ocean circulation and its fluctuations.
The practical applications of such information are clear,
whether related to management of fishing grounds, understanding the movement of pollutants, or assisting the more
efficient navigation of vessels.[36]

In addition to the above dedicated missions, there
will be a number of future opportunities to fly special
instruments on short-duration Space Shuttle missions and on
satellites whose main purpose is to serve another discipline. In addition to the Shuttle imaging radars flown by
NASA, which are aimed principally at geological applications but which have ocean applications as well, one of the
most intriguing instruments is the ocean color imager
(OCI). This instrument is an outgrowth of the highly successful coastal zone color scanner (CZCS) that was flown by
NASA on Nimbus-7. While this device was designed to determine the biological productivity of the ocean's sunlit
layer from a measurement of chlorophyll near the sea surface, it has also proved to have physical oceanography
applications as well.[23] The biological applications will
be discussed in Sec. VI. In the physical oceanography
area, the instrument has been found to provide important
information on sea surface temperature, oceanic mesoscale
structure and dynamics, aerosol distributions, and pollution mapping. At present no firm plans exist for flight of
the instrument beyond Nimbus-7, which is still functioning,
but studies are under way to place it either on the operational polar-orbiting weather satellites or on the French
SPOT satellite.

Earlier in this section, a statement was made about
the improvement that can be gained through a "coordinated
sum" of these missions, rather than an arithmetic sum. It
is evident to all reviewing the above that a number of
nations are about to make major investments in ocean
sensing satellites. More than a billion dollars will be
spent on satellite-based ocean measurements during the next
6-7 years. It is also evident that there is great potential for duplication of effort and for not extracting the
maximum possible scientific and operational value. Even
the simplest level of coordination on mission launch schedules and orbital parameters can yield huge dividends. For
example, the repeat observation cycle for the ERS-1 is
approximately 2-3 days, as is that for N-ROSS. If the two
missions overlap in time and the orbits are properly coor-

dinated, global ocean coverage will be available on a daily
basis from all instruments except the synthetic aperture
radar on ERS-1. This would create a quasioperational capability of immense value to the maritime community. It
would literally revolutionize man's view of the oceans.
Thus, the overall value of the two missions would be very
greatly enhanced and at no incremental cost to either
mission.

Just as the weather, the oceans change continually
and require continuous observation. And just as weather
patterns respect no national boundaries, neither do ocean
patterns. It seems inevitable that common interests in
observing the state of the oceans will lead toward at least
the international model of shared observational systems
that has become accepted in meteorology.

In the preceding paragraphs, the dynamic atmosphere
and oceans have been discussed. Both are coupled to the
solid Earth, which is the subject of the next section of
this paper.

V. The Solid Earth

No more spectacular insights have been gained from
spaceborne remote sensing, and space-related measurement
techniques in general, than those associated with the
lithosphere, the solid Earth. Some of the most remarkable
insights into plate tectonics are derived from even the
simplest photographs taken with hand-held cameras by the
astronauts. These photographs show the effect of the tear-
ing of the Earth's crust to produce the Sinai Peninsula,
the movement of Arabia away from Africa in the formation of
the Red Sea and the Persian Gulf, and the remarkable correspondence between the northern shore of the Gulf of Aden
and the northern shore of the Somali Peninsula as vivid
evidence of the dynamics of the Earth's crust.

These early achievements were quickly surpassed by
vastly more sophisticated measurements, including such
programs as Landsat, HCMM, Lageos, and Magsat. From the
earliest to the most recent in the Landsat series, the
complex geological structures of the Earth have been analyzed in an unprecedented manner.[37] The examination of the
effects of glaciation could now be made on a regional
scale. Geologic structures were now unmasked through the
uniform rendition and geometric accuracy afforded by the
Landsat images. Faults and fractures could now be observed
over far greater areas and features that were thought to
end at one point were found to reappear outside the view
of conventional reconnaissance techniques. Particularly

with the enhanced capabilities of the thematic mapper (TM)
flown on Landsat-4 and -5, the identification of rock types
and alteration products, such as hydrothermally altered
clays, was found to be feasible in a number of valuable
instances.[38]

One of the interesting aspects of the use of Landsat
data in geology is that certain deposits are more easily
seen on Landsat than they are in the field; this is particularly true for surface minerals (often clays) that are
indicators of the subsurface presence of other minerals.
The middle infrared bands that were added to Landsat-4
and -5 at the request of the geological community are
especially suited to the discrimination and mapping of
assemblages of minerals that are located in rocks and soils
containing clays, carbonates, and low-grade metamorphic
minerals.[38]

Another use of Landsat data is in cartography. Both
MSS data and TM data have found applications in updating as
well as producing maps. In the developed world, the TM
data have been used to update maps, including those of
metropolitan areas. One recent example involved a 1977 map
of San Francisco that shows a number of docks on the water-
front. When this was compared with a Landsat TM scene, it
was quickly noted that some of the docks no longer existed,
having been burned down after the earlier map was prepared.
The U.S. Geological Survey has recently printed experimental image maps of a number of U.S. metropolitan areas at
scales of 1:100,000 and 1:250,000. Particularly in the
developing world, Landsat has been found to be an economical way to prepare maps of regions where none previously
existed and to produce land use and land cover maps. Also,
in rapidly changing flood plains such as the Ganges,
satellite-derived maps effectively show the new channels
the river is opening or following.

Landsat has also been employed for shallow-water
bathymetry. From a mariner's perspective, the most critical regions are where uncharted reefs and rapidly changing
sandbars may pose a hazard to navigation. These features
are frequently visible on satellite images and, therefore,
older maps can be updated using it. In shallow areas, the
Landsat data can even be used to map the extent of benthic
vegetation.

In 1978, the United States launched the heat capacity
mapping mission (HCMM). The satellite produced day-night
temperature difference maps and apparent thermal-inertia
maps of selected areas in North America, Europe, North
Africa, and Australia. The resulting thermal images are
being used by investigators to evaluate their utility in

rock-type discrimination, soil moisture detection, thermal
current monitoring in water bodies, urban heat-island
studies, and other applications.[39] The mission illustrates
how data sets from one satellite can complement and extend
the data from another satellite. Overlaying the HCMM data
set on that from Landsat and other systems provides an
additional dimension to the analyses. For example, combining the Landsat data with stereo-like representation of
thermal gradients from HCMM produces a useful product and
HCMM data can be used to enhance the interpretation of
Landsat data and its classification. This benefit is
derived because the operating wavelength is farther into
the infrared than the Landsat multispectral scanner (MSS)
that was in orbit at the same time. It is also derived
from the difference in obervational times and conditions,
all of which add to the dimensionality of the total data
set.

As in the case of all remote sensing applications,
images do not stand alone, no matter how cleverly chosen or
enhanced. Correlative data are always required and some of
those data come from space measurements, as well as from in
situ or other conventional sources. In 1965 investigations
began of the Earth's magnetic field using the U.S. Orbiting
Geophysical Observatories and the USSR Cosmos-49 satellite.
More recently the United States launched the magnetic field
satellite called Magsat. It carried scalar and vector mag-
netometers and provided an accurate global map of the secu-
lar change in strength and direction of the magnetic field.
Such data are important in understanding the long-term
dynamics of the Earth's evolution and supporting geomagnetic field surveys that search for ferromagnetic metals or
nonferromagnetic metals frequently found in such deposits--
e.g., titanium.

The laser geodetic satellite, called Lageos, and a
similar French satellite, called Starlette, demonstrate the
use of space techniques in the Earth sciences. In this
instance, satellites specially designed to have minimum
solar radiation and drag forces are used as spaceborne geodetic benchmarks and are tracked with very high precision
by terrestrial laser stations. These satellites have
enabled very accurate measurements to be made of crustal
motion and the Earth's polar motion and, in conjunction
with other satellites and terrestrial measurements, have
provided new clues in understanding such important geological activities as the spreading of the sea floor.

As always, one set of measurements must be complemented, extended, and even understood through the use of
correlative measurements. In this instance, the next step

will be the detailed examination of the Earth's gravitational field by an innovative remote sensing satellite
formerly called Gravsat, but now known as the Geopotential
Research Mission (GRM).

The GRM satellite has been under study for a number of
years. A particularly perceptive report was published by
the National Research Council's Panel on Gravity Field and
Sea Level in 1979.[40] This was followed by a series of successively more detailed reports and analyses of the value
of the mission in geophysics, geodetics, and oceanography.
One of those reports is worth quoting:[41]

"In the last three decades, the earth sciences have
undergone a revolution of major scope and importance. To
the long-held model--a static earth dominated by slow,
rhythmic vertical motions--has been added the concept of
comparatively rapid and independent horizontal motions of
large slabs of the earth's crust, a concept encompassed
in the plate tectonics hypothesis. In this model the
earth has an everchanging surface; continents enlarge by
accretion of new material, divide, and reassemble in new
patterns, and new oceans form as old ones are destroyed
by subduction under the continents. The resulting
strains developed within the crust are evidenced by
devastating earthquakes and volcanic outbursts, but phenomena associated with the dynamism also create the conditions necessary for the formation of mineral deposits
and other natural resources."

Just as in the other discipline categories, the success of remote sensing of the solid Earth by U.S. satellites has encouraged other countries to enter this field as
well. Most notably, the Federal Republic of Germany,
France, Japan, and India have all initiated projects in
this area. Each country's activities will be summarized
below.

Germany has developed the metric camera facility for
flight on Spacelab. The facility uses a standard Zeiss
aerial camera, and produces 190 x 190 km images with an
approximate ground resolution of 20 m. The camera can use
black-and-white, color, or color infrared film.[42] Germany
has also developed a "push-broom" imaging system called the
modular optoelectronic multispectal scanner (MOMS) that
provides approximately 20 m ground resolution in the
visible and near-infrared spectra. This sensor is proposed
for the first "commercial" remote sensing space system by
the Sparx Corporation.[43] MOMS is presently configured for
use only on the Space Shuttle and short-duration flights,
but consideration is also being given to its use in a free-
flying mode as well.

The French SPOT satellite is planned for launch early in 1985 and will provide a number of advanced remote sensing features. It includes a 10 m ground resolution panchromatic mode, a 20 m ground resolution multispectral mode, and an offset pointing capability to reduce revisit time to a given ground target. The SPOT system will also provide stereo coverage that will be of value to the geologic and topographic mapping communities. As in the case of the Sparx Corporation initiative mentioned above, the SPOT system is intended to be a commercial venture.[44]

The Japanese Earth resources satellite mentioned previously under the ocean sensing category, JERS-1, will carry a push-broom electro-optic detector array with similar performance to that of the MOMS and SPOT sensors. It will be flown with a synthetic aperture radar system that will be used for both maritime and land applications.

India has launched two Earth resources satellites, Bhaskara-1 and -2, and is planning a new satellite called the Indian Resources Satellite (IRS). The Indian Space Research Organization has completed studies of the basic system parameters and has chosen a four-spectral-band sensor that operates in the push-broom mode in the visible and near-infrared spectra. The sensor is to provide two spatial resolutions, 73 and 37 m.[45]

As can be seen above, a staggering number of sensors are planned for flight during the next decade and the above list is by no means complete, nor does it take account of current U.S. efforts to create a private sector supplier of space remote sensing data. Particularly neglected above is any discussion of new cartographic applications of space remote sensing data or of the "orbital mapping system" concept, as has been advocated by Colvocoresses.[46]

Thus, once again the total system view of the Earth must prevail. And just as the motions of the seas and the atmosphere respect no national boundaries, the path of a geological fault or fracture is not interrupted by the custom official's toll gate either. Although legitimate arguments can be made about the distinctions between remote sensing of the oceans and atmosphere on the one hand and land remote sensing on the other, because of differing applications and political sensitivities, the distinction should not be drawn too finely, for the understanding of this dynamic Earth can be gained only through measurements beyond national boundaries and through the involvement of many nations and their researchers.

One of the most striking aspects of the Landsat program has been the early and intensive involvement of foreign countries. In the Americas, Canada, Brazil, and

Argentina have built Landsat ground stations. Interest-ingly enough, it was the Canadian station that provided vital coverage of the contiguous 48 states during the period of Landsat-4. In the Far East, Australia, Japan, Thailand, and India have operational stations, and Indonesia will soon. China is presently procuring a Landsat station.

In the Middle East and Africa, South Africa has a station and Saudi Arabia has begun planning for one as well. In Europe, the European Space Agency operates two stations, in Fucino, Italy, and Kiruna, Sweden. The cover-age circles of these stations include a substantial part of the inhabited world. The stations also represent a sizable investment in another nation's space system and, indeed, a substantial vote of confidence in international cooperation in remote sensing.

The international participation in land remote sensing extends far beyond the deployment of these ground stations and their associated processing centers. Landsat has changed the manner in which nations conduct their business and the way they think about the Earth. There are numerous striking examples that can be cited. In addition to the facilities mentioned above that have their own Landsat receiving stations, numerous facilities have been set up to apply the data gained from a variety of sources. One notable activity has been the East African Remote Sensing Center in Nairobi, Kenya, which has used Landsat data for mapping, ecological monitoring of rangeland, studying the effects of grass fires, and examining food, water, and fuel resources--all for a relatively modest annual budget.

All of the above categories of measurement (solar -terrestrial interactions, atmosphere, ocean, and solid Earth) gain importance to the human race through their effect on the next area that will be discussed, the biosphere.

VI. The Biosphere

While the importance of the biosphere as an entity in its own right is evident, it should not be overlooked that the biosphere is also an important cog in the total Earth machine. The interaction of the biosphere with the hydro-sphere, atmosphere, and lithosphere is pervasive, continu-ous, operational over many time scales and active at many nested levels.[47] All of the preceding sections relate to remote sensing systems and sensors that can observe various aspects of the biosphere, even though the primary purpose of those systems is elsewhere and the relationship to meas-urements of the biosphere may not be stated at all.

The Landsats observe geologic features, now land-
locked, that were once great reefs in ancient oceans and
that are made up of the remnants of sedimentary rocks,
coral, sponges, and algàe. These features, their location,
and makeup provide essential clues about the origins and
evolution of the Earth. Landsat also measures the extent
and types of plant cover on a global basis. This provides
data on the total Earth biomass. The weather satellites
observe huge forest fires that are contributing to climate
change both through additions to the global haze layer and
changes in the Earth's total biomass. Further, the weather
satellites provide on a global basis a rapid-update of
vegetation conditions. The experimental coastal zone color
scanner (CZCS) mentioned earlier in Sec. IV in reference to
its utility in measuring mesoscale ocean features also
measures pigment concentrations in the upper ocean. These
measurements are made with adequate accuracy to provide a
useful determination of phytoplankton biomass and in some
instances net productivity.[48] Thus, the biosphere is being
examined in many different ways by systems already in
place. The use of these systems in a number of experimental programs will be discussed in this section.

The biosphere-related measurements of Landsat are
often identified with the joint program conducted by the
U.S. Department of Agriculture (USDA), Department of the
Interior, NASA, NOAA, and the Agency for International
Development (AID) on agricultural surveys. The program is
called Agricultural and Resources Inventory Surveys Through
Aerospace Remote Sensing, or simply AgRISTARS. The objective of the program is "to determine the usefulness, cost,
and extent to which aerospace remote sensing data can be
integrated into existing or future USDA systems to improve
the objectivity, reliability, timeliness, and adequacy of
information required to carry out USDA missions."[49]

Although the AgRISTARS program has been troubled by
uncertainties in Landsat data continuity and program
budgets, as well as by the general lack of quick repeat-
cycle measurements, the basic objectives have been met.
Landsat has demonstrated that, in conjunction with the
meteorological satellites, it can assist in the development
of important international economic parameters related to
the agricultural sector. In particular, the combined
satellite data can contribute global, timely, and reliable
information on major food and fiber crops, in terms of
stocks on hand, expected production, future supply, and
import needs. One measure of the importance of agricultural data is evident in the $44 billion that agricultural
exports contributed to the U.S. trade balance in 1981. On

a humanitarian basis, the United States has also contributed enormous quantities of agricultural products to
countries beset by floods, droughts, and similar events.
Whether the measurement is made in economic or humanitarian
terms, it is evident that agricultural data, particularly
as advance warnings of impending difficulties, are both
important and potentially very sensitive.

The AgRISTARS program has spawned two interesting
paths for further research. Predictably, the early MSS
data at 80 m spatial resolution, and with limited spectral
capability, led to the desire for higher spatial resolution
data over a wider spectral range. These capabilities are
provided by the thematic mapper on the last two Landsats.
The second research direction was far less predictable, in
that it involved the use of much coarser resolution data
from the weather satellites, nominally 1 km in spatial
resolution. In this instance, the use of the higher-
resolution data gave sufficient confidence to investigate
the use of low spatial resolution data that are available
at low cost and at higher temporal resolution. Each
research direction and some recent results will be reviewed
below.

It was expected that Landsat's thematic mapper (TM)
would improve the discrimination of forest tree types and
acreages. This has proved to be true. For example, unlike
the MSS, it has been possible to discriminate among stands
of slash pine, young pine, loblolly pine, and natural pine
with TM data.[50] It was also expected that the discrimination of agricultural crops would be improved by the TM.
Again, this was verified and the middle-infrared bands of
the TM were found to improve the separability of corn and
soybeans in both single and multitemporal measurements.[51]

There are basically three parameters that can be
deduced from remotely sensed data of an agricultural area:
crop type, acreage, and condition.[52] Acreage, particularly
in the small fields common in developing countries,
requires high spatial resolution, but the acreage does not
vary greatly from one year to the next where agriculture is
a permanent land use--except as affected by climatological-
scale variables such as floods. Sometimes, crop type does
not change from year to year very much and the effect of
any changes can be reduced if data are available on the
crop rotation practices for a region. Again, the situation
in the developing countries is difficult to analyze because
such countries are typically in the tropics and the planting and harvest times may vary considerably. A given scene
may contain many plots at various stages of growth, leading
to considerable difficulties in interpretation, but never-

theless a fair amount of correlative data may be available
to reduce the error associated with crop identification.
Finally, the crop condition is usually assessed through the
sensitive relationship between the chlorophyll content of
healthy vegetation and its near-infrared reflectance. In
this instance, a number of the stressing conditions are
related to climatological variables and scales, e.g.,
droughts. Further, the assessment of such stresses
requires frequent measurements as the crop matures. These
last two points suggest that coarse spatial resolution
data, perhaps averaged over a week or so to remove cloud
cover, may be suitable for some applications--particularly
when they are used with appropriate correlative data. It
also suggests that the weather satellite data would be
particularly useful for the assessment of crops in large
fields and in rangeland management. This does not suggest
that they eliminate the need for higher-resolution data,
only that they are useful data for some purposes.

The latter approach has been examined by a number of
researchers. For example, the vegetation in the Nile Delta
was measured over a season and it was found that the
observed trends correlated very well with both growing conditions and agricultural practices.[53] A direct outgrowth
of the AgRISTARS effort is an activity relating meteorological satellite data to such agriculturally important variables as precipitation, insolation, maximum and minimum
temperatures, vegetation index, and snow cover.[54] Finally,
one private firm is now using the weather satellite data on
essentially an operational basis for crop yield forecasting
and is evaluating the use of higher-resolution Landsat data
as a calibration tool.[55]

Throughout this paper, the theme of the need for a
global view of environmental issues has been stressed,
where the term "environmental" is used in its broadest
possible meaning. This theme is appropriate because of the
global effects of solar radiation, the transnational movements of atmospheric and oceanic patterns, the coupling of
the intertropical convergence zone to the Sahelian droughts
and to the Asian monsoon, the geological structures that
can only be understood through a regional or global study,
and the common concerns that all nations have about the
future availability of nonrenewable Earth resources. But
nowhere is this theme more appropriate than in the consideration of the Earth's biomass and man's potentially
adverse impact upon it. This can be illustrated most
vividly in the example of deforestation in the tropics.[56]

Throughout the tropics, evidence is accumulating that
the forest resource is disappearing far more rapidly than

had been thought and, indeed, the estimates of available
forest cover have had to be reduced dramatically in India,
Thailand, the Philippines, Costa Rica, the Ivory Coast,
Brazil, and Indonesia.[57,58] Systematic, repetitive measurements are necessary to monitor this essential resource,
yet clearly this is again an area of great national sensitivity. Only space systems offer the potential to map
economically and objectively the state of the Earth's vegetative cover. The word "objectively" is crucial in this
sentence, because without objectivity the discussion is
reduced to a political contest between those having an
apocalyptic view of the Earth's future and those with an
antiapocalyptic view.

One of the most important linkages tying the atmosphere, lithosphere, the oceans, and biosphere together is
hydrology. Precipitation must occur with the proper quantity and timing to sustain the biosphere. Excessive precipitation produces floods and polluting runoff into water
bodies. The solid Earth nourishes the vegetation, while
the vegetation protects the solid Earth from erosion by
wind and water. Again the total system view of the Earth
is necessary.

As the population of the Earth increases, man must
look for increasing production from all food sources.
There is no doubt that the oceans must be regarded as perhaps the most important of the sources of new production.
Yet the ocean serves many purposes, including transportation, recreation, and waste disposal. These purposes must
be balanced and the adverse interaction of one use on
another must be carefully monitored. The most critical
regions of all are the continental shelves, the highly productive areas where some 95% of the total fishery yield
occurs.

The CZCS and its proposed successor, the ocean color
imager (OCI), have the capability of assisting in the
determination of the productivity of the sunlit upper layer
of the ocean. In this instance, the term "productivity" is
used to describe the conversion of inorganic matter (e.g.,
oxygen and carbon dioxide) into organic matter through the
process of photosynthesis. Because the tetravalent carbon
atom is the building block for organic molecules, productivity of the ocean is expressed in grams of carbon production per square meter per year. The sun's energy is
captured in the photosynthetics process, leading to the
creation of phytoplankton, the base of the marine food
chain whose abundance ultimately dictates the fertility of
an ocean region and the fish population it can support.
The density of phytoplankton reflects a changing concentra-

tion of chlorophyll, which in turn produces subtle variations in the color of the ocean. It is this color change
that the sensors detect.

The CZCS and OCI sensors can be used to aid in the
location of pelagic fish and in the determination of appropriate environmental conditions for the release of juvenile
salmon. The sensors can also track areas of ocean pollution through measurements of the diffuse attenuation
coefficient.

As with all of the other applications discussed above,
ocean color measurements cross national boundaries and
involve major economic interests. They also may involve
sensitive issues relating to ocean pollution, particularly
with respect to its source and the identification of
responsible parties. Also in common with the other applications, the coupling of the atmosphere, oceans, and solid
Earth to the biosphere is vital to understanding the Earth
and projecting its future. To this point in this paper,
the focus has been on near-term interactions and effects.
The next section will deal with long-term climate change
and its detection.

VII. The Earth's Climate

The focus of the preceding discipline areas was on
near-term results that could be derived from Earth observations, where the time-span associated with "near-term"
ranges from sensing a severe weather event and providing
adequate warning to the public to performing measurements
of a given area that may be used over a period of years in
exploring for minerals. In other words, there is a relatively near-term and direct tie between the measurement and
some foreseeable benefit. There is another class of measurements having to do with long-term climate change for
which space techniques are also suited. In this case, the
measurements may of necessity be indirect or at best be
carried out over a very long period. In the latter example, two issues immediately arise:

1) Can the measurements needed today in order to
unravel the puzzle of climate change detection in the next
century be adequately defined?

2) Can a self-consistent data record be created of
sufficient length and sensitivity to allow corrective
actions to be taken adequately far in advance, if they are
necessary?

As in many such sweeping questions, the only answer is
that scientists will do the best job that they can. The
questions do serve notice, however, that the scientific

underpinnings must be as rigorously developed as possible to support both the definition of the required measurements and the development of the criteria for the data record. Certainly, the greater the ambiguity in that record, the longer will be the period before the trends can be observed and the shorter will be the time available if man's actions must be corrected.

The question of climate change detection is being investigated by many researchers and it would be almost impossible to provide a synopsis of all of their activities. In the next few paragraphs, only a brief outline will be provided, with particular emphasis on the role of space-based measurements. A more complete discussion is available in a description NASA has published of its program and the relationship to the overall U.S. and world climate programs.[59]

The precise measurement of climate-related parameters from space platforms received a major advancement in the flight of the SMM/ACRIM (discussed previously in Sec. II) and the cavity pyrheliometer used in the Nimbus-7 Earth Radiation Budget Experiment. These provided the first a accurate measurements of the solar driving function for the Earth's climate. The next set of measurements related to the amount of energy emitted by the Earth back to space and used data from earlier weather satellites and Nimbus-7. These results will be extended considerably by NASA's Earth Radiation Budget Experiment, which consists of a free-flying satellite, the Earth Radiation Budget Satellite (ERBS), and sensors on the NOAA-F and -G weather satellites.

Before solar radiation can reach the Earth's surface, or pass back out to space, it must pass through clouds, atmospheric aerosols, and the atmosphere with its various trace gases. Each of these links in the chain is under investigation. The International Satellite Cloud Climatology Project (ISCCP), sponsored jointly by the International Council of Scientific Unions (ICSU) and the World Meteorological Organization's (WMO) World Climate Research Program, is designed to evaluate the clouds' contributions and involves the entire ring of geostationary weather satellites, as well as many other data sources.

Determining the effects of atmospheric aerosols, such as those that result from volcanic eruptions, will require much further research, but may not yield to satellite analysis beyond the simple tracking of dust plumes. The Stratospheric Aerosols and Gases Experiment (SAGE) on ERBS will provide insights, but not a complete picture. On the other hand, trace gases are the subject of a major NASA

research mission called the Upper Atmosphere Research
Satellite (UARS) and include such critical gases as ozone
and carbon dioxide. Ozone measurements will also be the
subject of the solar backscatter ultraviolet spectrometer
(SBUV/2) that will be flown on the NOAA polar-orbiting
weather satellites, as well as on UARS. Its objective
will be to determine the total amount of ozone in the
atmosphere, its vertical distribution, and its seasonal
variation.

The limited and somewhat incomplete listing above
accurately conveys the idea that a large number of climate-
related space measurements are planned for approximately
the next decade. It does not convey at all well the rather
incomplete scientific framework into which those measurements must be placed. To gain an understanding of the
wider structure, it is necessary to examine some of the
numerous studies addressing these issues. One of the first
was produced by an International Workshop on Climate Issues
that was chaired by R. M. White in 1978.[60] The report outlines the difficulties in projecting the climatic effect
of increases in atmospheric carbon dioxide and the even
greater difficulty associated with evaluating the socioeconomic effects. The report established the framework for
what became the World Climate Research Program.

This study was extended in 1979 by the Charney study
group on carbon dioxide and climate.[61] The study concluded
that, although there were uncertainties in the time scale,
the effects of the measured increases in atmospheric
carbon dioxide would result in a global warming with major
consequences.

These early studies, and many that accompanied and
succeeded them, noted the need for increased research on
the basic climate parameters, but also on the couplings
among them. It was this ground swell that led to the
establishment of the NASA Global Habitability Program and
the consideration of an International Geosphere-Biosphere
Program mentioned in the first paragraphs of this paper.
They have, in turn, led to analyses that are pointing the
way to a better understanding of the Earth's climate
system. The previously referenced Global Biology Research
Program document[56] has been followed by a thorough review
of land-related global habitability science issues[62] that
addresses such things as the global energy balance, hydrological cycle, and biogeochemical cycles. The biogeochemical cycle was the subject of another workshop chaired by
M. McElroy and aimed at understanding the present status of
and likely future evolution of the planetary life-support
system.[63]

The study of the Earth on all time scales is of
supreme importance; the study of the Earth's climate is
ultimately the study of man's survivability on "Spaceship
Earth." More than a decade ago, Aurelio Peccei wrote:[64]

"The human species is peculiar in that it complements
its slow biological adaptability with a social organization and cultural devices capable of interpreting
and modifying its environments. Hence, its ecological
fitness and survival depend essentially on continual
adaptation of this extraordinary sociocultural endowment
to changing conditions. But, since humans possess
another peculiarity--that of being themselves the principal agent of change on earth--and since manprovoked
change is nowadays revolutionary, their life and future
hinge on rapid and radical, continual cultural updating--
as is necessary to maintain the human system in dynamic
equilibrium and harmony both within and with respect to
its environments."

These words fittingly describe the need to understand the
coupled system that controls the Earth's climate.
It is evident that the examination of climate change
involves all of the disciplines discussed in this paper,
special measurements aimed at particular aspects of the
climate system, and the development of a deeper understanding of all of these disciplines and their interrelationships. It is not necessary to have an apocalyptic view of
the Earth's future to recognize the value of long-term
climate research. The environment is often the subject of
emotional--and even highly politicized--discussions, but
there should be no argument that scientifically accurate
foundations must be developed. It would also seem evident
that such important objectives would capture the enthusiasm
of researchers in all nations and carry more than adequate
justification for inclusion in the programs of all spacefaring nations.

VIII. The Problems of Categories

There are dozens of categories that can be used for
space remote sensing missions and sometimes it seems that,
however they are chosen, they create difficulties. Some of
those difficulties will be examined at this point.
There have, no doubt, been points in the above pages
where the use of discipline categories has seemed artificial. The reason for that appearance is that it is not an
appearance but a reality. It is artificial to categorize
space systems according to an orientation toward land,

ocean, or atmospheric applications. Weather (atmospheric)
satellites are used for ocean applications and even for
crop condition assessments. Landsats see the bottoms of
lagoons and the effluent plumes in water bodies. Synthetic
aperture radars aimed at the ocean produce images of geologic features when over land. The boundaries are not clear.
The only thing that is clear is that all represent large
investments of resources and share in many instances a
common "Earthview" from a particular orbit within a certain
range of times of day. Therefore, at least for nongeosta-
tionary orbits, the orbital parameters establish the application and, once they are selected, the passenger list of
possible instruments can be prepared. In the future, the
discipline distinctions will vanish.

Another peculiar categorization is made between
research and applications missions. This categorization is
sometimes used by those seeking identifiable beneficiaries
who might be assigned the cost of a given mission. On more
than one occasion, it appeared that likelihood of producing
tangible benefits became a negative rather than a positive
consideration. Why would any spacefaring nation omit from
its national program a vigorous effort in the practical
applications of space? A rather simple truth is that all
Earth-directed remote sensing missions are first and foremost scientific explorations of this planet. No measurements currently made rest upon a scientific base so sound
that there are not major research activities needed for
their interpretation. The images from weather satellites
may seem on occasion mundane, but they depict more accurately gaps in understanding rather than comprehension.

A related categorization is that of experimental and
operational missions. If operational carries with it a
connotation of routine and repetitive, then it is clear
that over some time scale there are no operational
missions, because all systems change and evolve with new
knowledge gained from earlier experience. Further, for
climate research, an experiment might continue for decades,
with consistent measurements being repeated rigorously to
protect the integrity of the data record. Still further,
even though an instrument on a satellite might be repeat-
edly flown--and, therefore, be considered "operational"--
its uses may be changing frequently and dramatically as its
companion ground system and human operators and users
become more sophisticated. Thus, it must be recognized
that in the future the distinctions among research, applications, experimental, and operational missions will
lessen, with each mission tailored to understand the Earth
through a combination of repeated or singular measurements.

Long-term experiments will have the character of an operational rather than an experimental system.

Sometimes people categorize space systems aimed at ocean or geological or other disciplines as somehow separate from the parent discipline of oceanography, etc. Out of the context of the parent discipline, space systems are without roots and sterile. It is only through their integration into the greater dimensionality of the overall science and its integrated theoretical and measurement milieu that they gain substance and advance understanding.

Finally, there is the separation of national and international programs. Observations of the Earth from space know no national boundaries. The passage ot a satellite from the space above one country to that above another requires no visa and technology has made obsolete the concept of complete national privacy. By the very things that they observe, however, all Earth observation programs are international programs, and--while no nation can prevent being observed (except via overtly hostile actions such as the use of antisatellite weapons)--it does not follow that helplessness leads to a lack of concern. This is an appropriate point to move to the next section of this paper that discusses the international concerns about remote sensing.

IX. International Concerns about Remote Sensing

Earth observation satellites have demonstrated incontrovertibly the contribution they can make to the understanding of the planet and to the daily activities of the planet's citizens. It is not surprising that a principal international concern is the future availability of these data. It is perceived that data could be denied to countries through a number of possible actions, both inadvertent as well as advertent. It is also perceived that unilateral changes by an operating nation may affect its ability to use data upon which it has become dependent. These points will be elaborated upon below.

Data denial could occur in a variety of ways:

1) An agreement with a neighboring country could contain an exclusive use clause, perhaps in exchange for some special consideration (a premium fee in a commercial system or a foreign policy advantage in a governmental system), that would bar distribution in the concerned country.

2) For some types of perishable data, the agreement would need only to stipulate a time period of exclusive use to render the data largely useless. Thus, delay may be as harmful as denial. Note that this is not only true of weather or oceanographic data, but could also be true for agricultural, hydrographic, or even some geological data.

3) If fees are involved for data, another de facto way
in which data could be denied occurs when the data can be
afforded by one group of countries, but not by others.
    Unilateral changes by an operating country can also
result in data denial in some of the following ways:
    1) Modifications to the design (transmission parame-
ters, data formats, etc.) of a sensing system are clearly
within the authority of the country or body funding and
operating a system that other users may not be able to
accommodate.
    2) The operation of a sensing system, or a particular
sensor element of the overall system, may be terminated.
Such abrupt actions, or the design modifications just mentioned, could also have been categorized as another form of
data denial.

    Thus, in the absence of financial, political, or moral
influence, the perception of helplessness alluded to above
can be heightened. It is this perception that has led to
so many international discussions, particularly within the
framework of the United Nations. These and other considerations were major issues at the second United Nations
Conference on the Exploration and Peaceful Uses of Outer
Space.[65]
    It may be surprising to some that the above discussion
opened with concern about access to data, rather than a
review of the concept of "prior consent." A number of
countries have taken the position in the past that a country's permission must be gained before data are taken of
its territory. This has largely passed (within a number of
spatial resolution bounds) because of the inability to prevent the imaging of national territories from space. This
was the earliest version of prior consent. It was quickly
supplanted by a modified version of prior consent--namely,
even though a country could not prevent unwanted data-
taking, the sensed country should have control over the
distribution of data taken of its territory. Hence, the
concept of "national privacy" has been raised, with its
extension into more established principles of national
sovereignty. Thus, the earlier principle of the right to
"prior consent to observe" has evolved into a principle of
"prior consent to distribute data."
    All of these issues have been largely academic up
until the present time, because many countries have bene-
fitted from civil remote sensing systems. An enlightened
data distribution policy was initiated for such data that
established the principle of equality of access to data.
Data obtained from the U.S. land and weather satellites
were made available to anyone desiring them on equal terms

(cost, schedule, etc.). The specter of one country using
privately held space data to the disadvantage of its neighbors was eliminated. Each of the foreign ground stations
participating in the Landsat program was required to sign a
"memorandum of understanding"committing it to nondiscriminatory data dissemination.

If remote sensing moves into the commercial world, the
protection of "copyrights" for data products will undoubtedly be sought. The copyright sought could encompass all
levels of data products and their derivative products, or
some fraction thereof. This is not necessarily incompat-
ible with the principle of nondiscriminatory data dissemination. That principle does not deny an organization the
right to protect its intellectual property, only that one
group of customers not be treated to favorable access to
data not available to other customers. In light of the
formidable business obstacles that governments could place
in the path of companies intending to do business within
their borders, nondiscriminatory data dissemination may
ultimately be a small price to pay.

It should be noted, however, that some members of the
private sector object vigorously to any restraint on their
activities. One such proponent, best known for his analysis supporting the cost effectiveness of the Space Shuttle,
has asserted a constitutional right to ". . . the freedom
to gather publicly and privately whatever information one
desires as part of the exercise of free speech."[66] He
recommends that a law be passed with the language:

> "Nothing in this Bill shall be construed to infringe in
> any form on the right of public and private persons to
> gather information at their expense for peaceful pur-
> poses; or to infringe in any form on any property rights
> from information thus gathered; nor shall any license or
> other regulation be required for such activities; nor any
> direction be given by any Government entity as to the
> uses of such information; nor shall any public or private
> person be denied access to space transportation and other
> services provided by the U.S. Government or any U.S.
> person for the pursuit of such activities; . . ."

If nothing else, this would remove any ambiguity about
foreign concerns with respect to remote sensing, if it were
adopted. It highlights, however, how divergent the views
are that must be reconciled. On the one hand, the private
sector view expressed above is unacceptable to a substantial segment of the international community; on the other
hand, a view that accounts for the concerns of that community may produce a business environment that is unaccept-

able to the private sector. It will take a considerable
time for these issues to be resolved.

Another issue that must be resolved is that of sensor
resolution, whether in the spatial, spectral, or temporal
domains. One reason for the early acceptance of weather
satellite data was not only its wide international utility,
but its relatively coarse resolution, which aroused no
concerns about national security. Thus far, as more and
more advanced sensors have been deployed, international
acceptance has stemmed from shared mutual benefits and the
fact that nations became accustomed to them--having experienced no bad effects from their predecessors. This may
continue, but nations may also find remote sensing objec-
tionable when it reaches the level of detecting military
activities or items considered to have critical national
economic value. This is also going to take time to
resolve. A still further issue is whether a radar system
or other active sensor is more intrusive than an imaging
sensor and subject to a different set of rules.

Once again in this paper the inherently international
nature of remote sensing is obvious. It seems self-evident
that the way the above concerns can best be resolved is by
international cooperation in which concerned nations can
participate and make their influence felt in a constructive
manner. This leads to the next section of this paper concerning the commercial opportunities in civil space remote
sensing.

X. Commercial Opportunities in Remote Sensing

There are many opportunities for the private sector
to participate in civil Earth observations systems. The
private sector, at least in western countries, is the
exclusive manufacturer of the space hardware. The private
sector is the dominant supplier of specialized services
derived from the basic data sets obtained from space systems, even though the data sets themselves may find their
principal role in government functions. Further, the private sector is the principal operator of spaceborne Earth
observation systems through contractual arrangements with
government agencies. The issue receiving a great deal of
current attention is whether the private sector role can
be expanded even further to encompass full management and
ownership, in a manner analogous to domestic communications
satellite services in the United States.

France and the United States are engaged in a great
experiment to determine if spaceborne land remote sensing
systems represent a viable commercial opportunity. As of

the date of this paper, it is premature to indicate the
outcome of this effort. The French SPOT program will have
its first launch in 1985. The current U.S. plan is to
transfer the Landsat-4 and -5 satellites to a private firm
(the Earth Observation Satellite Company, which is usually
called simply "EOSAT") late in 1984 and to have the first
launch of a satellite by that firm in 1987 or 1988. Both
France and the United States will retain substantial
government involvement in the program at least into the
early 1990s. There seems to be little doubt that the
present market cannot sustain the operating costs of a
land observing system, to say nothing of the capital costs.
It is at best speculative that an adequate market will
evolve with time and that government involvement will then
diminish.

One of the fundamental questions that has been avoided
with respect to land observing systems is, "If they are not
a commercial success, should they continue?" Because of
the early justification for the U.S. Landsat program--
justification that this author believes to have been most
unfortunate--there is a belief that the success or failure
of the Landsat program hinges upon its ability to survive
as a commercial entity. This is patently incorrect. Land
observing systems are simply another means to develop
specialized maps of the Earth. They map renewable and
nonrenewable resources, land use, urban change, and other
parameters. In common with many other mapping functions
(note that the less rigorous term of "mapping" is used,
rather than "cartographic"), the principal benefits lie in
secondary, tertiary, and higher-order applications of the
"maps." Because these higher-order benefits are distributed widely through society, the provision of the basic
maps has almost always been a governmental function that is
paid for by taxes. Capturing the appropriate cash value
resulting from the higher-order applications may be difficult or even impossible. Therefore, from a societal point
of view, a land observing system might be a commercial
failure on the basis of its ability to recover costs from
primary data sales and yet be a success from an overall
national perspective. Indeed, the greater tax base produced through a fostering of the development of new value-
added industries might warrant an indefinitely continued
government support of a land observing system.

While the above discussion considers only the narrow
subject of land observing systems, some of the same considerations apply to atmosphere and ocean observing systems.
In both cases the governmental use of primary data will
dominate for many years, because issues related to the

protection of life and property are associated with the
data and such protection is a traditionally governmental
function. Beyond the primary function, however, there
are numerous opportunities for private firms to provide
specialized services to a wide range of clients. The
growth of such private activities is dependent upon the
continued availability--at minimal cost--of the primary
data sets.

Another major issue that has yet to be satisfactorily
addressed is the question, "How many spaceborne earth
observations systems does the world need?" At present,
competition and a desire to ensure domestic technological
capabilities are driving more and more nations to seek an
Earth observations system of their own. On the global
scale, this produces inevitably a duplication of effort and
an inefficient application of scarce resources. Even more
seriously, this inefficient use of resources denies support
of the vitally important data communications, processing,
and analysis functions that are needed to gain the full
value of the space sensing system. As the first enthusiasm
wanes and national chauvinism becomes less important than
budgets, it seems likely that an international consortium
will emerge to meet global needs. As has been noted above,
international cooperation is already extensive in Earth
observations; it needs only to be extended to reap even
greater rewards.

XI. Future Opportunities for International Cooperation

During the next decade, it will be feasible for the
nations of the world to have a daily view of the Earth's
oceans and atmosphere, and even--at coarse resolution--
the land masses and ice. On a slower time scale, high-
resolution data of the land masses and ice will also be
available. The demands this effort will place on the Earth
observations community--in terms of sensor deployment, data
processing, and data distribution and application--will be
beyond the reach of any single nation if the full benefits
are to be obtained. International cooperation is a natural
and desirable avenue for sharing benefits and costs.
Precedents for joint programs exist and have been frequently mentioned above. The U.S. polar-orbiting weather
satellites are a splendid example of international cooperation. A further example is the activity being conducted
under the encouragement of the annual Economic Summit of
Industrialized Nations.

At the conclusion of the seventh meeting of the
Economic Summit, held in June 1982 at Versailles, a

Working Group on Technology, Growth, and Employment was established to identify areas for further cooperation among the members (Canada, Federal Republic of Germany, France, Italy, Japan, United Kingdom, United States, and the European Economic Community). Satellite remote sensing was one of 18 topics chosen for discussion and an international panel was formed to foster cooperation.

The objectives of this panel are to exchange information on remote sensing programs and plans, to coordinate remote sensing programs and plans with a view to avoiding duplication of efforts, fostering compatibility of activities to enhance the value of these programs in addressing global phenomena, and promoting more efficient uses of budget resources. All of these are consistent with international participation in cooperative Earth observation activities. Two working groups have been formed to coordinate activities. They are the Committee on Earth Observation Satellites (CEOS) and the International Polar-Orbiting Meteorological Satellite (IPOMS) Group.

CEOS provides a forum for the informal coordination of technical parameters of environmental, land, and ocean satellites. Membership is open to any country or agency with an approved remote sensing satellite program. At the first meeting in September 1984, participants included Brazil, Canada, the European Space Agency, France, India, Japan, and the United States.

IPOMS is exploring mechanisms for increased international cooperation in and support for polar-orbiting meteorological satellites and in ensuring their continuity. Members of the group are agencies currently contributing to or planning to contribute to the U.S. civil operational polar-orbiting environmental satellite system. Current contributors include Canada, France, and the United Kingdom. Potential future contributors include Australia, the Federal Republic of Germany, Italy, Norway, the European Space Agency, and others.

Thus, international cooperative mechanisms exist that can be built upon to foster greater integration of programs with the resulting increased benefits and program economies. Further, these forums also allow examination of the utility of NASA's planned space station program, both as a means to carry out Earth observations and as a vehicle for international cooperation.

XII. Possible Effect of NASA's Space Station Program on Earth Observations

The recent U.S. decision to proceed with the development of a manned space station program will provide a new

vantage point for Earth observations. There are three
principal elements to the NASA program: 1) the permanently
manned space station and its peripheral equipment in a low-
altitude orbit at 28.5 deg inclination, 2) an astronaut-
tended co-orbiting platform in the same orbit to be used
for materials processing and other experiments, and 3) an
astronaut-tended platform in near-polar, sun-synchronous
orbit. In the following paragraphs, the last element will
be referred to simply as the "polar platform." It is this
last element that has the potential to make a major contribution to Earth observations.

A polar platform can serve as the home for a multidisciplinary suite of instruments to monitor the ocean,
land, and atmosphere. The platform and its instrument
complement can be the product of international cooperation.
The instrument suite will be the result of the successful
flight of new sensors produced by research missions and the
continuing need to fly operational sensors. The rationale
for employing an astronaut-serviced platform will stand or
fall on the economics and ease of the servicing mission and
the ability of such a mission to make a clearly demonstra-
ble contribution to the Earth observation community's
objectives.

If a platform proves to be an economically attractive
alternative to expendable satellites, it can serve as the
carrier for a combined land, ocean, and atmospheric observation system of unparalleled capability. The need for
frequently updated global synoptic models will militate
toward the use of two platforms, both at an altitude of
800-1000 km, one using a morning southbound and the other
using an afternoon northbound equator crossing time.[68] The
nations of the world have the capability to participate
fully in this worthy enterprise. It requires only the per-
severance and willingness to create the administrative
innovations needed to make it happen.

XIII. Conclusions

To the author at least, the conclusions of this paper
are few and clear. Earth observations from space are an
inherently international activity that is justified by the
greater understanding it provides of the coupled, interdependent system called the planet Earth. It is deserving of
consistent, long-term support by all space-capable nations,
but--because of its great expense--opportunities must be
sought aggressively to expand international cooperation in
the coordination of missions and the sharing of mission
costs.

International sensitivities will be exacerbated by national programs, whether private or governmental, that do not acknowledge the legitimate concerns of other nations. Those same sensitivities will be alleviated by joint activities in which genuine partnerships are created for the investigation of the globe.

The future of space remote sensing is bright and can involve such new efforts as the space station program. If these potentials are realized and the space station program is accompanied by a vigorous effort in the Earth sciences, instrument development, experimentation, and data analysis, all of the visions of the Global Habitability or International Geosphere-Biosphere Programs can be realized. That is indeed a challenge worthy of the 21st century.

Acknowledgments

The draft of this paper was reviewed by a number of colleagues, all of whom suggested very constructive changes and improvements. Among them were John Bowman, Abraham Schnapf, M. T. Chahine, John Harries, David S. Johnson, Lawrence R. Pettinger, and W. Stanley Wilson. Their assistance was very much appreciated.

References

[1]Executive Committee, "Global Change: Impacts on Habitability, A Scientific Basis for Assessment," Jet Propulsion Laboratory, Pasadena, Calif., Rept. D-95, July 7, 1982.

[2]"Toward an International Geosphere-Biosphere Program, A Study of Global Change," Report of a National Research Council Workshop, National Academy Press, Washington, D.C., 1983.

[3]Barney, G. O., "The Global 2000 Report to the President: Entering the Twenty-First Century," U.S. Council on Environmental Quality and Department of State, Washington, D.C., 1980.

[4]Report of the Global 2000 Task Group on Data and Modeling Capability, prepared for the President's Task Force on Global Resources and Environment, Nov. 7, 1980.

[5]"Global Models, World Futures, and Public Policy, A Critique," Office of Technology Assessment, Congress of the United States, Government Printing Office, Washington, D.C., April 1982.

[6]"Solar-Terrestrial Research for the 1980's," Committee on Solar-Terrestrial Research, National Research Council, National Academy of Sciences, National Academy Press, Washington, D.C., 1981.

[7]Newell, H. E., Beyond the Atmosphere, Early Years of Space Science, NASA SP-4211, 1980.

[8]Willson, R. C., Gulkis, S., Janssen, M., Hudson, H. S., and Chapman, G. A., "Observation of Solar Radiance Variability," Science, No. 211, 1981, pp. 700-702.

[9]Hoffman, R. A. (ed.), "Dynamics Explorer," Space Science Instrumentation, Vol. 5, No. 4, 1981.

[10]Spencer, N. W. and Nagy, A. F. (eds.), "Dynamics Explorer Results," Geophysical Research Letters, Vol. 9, No. 9, Sept. 1982.

[11]Federal Coordinator for Meteorological Services and Supporting Research, "National Plan for Space Environment Services and Supporting Research," National Oceanic and Atmospheric Administration, Rept. FCM-P10-1983, July 1983.

[12]Shawhan, S. D., "International Solar-Terrestrial Physics Program -- Program Objectives and Relationship to IGBP," Presentation to the Board on Atmospheric Sciences and Climate, National Academy of Sciences, Washington, D.C., Feb. 16, 1984.

[13]Suess, S. T., "Operational Uses for a Solar Soft X-Ray Imaging Telescope," NOAA Technical Memorandum ERL SEL-66, July 1983.

[14]"The Global Weather Experiment -- Perspectives on Its Implementation and Exploitation," U.S. Committee for the Global Atmospheric Research Program, National Academy of Sciences, Washington, D.C., 1978.

[15]Johnson, D. S., "Twentieth Anniversary of the World Weather Watch: Opportunities and Outlook for an Improved WWW," World Meteorological Organization, Pub. 608, 1983.

[16]Hussey, W. J., "The Economic Benefits of Operational Environmental Satellites," National Environmental Satellite, Data, and Information Service, March 1983.

[17]Vonder Haar, T., "Comments on Satellite Meteorology from Geostationary Satellites," The Conception, Growth, Accomplishments, and Future of Meteorological Satellites, NASA CP 2257, 1982, pp. 72-83.

[18]Vaughan, W. W. (ed.), "Meteorological Satellites -- Past, Present, and Future," NASA CP 2227, 1982.

[19]White, R. M., "Land, Sea, and Air: Global Implications of the View from Space," Global Implications of Space Activities, edited by J. Gray and L. Levy, AIAA, New York, 1982.

[20]Lerner, E. J., "The Great Weather Network," IEEE Spectrum, Vol. 19, Feb. 1982, pp. 50-57.

[21]Wilson, W. S., "Oceanography from Satellites?," Oceanus, Vol. 24, No. 3, Fall 1981, pp. 9-16.

[22]Weeks, W. F., "Sea Ice: The Potential of Remote Sensing," Oceanus, Vol. 24, No. 3, Fall 1981, pp. 39-48.

[23]Ruttenberg, S. (ed.), "Needs, Opportunities and Strategies for a Long-Term Oceanic Sciences Satellite Program," NCAR TN 185, Nov. 1981.

[24]O'Brien, J. J. (chm.), "Scientific Opportunities Using Satellite Surface Wind Stress Measurements Over the Ocean," Report of the Satellite Surface Stress Working Group, NASA, June 1982.

[25]Wunsch, C., "The Promise of Satellite Altimetry," Oceanus, Vol. 24, No. 3, Fall 1981, pp. 17-26.

[26]Brown, O. B. and Cheney, R. E., "Advances in Satellite Oceanography," Reviews of Geophysics and Space Physics, Vol. 21, No. 5, June 1983, pp. 1216-1230.

[27]Stewart, R. H., "Oceanography from Space," Proceedings of the 33rd Congress of the International Astronautical Federation, International Astronautical Federation, Paris, Oct. 1982, pp. 246-248.

[28]Bernstein, R. L. (ed.), "Seasat Special Issue I: Geophysical Evaluation," Journal of Geophysical Research, Vol. 87, No. C5, April 30, 1982.

[29]Kirwan, A. D., Ahrens, T. J., and Born, G. H. (eds.), "Seasat Special Issue II: Scientific Results," Journal of Geophysical Research, Vol. 88, No. C3, Feb. 28, 1983.

[30]Gower, J. F. R. (ed.), Oceanography from Space, Plenum, New York, 1981.

[31]Allan, T. D. (ed.), Satellite Microwave Remote Sensing, Ellis Horwood Ltd., Surrey, England, 1983.

[32]"Technical Description for Design of MOS-1 Ground Stations," NASDA, Doc. DE-4052A, Sept. 1983.

[33]European Space Agency, "ERS-1 - A New Tool for Marine Applications and Science," Earth Observation Quarterly, No. 4, Dec. 1983.

[34]Langham, E., "Radarsat," Proceedings of the Pecora VIII Symposium, Sioux Falls, S. Dak., Oct. 4-7, 1983, pp. 246-258.

[35]Honhart, D., "NROSS Description," U.S. Navy, Feb. 1984.

[36]TOPEX Science Working Group, "Satellite Altimetric Measurements of the Ocean," Jet Propulsion Laboratory, Pasadena, Calif., Mar. 1, 1981.

[37]Short, N. M., Lowman, P. D. Jr., Freden, S. C., and Finch, W. A. Jr., Mission to Earth: Landsat Views the World, NASA SP-360, 1976.

[38]Henderson, F. B., "Geological Mapping by Satellite," Optima, Vol. 31, No. 3, Sept. 15, 1983, pp. 124-139.

[39]Short, N. M. and Stuart, L. M. Jr., The Heat Capacity Mapping Mission (HCMM) Anthology, NASA SP-465, 1982.

[40]Harrison, J. C. and Rapp, R. H. (chm.), "Applications of a Dedicated Gravitational Satellite Mission," National Academy of Sciences, 1979.

[41]"Geodynamics in the 1980's," U.S. Geodynamics Committee, National Academy of Sciences, 1980.

[42]Simonett, D. S., "The Development and Principles of Remote Sensing," Manual of Remote Sensing, Vol. 1, 2nd ed., American Society of Photogrammetry, Falls Church, Va., 1982, p. 12.

[43]"SPAS Team to Compete with Landsat," Aviation Week and Space Technology, Nov. 7, 1983.

[44]Courtois, M., "SPOT System Conception and Program Status," Proceedings of the Pecora VIII Symposium, Sioux Falls, S. Dak., Oct. 4-7, 1983, pp. 269-278.

[45]Kasturirangan, K., "IRS Satellite System," ISRO Satellite Centre, Bangalore, India, to be published.

[46]"Acquisition and Processing of Space Data for Mapping Purposes," Report of Working Group IV/3, International Society of Photogrammetry and Remote Sensing (ISPRS), Feb. 22, 1984.

[47]Cloud, P., "The Biosphere," Scientific American, Vol. 249, No. 3, Sept. 1983, pp. 176-189.

[48]Walsh, J. J. (chm.), "The Marine Resources Experiment Program (MAREX)," Report of the Ocean Color Science Working Group, NASA Goddard Space Flight Center, Dec. 1982.

[49]"AgRISTARS Annual Report, FY 1981," NASA Johnson Space Center, Houston, Jan. 1982.

[50]Hill, C. L., "Analysis of Landsat 4 Thematic Mapper Data for Classification of Forest in Baldwin County, Alabama," Proceedings of the Pecora VIII Symposium, Sioux Falls, S. Dak., Oct. 4-7, 1983, pp. 110-121.

[51]Pitts, D. E. et al., "Agricultural Applications of TM Data," Proceedings of the Pecora VIII Symposium, Sioux Falls, S. Dak., Oct. 4-7, 1983, pp. 122-133.

[52]Myers, V. I., "Remote Sensing Applications in Agriculture," Manual of Remote Sensing, Vol. 2, 2nd ed., American Society of Photogrammetry, Falls Church, Va., 1982, pp. 2111-2228.

[53]Tucker, C. J., Gatlin, J. A., and Schneider, S. R., "Monitoring Vegetation in the Nile Delta with NOAA-6 and NOAA-7 AVHRR Imagery," Photogrammetric Engineering and Remote Sensing, Vol. 50, Jan. 1984, pp. 53-61.

[54]Yates, H. W. et al., "The Role of Meteorological Satellites in Agricultural Remote Sensing," Remote Sensing of Environment, Vol. 14, 1984, pp. 219-233.

[55]Merritt, E. S., "Space Observations in Agricultural Information Systems -- A Review of Today's Systems with Requirements for Tomorrow," to be published.

[56]Rambler, M. B. (ed.), "Global Biology Research Program," NASA TM 85629, Jan. 1983.

[57]Botkin, D. B. (chm.), "Towards a Science of the Biosphere," Committee on Planetary Biology, National Academy of Sciences, 1984.

[58]Lanly, J. P., "Tropical Forest Resources," United Nations Food and Agriculture Organization, FAO Forestry Paper 30, Rome, 1982.

[59]"Understanding Climate: A Strategy for Solar and Earth Radiation Research (1984-1994)," Office of Space Science and Applications, NASA Headquarters, Washington, D.C., Oct. 1983.

[60]White, R. M. (chm.), "International Perspectives on the Study of Climate and Society," Report of International Workshop on the Study of Climate and Society, National Research Council, National Academy of Sciences, Washington, D.C., 1978.

[61]Charney, J. G. (chm.), "Carbon Dioxide and Climate: A Scientific Assessment," National Academy of Sciences, Washington, D.C., 1979.

[62]"Land-Related Global Habitability Science Issues," Office of Space Science and Applications, NASA TM 85841, July 1983.

[63]McElroy, M. (chm.), "Global Change: A Biogeochemical Perspective," Jet Propulsion Laboratory, Pasadena, Calif., Rept. 83-51, July 15, 1983.

[64]Peccei, A., "Human Settlements," Who Speaks for Earth?, edited by M. F. Strong, Norton, New York, 1973, p. 155.

[65]"Report of the Second United Nations Conference on the Exploration and Peaceful Uses of Outer Space," Vienna, Aug. 1982, UN Doc. A/CONF. 101/10, 1982.

[66]Heiss, K., Testimony before the U.S. Senate Committee on Commerce, Science, and Transportation, Subcommittee on Science, Technology, and Space, March 22, 1984.

[67]Gille, J., "Middle Atmosphere Science," Earth Observing System, NASA TM 86129, 1984, p. A49.

[68]McElroy, J. and Schneider, S., "Utilization of the Polar Platform of NASA's Space Station Program for Operational Earth Observations," NOAA Tech. Rept. NESDIS 12, Sept. 1984.

Chapter II.   Meteorological and Environmental Satellites

The TIROS Meteorological Satellites—
Twenty-five Years: 1960-1985

A. Schnapf*

Aerospace Systems Engineering, Willingboro, New Jersey

Abstract

The TIROS meteorological satellite program has completed a quarter century of orbital space observtions.
During the period between 1960 and 1985 four generations
of the TIROS/ESSA/ITOS/TIROS N-NOAA family of satellites
evolved. A total of 30 satellites were launched, all meeting or exceeding the mission objectives.

The TIROS I-X series, the development and semi-operational system were orbited between 1960 and 1965. The
ESSA (Environmental Satellite Service Administration) 1-9,
the world's first global operational system were placed in
orbit in 1966-1969. The ITOS (improved TIROS operational
system) were launched between 1970 and 1977, providing day
and night global observation including temperature sounding
of the atmosphere. TIROS N/NOAA A-J (National Oceanic and
Atmospheric Administration) were introduced in 1978 and the
advanced TIROS N was orbited in 1983. This fourth generation provides enhanced data and expanded observations over
its predecessors. NOAA (G-J) spacecraft will be launched
between 1985 and 1989 to assure continuity of meteorological data.

The TIROS program built by RCA Astro-Electronics for
NASA and NOAA has been the mainstay of the U.S. low-earth
polar orbiting meteorological and environmental satellite
system for this country and the world at large.

Introduction

On April 1, 1960, TIROS-1 (Television Infrared Observation Satellite) was orbited successfully from Cape
Canaveral, Fla. It was the world's first meteorological

satellite, ushering in a new era in meteorological observations. From its very first orbit around the Earth, TIROS
demonstrated the ability of the satellite to perform global
observations on a timely basis. The TIROS meteorological
satellite system was designed and built at RCA Astro-Electronics, Princeton, N.J., for the National Aeronautics and
Space Administration (NASA). With the success of TIROS-1,
there followed an orderly growth and evolution of the TIROS
family of meteorological satellites through the 1980s.
Figure 1 depicts the chronology of the TIROS satellites.
A total of 30 TIROS/ESSA/ITOS/(TIROS-N)/NOAA series of
satellites was orbited successfully, all meeting or exceeding the mission requirements. Table 1 shows the orbital
performance of the TIROS satellites. In 1960-1965, 10
TIROS research and development spin-stabilized satellites
were placed in orbit to provide data for researchers and
the U.S. meteorological community. TIROS-VIII, launched
in 1963, with its special automatic picture transmission
(APT), provided the first real-time direct readout of the
satellite's observations to simple ground stations located
in various parts of the world.

The world's first operational meteorological satellite
(as well as the world's first operational application satellite) was introduced into service in February 1966 with
the successful launch of ESSA 1 and 2. The Environmental
Science Service Administration's (ESSA) spin-stabilized
satellite series provided two satellite configurations, an
ESSA APT for direct real-time readout of observed data to
relatively low-cost Earth receiving stations located
throughout the planet and a second ESSA-AVCS capable of

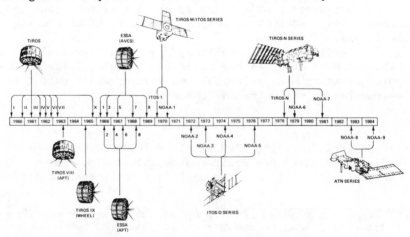

Fig. 1 TIROS polar-orbiting global operation meteorological
satellite system evolution.

Table 1 TIROS/ESSA/ITOS/NOAA satellites in orbit

Name	Launched	Weight (lbs)	Period (min)	Perigee (km)	Apogee (km)	Inclination (deg)	Life (days)	Remarks
TIROS I	01APR60	263	99.2	796	867	48.3	89	1 TV-WA and 1 TV-NA
TIROS II	23NOV60	278	98.3	717	837	48.5	376	1 TV-WA, 1 TV-NA, passive & active IR scan
TIROS III	12JUL61	285	100.4	854	937	47.8	230	2 TV-WA, HB, IR, IRP
TIROS IV	08FEB62	285	100.4	817	972	48.3	161	2 TV-WA, IR, IRP, HB
TIROS V	19JUN62	287	100.5	680	1119	58.1	321	1 TV-WA, 1 TV-MA
TIROS VI	18SEP62	281	98.7	783	822	58.2	389	1 TV-WA, 1 TV-MA
TIROS VII	19JUN63	299	97.4	713	743	58.2	1809	2 TV-WA, IR, IP, HB
TIROS VIII	21DEC63	260	99.3	796	878	58.5	1287	1st APT TV direct readout & 1 TV-WA
TIROS IX	22JAN65	320	119.2	806	2967	96.4	1238	First "wheel"; 2 TV-WA global coverage
TIROS X	02JUL65	320	100.6	848	957	98.6	730	Sun synchronous, 2 TV-WA
ESSA 1	03FEB66	320	100.2	800	965	97.9	861	1st operational system, 2 TV-WA, FPR
ESSA 2	28FEB66	290	113.3	1561	1639	101.0	1692	2 APT, global operational APT
ESSA 3	02OCT66	350	114.5	1593	1709	101.0	738	2 AVCS, FPR
ESSA 4	26JAN67	290	113.4	1522	1656	102.0	465	2 APT
ESSA 5	20APR67	350	113.5	1556	1635	101.9	1034	2 AVCS, FPR
ESSA 6	10NOV67	290	114.8	1622	1713	102.1	763	2 APT TV
ESSA 7	16AUG68	350	114.9	1646	1691	101.7	571	2 AVCS, FPR, S-Band
ESSA 8	15DEC68	290	114.7	1622	1682	101.8	1103	2 APT TV
ESSA 9	26FEB69	350	115.3	1637	1730	101.9	1030	2 AVCS, FPR, S-Band
ITOS 1	23JAN70	683	115.1	1648	1700	102.0	510	2 APT, 2 AVCS, 2 SR, FPR, 3-axis stabilization
NOAA 1	11DEC70	683	114.8	1422	1472	102.0	252	2 APT, 2 AVCS, 2 SR, FPR
NOAA 2	15OCT72	750	114.9	1451	1458	98.6	837	2 VHRR, 2 VTPR, 2 SR, SPM
NOAA 3	06NOV73	750	116.1	1502	1512	101.9	1029	2 VHRR, 2 VTPR, 2 SR, SPM
NOAA 4	15NOV74	750	114.9	1447	1461	101.6	1463	2 VHRR, 2 VTPR, 2 SR, SPM
NOAA 5	29JUL76	750	116.2	1504	1518	102.1	1067	2 VHRR, 2 VTPR, 2 SR, SPM
TIROS-N	13OCT78	3127	98.92	849	864	102.3	868	AVHRR, HIRS-2, SSU, MSU, HEPAD, MEPED, DCS, TED
NOAA 6	27JUN79	3127	101.26	807.5	823	98.74	857*	AVHRR, HIRS-2, SSU, MSU, HEPAD, MEPED, DCS, TED
NOAA 7	23JUN81	3127	101.9	845	879	98.9	131*	AVHRR-2, HIRS-2, SSU, MSU, HEPAD, MEPED, TED, DCS & SAR
NOAA 8	28MAR83	3800	101.2	801	826	98.7	533	AVHRR-2, HIRS-2, SSU, MSU, HEPAD, MEPED, TED, DCS & SAR
NOAA 9	12DEC84	3800	102.0	842	862	98.9	19*	AVHRR-2, HIRS-2, SSU, MSU, HEPAD, MEPED, TED, DCS & SAR, SBUV, ERBE

*Still Operational as of 1/1/85

APT	Automatic Picture Transmission TV
AVCS	Advanced Vidicon Camera System (1" Vidicon)
AVHRR	Advanced Very High Resolution Radiometer – 4 ch.
AVHRR-2	Advanced Very High Resolution Radiometer – 5 ch.
DCS	Data Collection System
ERBE	Earth Radiation Budget Exp.
FPR	Flat Plate Radiometer
HB	Heat Budget Instrument
HEPAD	High Energy Proton and Alpha Particle Detector
HIRS-2	High Resolution Infrared Sounder
IP	Ion Probe
IR	Infrared 5 Channel Scanner
IRP	Infrared Passive
MEPED	Medium Energy Proton and Electron Detector
MSU	Microwave Scanner Unit
SAR	Search & Rescue
SBUV	Solar Backscatter Ultra – Violet Radiometer
SEM	Solar Environmental Monitor, TED, MEPED, HEPAD
SPM	Solar Proton Monitor
SR	Scanning Radiometer
SSU	Stratospheric Sounding Unit
TED	Total Energy Detector
TV	Television Cameras (1/2" Vidicon)
	NA Narrow Angle – 12°
	MA Medium Angle – 78°
	WA Wide Angle – 104°
VHRR	Very High Resolution Radiometer
VTPR	Vertical Temperature Profile Radiometer

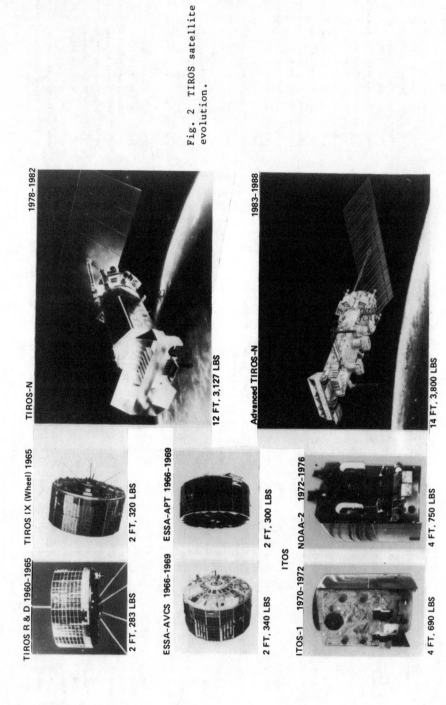

Fig. 2 TIROS satellite evolution.

remote sensing and storage of data and playback to the two
principal U.S. command and data acquisition stations. Each
satellite viewed the entire planet on a daily basis. A total of nine ESSA satellites was orbited successfully between 1966 and 1969.

The third generation of TIROS satellites, TIROS-M
(ITOS), was placed into orbit in December 1970. ITOS, by
means of infrared scanning radiometers and television cameras, provided day-and-night observation of the entire
planet. Further improvements were introduced in this
three-axis stabilized satellite with the ITOS-D series.
The very high resolution radiometer VHRR was added for 1
km (0.6 mi) resolution in the visible and infrared (i.r.)
channels, and the vertical temperature sounding instrument
for temperature profiles of the atmosphere from sea level
to 30 km. Each of the ITOS satellites was capable of observing the planet every 12 h. A total of six ITOS/NOAA
satellites was placed into operation between 1970 and 1976.

The fourth satellite generation, TIROS-N, was introduced into service in October 1978 and its companion satellite, NOAA-6, in June 1979. A third satellite, NOAA-7,
was placed into orbit on June 23, 1981. These new, sophisticated environmental satellites were configured with improved sensors that provided more refined observations, a
data collection platform, and a solar energetic particle
monitor. The satellites were on station to support the
First Global Atmospheric Research Program (GARP) global
experiment (FGGE) during 1978-1979. NOAA-8 the first of
the advanced TIROS-N (ATN) series was launched on March
29, 1983, and NOAA 9 was launched on Dec. 12, 1984. Additional ATN spacecraft are under construction to assure
continuous global observation into the 1980s. These will
have additional payloads to monitor the Earth's ozone and
measure radiation gains and losses to the planet for climatology use. They will be configured with an experimental
search and rescue payload for locating downed aircraft and
ships in distress. Figure 2 shows the evolution of the
TIROS/ESSA/ITOS/NOAA series of satellites.

The National Oceanic and Atmospheric Administration
(NOAA) owned and operated the operational ESSA and NOAA
satellites. NASA developed the initial spacecraft and
managed the procurement of the satellites.

Evolution of the TIROS Program

Early Development Phase of TIROS

Early in this century, aircraft began to gather data
to enlarge the knowledge of the atmosphere. In the mid-

1930s radiosondes were routinely used for upper atmosphere
observations. Small sounding rockets were used before
World War II for upper atmospheric measurements. Following
the war, the captured V-2 and Viking rockets were used for
further research. The Navy Aerobee rocket returned high
altitude motion pictures of the Earth and its cloud cover
in 1954. Early satellite observations were attempted by
Vanguard II in February 1959. However, due to a poor orbit
and a large spin-axis nutation, the data were unusable.

The initiation of TIROS I program in mid-1958 and the
successful launch and operations of TIROS I on April 1,
1960 opened a new era in Earth observations. In its time,
TIROS I was one of the most sophisticated satellites
launched in the U.S. space program. The development that
led to the first successful TIROS I, which has gone on to
produce four generations of meteorological and environmental satellites totaling 30 in orbit over the past 25
years, has had a very colorful beginning and a number of
iterations in design and launch vehicles and supervising
government agencies.

As a result of studies by RCA with the Rand Corporation in the 1950s as to the use of television in space and
discussions of weather reconnaissance via satellite by
S.M. Greenfield, W.W. Kellogg, H. Wexler, and S.F. Singer,
the concept for meteorological satellites came forth.

The initial development of the TIROS program material-
ized when the Army Ballistic Missile Agency at Redstone
responded favorably to an RCA proposal. RCA's initial
award in 1956 was to conceive a TV system for a satellite
for weather reconnaissance to be launched by Jupiter C
rocket. The program was designated Janus. The resultant

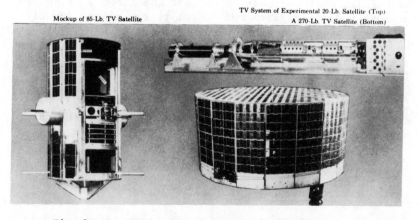

Mockup of 85-Lb. TV Satellite

TV System of Experimental 20-Lb. Satellite (Top)
A 270-Lb. TV Satellite (Bottom)

Fig. 3   Janus and Janus II spacecraft development.

design was a slender rod-shaped 20 lb spacecraft, measuring
5 in. in diameter and approximately 30 in. long and with a
single TV camera. In mid-1958 the configuration was
changed with the availability of a larger booster designated Juno-II. The Janus-II weight limit increased to 85
lb and a drum-shaped satellite 18 in. in diameter and 30
in. long was configured. Figure 3 depicts the Janus and
Janus II spacecraft development.

In late 1958 the Thor-Able rocket was made available
and the project, then called Cloud-Cover, finally became
the disk-shaped TIROS spacecraft. The TIROS weight limit
was set at 270 lb, and its size increased to 42 in. in
diameter and 22.5 in. high plus the extended antenna on
top and bottom of the spacecraft. Two complete 1/2 in.
vidicon TV cameras, plus two video recorders, cylindrical
solar array hat, rechargeable batteries, spin-up rockets,
nutation dampers, remote command, telemetry, beacons,
command receivers, and TV transmitters were included in
the spacecraft. During these early development years the
management of the program shifted from the Ballistic
Missile Agency to the Advanced Research Projects Agency,
to the U.S. Signal Corps, and finally in early 1959 to
NASA Goddard Space Flight Center.

Fig. 4 TIROS I, world's first
meteorological satellite,
launched April 1, 1960.

The TIROS I-X System Development

TIROS I was launched April 1, 1960 by the Thor-Able, as shown in Figure 4, with the primary objective of demonstrating the feasibility of observing the Earth's cloud cover by means of slow-scan television cameras on an Earth-orbiting, spin-stabilized satellite. This satellite included both wide-angle and a narrow-angle TV cameras, and was placed in a circular orbit at an altitude of 400 miles, with the orbit inclined 48 deg to the equator.

The first, historic television pictures from space were received on the very first orbit of TIROS I, immediately and clearly demonstrating the feasibility of the system. Figure 5 shows the first picture taken on the first orbit, a wide-angle picture showing the Earth's cloud cover from space of the northeastern part of the United States and Canada. With the reception of pictures from TIROS I, a new and powerful tool for the meteorological community became a reality.

TIROS II was launched Nov. 23, 1960, to demonstrate, in addition to the wide- and narrow-angle television cameras, an experimental five-channel scanning i.r. radiometer and a two-channel nonscanning i.r. device. Both were developed by the NASA Goddard Space Flight Center. They measured the thermal energy of both the Earth's surface and atmosphere in order to provide data on the planet's heat balance and

Fig. 5 First television picture from space, from TIROS I, April 1960.

add a new dimension for the understanding of weather. A magnetic torquing coil was added to TIROS II (and all TIROS satellites thereafter) so that a controlled magnetic field about the satellite would interact with the Earth's field in space and, hence, provide control of the satellite's attitude. In this way, camera pointing, thermal control, and the use of available solar power were enhanced.

TIROS III-VII were launched between July 1961 and June 1963 to provide continuous observation of the Earth's cloud cover for limited operational use. With each of these satellites, particular emphasis was given to provide early warning of severe tropical storms, hurricanes, and typhoons. In addition to cloud-cover observation, the satellites were employed experimentally to detect sea ice and snow cover. The initial 104 deg wide-angle, 1/2 vidicon TV camera and 12 deg narrow angle TV were converted to two wide-angle TV on TIROS III and again changed to one wide-angle and one 78 deg medium angle TV on TIROS IV-VI.

TIROS VIII, launched in December 1963, included both a 1/2 in. TIROS camera and a 1 in. automatic picture transmission (APT) camera. This marked the first in-space use of the APT system. The APT camera utilized a very-slow-scan vidicon, as compared to the 1/2 in. TV camera. The latter required 2 s to scan its 500 TV-line image; the APT camera required 200 s for readout of its 800 TV-line image. By virtue of the 2 kHz bandwidth of the APT system, TIROS VIII was able to transmit direct, real-time television pictures to a series of relatively inexpensive APT ground stations located around the world.

TIROS IX, the first "wheel-mode" satellite, was launched in January 1965 with the objective of expanding the capability of the TIROS satellites to provide complete global weather observation on a daily basis. This represented an increase of four times the daily observation provided by the predecessor TIROS satellites. With its new design, TIROS IX differed from its predecessors in many aspects and was the forerunner of the satellites used in the TIROS operational system. A primary difference was that in TIROS I-VIII, the two TV cameras were mounted on the baseplate of the satellite with the optical axes parallel to the inertially stabilized spin axis. Hence, the camera axes were parallel to the orbit plane and viewed the Earth for about 25% of each orbit. In the TIROS IX configuration, the TV cameras were mounted radially perpendicular to the spin axes and diametrically opposite one another and looked out through the sides rather than through the baseplate of the satellite. The satellite was injected into a higher inclination orbit with

the spin axis in the orbital plane; however, the spin axis
was then maneuvered by an improved magnetic-torquing system
to an attitude normal to the orbit plane. Thus, the spinning satellite "rolled" along its orbital path and the
field of view of each camera passed through the local vertical once during each spin or "roll." At the proper interval in the picture-taking sequence, the camera shutter
was triggered to take a photo of the local scene when the
camera was looking down at the Earth. Hence, throughout
the sunlit portion of the orbit, the Earth below the satellite could be observed by means of a sequence of overlapping photos. By placing the wheel satellite in a near-
polar, sun-synchronous orbit, the entire Earth could be
observed on a daily basis. Figure 6 is a mosaic of TIROS
IX pictures depicting global coverage in a 24 h period.
TIROS IX was the forerunner of the Global Operational ESSA
system.

TIROS X, the last of the research and development
series of standard TIROS satellites, was launched in July
1965 to provide hurricane and tropical storm observations.

ESSA Global Weather Satellite System

The commitment to provide daily routine worldwide observations without interruption in data was fulfilled by
the introduction of the TIROS Operational System (TOS) in
February 1966. This system employed a pair of ESSA (Environmental Science Services Administration) satellites,
each configured for its specific mission. Through their
onboard data storage systems, the odd-numbered satellites
(ESSA 1, 3, 5, 7, 9) provided global weather data to the
U.S. Department of Commerce's command and data acquisition
(CDA) station in Wallops Island, Va. and Fairbanks, Alaska,
and retransmitted it to the National Environmental Satellite Service at Suitland, Md., for processing and forward-
ing to the major forecasting centers of the United States
and to nations overseas. Nine ESSA satellites were
successfully launched between 1966 and 1969. One of them,
ESSA-8, remained in operation for over 7 years.

ESSA 1 was launched Feb. 3, 1966 into a 400 n.mi. near-
polar sun-synchronous orbit to become the first operational
satellite providing global observations on a daily basis.
This satellite (like its predecessor, TIROS IX) utilized
two 1/2 in. vidicon camera systems, wherein a pair of
pictures (one from each camera) produced a picture swath
2200 miles wide and 800 miles long along the orbit track.
With the 14.5 orbits completed each day, a total of 450 TV
photos were available.

Fig. 6 First complete view of the Earth's weather, from TIROS IX, February 13, 1965.

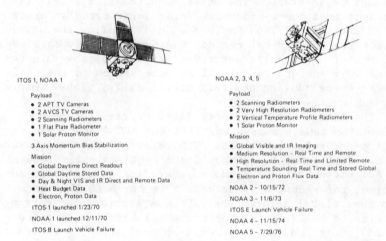

ITOS 1, NOAA 1

Payload
- 2 APT TV Cameras
- 2 AVCS TV Cameras
- 2 Scanning Radiometers
- 1 Flat Plate Radiometer
- 1 Solar Proton Monitor

3-Axis Momentum Bias Stabilization

Mission
- Global Daytime Direct Readout
- Global Daytime Stored Data
- Day & Night VIS and IR Direct and Remote Data
- Heat Budget Data
- Electron, Proton Data

ITOS-1 launched 1/23/70

NOAA-1 launched 12/11/70

ITOS-B Launch Vehicle Failure

NOAA 2, 3, 4, 5

Payload
- 2 Scanning Radiometers
- 2 Very High Resolution Radiometers
- 2 Vertical Temperature Profile Radiometers
- 1 Solar Proton Monitor

Mission
- Global Visible and IR Imaging
- Medium Resolution - Real Time and Remote
- High Resolution - Real Time and Limited Remote
- Temperature Sounding Real Time and Stored Global
- Electron and Proton Flux Data

NOAA 2 – 10/15/72

NOAA 3 – 11/6/73

ITOS E Launch Vehicle Failure

NOAA 4 – 11/15/74

NOAA 5 – 7/29/76

Fig. 7 ITOS/NOAA improved TIROS operation system, 1970-1978.

ESSA 2 was successfully placed in orbit on Feb. 28, 1966. ESSA 2 was actually the first of the TOS-design spacecraft. It was launched into a 750 n.mi., sun-synchronous orbit to complement ESSA 1 in the TIROS Operational System by providing direct, real-time readout of APT pictures to the APT ground stations located throughout the world. The pair of ESSA satellites fulfilled the commitment made by the United States to provide an operational meteorological satellite system in the first quarter of 1966. On Oct. 2, 1966, the ESSA 3 satellite was launched, replacing ESSA 1. ESSA 3 was launched into a 750 n.mi., sun-synchronous orbit. This satellite was configured with the advanced vidicon camera system (AVCS), which provided higher resolution and a larger picture area than the 1/2 in. TIROS cameras. To ensure uninterrupted daily global

photo coverage, three additional APT satellites were
launched, ESSA 4, 6, and 8. Likewise, three more AVCS
were orbited, ESSA 5, 7, and 9, to assure continuous
operational service.

ITOS - The Improved TIROS Operational System

TIROS-M Configuration

The ITOS system was designed as a third-generation
meteorological satellite system that would meet NOAA's
requirements for obtaining systematic, world-wide, day-
and-night weather observations routinely and reliably from
a single spacecraft. The Delta-launched ITOS satellites
operated in a sun-synchronous, near-polar circular orbit
at an altitude of 1463 km (908 miles). During the satellite's 115 min orbital period, the Earth rotates 28.5 deg.
The sensor view angles assured contiguity of coverage between adjacent orbits as well as observation in the orbit
track; hence, during the 12.5 orbits daily, global imaging
was achieved.

The ITOS-1 series of satellites carried redundant
television camera subsystems (APT and AVCS) and scanning
radiometer subsystems. The ITOS television sensors, proved
on the ESSA satellites, provided direct real-time readout
of APT pictures to stations anywhere in the world; in addition, the recorded video data from the AVCS TV system
provided global data to the U.S. CDA stations for retransmission to the National Environmental Satellite Service
(NESS), Suitland, Md. The dual-channel scanning radiometer
and its associated signal processor and recorders provided
for day and night observations, and the recording of surface temperatures of the Earth, sea, and cloud tops. The
recorded data was played back to the CDA stations; the
real-time data were directly read out to APT stations.
These satellites were also equipped with a solar proton
monitor, which provided NOAA's Space Disturbance Center at
Boulder, Colo., with timely warnings of solar energy bursts
in the vicinity of Earth.

A flat-plate radiometer (FPR) on board each spacecraft
gathered heat balance data. The ITOS system provided for
continuous Earth orientation of the spacecraft surface
containing the primary sensors and maintained three-axis
orientation of the spacecraft to better than ± 0.5 deg at
all times.

The general physical configuration of the ITOS satellite is shown in Fig. 7, which shows the similarity between the NOAA-2 (ITOS-D) and ITOS-1 spacecraft. The sat-

ellite was a rectangular, box-shaped structure, approximately 101.6 cm x 101.6 cm (40 x 40 in.) x 121.9 cm (48 in.) long. On the bottom of the structure, a cylindrical transition section attaches to the 94 cm (37 in.) diameter adapter section of the second stage of the Delta launch vehicle. The ITOS-D series spacecraft weigh approximately 340 kg (750 lb) compared with the 310 kg (683 lb) of the ITOS-1 (TIROS-M) spacecraft. The three solar panels, each measuring 92.7 x 161.3 cm (36.5 x 63.5 in.) are mounted along the main body of the satellite with their hinge lines at the top of the structure. In the deployed position, the 4.5 m^2 array lies in the orbit plane. A total of 10,260 2 x 2 cm silicon cells comprised the solar array that provided an initial power output of over 400 W. The power system provided an adequate margin of power over a sun-angle range of 30-60 deg. Thermal control was achieved by the application of passive and active thermal control techniques. Most of the satellite was covered by multi-layer insulation blankets, except for the primary sensor openings and the areas used for the active and passive thermal control systems.

ITOS-D Configuration

The second configuration of the ITOS spacecraft series, ITOS-D, expanded the operational capability of the ITOS system and its ability to achieve the long-term objectives of NOAA for sensing the environment of the planet. This system utilized the ITOS basic space bus with a new complement of operational environmental sensors: a redundant, very-high-resolution radiometer (VHRR); a redundant vertical temperature profile radiometer (VTPR); an improved, redundant, scanning radiometer (SR); and the solar proton monitor (SPM). The APT, AVCS, and FPR systems have been deleted in this new configuration.

The ITOS-D spacecraft series again, as in the ITOS-1 series, provided both real-time direct data to APT-type receiving stations throughout the world and stored data to the two primary NOAA CDA stations. Three types of real-time data were available to the local users: SR over the APT vhf link, VHRR over the S-Band link, and VTPR over the beacon link. The SR data, which was similar to that of ITOS-1, provided to local users 0.52-0.73 μm visible data and 10.5-12.5 μm i.r. data with a resolution of 3.7 and 7.4 km, respectively. The VHRR two-channel scanning radiometer provides data in two spectral regions to the local user: 0.6-0.7 μm visible and 10.5-12.5 μm i.r. The resolution at local vertical for the VHRR was 0.9 km,

both in the i.r. and visible channels. The vertical temperature profile radiometer provided sounding of the temperature profile from the surface of the Earth to about
30,500 m (100,000 ft). The temperature sounding was made
in the 15 μm Q-branch region of the CO_2 spectrum. The
soundings are made through eight narrow channels. The
NOAA processed VTPR data yielded a global temperature map
on a 450 km grid. The solar proton monitor (SPM) continuously measured proton and electron flux at orbit altitude. The SPM monitored the environment with six solid-
state detectors. 3 NOAA-D series satellites were launched.

The Current TIROS-N/NOAA Operational System

The fourth-generation polar-orbiting environmental
satellite system, designated TIROS-N, completed development and was placed into operational service in 1978.
Eleven spacecraft in this series will provide global operational service in 1978-1989. TIROS-N provides NOAA with
the global meteorological and environmental data required
to support both the operational and the experimental portions of the World Weather Watch Program. This current
series has a new complement of data gathering instruments.
One of these instruments, the advanced very-high-resolution
radiometer (AVHRR), increases the amount of radiometric information for more accurate sea-surface temperature mapping
and identification of snow and sea ice, in addition to day-

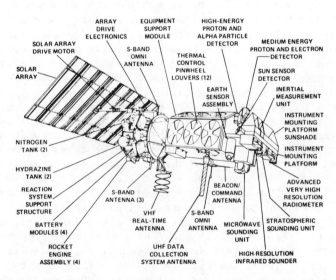

Fig. 8 TIROS-N spacecraft.

and-night imaging in the visible and infrared bands. Other
instruments, contained in a subsystem known as the TIROS
operational vertical sounder (TOVS), provide improved vertical sounding of the atmosphere. These instruments are
the high-resolution infrared sounder (HIRS/2), the stratospheric sounding unit (SSU), and the microwave sounding unit
(MSU). A data collection system (DCS) receives environmental data from fixed or moving platforms such as buoys or
balloons and processes it. A solar environmental monitor
(SEM) is included to measure proton, electron, and alpha
particle densities for solar disturbance prediction.

The data collected by the satellite's advanced instrument complement are processed and stored on board for
transmission to NOAA's central processing facility at Suitland, Md., via the CDA station. Data are also transmitted
in real time, at vhf and S-Band frequencies, to remote
stations distributed about the globe. Figure 8 depicts the
TIROS-N equipment layout.

The TIROS-N satellite, launched by an Atlas E/F from
the Western Test Range, operates in a near-polar circular
sun-synchronous orbit with a nominal altitude of either 833
or 870 km. In the operational configuration, two satellites are positioned with a nominal orbit plane separation
of 90 deg.

The instrument payload for TIROS-N consists of:

1) The advanced very-high resolution radiometer
(AVHRR), initially a four-channel currently a five-channel
instrument, cross-track scanning instrument providing image
and radiometric data in the visible, near-infrared, and
far-infrared portions of the spectrum. The instrument is
used to observe clouds, landwater boundaries, snow and ice,
water vapor, temperature of clouds, land and sea surface.

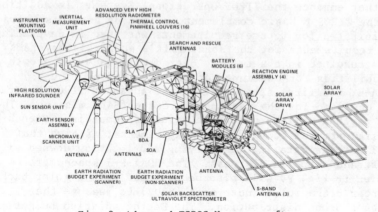

Fig. 9 Advanced TIROS-N spacecraft.

2) The TIROS operational vertical sounder (TOVS), a
subsystem consisting of three instruments, providing temperature profiles of the atmosphere from sea level to 20
miles, water vapor contents, and total ozone content. It
includes:

a) The high-resolution infrared sounder (HIRS/2), a
20-channel step-scanned, visible and infrared spectrometer
used to produce tropospheric temperature and moisture
profiles.

b) The stratospheric sounding unit (SSU), a three-
channel, pulse-modulated, step-scanned, far-infrared
spectrometer used to produce temperature profiles of the
stratosphere.

c) The microwave sounding unit (MSU), a four-channel,
step-scanned spectrometer with response in the 60 GHz O_2
band used to produce temperature profiles in the atmosphere
in the presence of clouds.

3) The data collection system (DCS), a random-access
system for the collection of meteorological environmental
and scientific data from in situ platforms, both movable
and fixed, such as buoys, balloons, and remote stations.

4) The space environment monitor (SEM), a three-in-
strument multidetector unit used to monitor solar particulate energies in the vicinity of the satellite. SEM will
measure solar proton, alpha particle and electron flux-
density energy spectrum in the vicinity of the satellite.

Advanced TIROS-N (NOAA-E, -J)

The last six spacecraft in the TIROS-N series (NOAA-E,
-J) have been designed for a larger payload complement to
further enhance the TIROS Operational System. In addition
to the TIROS-N basic complement, a list of growth sensors
anticipated for future requirements was used in developing
the requirements for the spacecraft's support subsystems.
This resulted in a satellite design with inherent growth
capabilities for continued orderly evolution. Thus,
NOAA-E, the first spacecraft in the advanced TIROS-N series
was equipped for the search and rescue (SAR) mission. The
SAR payload will be used in a joint USA-Canadian, French-
Russian program to perform an experimental mission that
will provide data for identifying and locating downed aircraft and ships in distress. The NOAA-F-J spacecraft
(refer to Fig. 9) will also be equipped with a solar backscatter ultraviolet instrument (SBUV) to measure the
Earth's ozone distribution. The Earth Radiation Budget

Table 2 Polar satellite system launch schedules and spacecraft systems (two satellite system)

Satellite	Planning date	Time of day	Instrument complement								
			AVHRR/2	HIRS/2	MSU	SSU	SEM	DCS	SAR	SBUV	ERBE
TIROS-N	10/78	PM	4-Channel	X	X	X	X	X			
NOAA 6	6/79	AM	4-Channel	X	X	X	X	X			
NOAA 7 (C)	6/81 Actual	PM	5-Channel	X	X	X	X	X			
NOAA 8 (E)	3/83 Actual	AM	4-Channel	X	X	X	X	X	X	D	D
NOAA 9	12/12 Actual	PM	5-Channel	X	X	X D	X 2,3	X	X	X	X
NOAA G	8/85	AM	4-Channel	X	X	X	2) 2,3	X	X	3)	X
NOAA H	10/86	PM	5-Channel	X	X	X	X	X	X	X	
NOAA D	3/87	AM	5-Channel	X	X	1)	2)	X		3)	
NOAA I	10/88	PM	5-Channel	X	X	X	X	X	X	X	
NOAA J	3/89	AM	5-Channel	X	X	1)	2)	X	X		
NOAA NEXT	10/90	PM	6-Channel	HIRS/3	AMSU	X	X	X		3)	

1) Two satellites will fly without an SSU
2) Three satellites will fly without an SEM
3) SBUV will fly only on PM satellites
4) D - Dummy Unit

Table 3 TIROS-N/NOAA (A-J) physical characteristics

Characteristic	TIROS-N/ NOAA A-D	Advanced TIROS-N (NOAA E-J)
Weight, lb		
Liftoff	3127	3725
On-orbit	1640	2235
Payload	510	810
Size, in.		
Length, nondeployed	146	165
Diameter	74	74
Length, deployed	256	294
Power, W		
Array	1260	1470
Bus load	266	286
Payload	146	263

Experiment (ERBE) will be used to determine the radiation
loss and gain to and from the planet. Table 2 depicts the
instrument complement for the TIROS-N/NOAA A-J series.
Table 3 summarizes the physical characteristics of this
series. NOAA-8 (formerly NOAA-E) was launched on Mar. 23,
1983, and NOAA-9 (formerly NOAA-F) was launched on Dec.
12, 1984.

Benefits

Over the past 22 years, the U.S. TIROS/ESSA/ITOS/
NOAA meteorological satellite systems have evolved where
the products, the quantity, quality, and reliability of
satellite coverage have improved greatly. Since 1966 the
entire Earth has been photographed at least once daily on

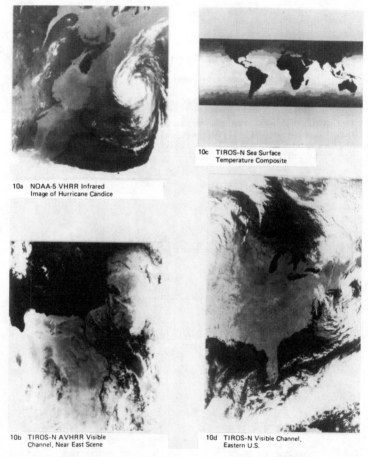

10a   NOAA-5 VHRR Infrared
      Image of Hurricane Candice

10c   TIROS-N Sea Surface
      Temperature Composite

10b   TIROS-N AVHRR Visible
      Channel, Near East Scene

10d   TIROS-N Visible Channel,
      Eastern U.S.

Fig. 10 Representative pictures from the TIROS/NOAA series.

a continuous basis. The photographs are not only used in real-time operations, but are also placed in archives from which they can be retrieved for use in research case studies. From its inception as a new research tool with its potential not fully realized, satellite data have steadily increased in importance. It is now being used by meteorologists and environmental scientists on a widespread basis in routine operations throughout the world and is considered almost indispensable for analyses and short-range forecasts.

The meteorological data from around the Earth are received at the National Environmental Satellite Service (NESS) in Washington, transformed into a broad variety of products, and distributed throughout the world. Selected images from several satellites are shown in Fig. 10. Although the processing necessary to reduce these images to the printed page results in the loss of detail, their scope and potential usefulness are readily apparent.

The satellite information has proved extremely useful in two broad types of situations. First, there are extensive areas of the Earth from which conventional reports are sparse, namely: the oceanic regions of the Northern and Southern Hemispheres, deserts, and the polar regions. Satellite information fills these voids by locating the large-scale features depicted by the cloud formations. These features include storm systems, fronts, upper level troughs and ridges, jet streams, fog, stratus, sea ice conditions, area of snow cover, and to some extent upper level wind directions and speeds. The satellite data are also used in conjunction with other data to provide quantitative heights of constant pressure surfaces as inputs to conventional analyses.

The second type of situation to which satellite data are usefully applied is the location and tracking of hurricanes, typhoons, and tropical storms. Coastal and island stations with little or no adjacent conventional weather information can make maximum use of APT data. The satellite data provide information on the presence and the position of frontal patterns, storms, and general cloud cover. Storms are usually spotted in their developing states, often beyond the normal range of weather reconnaissance aircraft from their bases of operation. The APT, direct readout infrared (DRIR), and processed-stored visible and infrared data are available at most offices with tropical storm forecast responsibilities. All the tropical regions of the world are completely monitored through satellite data received by the National Environmental Satellite Service.

The infrared data from the TIROS-N/NOAA satellites
can be used to produce charts showing the sea-surface
temperature over a larger area and with more frequency
than is possible from any other source. This information
is useful to shipping interests and the fishing industry
and is a vital input to meteorological forecasts. Satellite pictures display the extent and character of ice
fields in the Arctic and Antarctic Seas and on the Great
Lakes with a frequency and geographic coverage never
before approached.

Worldwide atmospheric temperature soundings provided
by the satellite result in more complete and accurate
analyses for use in weather forecasts. Soundings by satellite provide coverage over oceans and remote areas not
covered by conventional sounding instruments. TIROS direct
readout data are received by over 900 ground stations in
over 100 countries. The AVHRR images have been utilized
in the support of the Earth Resources Programs in the
determination of vegetation growth.

Summary

The TIROS series of satellites will continue to provide beneficial data to the United States and the world
community. The meteorological products for this highly
successful program have grown. Initially gathering daytime cloud observations in 1960, TIROS today provides data
used for atmosphere temperature and moisture profiles, sea
surface temperature, and sea ice and snow-cover observation. It collects and locates data from fixed or moving
platforms and monitors electron and proton particles
emanating from the sun. Its broad international acceptance and use is unmatched. The additional spacecraft in
the TIROS series will assure global coverage during most
of this decade.

Acknowledgment

I want to express my gratitude to Eileen Kennedy and
Joseph M. Paoletti for their assistance in the preparation
of this paper.

The Nimbus Satellite System: Remote Sensing R&D Platform of the 1970s

I.S. Haas*

General Electric Co., Philadelphia, Pennsylvania

and

R. Shapiro†

NASA Goddard Space Flight Center, Greenbelt, Maryland

Abstract

Originally conceived by the U.S. Weather Bureau (now NOAA) and the National Aeronautics and Space Administration during the earliest days of the Space Program to be the future operational weather satellite, the Nimbus series of seven satellites became the work horse and experimental backbone of the NASA/NOAA space research program during the next 15 years. Early problems in developing the attitude control system and proving its operational characteristics in the simulated space environment contributed to cost growth and schedule delay, encouraging Federal agencies to reconsider their operational commitment. The resulting program proved itself many times over by orbiting more than 35 remote sensing instruments, contributing substantially to the scientific knowledge of atmospherics and weather, and paving the way for operational sensors on both U.S. and other country's Metsats.

Introduction

The Nimbus observatory satellite project, initiated by the National Aeronautics and Space Administration in the early 1960s matured to become the nation's principal satellite platform for remote sensing research. Starting with the launch of Nimbus-1 in 1964, the satellites have grown significantly in sophistication, complexity,

*Senior Consultant.
†Department Project Manager OSP-A.

weight, capability, and performance. Each mission has
advanced man's understanding of Earth's atmospheric
environment and its structure.

Nimbus spacecraft are placed in sun-synchronous,
near-polar orbits and provide global coverage twice in
every 24 h period. The spacecraft is butterfly shaped,
3.1 m (10 ft) tall and 1.5 m (5 ft) in diameter. Figure
1 is a detailed illustration of Nimbus-7 that shows the
location of various elements of the satellite, including
the complement of nine experiments. A circular structure
at the base of the satellite houses the major subsystems
and experiments. A three-axis active attitude control
subsystem mounted above the sensory ring keeps the
spacecraft oriented to Earth's center with an accuracy of
better than 1 deg. Two solar paddles track the sun
during daylight operation and convert its energy into
electrical power for the spacecraft's subsystems.

As application/research vehicles, the seven Nimbus
spacecraft have been used for the development, test, and
application of a variety of new and advanced
meteorological and geophysical remote sensing instruments
and associated data transmission and processing
techniques. A wealth of new data applicable to
meteorology, oceanography, geology, geography, and

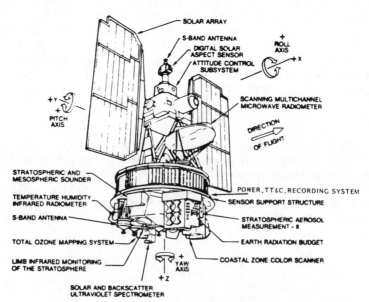

Fig. 1 Nimbus-7 spacecraft.

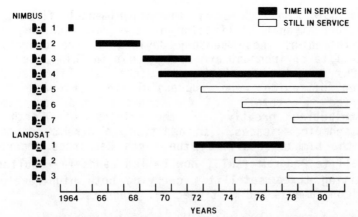

Fig. 2 Decades of experimental performance, Nimbus/Landsat.

hydrology has been transmitted to Earth. Beneficial results are still being obtained from the last Nimbus which is still operational. The launch dates and operating lifetimes of both the Nimbus and Landsat observatories are outlined in Fig. 2.

In spite of an improper orbit (elliptical instead of circular at 575 miles), Nimbus-1, the first three-axis fully stabilized satellite launched by NASA on an Air Force Agena, achieved operational status a few days after its launch on Aug. 28, 1964. On that day, a new era was initiated in the science of meteorology, leading to a worldwide dependence on space for synoptic digital data to feed the "hungry machines" to be applied later by the world's meteorological community.

To quote a representative of the Weather Bureau who was present at the Nimbus-1 NASA press briefing on September 2, 1964, and was asked about the meteorological community dependence on satellite data (at that time, two TIROS spin-stabilized satellites were actively providing image data to the U.S. only): "Are we dependent on them? Yes, we certainly are. --- When the world sees the quality of APT (the automatic picture taking vidicon capability on Nimbus-1 -- a first) they will be demanding it more and more. As you can see, it's absolutely marvelous. We have been using it every day since Nimbus went up and are using it to good advantage."

The continuance of the TIROS and Nimbus programs, one operational and the other experimental, was assured from

this point on.   Some of the experimental firsts, the
quasioperational utilization of the data and the later
adaptation of those sensory devices to the operational
satellite environment are brought out in this paper.   The
Nimbus Program, consisting of eight satellite launches,
seven of which were successful in achieving orbit,
carried a total of 48 sensors and experiments
contributing greatly to the fields of Earth and
atmospheric sciences.   In addition, a direct adaptation
of the Nimbus satellite, the Earth Resources Technology
Satellite Program (ERTS, now called Landsat) resulted in
orbiting three satellites carrying both high-resolution
vidicon cameras and multispectral scanners.

    To the basic Nimbus bus were added a wideband
recording and transmission system, the RBV (return beam
vidicon) and MSS (multispectral scanner) sensors.   A
slight modification to the solar array and attitude
control system provided a 9:30 a.m. orbit instead of the
standard Nimbus 12:00 noon orbit.   An artist rendition of
the Landsat satellite is shown in Fig. 3.   The data from
Landsat, processed through a dedicated high throughput
ground data handling system and highly organized cadre of
scientific investigators, opened the door to an entirely
new set of scientific analyses, techniques, and
applications.   The then NASA Administrator, Dr. James
Fletcher, had this to say about the contribution of the
ERTS Program to our society: "If I had to name one space
age development to help save the world, I would pick
ERTS" (September 1973).

Fig. 3 Artist's rendition of ERTS/Landsat.

Satellite System Design

The Nimbus satellite design had its origins very early in the evolutionary development of the NASA Goddard Space Flight Center(GSFC)as a satellite system designer, implementer, and contracting agency responsible for scientific and applications satellites in the 1960s. Originally conceived as an "in-house" project, where subsystems and payloads would be "contracted out" with final integration at GSFC, the Center management eventually decided to fund an integrating contractor. This role, together with the attitude control subsystem development, was assigned to the General Electric Company. Many features of the design resulted from GSFC's early experience with space flight and, in large part, the eventual long life experienced by almost all of the satellites was due to the configuration and conservative nature of the original design. (Life expectancy in the contract was specified to be at least 6 months.) In today's broadened knowledge of the space environment and with a generation of experience in reliable/redundant design, the original life requirement sounds overly simplistic and shortsighted. Indeed, by the time the Nimbus configuration was employed for Landsat in the early 1970s, the life expectancy was raised to 3 years. Current technology affords greater than 5 year life from similar performing satellites and there is no question that the goals have been raised based on the demonstrated performance of the Nimbus satellite and others of similar complexity.

At the inception of Nimbus design, several methods of stabilization in orbit were known, i.e., spin, gravity gradient, and reactive control. It was decided to combine, some features of both reactive and gravity gradient control into Nimbus, explaining to some degree the two-mass design (sensory ring with strut separation of the attitude control subsystem). See Fig. 1 where the Nimbus-7 configuration is described. In fact, on Nimbus-4, the gravity gradient feature was actively explored with the addition of a gravity gradient deployable mass on the top of the attitude control subsystems and successfully demonstrated in orbit. This feature, combined with the roll, pitch, and yaw reaction wheel, has been beneficial in providing Nimbus with very low rotational rates, resulting especially in very reduced data correction requirements for experimental data processing.

Other benefits accrued from the decision to separate the attitude control subsystem from the sensory ring. The Nimbus Program had an extraordinarily high content of government-furnished equipment, resulting in a continuing need to integrate a multitude of "black boxes" and remote sensor instruments from various suppliers into a single integrated functioning system. The process of integration, and thereby the cost of integration, was simplified to a great degree by the ability to do separate and parallel integration and test of these elements of the system. The Multimission Satellite, (MMS) later developed by NASA GSFC, had this same concept in the scope of the program and the development of the subsystems. On Nimbus, this concept was particularly useful since it permitted easy interchangeability of the major system elements between concurrently produced satellites and between Nimbus and Landsat in later years.

As the program evolved from its original concept as an operational Metsat into a research/experimental observatory system, many varied improvements were introduced into the satellite design to accommodate increasingly sophisticated payloads. For Nimbus-3 a new power system was designed, providing increased efficiency solar conversion and a significant increase in electrical power capability during satellite night. Earlier designs carried instruments mainly utilized for daytime sensing. The experiment complement on Nimbus-3 and beyond became more focused or remote sensing during the entire orbit, with sensors operating in the i.r., uv, and microwave protions of the spectrum. Table 1 summarizes the significant growth and dramatic changes in operating payloads of all seven Nimbus observatories. The satellite configuration readily adjusted to each successive vehicle in terms of sensor view angle requirements, RFI, thermal isolation, and radiation cooling requirements.

Nimbus-4 provided a significant upgrade of the attitude control subsystem that provided higher reliability and improved stability and, of equal importance, the addition of the versatile information processor (VIP). Together with the command system clock and tape recorders, VIP represented a complete real-time

Table 1   Growth of sensor technology
Nimbus observatories

	NIMBUS						
	1	2	3	4	5	6	7
NUMBER OF EXPERIMENTS	3	4	9	9	6	9	9
NUMBER OF SPECTRAL CHANNELS	3	8	28	43	34	62	79
SPECTRAL REGIONS							
VISIBLE	X	X	X	X	X	X	X
INFRARED	X	X	X	X	X	X	X
FAR INFRARED		X	X	X	X	X	X
ULTRAVIOLET			X	X		X	X
MICROWAVE					X	X	X

and delayed capability to execute, precision clock,
sample and hold, store, and transmit in a completely
flexible and reprogrammable way the experimental data
from the differing payload complements carried on each
successive observatory.

Nimbus Achievements

Growth of Earth Science Applications

Named after the Latin word for raincloud, Nimbus was
originally conceived as a meterological satellite
concerned primarily with providing atmospheric data for
improved weather forecasting. With the addition of more
sophisticated sensing devices on each succeeding vehicle,
this applications/research observatory program grew
significantly in capability and performance through a
total of seven launches to cover a wide range of Earth
sciences.

Data produced by the sensing instruments on Nimbus-5,
-6, and -7 are still being studied and applied in the
following fields:

1) Oceanography (geograghy of oceans and related
phenomena).

2) Hydrology (study of water, especially on surface
of the land, in the soil and underlying rocks, and in the
atmosphere).

3)   Geology (science of the Earth's composition, structure, and history as recorded in rocks).

4)   Geomorphology (study of the form of the Earth, general configuration of its surface, distribution of land and water, and evolution of land forms).

5)   Geography (description of land, sea, and air and distribution of life, including man and his industries).

6)   Cartography (map making and map revision).

7)   Agriculture (soil conditions, vegetation patterns, crop production).

8) Meterology (concerned with global water vapor distribution and temperature profiles as they affect weather forecasting).

Table 2 summarizes the experiments, arranged alphabetically, that have been used one or more of the seven Nimbus observations. The listing illustrates the wide variety of remote sensing techniques that have contributed to the growth and increased maturity of remote sensing technology.

The Experiments and Their Achievements

The growing list of achievements attained by the Nimbus observatories attests to the success of NASA's satellite program.   The technological growth of the devices flown on the Nimbus spacecraft is a complex story and the following discussion summarizes only a small portion of what has been accomplished. The continuous flow of sensor data from space and the new quasi-operational technnniques that have evolved are contributing greatly toward improved, long-range weather forecasts and further understanding of the Earth's complex environment. Selected experiments are described and representative pictures of the many data types and application areas are presented.

Earth Nimbus Experiments. Nimbus-1 carried three experiments that successfully demonstrated the design concept, with all sensors performing exceptionally well. The automatic picture transmission (APT) subsystem transmitted photographic data (Fig. 4) of synoptic meteorological conditions to local weather stations anywhere in the world that were equipped with relatively inexpensive receiving equipment. The advanced vidicon camera subsystem (AVCS) recorded three pictures simultaneously with overlapping field of view for subsequent readout. The high-resolution infrared radiometer (HRIR) provided nighttime infrared coverage of the Earth and cloud cover so that mosaics of worldwide weather conditions could be produced.

The vehicle provided an exceptionally clear photo of Hurricane Cleo during its first day in orbit and subsequently tracked other hurricanes and Pacific typhoons. In addition, the pictures enabled cartographers to correct inaccuracies on relief maps and supplied better definition of the formation of the Antarctic ice front.

At the time of Nimbus-2 launch, the number of APT stations had grown from 65 to over 300, located in 43 countries. The system was modified to enable HRIR data to be read out in real time, another first for space meteorology. Temperature patterns could be obtained of lakes and ocean currents (of vital interest to shipping and fishing industries) and thermal pollution could be identified.

Medium-Resolution Infrared Radiometer (MRIR). A new experiment on Nimbus-2, the MRIR, measured radiation emitted and reflected from the Earth in five wavelength intervals from visible to infrared. The data permitted detailed study of the effect of water vapor, and ozone on

Fig. 4   Annotated APT photograph returned from Nimbus-1.

I.S. HAAS AND R. SHAPIRO

Table 2 Nimbus experiment summary

Abbreviation	Experiment Name	Experimenter	Equipment Contractor	Type of Sensor	Scientific Objective
APT	Automatic Picture Taking	GSFC	RCA	Slow Readout Vidicon Camera	Local Cloud Cover Images (pictures)
AVCS	Advanced Vidicon Camera	GSFC	RCA	Wide Angle Multi-vidicon Camera	High Resolution Cloud Cover Images
BUV	Backscatter Ultraviolet Spectrometer	NCAR/GSFC	Beckman	Radiometer/ Spectrometer	Spatial Distribution of Atmospheric Ozone
CZCS	Coastal Zone Color Scanner	GSFC	Ball Bros.	Multispectral Imaging Radiometer	Ocean and Coastal Area Measurement of Chlorophyll, Vegetation, Temp. and Gelbstoff
ESMR	Electrically Scanning Microwave Radiometer	GSFC	Aerojet	Scanning (imaging) Microwave Radiometer	Thermal Image of the Earth and Ocean Unobscured by Clouds
ESMR-F	Electrically Scanning Microwave Radiometer	GSFC	Aerojet	Two Polarization, Scanning Microwave Radiometer	Map Liquid Water Content of Clouds Sea-Ice Cover, Gross Characteristics of Land.
ERB	Earth Radiation Budget	NOAA	Gulton	Fixed and Scanning Radiometer	Measure Planetary Heat Budget total Solar Radiation and Angular Distribution of Earth Flux
FWS	Filter Wedge Spectrometer	GSFC	ITT	Radiometer/ Spectrometer	Vertical Distribution and Temperature Profile of Water Vapor and Carbon Dioxide
HIRS	High Resolution Temperature Sounder	GSFC/NOAA	ITT	Scanning Spectral Radiometer	Vertical Temperature Profile and H_2O Distribution
HRIR	High Resolution Infrared Radiometer	GSFC	ITT	IR Imaging Radiometer	Night Cloud Cover
				Dual Channel Imaging Radiometer	Day/Night Cloud Cover
IDCS	Image Dissector Camera	GSFC	ITT	Imaging Radiometer	Day Cloud Cover
IRIS	Infrared Interferometer Spectrometer	GSFC	TI	Radiometer/ Spectrometer	Vertical Temperature & Moisture Profile and Distribution of Other Atmospheric Gases
IRLS	Interrogation, Recording, and Location System	GSFC	Radiation Inc.		Locate, Interrogate and Record Data from Remote Stations (balloons and buoys)
ITPR	Infrared Temperature Profile Radiometer	ESSA	Gulton	Radiometer/ Spectrometer	Vertical Temperature Profile (CO_2)
LIMS	Limb Infrared Monitoring of the Stratosphere	LRC	Honeywell	Multispectral Scanning Radiometer	Stratospheric Measurement of Temp., Ozone, Water, Vapor, Nitric Acid, Nitrogen Dioxide
LRIR	Limb Radiance Inversion Radiometer	NCAR U. of Florida	Honeywell	Scanning Spectral Radiometer	Stratospheric Measurements of Temperatures, Water Vapor, and Ozone Profiles
MRIR	Medium Resolution Infrared Radiometer	GSFC	SBRC	Imaging Radiometer/ Spectrometer	Vertical Temperature Profile, Heat Balance, and Distribution of Atmospheric Gases
MUSE	Monitor Ultraviolet Solar Energy	GSFC	Adcole	Radiometer/ Spectrometer	Measurement of Solar Ultraviolet Energy
NEMS	Microwave Spectrometer	JPL/MIT	JPL	Radiometer/ Spectrometer	Vertical Temperature Profile Using O_2 Line. Water and Water Vapor Distribution
PMR	Pressure Modulated Radiometer	Oxford	Marconi	Scanning Spectral Radiometer	Vertical Temperature Profiles to 85 KM
RMP	Rate Monitoring Package	GSFC	Sperry		Measurement of Angular Rate by Gas Bearing Gyro
RTG	Radioisotope Thermoelectric Generator	AEC	Martin		Assess the Usefulness of Radioactive Power Supplies
SAM II	Stratospheric Aerosol Measurement II	LRC	University of Wyoming	Spectral Radiometer	Measure and Map Global Aerosol Concentration and Optical Properties in Stratosphere and Troposphere
SAMS	Stratospheric and Mesospheric Sounder	Oxford	Hawker-Siddley	Pressure Broadening Spectral Radiometer	Global Measurement of Temperature and Select Gaseous Distribution
SBUV/TOMS	Solar Backscatter UV Energy and Total Ozone Mapping Spectrometer	GSFC	Beckman	Monochro Monitor Photometer	Map Total and Vertical Distribution of Ozone Measure Solar Irradiance
SCAMS	Scanning Microwave Spectrometer	JPL/MIT	JPL	Scanning Spectral Radiometer	Vertical Temperature Using O_2 line Water Vapor Distribution
SCMR	Surface Composition Mapping Radiometer	GSFC	ITT	Imaging Radiometer/ Spectrometer	Identification of Surface Minerals (ERS)
SCR	Selective Chopper Radiometer	Reading & Oxford University	Marconi	Radiometer/ Spectrometer	Vertical Temperature Profile and Distribution of Atmospheric Gases
SMMR	Scanning Multichannel Microwave Radiometer	GSFC	JPL	Scanning Microwave Radiometer	Seal Temp., Surface Winds, Ice Extent, Soil Moisture, Snow Cover, Continental Ice Atmospheric Moisture Water. Vapor and Rainfall
SIRS	Satellite Infrared Spectrometer	ESSA	ESSA Gulton/ SBRC	Radiometer/ Spectrometer	Vertical Temperature Profile and Distribution of Atmospheric Gases
T&DRE	Tracking and Data Relay Experiment	GSFC	GSFC/GE/ BBC	S-Band Trans-ponder	Range and Range Rate Measurements; Data Relay
THIR	Temperature/Humidity Infrared Radiometer	GSFC	SBRC	Imaging Radiometer/ Spectrometer	Cloud Cover, and Water Vapor Mapping
TWERLE	Tropical Winds Energy Conversion Reference Level Experiment	GSFC/Univ. of Wisconsin	TI	RF Receiver Balloon Transmitter	Measure Large Scale Atmospheric Motions, Conversion of Potential to Kinetic Energy, Provide 150 mb Reference Level

(Table 2 continued on the next page.)

Table 2 (continued)   Nimbus experiment summary

Abbreviation	Special Instrument Technique	Number of Data Channels (Sensor Only)	Spectral Interval	Pointing Direction	Angular Resolution (Degrees)	Scanning	Nimbus Spacecraft
APT	Stored Image Vidicon (slow scan)	1	0.5 to 0.75 μm	Nadir	2.5 nm**	77°	1, 2
AVCS	Vidicon Camera	3	0.5 to 0.75 μm	Nadir	1.0 nm**	107°	1, 2
BUV	Grating Spectrometer	12	2500 to 3888 Å	Nadir	12.0	None	4
CZCS	Mechanically Scanned Radiometer	6	.433 to .800 μm 10.5 to 12.5 μm	Nadir	0.05	Across Track ± 40° Along Track ± 20°	7
ESMR	Electronically Scanned Phased Array Antenna Dicke Switch	1	19.35 GHz	Nadir	1.4	74°	5
ESMR-F	Electronic Conical Scanned Phased Array Antenna. Measure both Horizontal and Vertical Simultaneously. Dicke	2	37 GHz	Nadir	1.1	74°	6
ERB	Two Axis Gimbal Mounted Scanning Radiometer	22	2000 Å 50 μm	Nadir and Towards the Sun	5.14 x +0.25 Scan Channels 1.5 Fixed Channels	Horizon to Horizon, Along Track and Across Track	6, 7
FWS	Continuously Variable Interference Filter Disk	1	1.2 2.4 μm 3.2 6.4 μm	Nadir	2.6	None	4
HIRS	Mechanically Scanned Radiometer with Spectral Selection by Interference Filters Radiation Cooler	17	0.7 - 15 μm	Nadir	1.5	72°	6
HRIR	Mechanically Scanned Imaging Radiometer Spectral Dispersion by Interference Filters	1	3.4 to 4.2 μm	Nadir	0.5	Horizon to Horizon	1, 2
		2	3.4 to 4.2 μm 0.7 to 1.3 μm	Nadir	0.4		3
IDCS	Electrically Scanned Imaging Radiometer	1	0.5 to 0.75 μm	Nadir	1.2 nm**	98.2°	3, 4
IRIS	Michaelson Interferometer with Self Calibration	1	5 to 25 μm	Nadir	8.0	None	3
					5.0		4
IRLS				Nadir	120.0 (beamwidth)	None	3, 4
ITPR	Fixed Spectral Filters Mech. Step Scan	7	3.8 to 15 μm	Nadir	1.5	76°	5
LIMS	Mechanical Scanning Radiometer	6	6.1 to 15.8 μm	Earth Limb	0.03°	Horizon to Space 12°	7
LRIR	Mechanically Scanned Radiometer. Interference Filters CH$_3$/NH$_3$ Cryo Cooler	4	8.7 25 μm	Towards the Horizon	0.3 x 0.03	10° Acquisition 2° Track Vertically	6
MRIR	Mechanically Scanned Radiometer with Fixed Interference Filters	5	0.5 to 29 μm	Nadir	2.7	Horizon to Horizon	2, 3
MUSE	Fixed Spectral Filter	5	1120 to 3100 Å	Towards Sun	90	None	3, 4
NEMS	Microwave Radiometer (Dicke Superheterodyne)	5	20 to 60 GHz	Nadir	10.0	None	5
PMR	Pressure Broadening Spectral Filter	2	15 μm	Nadir	4.0 x 20.0	15°	6
RMP	Hydrodynamic Gas Bearing Gyroscope					None	3
RTG						None	3
SAM II	Mechanically Scanned Radiometer	1	1 μm	Spacecraft Sunrise/Sunset	0.01°	10° Vertical Scan	7
SAMS	Mechanically Scanned Radiometer	9	2.7 to 15 μm 25 to 100 μm	Towards Horizon	1.6° x .16°	Horizon +5° to –9° ± 15° About	7
SBUV/TOMS	Fixed and Spectral Scanning Radiometers (TOMS/SBUV)	20	.16 μm to .80 μm	Nadir	SBUV 11° TOMS 3°	Vertical and Cross Track	7
SCAMS	Mechanically Scanned Microwave Radiometer (Dicke Superheterodyne)	5	20 60 GHz	Nadir	7.5	86°	6
SCMR	Spectral Filters and Cooled Detector	3	0.8 to 1.1 μm 8.3 to 9.2 μm 10.5 to 11.3 μm (Far IR & Visible)	Nadir	0.03	Horizon to Horizon	5
SCR	Selective Absorbtion of Gas	6	2 to 200 μm (Near to Very Far IR)	Nadir	3.0 & 5.0	None	4
		16			1.5 & 2.2		5
SMMR	Mechanically Scanned Radiometer	10	6.33, 10.69, 18.00, 21.00, 37.00 GHz	42° Conical Off Nadir	0.8° ~ 4.2°	Conical Forward of Nadir ± 25°	7
SIRS	Grating Spectrometer	8	11 to 15 μm (Far IR)	Nadir	12.0	None	3
		14	11 to 35 μm (Far IR)			35"	4
TADRE	Doppler Shift			Zenith			6
THIR	Mechanically Scanned Radiometer	2	6.5 μ to 7.5 μm (Far IR)	Nadir	1.2	Horizon to Horizon	4, 5, 6, 7
			10.5 to 12.5 μm (Far IR)		0.4		
TWERLE	Antenna Receiver, and Random Access Computer	8	400 MHz				6

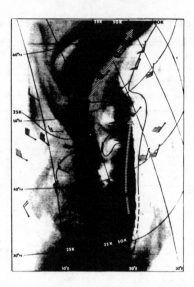

Fig. 5 Wind field analysis of THIR photograph taken over Europe.

the Earth's heat balance. A data composite of all five
spectral channels, together with spacecraft annotated
data and a calibrated gray scale, was generated for each
orbit. With rapid turnaround at the Nimbus ground
system, these weather annotated data sheets found their
way into early experimental operational weather analysis.

Image Dissector Camera Subsystem (IDCS). On Nimbus-3 and
-4, both the APT and the AVCS subsystems were replaced by
the image dissector camera subsystem. The IDCS was
designed to provide daytime cloud-cover pictures in both
real time using the real-time transmission subsystem
(RTTS) and by stored playback data using the high-data-
rate storage subsystem (HDRSS). Each frame of IDCS
provided effective Earth coverage of approximately 2500
km on side with a resolution of 800 lines. The average
picture resolution was approximately 4 km.

After demonstrating the enormous value of visible
sensors, like APT, AVCS and IDCS on early Nimbus
satellites, the use of visible sensors was discontinued
on Nimbus with IDCS (Nimbus-4). For reference purposes,
the THIR sensor was evaluated on Nimbus-4 and used
operationally on subsequent satellites.

Temperature Humidity Infrared Radiometer (THIR). The Nimbus THIR, which replaced the HRIR and MRIR used on previous Nimbus spacecraft as well as the IDCS, produced data of exceptional quality. The instrument is a two-channel scanning radiometer. The 6.7 μm (water vapor) channel, designed to show moisture distribution in the stratosphere and upper troposphere, provided a vivid portrayal of jet streams and large storm systems. Water vapor and ice concentration in the middle and upper tropospheres are strongly influenced by vertical as well as horizontal motion and often appear on THIR data as areas of convergence in the windblown patterns, indicating jet stream activity. These jet streams, lying in zones of maximum temperature contract, often denote regions of greatest storminess.

Fig. 5 was taken over central Europe on the night of April 12, 1970. A wind-field analysis has been added showing wind arrows, wind contours for 25 and 50 knots/h, and locations of two jet streams.

The 10-12 μm long wave window on THIR, where there is virtually no reflected sunlight, eliminated the problem often seen with data from the HRIR instruments flown previously and provided pictures of unusual clarity and contrast. Fig. 6 shows the coastal region of the United States with the warm water of the Gulf Stream registering much darker than that of the cold water. Improved versions of THIR were successfully carried on Nimbus-5, -6, and -7.

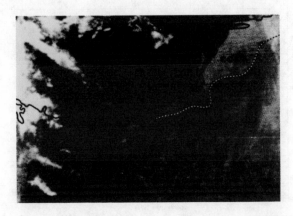

Fig. 6 Annotated photograph of Gulf Stream transmitted from Nimbus-4 THIR subsystem.

Satellite Infrared Spectrometer (SIRS). The excellent
performance of the satellite infrared spectrometer (SIRS)
on Nimbus-3 inaugurated a new era in using satellites for
meteorological observations. The device simultaneously
measured infrared spectral radiances in narrow intervals
of the carbon dioxide absorption band, from which
temperature profiles of the Earth's atmosphere can be
developed.

The now famous first temperature profile (Fig. 7) was
constructed from SIRS data on April 14, 1969, and provided excellent correlation with radiosonde measurements
from Kingston, Jamaica. Subsequent correlation with data
taken over the United States and the Pacific Ocean was
also excellent.

The first SIRS instrument, on Nimbus-3, sensed data
only along the subsatellite ground track. The Nimbus-4
SIRS had the added capability of making measurements to

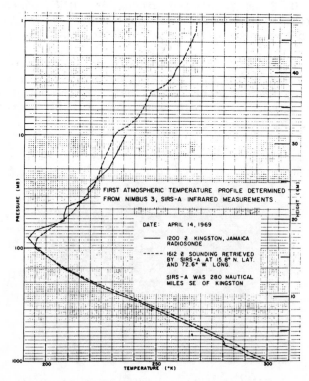

Fig. 7 Comparison of radiosonde and SIRS data.

either side of the subsatellite track so that full global coverage was obtained twice each day.

These satellite-derived profiles have become a part of the total set of meteorological observations used in numerical weather analysis and prediction by the National Weather Service. Early operational utilization of data from Nimbus led the way for smooth adaptation and utilization from TIROS temperature-sounding instruments ITPR.

Monitor of Ultraviolet Solar Energy (MUSE). The MUSE experiment measured solar radiation otherwise undectable at the Earth's surface because of the atmosphere's screening effect that absorbs all energy below 3000 Å. The purpose of the MUSE experiment was to look for changes with time in the ultraviolet solar flux in five broad bands at 1150 - 30000 Å (0.115 - 0.300 μm), to measure the solar flux in these regions, and to measure the atmospheric attenuation at these wavelengths as the sensor views the setting sun after the spacecraft has crossed the terminator in the Northern Hemisphere.

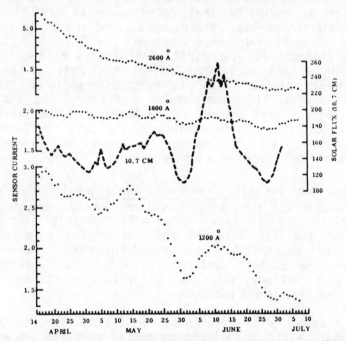

Fig. 8 Daily averages for three MUSE sensor channels. Ordinates for the top two plots are multiplied by 10^{-8} A and for the bottom plot by 10^{-10} A. Ordinate for the 10.7 cm (2800 MHz) solar flux is on the right.

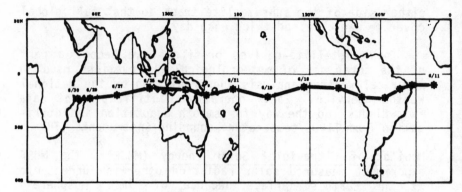

Fig. 9 Flight path of balloon interrogation package launched from Ascension Island on June 11, 1970.

Shortly after the Nimbus-3 launch, channels with responses at 2000 and 16000 Å suffered severe degradation due to a violent solar proton storm. The most significant finding from these three operating channels of MUSE was that there is a pronounced periodic variation in solar uv radiation that corresponds to the 27 day solar rotation period. Nimbus-4 data confirmed the variations. Fig. 8 shows sensor currents for 2600, 1800, and 1200 Å channels for the first three months of satellite operation. Such variations affect the rate at which atmospheric oxygen (O_2) is photodisassociated into atomic oxygen (O) and could influence the ozone concentrations that control the uv heating of the Earth's upper atmosphere. These studies of the sun, the Earth's heat source, are continuing in order to determine long-range influences on Earth's weather.

Interrogation, Recording and Location System (IRLS). The IRLS package was used on Nimbus-3 and -4 to demonstrate the feasibility of using polar-orbiting satellites to determine position location and to collect data from remote instrumented platforms around the globe, either on or above the Earth's surface. Five types of platforms were used: ballons, ships, an ice island in the Arctic, buoys, and land-based packages.

A tropical wind experiment, utilizing approximately 30 constant-altitude balloons conducted with the Nimbus-4 IRLS, revealed that the balloons stay at a fairly constant latitude as they circle the globe (Fig. 9). The Nimbus-4 IRLS, which had a greater slant range than that

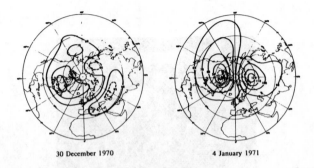

30 December 1970   4 January 1971

Fig. 10 SCR radiance maps showing stratospheric warming of northern polar region.

of Nimbus-3, was able to monitor the exact location on any given orbital pass to within +1 n.mi. This experiment system was followed by the highly successful TWERLE/RAMS experiment on Nimbus-6.

TWERLE Experiment. The TWERLE experiment, tropical wind energy conversion and reference level experiment/random access measurement system (RAMS), has had worldwide participation in the evaluation of meteorological circulation, ocean currents, and ice movement. At the end of 1 year of satellite operation, over 700 platforms had been activated by 31 investigations representing seven countries.

Selective Chopper Radiometer (SCR). The SCR determined the global temperature of six successive layers of the atmosphere by radiometric measurements of the emission of carbon dioxide in the 15 μm band. The refinement of the system enabled high-spatial resolution measurements of Earth or cloud-top temperatures to be taken, the field of view being a strip 7 miles wide. The calibration data were computerized and placed on tape for transformation into temperature profiles similar to those obtained with the IRIS and SIRS experiments.

SCR data were also used to prepare radiance maps that indicate "sudden warmings" of the winter stratosphere near the poles, where the temperature over a small area may rise as much as 50 K in a few days, accompanied by a major circulation change. Radiance maps for December 30, 1970, and January 4, 1971, (Fig. 10) illustrated how a warming region developing over central Asis intensified in four days and moved northeast over Siberia.

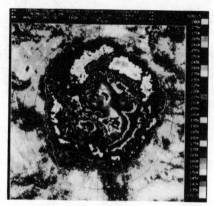

Fig. 11 Microwave image of Antarctic continent and sea ice, winter 1974.

Fig. 12 Water vapor (top) and liquid water (bottom) images over the ocean, Oct. 1-14, 1975. White represents high humidity; the apparent fringes of liquid water around the coastline are artifacts of the data processing.

A much more sophisticated design with 16 channels was flown successfully on Nimbus-5. A British experiment, its SCR data was found to be near-operational utility by the British Meterological Service for several years after the Nimbus-5 launch.

ESMR Global Thermal Mapping. The electrically scanning microwave radiometer (ESMR) on Nimbus-5 provided the first microwave device for globaly mapping thermal radiation from the Earth's surface and atmosphere. Differences between snow and ice and between rain and clear areas over oceans are emphasized by using the gray scale to represent sensed temperatures of 190-250K.

From polar images reconstructed from ESMR data, ice cover has been measured by the U.S. Geological Survey Ice Dynamics Project. Images of both polar regions have been measured and analyzed[1]. A sample reproduction of the images analyzed is presented in Fig. 11. The detailed analysis showed differences between earlier ice boundaries taken from the U.S. Navy Atlas and those presented by ESMR. ESMR 5 has proven that large discrepancies exist between long-term ice cover depicted in various Atlas measurements and actual ice canopies. This experiment was continued with excellent results from the ESMR F flown on Nimbus-6.

SCAMS Scanning Microwave Spectrometer. Fig. 12 shows global images of water vapor and liquid water obtained from the SCAMS experiment flown on Nimbus-6. The most prominent feature in these images is the intertropical convergence zone. Also prominent are the averaged traces of storms carrying moisture from the western tropical oceans into the midlatitudes of each hemisphere.

Nimbus - 7 Application Teams. The Nimbus-7 payload complement provided significant departures from a purely meteorological science direction, offering remote sensing coverage over a vast percentage of the electromagnetic spectrum. This is shown schematically in Fig. 13.

The complex of remote sensors carried on Nimbus-7 and the interrelationships of certain data types necessitated a slightly different arrangement in the planned data utilization. Where previous Nimbus sensor data were generally restricted to the instrument scientist for early proof and analysis, data from Nimbus-7 are distributed to teams of investigators. The principal applica-

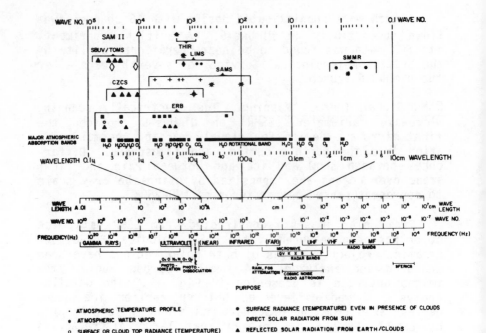

Fig. 13 Relation of Nimbus-7 experiments of the electromagnetic spectrum.

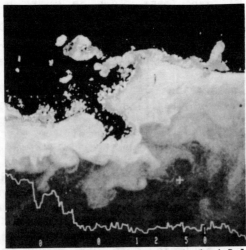

Fig. 14 Nimbus-7 CZCS image of the Mississippi Delta showing concentrations of phytoplankton.

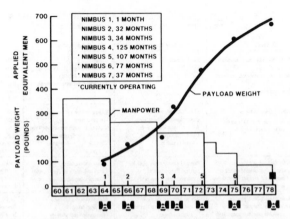

Fig. 15 Nimbus Program efficiencies.

tions and wide distributions of users working together in evaluation of each of the seven major sensors is summarized in Table 3. The quasioperational nature of this experimentation has significant advantages in both the improvement in evaluation techniques and the early determination of operational utility. The usefulness of BUV/ SBUV data to the meteorological community has led to plans for incorporation of this technique into the TIROS operational program.

Coastal Zone Color Scanner (CZCS). One of the most important sensors to be flown on Nimbus-7 is the CZCS. Increasing uses for the data are currently being explored by the experiment team. This image (Fig. 14) from the Nimbus-7 CZCS taken in November 1978 shows the area of the Mississippi River Delta to Mobile Bay, including Mississippi Sound and Lake Pontchartrain. The nutrient-enriched waters with high phytoplankton concentrations around the mouth of the Mississippi are shown in this gray scale representative of a color image. The gray scale is labeled in milligrams per cubic meter at the bottom of the image. To the south of the Mississippi Delta, one sees the clear water of the Gulf of Mexico with the chlorophyl concentrations dropping into the range 0.05 mg/m^3. A gradient of pigment concentration is shown by the graph in white, made by scanning between the two cursor marks shown as white crosses. The scan direction is from the northern cursor to the southern cursor. The values along the graph in milligrams per cubic meter are shown on the Y axis of the image, ranging 0-0.5.

Table 3   Nimbus-7 data products and their uses

Sensor	Film and Tape Output Products	Scientific Parameters	Applications	Users
ERB	Daily, monthly and seasonal world grids Monthly and seasonal contour maps Zonal statistics	Earth fluxes Solar fluxes Zonal insolation	Climatology Ocean/atmosphere dynamics Weather modeling Terrestrial reflectance studies	GSFC, NOAA, LaRC CSU Drexel U of C (Davis) Eppley Lab Cal Tech
SMMR	Orbital Observations Bi-daily and monthly color contour maps	SEH/ICE parameters Ocean surface conditions Atmospheric conditions Land parameters Glacial features	Ocean dynamics Ice dynamics Ocean/atmosphere interactions Cryospheric dynamics Climatology and weather modelling	GSFC, MIT, U of Wash. NOAA, JPL U.K., Switzerland Denmark Canada
SAM-II	Daily aerosol profiles Seasonal and annual contour maps and atmospheric cross sections	Aerosol backscatter profiles Optical Properties of stratospheric aerosols	Atmospheric sinks Earth radiation budget studies Aerosol injection dynamics	LaRC, U of Wyo. NCAR, SRI, U of Ariz. NOAA
LIMS	Daily atmosphere profile Daily, monthly and seasonal contour maps and atmospheric cross sections	Gas concentrations and temperature profiles in the stratosphere	Atmospheric pollution monitoring Photo-chemical studies Atmospheric gas dynamics Climatology	LaRC, NCAR, NOAA Drexel, U of Mich U of Wash, JPL UK France
SAMS	Daily atmospheric profile Daily, monthly, and seasonal contour maps and atmospheric cross sections	Gas concentrations and temperature profiles in the stratosphere and mesophere	Atmospheraic pollution monitoring Photo-chemical studies Atmospheric gas dynamics Climatology Wind dynamics	Oxford GSFC LaRC Drexel NCAR
SBUV/TOMS	Daily profiles of O_3 Daily, monthly and seasonal contour maps Solar spectra Zonal O_3 statistics	O_3 profiles Total atmospheric O_3 Solar irradiances Terrestrial radiances	O_3 dynamics/modelling Climatology and meteorology O_3 solar relationships	GSFC, NOAA, MIT, CDC, U of Fla. NSF, LARC Lockheed, Oxford Cal Tech Canada
CZCS	2-minute images	Temperature Spectral radiances Chlorophyll Sediment	Geodynamics of coastal regions Chemical and thermal pollution studies Fishery resources Deep ocean monitoring Oil spill monitoring	GSFC, NOAA, U of Cal (Davis) U of Fla. AMES Tex ARM EURASEP
THIR	Daily montages of temperature	Surface temperature Cloud top temperature	Effects of cloudiness or other Nimbus-G instruments data	All sensors

Table 4   Transfer of Nimbus technology to operational spacecraft

	NIMBUS INSTRUMENT		OPERATIONAL INSTRUMENT
APT	AUTOMATIC PICTURE TRANSMISSION SYSTEM	APT	AUTOMATIC PICTURE TRANSMISSION SYSTEM
AVCS	ADVANCED VIDICON CAMERA SYSTEM	AVCS	ADVANCED VIDICON CAMERA SYSTEM
SIRS	SATELLITE INFRARED SPECTROMETER	ITPR	INFRARED TEMPERATURE PROFILE RADIOMETER
IRLS	INTERROGATION, RECORDING AND LOCATION SYSTEM	DCS	DATA COLLECTION SYSTEMS
		SARR	SEARCH AND RESCUE PROCESSOR AND REPORTER
HIRS	HIGH RESOLUTION TEMPERATURE SOUNDER	HIRS	HIGH RESOLUTION TEMPERATURE SOUNDER
THIR	TEMPERATURE HUMIDITY INFRARED RADIOMETER	AVHRR	ADVANCED VERY HIGH RESOLUTION RADIOMETER
		SR	SCANNING RADIOMETER
NEMS	NIMBUS EXPERIMENT MICROWAVE SPECTROMETER	AMSU	ADVANCED MICROWAVE SOUNDING UNIT
		MSU	MICROWAVE SOUNDING UNIT
PMR	PRESSURE MODULATED RADIOMETER	SSU	STRATOSPHERIC SOUNDING UNIT
BUV	BACKSCATTER ULTRAVIOLET	SBUV	SCANNING BACKSCATTER ULTRAVIOLET
SBUV	SCANNING BACKSCATTER ULTRAVIOLET		

Application Technology Transfer. Table 4 is a summary of the remote sensing instruments that had their beginnings in the Nimbus Program. These experimental sensors became principal elements of the operational program of NOAA and, in so doing, are today contributing to the public welfare - - a tribute to the high degree of integration that exists in our nation's space program.

Lessons Learned

The current Administration, specifically the Department of Defense, has completed several studies aimed toward a better understanding of the processes involved in what is popularly called P^3I or preplanned product improvement. While Nimbus was not one of the programs selected for this study (aircraft and tanks were better suited to the task at hand), after-the-fact statistics on Nimbus are interesting if viewed in this perspective.

While there are many differences in relating one-at-a-time satellites, prepared for launch over a period usually lasting two or more years, to repetitive fabrication of military aircraft, the principal factors involved are pretty much the same -- mainly people.

Building, assembling, and testing satellites, while it is a one-at-a-time experience, is very dependent on what came before. The first of a kind has only related experience to provide the backdrop and very often the related experience is not as related as originally thought. Engineers find themselves experimenting more often than they are producing. Fig. 15 is a good example of how the people-related activity can be effectively employed, providing the same degree of skills, turning out a reliable, long-lived space vehicle in a repetitive manner, even over a period of years, while becoming more and more efficient in the process. It seems to be symptomatic in the space business that people and programs stay pretty much together, and I am sure that the General Electric Company experience with Nimbus has been repeated at other contractor facilities. Fig. 16 is related to the Boeing experiences over the years in the repetitive production of 727 airplanes.

Just as the data on Nimbus include the addition of significant nonrecurring cost improvements in the system (new command system, new attitude control system, improved power system, upgraded structure), so too do the

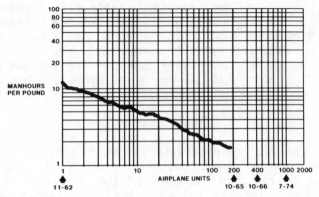

Fig. 16 Cost of nonrecurring product improvements (727 aircraft program).

data from the 727 program include approximately a 50% of initial investment nonrecurring cost for improvements made. The significance of repetitive activities, and not unexpectedly, the maintainance of a continuous technical/ cost team is stressed by Boeing as key factors in contributing to this improved performance. The NASA/General Electric continuous technical/cost team was instrumental in providing the results shown for Nimbus.

In a quantitative way, Fig. 17 describes the real payoff of P^3I. As described, Nimbus became the principal remote sensing research satellite for NASA and, in so becoming, hosted an ever-growing list of payload devices, each one more complex than the previous, each one demanding more power, each one demanding more transmission bandwidth needed to return significantly more data to the experiment community. Yet as the plots and the data show, the ratio of payload to spacecraft in terms of real dollar cost and total payload weight shows an ever increasing capability.

The Nimbus Program was indeed fortunate in that the early visionary designers selected a configuration, stuck to the principal of a highly accurate attitude control system, and designed an active thermal control system that simplified the individual payload designers' task. In addition, as mentioned briefly in this paper, the degree of adaptability of the basic Nimbus spacecraft design was further demonstrated in its direct application to the Earth Resources Technology Satellite (ERTS, now Landsat) Program launches 1-3. If similar data for ERTS

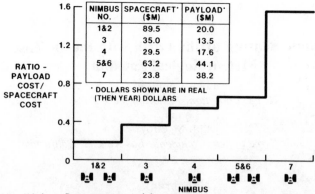

Fig. 17 Nimbus Program cost history and rate of information return.

were examined, it would be seen that the favorable ratios demonstrated for Nimbus-7 were exceeded by all three ERTS satellites.

Whether by accident or by design, it would appear that the prerequisites for successful P^3I are several and varied:

1) Vision and imagination to believe that the first prototype will be the precursor to a successful new series of flight articles.

2) Hard and fast design principals that demand just a little bit more capability than is really needed to meet the near-in objectives.

3) A qualified and dedicated team that sincerely believes in the product it is busy evolving, and a responsible management structure that helps to encourage their continuity.

With all the near-in problems that seem to be plaguing NASA today and the difficulty in initiating new program starts, it would certainly appear that the "Nimbus experience" could be used to good advantage and help to influence the future United States space program policy in the area of space applications.

Reference

[1]H.J. Zwally and P. Glorsen, "Passive Microwave Images of the Polar Regions and Research Applications," Polar Record, Vol. 18, No. 116, 1977, pp. 431-450, printed in Great Britain.

Remote Sensing of the Earth with the Defense Meteorological Satellite

Louis Gomberg*

RCA Corporation, Princeton, New Jersey

and

S.M. McElroy†

U.S. Air Force System Command, Los Angeles, California

Abstract

The Defense Meteorological Satellite System (DMSS) provides meteorological and environmental data for the Armed Forces of the United States. A key element in the system is the remote sensing platform, or spacecraft. This paper describes the DMSS and traces its evolution. Emphasis is placed on the space segment, particularly the spacecraft, which has evolved from a simple spin-stabilized vehicle weighing less than 200 pounds to the present three-axis satellite capable of virtually autonomous operation and weighing almost 2500 pounds. This paper describes the spacecraft evolution and compares it with the corresponding Polar Orbiting Environmental Satellite (POES). Detailed subsystem descriptions are provided, with particular emphasis on the attitude determination and control subsystem because of its sophistication. Future trends in the DMSS evolution are described, and other applications of this space platform are provided.

Background

The purpose of the Defense Meteorological Satellite Program (DMSP) is to provide high-quality weather and other environmental data in a timely fashion to the Armed Forces of the United States for tactical and strategic missions and to other authorized ancillary organizations such as NOAA. The satellite evolution has paralleled the civilian polar-orbiting environmental satellite (POES), more familiarly known as TIROS. However, DMSP has its own mission objectives, which requires unique sensor payloads and nodal crossing times.

---

*Division Vice President, Remote Sensor Programs, Astro-Electronics Division.

†Deputy for DMSP, Space Division; Colonel, U.S. Air Force.

The system is comprised of three major segments: space, ground, and launch. The program is managed by the Air Force System Commands (AFSC) Space Division in Los Angeles. Orbit operations are the responsibility of the Space Command in Colorado Springs. Aerospace Corp. is responsible for general systems engineering. The current DMSP Block 5D-2 satellites are extremely sophisticated and are capable of virtually autonomous operation in all mission phases. The satellite operates in a 833-km (450-n.mi.) sun-synchronous polar orbit with an inclination angle of 98.69° and can accommodate sun angle ranges of 0 to 95 deg.

The ground segment provides command and control functions, receives the sensor data, and processes and disseminates the data. To accomplish command and control, the Air Force Space Command site at Omaha (Central Command and Control, CCC) is linked through an Integrated Command System (ICS) to the command readout stations (CRS) at Loring AFB in Maine and Fairchild AFB in Washington. Additionally, the satellite has space/ground link system (SGLS) compatible links and can be controlled by the worldwide Air Force Satellite Control Facility (AFSCF) network to back up the Space Command's CRSs. Additional data receiving stations have been established at Kaenna Pt., Hawaii, and another is planned for Thule, Greenland.

Stored sensor data are transmitted from the CRSs to Air Force Global Weather Central (AFGWC) at Offutt AFB, Neb., through commercial communications links. The AFGWC processes and disseminates the data worldwide. Data are also transmitted to the Navy Fleet Numerical Operations Center (FNOC) at Monterey, Calif., via domestic commercial communications satellites. Real-time local day-and-night cloud-cover pictures are transmitted directly from the satellite to ground tactical terminals and Navy aircraft carriers. See Fig. 1.

The current launch vehicle is the Atlas E, which is a refurbished ICBM. The spacecraft is launched from the Western Test Range (WTR) at Vandenberg Air Force Base (VAFB) in California. The satellite navigates while on the Atlas and after separation injects itself into orbit autonomously using its own guidance and control capabilities. The heart of the G&C subsystem is a reprogrammable on-board computer.

The DMSP has been in existence for approximately 20 years. In that time, the satellite has evolved from a simple spin-stabilized vehicle using vidicon cameras for cloud-cover data to a very sophisticated three-axis zero-momentum satellite whose in-orbit weight is approximately 840 kg (1850 lb) depending on the payload sensor mix. The primary sensor (oscillating radiometer), supplied by West-

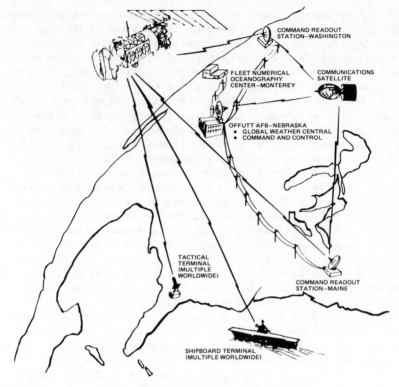

Fig. 1   Defense Meteorological Satellite System.

inghouse, provides high-resolution 0.5- and 3-km (0.3- and 2-n.mi.) and infrared (i.r.) pictures with constant resolution across the 2909-km (1600-n.mi.) scan and is capable of operating across the Earth's terminator.

The satellite carries other mission sensors: passive microwave temperature sounder (provided by Aerojet) and an i.r. sounder (provided by Barnes Engineering) to measure temperature and moisture content as a function of altitude above sea level. A microwave imager, built by Hughes Aircraft Corp. and to be launched aboard a DMSP spacecraft in 1985, will provide data on sea state, ice, soil, and cloud moisture. Additionally, other sensors measure charged-particle activity in the proximity of the satellite and the Earth's aurora and Earth's limb, which are used to characterize the ionosphere to make low-frequency radio wave propagation predictions. New payloads such as a laser radar (lidar--light detection and ranging) and vacuum ultraviolet (VUV) sensor are planned for future flights. The lidar instrument will provide temperature, humidity as a function of altitude, and wind information. The VUV will provide information on the ultraviolet activity which will allow characterization of the ionosphere.

This paper traces the evolution of the DMSP program-- with particular emphasis on the space segment--and points out the differences between the civilian polar-orbiting meteorological satellite and the military version. It also traces the evolution of the program and defines the objectives of each major change and how the mission objectives were achieved using a variety of strategies.

Introduction

This paper provides an overview of the Defense Meteorological Satellite Program (DMSP) and describes its evolution from a simple spin-stabilized satellite providing visible cloud-cover data to a three-axis precision-pointing meteorological and environmental remote sensing platform. It describes the different satellite configurations with emphasis on the spacecraft design, particularly on the current satellite series, which is one of the most sophisticated and autonomous satellites. In a companion paper in this volume, Meyer describes the DMSP remote sensing payloads and their applications in detail.

The DMSP had been in existence for a considerable period of time before John L. McLucas, Under Secretary of the Air Force, publicly disclosed on March 6, 1973, the existence of a Defense Meteorological Satellite Program. In this announcement, Dr. McLucas stated: "The various features which I will describe contribute to form the most responsive operational data system of its kind. Note, I stress responsive and operational." This requirement, "responsive and operational," led to unique spacecraft designs necessary to meet DMSP user needs in light of changing military requirements and provided a modus operandi for tracing the evolution of the spacecraft toward meeting these requirements. Table 1 summarizes the capabilities of the DMSP spacecraft.

The satellite evolved from a spin-stabilized spacecraft employing TV cameras to a sophisticated three-axis, zero-momentum system capable of virtually autonomous operation. Figure 2 depicts the satellite evolution from the spin-stabilized Block IV through the three-axis, zero-momentum, integrated, smart Block 5D satellites.

The program was initiated by the U.S. Air Force when it perceived the possibility of obtaining meteorological data through the use of orbiting satellites from areas of the world that proscribed access to the United States.

Table 1 DMSP satellites

Parameter	IV	5A	5B	5C	5D-1	5D-2	5D-2 FD	S11-14	S15
Weight, lb	180	220	411	411	1064–1132	1656	1850	2000	2400
Size, ft	3X3 Cylinder	3X3 Cylinder	4.3	tapering to 3.5 X 7	10 X 4	11.5 X 4	11.5 X 4	11.5 X 4	13.0 X 4
Power,[a] W									
BOL	70	140	285	285	1000	1250	1300	1300	177
EOL	60	70	150	150	350	550	600	600	750
Des life, month	6	12	18	18	30	48	48	48	60
Solar Array, ft^2	28.3	37.6	86	86	100	125	125	125	155
Launch vehicles	Thor, BII	Thor, BII	Thor, BIIA	Thor, BIIA	Thor, 364-15 and -4	Atlas, 364-15	Atlas, 364-15	Atlas, 364-15	Titan II
Orbit elements									
Altitude, n.mi.	450	450	450	450	450 ±10	450 ±10	450 ±10	450 ±10	450 ±10
Inclination, deg	98.69	98.69	98.69 ±0.2	98.69 ±0.2	98.69 ±0.15	98.69 ±0.15	98.69 ±0.15	98.69 ±0.15	98.69 ±0.15
A/P	60	60	60	60	30	30	30	30	30
Attitude control									
pointing, deg	0.5	0.3	0.3	0.3	0.01 precision / 0.1 basic	0.01 precision / 0.1 basic	0.01 precision / 0.1 basic	0.01 precision / 0.1 basic	0.01 precision / 0.1 basic
Memory bits	1600	1600	6400	512 k	896 k	896 k	896 k	1024 k	2816 k
Telemetry									
Analog	64 PAM	64 PAM	128 PCM	128 PCM	256 / Discrete-250	384 / 256	384 / 256	384 / 256	384 / 256
Digital					CPU data 120 words	CPU data 120 words	CPU data 120 words	CPU data 120 words	CPU data 120 words
					2, 10, or 60 kilobit/s	2, 10, or 60 kilobit/s	2, 10, or 60 kilobit/s	2, 10, or 60 kilobit/s	2, 10, or 60 kilobit/s
Uplink									
Encrypt.	No	No	Yes	Yes	Direct Data	Direct Data	All Data, TLM, Comm.	All Data, TLM, Comm.	All Data, TLM, Comm.
Frequency	UHF	UHF	UHF	UHF	High S	High S	High S	High S	High S
Command rate, kilobit/s	1	1	1	1	1	2	2	2	2

aBOL = beginning of life; EOL = end of life.

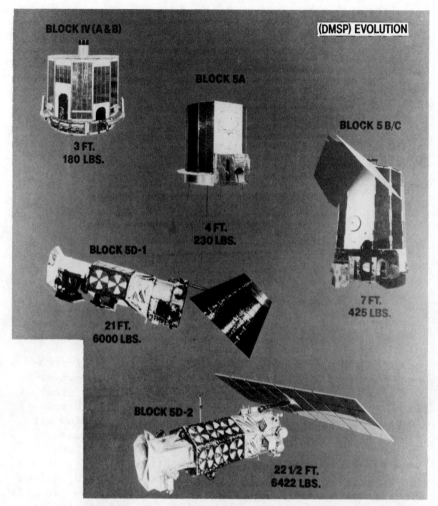

Fig. 2 Evolution from Block IV to 5D-2 satellites.

Block IV

The first series of satellites described here are the
Block IV, eight of which were designed and built and seven
launched. These were cylindrical spin-stabilized vehicles
weighing 82 kg (180 lb), 91.4 cm in diameter, and 91.4 cm
high (36 x 36 in.). The satellites were orbited in a 833-
km (450-n.mi.) sun-synchronous polar orbit (inclination
98.69 deg). The initial satellites were capable of daylight cloud-cover information provided by vidicon cameras,
and the last three satellites carried an i.r. detector

array that provided limited nighttime information. The
satellite utilized spin stabilization and magnetic torquing
for attitude control. The launch vehicle was a refurbished
IRBM-Thor LV-2F with a Burner II upper stage. The limited
throw weight capability of this combination resulted in a
minimum selective redundancy design philosophy. Only those
components with limited life—moving mechanical assemblies,
vidicon cameras, and tape recorders—were redundant. This
contrasted with the civilian meteorological satellites
(TIROS/ESSA) that were completely redundant because the
booster, a Delta, had a higher throw weight capability:
the Block IV weighed 82 kg (180 lb), whereas the TIROS
series weighed 136 kg (300 lb).

The use of the Thor LV-2F and a military launch team
resulted in a very austere cost-effective program. (In
fact, the program was so inexpensive that trade-offs showed
the cost of implementing total redundancy would result in
higher costs despite the increase in reliability and life.)
The use of refurbished IRBMs and ICBMs (Thor LV-2F, Atlas
Es, and TITAN 2s) for launching DMSP satellites continues
to this day.

The satellite had two vidicon cameras and used video
tape recorders for storing the cloud-cover data when out
of sight of a ground station.

The vidicon cameras used 1-in. tubes and an electro-
mechanical shutter. These provided visible cloud-cover
pictures. Nighttime pictures were provided by an array of
i.r. detectors (bolometers) located in the lower circumference of the spacecraft cylinder. The scan motion was
provided by the spacecraft spin about its pitch axis.

The major elements of the DMSP ground segment were
established during this era. The control readout stations
(CRS) were established at SAC bases—at Loring AFB, Maine,
and at Fairchild AFB, Washington. Controlling the two CRSs
was the Command & Control Center (CCC) at Offutt Air Force
Base in Omaha, which was in close proximity to the Air
Force Global Weather Headquarters. Operational responsibility initially given to SAC was transferred to Space
Command in 1983. There are other sites worldwide that
received tactical data, such as the Mark IV portable terminals and aircraft carriers.

Block 5A

The Block 5A spacecraft, launched in early 1970, was
the first operational, three-axis, body-stabilized meteorological spacecraft. The major reason for going to three-
axis body-stabilized satellites was the development of line

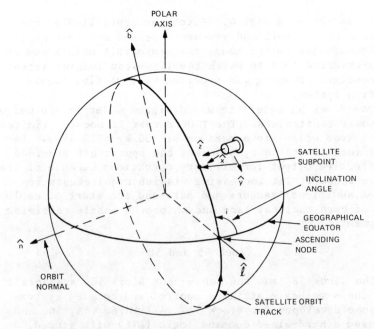

Fig. 3 Satellite coordinate geometry and sensor scan motion.

scan imagers that provided visual and i.r. data simultaneously. The spacecraft orbital velocity provided one scan
direction and a scanning mirror that is a part of the sensor provided the other. The operational scan mode of the
Block 5A spacecraft is shown in Fig. 3.

This spacecraft used a momentum-bias attitude control
system in which pitch-axis control was achieved by employing a combined momentum wheel and CO_2 band (13 μm) horizontal scanner located on the pitch axis. The momentum
wheel provided 35 in-lb-s and imparted a gyroscopic stiffness to the pitch axis. The roll and spin axes were controlled by magnetic coils that allowed replacement of the
momentum dissipated by friction in the bearing between the
momentum wheel and the main body of the spacecraft.

After injection into 833-km (450-n.mi.) circular sun-
synchronous orbit by the Thor/Burner II launch vehicle
system, the spacecraft was yawed 90 deg by the Burner II,
spun up to 4.5 rpm, and released using ball-lock separa-
tors. The momentum wheel was then spun up to approximately
150 rpm to despin the main body (by a momentum exchange
between the main body and the momentum wheel). The spin
rate along the orbit normal was observed by the horizon
sensor, looking through the motor shaft of the momentum

wheel, as shown in Fig. 4. Pitch was controlled by the
momentum wheel; roll and yaw were coupled and controlled
by the magnetic coils; thus, the spacecraft maintained an
Earth-oriented face to which the line-scan imaging sensor
was mounted. Damping was provided by a passive liquid
nutation system.

The Block 5A satellite was designed under severe weight
and power constraints. The Thor/Burner II booster limited
the payload weight to a maximum of 100 kg (220 lb). Despite such limitations, however, the spacecraft provided
an effective output for military operations because of its
unique sensor. The increasing mission requirements included additional sensors and data and the start of deployment of both tactical land and shipborne mobile receiving
equipment.

Block 5B and 5C

The Block 5B (and the subsequent Block 5C) spacecraft
used the same basic attitude control and command systems
as those developed for Block 5A. All three (5A, 5B, and
5C) used a hard-wired command logic (RTL) with stored,
time-tagged commands; however, the number of available
commands was doubled (64 to 128) in Blocks 5B and 5C.
Other basic capabilities were changed to meet the expanding requirements for direct readout capability, which more
than tripled. A second S-band data transmitter was added
to meet the needs for global coverage, doubling the mission data recording capability. Table 2 provides a com-

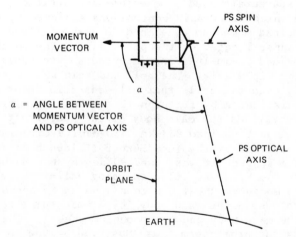

Fig. 4 Pitch momentum wheel conical horizon sensor and scan
geometry.

Table 2 Comparison of Block 5A and 5B/C capabilities

Parameter	Block 5A	Block 5B/C
Tape recorder storage		
High-resolution data	2 orbits	4 orbits
Very-high-resolution data	20 min	20 min
Direct readout/orbit	$\geq$11 (10 min ea.), 5 W	$\geq$20 (10 min ea.), 5 W
		+7 (10 min. ea.), 20 W
Sensor payload	Line scan imager (Visual)	Line scan imager (Visual and i.r.) Very-high-resolution radiometer (0.47 km) Precipitating electron sensor I.R. temperature sounder
Number of 25-bit stored commands	64	128
Transmitters		
Data	1 5 W	2 5 W
Telemetry	1 0.5 W	1 0.5 W

parison of the Block 5A and 5B/5C capabilities. A larger Earth-facing area was provided for mounting sensors, and the power capability was increased by more than doubling the size of the solar array hat and batteries. On the Block 5A through Block 5C, the hard mounting surface for the sensors was a chord of the rigid magnesium baseplate, which was the main structural element (Fig. 5). The chord length available for mounting was increased from 45 cm (17.7 in.) on Block 5A to 107 cm (42 in.) on Blocks 5B and 5C. The other major structural change was in the solar array "hat" structure, where the available solar cell area was doubled in Blocks 5B and C. This improved power system allowed an increase in direct readout (DRO) time to tactical sites from 60 min/day in Block 5A to 270 min/day in Blocks 5B and C. The Block 5B and C spacecraft carried a second 5W S-band transmitter. The transmitters employed UHF amplifiers followed by two X2 multipliers to obtain the S-band frequency (2207 MHz) and had a 10% efficiency.

The expanded command system provided for additional sensors (including a precipitating electron sensor, an i.r. temperature sounder, a cooled i.r. image channel and a classified sensor) and for greater flexibility in programmed direct readouts (DROs) as tabulated in Tables 2-4. Further improvements to enhance reliability and to increase mission effectiveness were also made to the spacecraft. In addition to the second transmitter, a redundant primary data recorder was added to increase the data storage capability and system reliability. In total, the changes made to meet increased mission requirements almost doubled the total satellite weight of 100 kg (220 lb) for Block 5A to 187 kg (411 lb) for Block 5B/5C.

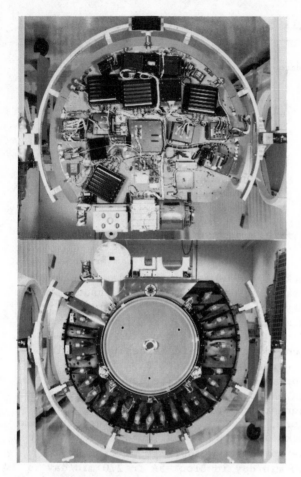

Fig. 5 Baseplate
mounting for sensors.

The launch sequence for Blocks 5A-5C was virtually identical. However, the increased weight of the Block 5B and C spacecraft necessitated the use of a two-stage Burner IIA in place of the one-stage Burner II atop the Thor booster. The Thor trajectory was reprogrammed to a hotter (shallow) trajectory, which caused concern about the spacecraft's aerothermal heating after separation of the heat shield. The other major modification was an extension of the heat shield to accommodate the increased size. Fins were also added to the Thor booster, returning it to its early configuration.

A total of three Block 5A, five 5B, and three 5C spacecraft were launched between 1968 and 1976.

The Block 5B and 5C spacecraft provided DMSP with data through the mid-1970s. Changing operational requirements to support changing military needs again drove DMSP into a

Table 3 Block 5 series spacecraft capabilities

Parameter	Block 5A	Block 5B/C	Block 5D-1	Block 5D-2	Block 5D-3
Tape recorder storage					
High-resolution data	2 orbits	4 orbits	6 orbits	9 orbits	9 orbits
Very-high-resolution data	20 min	20 min	40 min	60 min	60 min
Direct readout/orbit	11 (10 min ea)	20 (10 min ea)	72 (10 min ea)	100 (10 min ea)	100 (10 min ea)
Sensor payload	50 lb	110 lb	300 lb	650 lb	800 lb
Transmitter					
Power	1 5 W	1 5 W	2 5 W (1 dedicated to DRO)	2 5 W (1 dedicated to DRO)	2 5 W (1 dedicated to DRO)
	1 0.5 W	1 20 W	1 10 W	1 5 W	1 5 W
		1 0.5 W	2 5 W	2 5 W	2 5 W
Telemetry	64 25-bit words	128 25 bit words	16k 16-bit words	32k	64k
Memory size			52 microprogram instructions (read only)	52 microprogram instructions (read only)	52 microprogram instructions (read only)
			4096 18-bit words, in primary sensor system	4096 18-bit words, in primary sensor system	4096 18-bit words, in primary sensor system

^{a}Each of two CPUs; read/write can be reprogrammed in orbit.

Table 4 Sensor payloads

Block 5A	Block 5B/C	Block 5D^a	Block 5D-2	Block 5D-3
Line scan imager (visual)	Line scan imager (visual and i.r.)	Line scan imager (visual and i.r.) producing both high-resolution and very-high-resolution data	Line scan imager (visual and i.r.) producing both high-resolution and very-high-resolution data	Line scan imager (visual and i.r.) producing both high-resolution and very-high-resolution data
	Very-high-resolution i.r. imager	Gamma detector	Gamma detector	Gamma detector
	Precipitating electron sensor	Precipitating electron spectrometer	Precipitating electron spectrometer	Precipitating electron spectrometer
	I.R. temperature sounder	Density sounder	Density sounder	Density sounder
	Gamma detector	I.R. temperature, water vapor, and ozone sounder	I.R. temperature, water vapor, and ozone sounder	I.R. temperature, water vapor, and ozone sounder
		Plasma monitor	Plasma monitor	Plasma monitor
		Passive ionospheric monitor	Passive ionospheric monitor	Passive ionospheric monitor
		Microwave temperature sounder	Microwave temperature sounder	Microwave temperature sounder
		I.R. fluxmeter	I.R. fluxmeter	I.R. fluxmeter
		Plume sensors	Microwave Imager	Microwave Imager
				Vacuum Ultra-violet Sensor

^{a}Line scan imager carried on all spacecraft. Complement of other sensors varies with each spacecraft.

Tape Recorders:
1 very high resol. analog   1 very high resol.(analog)   3 - 1.67 x 10^9 bits   4 - 167 x 10^9 bits
1 med resol. analog   1 med resol. (analog)   digital recorders   digital recorders

new and, in this case, unique spacecraft design, the Block
5D-1, which eventually became the Block 5D-2 and was
adopted by NOAA for the successful TIROS-N program (POES).
See Fig. 6.

Block 5D-1

The new requirements were location of the primary image
data to within 0.6 km (0.3 n.mi.) without the benefit of
landmarks or other correlations (essential for rapid grid-
ding of the tactical data with minimum location error) and
rapid computer analysis of data for the automated cloud
nephanalysis. This required very precise attitude pointing and control accuracy (less than 0.01 deg or 36 sec)
and required that the primary sensor maintain a constant
spatial resolution across the 2909-km (1600-n.mi.) wide
data field. The nephanalysis provides rapid, automated
interpretation of cloud conditions. It also provides a
means for combining meteorological data obtained from satellites with that obtained from conventional sources. To
provide a statistically consistent sample, it was necessary
to provide constant spatial resolution over the total image
area. As an added benefit, this also improved the basic
image for manual integration. The sensor was also required
to produce pictures across the terminator where the light
band varied by over 100 dB. Figure 7 shows still another
benefit of constant spatial resolution: the possibility
of electronic enlargement of specific areas. The picture
on the right represents an electronic enlargement of a portion of the picture on the left.

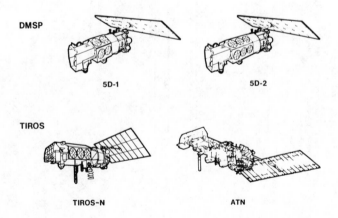

Fig. 6   Meteorological satellite configurations.

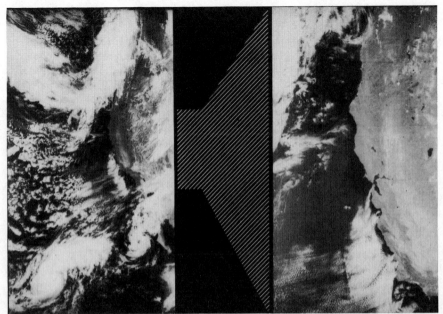

Fig. 7   Example of electronic enlargement; F2 real-time data, Sept. 22, 1977, high-resolution, low-light level, visible spectrum.

These requirements together with the mandated use of the Thor LV-2F with its 142.24-cm (56-in.) diameter influenced the design of the spacecraft and sensor. The most important requirement was translated into the need for a platform capable of pointing and controlling the optical axis of the primary imaging sensor to within 0.01 deg (36 sec) (in effect a spaceborne optical bench). Considering the error budget, this requires the spacecraft to maintain its pointing control to within 0.003 deg with negligible jitter rates. The accuracy was required for all disturbances including the uncompensated momentum from the primary imaging sensor. Such momentum varies sinusoidally at 5.94 Hz, reaching a peak as high as 2.2 in-lb-s about the spacecraft pitch axis.

Other design requirements were increased secondary payload capability, more flexible data handling, higher reliability, and longer mission life. Before beginning a discussion of this development, a comparison of the changing capabilities resulting from changing requirements is useful. Tables 3 and 4 tabulate this comparison for the Block 5 series.

To meet these requirements in a cost-effective manner, the Block 5D spacecraft is an integrated spacecraft. The term "integrated" means that some of the spacecraft components are used in the boost phase as well as in the on-orbit mode, resulting in substantial cost savings. The on-board flight computers and attitude determination and control equipment (the inertial measurement unit--IMU) are used to guide and control tne entire system, including the Thor booster, during the ascent and orbit injection phases, as well as performing their on-orbit role of spacecraft control of command and attitude. The spacecraft power and telemetry subsystems, and reaction control equipment, are also used for the ascent phase, and the residual GN_2 is used on-orbit in the event that high-momentum unloading is required.

The integrated spacecraft system includes everything above the booster interface mounting ring. This includes the satellite's two solid rocket motors, TEM-364-4 and TEM-364-15, which replaced the Block 5B/C upper stage (Burner IIA).

First put into operation in 1976, the Block 5D sat-ellites have also been called the "smart" satellites. The satellite is "smart" because it performs satellite opera-tional functions autonomously using a predetermined (but reprogrammable in orbit) software code in each of two cen-tral computers. Such functions include, for example, con-trol of the complex launch sequence, including all events associated with engine firing, steering the launch vehicle, separation, staging, and attaining a precision circular or-bit. Further, the spacecraft autonomously attains mission attitude through a series of maneuvers and deployments of such elements as the solar array. A typical launch se-quence is shown in Fig. 8. This demonstrated capability to autonomously achieve orbit and mission attitude, with-out ground control intervention, is essential to any space-craft flying from the vicinity of the Space Transportation System (STS) Orbiter to its predetermined mission orbit. Another reason for the "smart satellite" label is that the Block 5D spacecraft, because of the on-board computers, provide for a redundancy manager (artificial intelligence) as well as giving the mission controller the ability to reconfigure the system by reprogramming the on-board cen-tral computers (CPU). The flight software (S/W) can be and, in fact, has been modified to cope with unplanned events, thus extending the satellite's operational life or permitting more efficient operation of the satellite in response to mission changes.

The usefulness of the on-board reprogrammable computers was illustrated when, in the first launch, an unexpected large disturbance torque, which exceeded the reaction wheel and the torquing coil authority, caused the satellite to tumble. Some weeks later, intermittent communication with

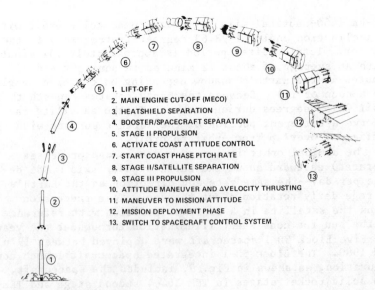

1. LIFT-OFF
2. MAIN ENGINE CUT-OFF (MECO)
3. HEATSHIELD SEPARATION
4. BOOSTER/SPACECRAFT SEPARATION
5. STAGE II PROPULSION
6. ACTIVATE COAST ATTITUDE CONTROL
7. START COAST PHASE PITCH RATE
8. STAGE II/SATELLITE SEPARATION
9. STAGE III PROPULSION
10. ATTITUDE MANEUVER AND ΔVELOCITY THRUSTING
11. MANEUVER TO MISSION ATTITUDE
12. MISSION DEPLOYMENT PHASE
13. SWITCH TO SPACECRAFT CONTROL SYSTEM

Fig. 8   Block 5D integrated spacecraft ascent, orbit injection, and array deployment.

the tumbling satellite was established and, by uplinking special despin S/W, the rates were gradually reduced using the magnetic torquers until the satellite was stabilized and became operational in a mode not originally envisioned. The in-orbit recovery of a satellite considered "dead" was made possible only by the extreme versatility and flexibility of the design. To preclude recurrences, a new S/W module was developed to measure the satellite's momentum continuously. When the momentum exceeds 25 in-lb-s, the GN_2 is brought on-line by opening a latch valve and the S/W automatically reduces this momentum by firing the appropriate GN_2 thrusters. Other problems overcome by modifying the flight software were the incorporation of new gyro and Earth sensor biases to compensate for orbital shifts, revision of the attitude control laws to compensate for structural damage, and a modification to the star processing software to cope with spurious star transits due to protons striking the celestial sensor.

In the first of the Block 5D series, 5D-1, flight S/W employed virtually all of the 16 kW of random access memory (RAM), which necessitated a progressive evolutionary increase in RAM in succeeding blocks until 32 kW is now standard. The next block 5D-3 will use 64 kW.

The 5D-1 is a three-axis-stabilized spacecraft with the same orbital elements as the 5B/C. It is launched into an

833-km (450-nautical mile) circular, near-polar orbit with
an inclination angle of 98.69 degrees (retrograde) to the
equator. Total orbital period is approximately 101 minutes
(with an average of about 72 minutes in sunlight and 29
minutes in the Earth's shadow depending on the clock angle
for a noon orbit). Because the Earth rotates beneath the
orbit 25.59 degrees during each orbit, the satellite can
observe a different portion of the Earth's surface with
sufficient overlap from orbit to orbit.

The nominal orbit is sun-synchronous and precesses
(rotates) eastward about the Earth's polar axis 0.986 degree per day--the same rate and direction as the Earth's
average daily rotation about the sun. This precession
keeps the satellite in a constant position with reference
to the sun for consistent illumination throughout the year.

Five Block 5D-1 spacecraft were deployed between 1976
and 1980. The Block 5D-1 integrated spacecraft launch configuration, as shown in Fig. 9, included the spacecraft,
two solid rocket stages (a TEM-364-4 second stage and TEM-
364-15 third stage), and a hydrazine (N_2H_4)/GN_2 pressurized
reaction control subsystem. The attitude determination
sensors, gyros, sun and Earth sensors, reaction control
wheels, and on-board computing facilities are part of the
spacecraft. The integrated spacecraft controls the entire
launch and orbit injection phase, including achievement of
a precise orbit and maneuvering to the mission attitude,
which continuously points the primary imaging sensor payload along the local vertical toward the Earth's geocenter.
The component that makes the Block 5D-1 "unique" is the
reprogrammable on-board computers (OBC). The DMSP was the
first operational satellite to use OBCs for command and

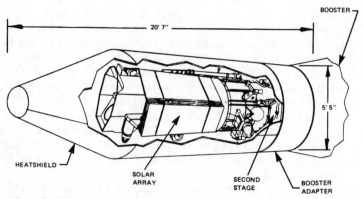

Fig. 9 Block 5D integrated spacecraft launch configuration.

control, attitude determination and control, redundancy management, ascent guidance and control, and power management. The Block 5D-1 SCP-234 utilizes bulk CMOS MSI devices. On the 5D-2, the memories now employ 4k CMOS SOS RAM. The OBCs interface with virtually every subsystem on the satellite, as show in Figure 10.

The on-board computers process inertial measurements and compute control commands of several spacecraft functions on a time-shared, priority-interrupt basis. From the moment when the "lift-off" signal ignites the booster, the main ascent guidance algorithms are in control. Once on orbit, the OBC "hands over" control to the orbit attitude determination and control algorithms. As shown in Fig. 11, the ascent guidance algorithms accept vehicle rate and acceleration data from the spacecraft inertial measurements unit (IMU) and compute spacecraft position, velocity, and attitudes during ascent. The current position is compared to a stored trajectory, and error signals in the form of corrective steering commands are transmitted to the proper element of the spacecraft to attain orbital altitude and inject it into orbit. After third-stage burnout, the orbit is made circular by a final velocity trim (ΔV) from the spacecraft's N_2H_4 thrusters. A ΔV of 30 m/s is provided.

The first-stage burn and attitude was controlled by the Thor autopilot through a gimballed main engine. The spacecraft computer and IMU gyros and accelerometers monitor the trajectory and issue commands that steer the total booster

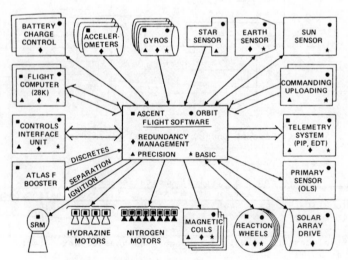

Fig. 10 Flight software overview.

stack by torquing the Booster integrating gyros (HIGS) to
trim the nominal trajectory to ensure the desired orbit
with the remaining states. The spacecraft computer then
issues discrete commands for main engine cutoff, vernier
engine burn, and heat shield jettison. Spacecraft separation is achieved by firing the 668-Nm (150-1b) N_2H_4 engines under control of the guidance software. Second-stage
ignition and cutoff and pitch and cutoff are also controlled by the spacecraft. After the spacecraft has
achieved orbit, the OBC calculates and issues steering commands for the eight GN_2 thrusters to torque the spacecraft to its operational attitude. When the vehicle is in
proper mission attitude, with the yaw axis pointed toward
the Earth along the local vertical and the vehicle rates
are less than 0.25 deg/s/axis, handover to the on-orbit
attitude determination and control software is initiated.
The typical orbits achieved by the Block 5D-1 and 5D-2
spacecraft are shown in Table 5.

   The 5D satellites utilize a monopropellant GN_2 pressurized hydrazine propulsion subsystem during the ascent
phase for attitude control and apogee trim and, later in
the mission, the residual GN_2 provides a backup for the
attitude control subsystem (ACS) on orbit. The pressure-
regulated, mixed-mode propulsion subsystem includes large

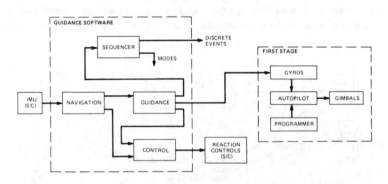

Fig. 11   Ascent phase, functional block diagram.

Table 5   Typical orbital elements

	Alt, n.mi.	A-P, n.mi.	Inclination, deg
Block 5D-1[a]	448	9	98.8
Block 5D-2[b]	443	6	98.69

[a]Includes one at 99.3 deg because of booster hard start
   at 98.69°.
[b]Two satellites.

668-Nm (150-lb$_f$) hydrazine rocket engines for major velocity corrections and eight 8.9-Nm (2-lb$_f$) gaseous nitrogen thrusters for attitude control functions in all three axes.

For on—orbit operations, the Block 5D spacecraft includes both a precision attitude and basic attitude determination and control systems. The basic elements of these systems are shown in the block diagrams in Figs. 12 and 13. Their location is shown in Fig. 14.

Upon handover to the on—orbit mode, the spacecraft automatically sequences through its initial attitude acquisition modes of rate nulling, Earth search and lock, and yaw gyrocompass. Upon ground command, the spacecraft enters its basic pointing mode, in which Earth sensor data are used to compute the pitch and roll torque commands. The IMU provides the basic attitude reference, utilizing four gyros (three orthogonal and one skewed at 57 deg as a backup to any of the other three). The skewed gyro data are also used to compute the yaw torque commands, with the sun sensor providing gyro drift calibration measurements once per orbit. The basic system pointing accuracy is less than 0.12 deg (3σ) per axis.

Attitude Determination and Control

The Block 5D attitude determination and control system is one of the most sophisticated ever launched and has proven itself in 13 missions--7 DMSP and 6 POES.

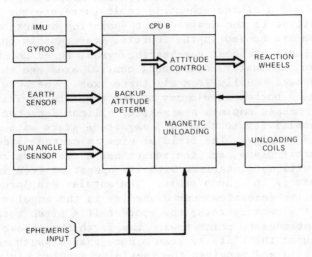

Fig. 12 Basic attitude determination and control subsystem, functional block diagram.

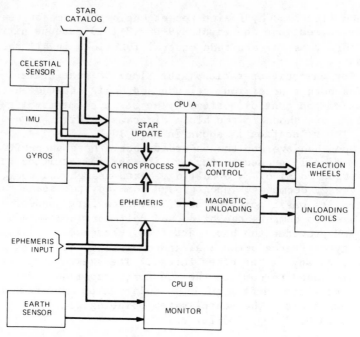

Fig. 13 Precision attitude determination and control subsystem, functional block diagram.

The precision attitude determination system uses gyro signals as a short-term reference, star mapper inputs for updates, and a stored ephemeris table to relate the inertial attitude to the desired Earth-pointing direction. The gyros are housed in the inertial measurements unit (IMU). There are four gas-bearing gyros, three mounted along the (nominally) orthogonal control axes and the fourth skewed equally from all three axes. The skew gyro serves as a backup should any of the other three fail. The star mapper employs a six-slit, silicon detector and has a sensitivity to about 4.5 magnitude stars with a 10-deg field of view. The field of view is canted 35 deg out of the orbit plane, and the sensor has a sun shade so that the sun will not interfere with its operation even if the spacecraft is in a noon orbit. The angular displacement of the slits generates some diversity in the angular direction of the measurements; the spacecraft's pitch rotation as it continues to point toward the Earth throughout the orbit causes the slits to scan a cone-shaped swath through a star field and provides the remaining angular diversity for full three-axis measurement capability. See Fig. 15.

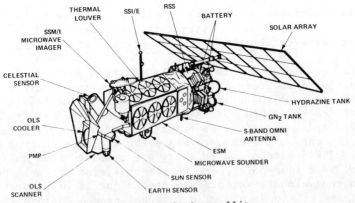

Fig. 14   DMSP 5D-2 satellite.

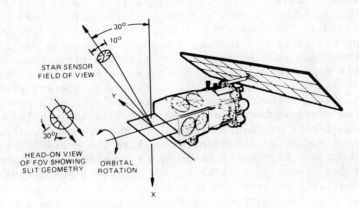

Fig. 15   Star mapper geometry.

The signals from these instruments are processed by the flight software. The gyro signals are digitized representations of the torquer rebalance current, transmitted at 10 samples/sec. The first software processing is to filter the rate signals; the filter provides additional stability margin at frequencies where the lowest structural bending modes occur. The filter output is resampled at 2 samples/sec; this timing drives the majority of the software and is the basic sampling rate of the attitude control loops as a whole. The rate signals are then corrected for known bias and misalignment; selection of the appropriate alignment matrix implements the use of the skew gyros as a replacement for an orthogonal gyro. A fine bias correction

is added (derived as described below). The resulting rate
signals are then used to integrate the directional cosine
matrix representing the inertial attitude of the spacecraft.

The ephemeris module provides position and velocity
vectors used to generate the reference pointing matrix, the
x (yaw) axis of which is directed normal to the (ellip-
soidal) earth. When combined with the measured attitude
matrix, this matrix yields pointing errors that, together
with the rates, are used to close the attitude control
loop. The position and velocity are computed each half-
second by a four-point Hermite interpolation scheme. Position and velocity vectors are stored for 12-min intervals
for a day (15+ orbits). The interpolation equations are
renewed every 12 mins. The calculations are done in 32-bit
double-precision values (as are all of the attitude determination calculations), but to conserve storage, a scheme
is employed whereby only single-precision values need to
be stored in the ephemeris table. This involves approxi-
mating the orbit by deriving a harmonic expansion for each
component and tabulating only the residues after removal
of this approximate value. The harmonic expansion by itself has low accuracy, but will continue to operate even
if the daily reload of the stored table (and new parameters
for the approximations) are omitted. This is important because, as will be seen subsequently, the ephemeris outputs
are used for other functions as well as the present one.

The remaining functions comprise a Kalman filter, which
is called whenever the star mapper detects a star transit.
This software is executed at a low priority level and need
not be completed within a half-second cycle. (The state
transition matrix is updated at a 2-Hz rate, so that it
will be current whenever a transit occurs.) The filter
estimates the three components of attitude error and three
of gyro bias.

The entire ADAC system is shown in the block diagrams
of Fig. 16 and 17.

The star mapper provides two items of information: the
time that a transit occurred and the slit that detected
the transit. See Fig. 15. The attitude at the instant of
transit is computed and used to define the (presumed)
inertial orientation of the active slit. The covariance
matrix, representing the filter's estimate of uncertainty
as of the previous accepted transit, is updated for attitude change since that time and is augmented by the "plant"
noise, which consists of an estimate of gyro random drift
plus an allowance for unmodeled errors, such as roundoff
effects. A loop is then entered, comprising a search

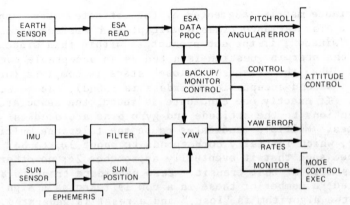

Fig. 16   Basic attitude determination.

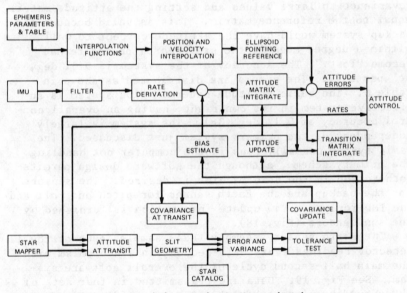

Fig. 17   Precision attitude determination.

through the star catalog, to determine which star caused
the transit. The catalog contains up to 80 stars (typically 50) and is updated daily to track the precession of
the orbit. Only those stars close (less than 7.25 deg) to
the line of sight are considered, although there would be
enough CPU time to search the whole table if necessary.
For each star, the measurement variance is then computed
using the slit-star geometry and the above-mentioned

covariance matrix, augmented by the estimated star mapper
error. The variance times a multiplier comprises a tolerance "window"; if the dot product is within this window,
then the star in question is noted as an acceptable candidate. When the search of "close" stars is complete (or
when a second acceptable candidate is found), the search
ends. If exactly one candidate is found, the associated
corrections to the attitude and gyro bias are used as
updates. Multiple candidates cause the tolerance multiplier, which initially corresponds to about 3σ, to be
reduced such that it eventually approaches 2σ; no other
use is made of that transit. Zero candidate transits are
counted; a number of these in a row is taken as a sign
that the algorithm is "lost," and a reset is generated.
Finally, the covariance matrix is adjusted as a result of
the update.

Initialization of the filter is done by setting the
covariance to large values and setting the attitude matrix
equal to the reference matrix. This is valid because the
backup system would have the attitude correct to well
within a degree even if the star search procedure had
become "lost." The accuracy of the system is 0.01 deg,
3σ per axis. The errors are distributed as shown in
Table 6. The basic attitude determination system is an
effective system in its own right, having an overall control accuracy of 0.12 deg (3σ). The system is largely
independent of the primary system just discussed. The
basic system normally runs in the computer not handling
the primary scheme, although the software design permits
both to run in the same machine if desired. The sensors
for the backup are the Earth sensor for pitch and roll and
the IMU for yaw. Yaw update information is furnished by
the sun sensors (Fig. 18).

The Earth sensor assembly (ESA) samples each of the 12
detector readings every half-second, in synchronism with
the main half-second cycle of the overall software system. See Fig. 19. Data are transmitted in four sets of
three readings (one quadrant) at regular intervals during
the half-second cycle and are accumulated by the Earth sensor read software, which also applies calibration corrections to the readings. The priority structure of the OBC
(SCP-234) facilitates reading the ESA when required without significant delays to other computational tasks.

The Earth sensor data processor decides whether the
four quadrant readings (see Fig. 19) are useable or off
the Earth, then computes the angle measurements just described, corrects for alignment calibration, and resolves
the readings into the pitch and roll control axes. If any
quadrant is unusable because of saturation, sun blockage,

Table 6   Pointing accuracy error sources, sec

Ephemeris predication accuracy	27
Attitude determination accuracy	15[a]
Attitude control errors	12
Alignment uncertainties	10
rss	< 36

[a]18 using the skew gyro.

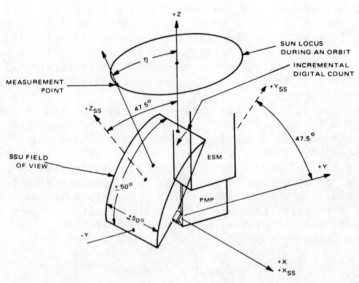

Fig. 18   Sun sensor geometry.

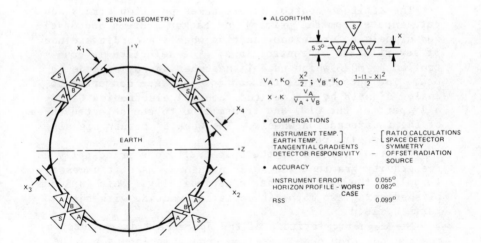

Fig. 19   Earth sensor geometry.

or hardware failure, the attitude is calculated by an
alternate scheme using the three remaining quadrants.

It has been mentioned that the basic monitor control
module is notified if any Earth sensor quadrant leaves the
Earth. This would initiate the acquisition sequence, the
first phase of which is to null the body rates. Next, a
search procedure is entered that consists of determining
which Earth sensor quadrants are off the Earth and establishing appropriate pitch and/or roll rates to drive the
Earth sensor back onto the Earth. The logic will account
for all cases, even the "upside-down" case in which all
quadrants are off the Earth. Once all four quadrants are
on the Earth, the yaw gyrocompassing mode is entered and
the normal (integration) yaw mode is established later by
ground command.

As stated, the usual mode of the basic system is "monitor," which simply means that the system measures but
does not control attitude. However, if a large error is
detected, the basic system takes control of the spacecraft.
At the time of such a takeover, an automatic "passive" test
is made to determine if the error was caused by a failure
of a reaction wheel. If the error persists after takeover,
it is attributed to a wheel failure. As with the gyros,
there is a fourth (skew) reaction wheel for use in case of
such a failure.

Control Functions

Everything has been discussed except the functions
exercising the actual control over the spacecraft dynamics.

The attitude control module takes position errors and
rate inputs from the primary and backup systems and devel-
ops signals to drive the reaction wheels according to one
of several sets of control laws. The selection is controlled by MCXS which establishes what backup submode to
use. The outputs from the control laws are converted to
analog signals by the attitude control electronics (actually part of the CIU) and transmitted to the selected three
of the four reaction wheels. The wheels' return signals
indicate their speed.

External torques on the spacecraft, due principally to
the gravity gradient and solar pressure, make it necessary
to unload the reaction wheels periodically. This is accomplished using two magnetic coils interacting with the
Earth's field.

The magnetic latitude of the spacecraft is computed by
the sun position code, based on ephemeris inputs and the
position of the Earth. The "magnetic momentum unload"

module defines the unloading regions, tests the wheel speeds to determine whether unloading is necessary, and generates the commands to energize the direction and to turn them off when the unloading is complete. The commands are issued by the attitude control software, so that the compensation terms can be set and cleared at the proper times, because the unloading code operates at a very low priority level.

The final function to be discussed is the control to keep the solar array drive running at one revolution per orbit. The drive itself is a constant-speed device operating at one of three speeds; these values are selected to just exceed the range required by the design tolerance on the orbit altitude. A skew rate of about five times the orbital rate is also provided. The drive contains a coarse resolver that furnishes a position signal; the desired array position is calculated by the sun position software. The solar array control module compares these and selects the appropriate rate.

The emphasis here has been on the attitude control subsystem; however, resolution of other unique design problems was also a key to this versatile space system. For example, to translate the high pointing accuracy of the attitude system to the pointing of the optical axis of the primary sensor, a unique mounting platform had to be developed. This precision mounting platform (PMP) is of optical bench quality and through a very careful thermal design is maintained in a virtual isothermal condition around the orbit. The primary elements of the attitude control subsystem (the IMU and the star and Earth sensors, as well as the primary imaging sensor and some secondary sensors) are all mounted and precisely aligned on the PMP. This approach allows the spacecraft to meet the mission requirement of pointing and optical axis of the primary imaging sensor to an accuracy of within 0.01 deg (3σ) in all axes. Another uniquely military requirement is the capability to achieve any local sun time for the sun-synchronous orbit. This was the major factor in designing the articulating array and the spacecraft power and thermal subsystems. The TIROS-N and ATN spacecraft (see Fig. 20) operate in a similar fashion but do not have a celestial sensor because they do not require the pointing accuracy.

As stated earlier, the mission capability and flexibility required to meet the unique military needs further dictated the use of two on-board reprogrammable computers. Each OBC is a multilevel, microprogrammed unit built with CMOS bulk and CMOS/SOS logic and each includes a reprogrammable 16k CMOS memory. It operates at a 100 kips

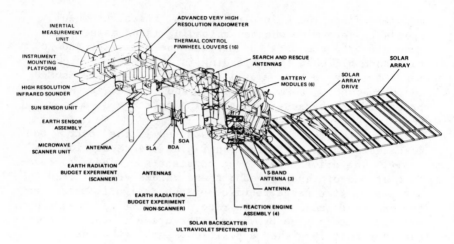

Fig. 20   ATN spacecraft configuration.

fixed point and consumes less than 5W of 10V power.   In
the spacecraft architecture, the OBCs are involved in
command and control and stored command functions for all
spacecraft activities, solar array drive signal computation, ascent guidance, and on-orbit attitude determination
and control, as shown in Fig. 10.   Moreover, they have the
potential of a host of other functions.   New algorithms
are under development to provide greater autonomy, such as
power management software.   They are also used to provide
the redundancy management (the skewed wheels and gyros),
gyro power supplies, array drive electronics, and celestial
sensor detector in extended lifetime applications.

The Block 5D-2 satellite is very similar in implementation and operation to the Block 5D-1 and are virtually
identical to the POES (TIROS-N) with the exception of the
celestial sensor that DMSP requires to meet the 0.01-deg
attitude pointing requirement.   See Fig. 21.   The changes
were driven by the need to increase payload capability
and reliability.   As a result, the basic structure was
increased by 45.7 cm (18 in.) and the solar array panels
were lengthened by 45.7 cm (18 in.), resulting in a solar
array area of 11.6 m^2 (125 ft^2) (a 25% increase).   The number of batteries was increased from one to two, and the
power supply electronics was upgraded to accommodate the
increase in power.

The primary sensor (OLS) reliability was improved by
making the sensor electronics redundant and increasing the
number of tape recorders (storage capacity of 1 x 10^9 bits)
from three to four.   A microwave imager was added to the
spacecraft.   See Fig. 22 for the current sensor complement.

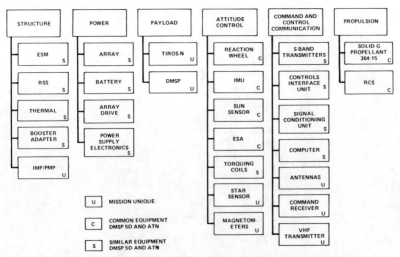

Fig. 21 DMSP and TIROS subsystem commonality.

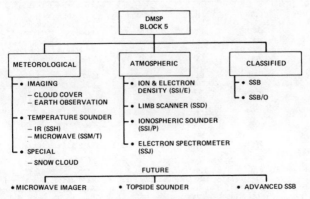

Fig. 22 DMSP sensor complement.

The spacecraft components were modified to eliminate all single-point failures. The telemetry processor was made redundant, and its capabilities were increased. The computers were upgraded by increasing the RAM from 16 to 32 kW, and two-bit error detection and one-bit error correction was added. The memory devices were changed from bulk CMOS to CMOS/SOS. The latter has worked well in orbit and has an inherently high immunity from single-event upset (SEU).

As a consequence of these changes, the satellite on-orbit weight increased from 514 to 840 kg (1131 to 1850

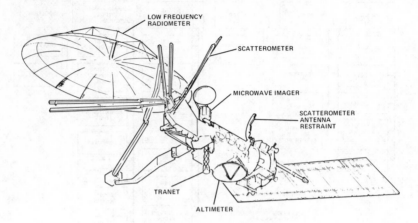

Fig. 23 NROSS satellite.

Table 7 DMSP, TIROS, ATN, NROSS spacecraft features and capabilities

Parameter	5D-1	5D-2	TIROS-N	ATN/POES	5D-3	NROSS
TECO weight (lb)	1131	1380 ↕ 1850	1680	1835-2250 ↕ 2470-2900	1697 ↕ 2470	3000
First stage	LV-2F	Atlas F	Atlas F	Atlas F	Titan II	Titan II
Second stage	TEM-364-4	none	none	none	none	none
Third stage	TEM-364-15	TEM-364-15	TEM-364-15	TEM-364-15	TEM-364-15	TEM-364-15
N_2H_4 (lb)	35	35	35	35	35	110
Power (W)						
BOL (array output)	770	910	1095	1270	1300	1300
EOL (load capability)	300	400	465	520	600	600
Sun angle	0°-95°	0°-95°	0°-68°	0°-68°	0°-95°	0°-45°
Payload weight (lb)	300	400 ↕ 650	650	808	650 ↕ 1285	1000
No. of batteries	1	2	2	3	3	3
No. and size of solar array	8(6'x2')	8(7.5'x2')	8(7.5'x2')	8(7.5'x2')	10(7.5'x2')	10(7.5'x2')
Fairing diameter (ft)	5	7	7	7	10	10
ADACS						
Pointing and control	0.01°	0.01°	0.1°	0.1°	0.01°	0.05°
Control method	RWA & coils	RWA & coils	RWA & coils	RWA & coils	RWA & coils	RWA & coils
Determination sensors	CSA, SSA, ESA, IMU	CSA, SSA, ESA, IMU	SSA, ESA, IMU	SSA, ESA, IMU	CSA, SSA, ESA, IMU	SSA, ESA, IMU
Modes	primary backup gyro compass GN_2 muls	primary backup gyro compass guls	basic gyro compass GN_2 muls	basic gyro compass GN_2 muls	basic gyro compass guls	basic gyro compass guls
Computers	2	2	2	2	2	2
memory	16k words	28k words	18k words	18k words to 32k words	64k words	32k words
tech	CMOS bulk PMOS	CMOS bulk & SOS & PMOS*	CMOS bulk & SOS & PMOS	CMOS bulk & SOS & PMOS*	CMOS bulk & SOS	CMOS bulk & SOS

*Replaced with CMOS.

lb). To accommodate the increased weight, the launch
vehicle was changed from a Thor LV-2F to an Atlas E. The
propulsion system was modified by changing to a single
thrust mode and reducing the hydrazine thrust impulse from
668- to 445-Nm (150- to 100-lb) units.

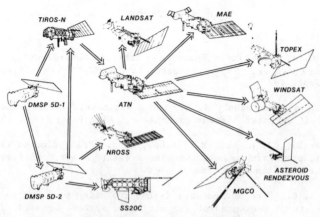

Fig. 24   Remote sensing satellite.

Because the Atlas is radio guided, the ascent guidance software was modified so that it navigates only while riding the Atlas. After separation, it performs the control and orbit injection.

The flight software package was reorganized to take advantage of the memory increase to add more capability and to implement additional reliability and autonomous capabilities such as power management and a formal hardware redundancy management module. See Fig. 10.

Two of these satellites have been launched to date, and both are operating well.

Because it is integrated and is in fact capable of being launched from the Shuttle as well as an expendable launch vehicle, the Block 5D bus provides a high degree of flexibility for the future. It will survive into the 1990s providing real-time, remotely sensed environmental information for the military and other applications, such as NROSS (see Fig. 23), in a cost- and system-effective manner. In fact, the AF is procuring additional satellites for launch on a TITAN II. Their length has been increased by 46 cm (18 in.), and additional solar array panels and batteries have been added for a longer life. Table 7 compares the major features of the DMSP, TIROS, and NROSS spacecraft.

Finally, the basic integrated Block 5D bus concept has performed so well and has so much versatility that it is being employed for the civilian polar orbiter, Advanced TIROS-N, and is the basis for the commercial Landsat, Mars Geoscience Climatological Orbiter (MGCO), the Navy Remote Observation Sensing Satellite (NROSS), and a host of other remote sensing satellite missions. See Fig. 24.

Bibliography

Beck, G. A., "Precision Spacecraft Attitude Control Using an On-Board Computer," Paper presented at EASCON '75, Washington, D.C., Sept. 1975.

Beck, G. A., Buntschuh, R. F., and Aukstikalnis, A. J., "Adaptable Spacecraft Computer Systems Experience," AIAA Paper, Oct. 1979.

Blankenship, J. R. and McGlinchey, J. J., "Evolution of the Block 5 Spacecraft to Meet Changing Military Needs," Military Aerospace, Weisbaden, Germany, 1978.

Daly, K. C., "The 5D Spacecraft--The Evolution of a Spacecraft System," presented at the Air Force Systems Command Science and Engineering Symposium, Kirtland AFB, New Mexico, Oct. 2, 1973.

Gomberg, L., TeBeest, R., and McElroy, S., "Block 5D-1 Computer Controlled Spacecraft," Paper presented at Telemetry Conference, San Diego, 1978.

Oey, K. K. and Teitelbaum, S., "Highly Reliable Spaceborne Memory Subsystem," AIAA Paper 81-2113-CP, Oct. 1981.

Staniszewski, J. R., "Lazarus Sleeps No More - Satellite Recovered from Tumble," RCA Engineer, August/September 1978.

The Defense Meteorological Satellite Program:
A Review of Its Impact

Walter D. Meyer*

Control Data Corporation, Englewood, Colorado

Abstract

Since its inception, the Defense Meteoroligical Satellite Program (DMSP) has matured into a program that supports virtually all elements of the Defense Department that
operates systems sensitive to weather changes. The purpose
of this paper is to reflect on the past 18 years, to examine the increases in capability that have taken place, and
to highlight some of the key contributions that the DMSP
has made. It is intended to be a scientific review with an
emphasis toward the operational use of such data in every-
day activities--both military and civilian. The DMSP originated in the mid-1960s with the mission of providing
daily cloud-cover information over selected areas of the
world in support of Department of Defense operations.
Uniquely tailored to meet specific military needs, it quickly became a vital element of the United States Air Force
Air Weather Service (AWS) support capability. In the early
1970s, the United States Navy formally joined the DMSP and
arranged for image data to be relayed to their Fleet Numerical Oceanographic Center (FNOC) in Monterey, California, as
well as to a number of ground and seaborne terminals.
Following the declassification of the DMSP in early 1973,
an increasing number of military and non-military applications and benefits occurred. Image data were made available to the scientific community through an archival facility at the University of Wisconsin's Space Sciences and
Engineering Center. These data have been used in studies
ranging from the morphology of the auroral borealis to the
dynamics of tropical wave disturbances, to the monitoring
of the polar ice edge. As the DMSP has grown and evolved
over the past 18 years, its applications have expanded by

This paper is declared a work of the U.S. Government and
therefore is in the public domain.

*Manager; Lt. Col. (Ret.), U.S. Air Force.

leaps and bounds. The impacts on military operations have
been many and a number of examples are shown. Additional
non-military benefits have made the DMSP a truly national
asset. The continued increase in both the DMSP capabilities
and the data applications will result in even greater benefits in the future.

Introduction

The use of satellites to gather weather information was
one of the first "operational" applications explored by our
space pioneers. In fact, only a little over 2 years after
the United States launched its first satellite, a spacecraft
with the expressed goal of taking "weather" pictures was put
into orbit. That satellite, TIROS-1 (Television, Infrared
Observation System), paved the way for an effort that has
launched over 70 spacecraft providing either research and
development or operational weather and environmental support to the nation. Both the U.S. Department of Commerce
(DOC) through the National Oceanic and Atmospheric Administration (NOAA) and the Department of Defense (DOD) through
the Defense Meteorological Satellite Program (DMSP) have
come a long way in advancing the state-of-the-art of both
the hardware technology and the application of the resulting data to operational needs.

The evolution and description of the National Weather
Satellite Programs have been summarized by NASA.[1] It is
not the intent of this treatise to repeat this information,
but rather to amplify on the description and evolution of
the DMSP. It will focus on how the program has changed
over the years and how those changes have resulted in
greater utility and importance of program data. References
2-14 and many others describe selected aspects and applications of the DMSP.

Several key events in the life of the DMSP have inex-
orably altered the mission and therefore the character of
the program. Initially conceived to satisfy DOD and Air
Force requirements that were well beyond the requirements
of the early TIROS system, the program became triservice in
1969, was declassified in early 1973, survived (along with
the NOAA TIROS program) an extensive governmental review of
the nation's weather satellite programs in 1978-1979, and
picked up at least a portion of the DOD oceanographic satellite responsibilities in 1983. The impacts of these big
changes will be discussed during the course of this paper.
In every case, the result has been to make the DMSP responsible and responsive to a larger segment of the nation.

The Early Years: 1965–1972

The DMSP originated in the mid–1960s with a narrow set of well-defined military objectives. Chief among these was that of providing daily cloud-cover data worldwide. Very soon after its inception, however, its tactical use in supporting U.S. forces anywhere in the world was recognized. A specially configured DMSP satellite was launched with the express purpose of providing the U.S. Military Command in Vietnam with high-quality weather pictures over North Vietnam, Laos, and China, areas where conventional weather information was being withheld. The DMSP became a triservice system in late 1969 when the Navy joined the program. The Navy achieved its initial capability with a readout terminal for the data on board the aircraft carrier USS Constellation in 1971.

The Hardware

From mid–1965 to early 1970, the series of DMSP satellites was known as the Block IV series. A complete description of this series, its sensors, and the ground system is found in Ref. 15. Since this document is not readily available, the following additional information is provided. (See also Ref. 1) The spacecraft was a spin-stabilized octagon weighing approximately 100 lb. It employed two vidicon cameras to gather high-resolution TV pictures, 2.4km (1.5n.mi.) at the center to about 16km (10n.mi.) at the edge of the picture as the spacecraft moved in its orbit. Some spacecraft also had a low-resolution "visible" (0.4 – 4.0μm) and infrared (8.0 – 12.0μm) system. From these latter systems emerged the first attempts to combine reflected energy and emitted energy in the cloud analysis problem.

Beginning in early 1970, a new generation of satellites was inaugurated, the Block 5. It was a three-axis stabilized spacecraft that initially employed as its imaging sensor a three- and then a four-channel scanning radiometer. Detailed information on the instrument is contained in Refs. 4 and 16. The visible channels had a spectral band of 0.4 – 1.1μm and the lower-resolution [approximately 3.6km (2.0n.mi.) at nadir] channel also had a low-light-level amplification system. These two design factors enhanced the utility of the visible data by providing good land–sea contrast (land is much more reflective a 1μm than water) and by obtaining some interesting nighttime visible data (for half moonlight or brighter). A number of examples of the latter are found in Ref. 3.

In the evolution from the Block IV to the Block 5, the DMSP successfully maintained the concept of total system integration from spacecraft through data reduction. This concept, vital to meeting the short timelines associated with the application of cloud information, has been a trademark of the program. It involved contractors and various government agencies working together to design and build a total system from spacecraft to sensors, data communications, and data processing and display. The result was to put a cloud image from almost anywhere in the world in the hands of an analyst within 1.5h of the time the scene was imaged.

The space system was controlled from a Strategic Air Command Center at Offutt AFB, Neb., through two command readout sites at Fairchild AFB, Wash., and Loring AFB, Maine. High-speed communication lines tied the system together and the system was operated in a total "blue suit" Air Force environment.

The success of the mobile satellite receiving van deployed to Vietnam, combined with the incorporation of the U.S. Navy into the program in 1969, led to a gradual but substantial increase in the number of direct readout ground stations. By the end of 1972, 13 Air Force terminals, all equipped to receive Block 5 image data, were deployed worldwide and the Navy had installed its first shipboard receiving terminal.

The Product

Block IV data initially consisted of polaroid prints of the output of the vidicon. These prints, complete with two-dimensional distortion, were hand analyzed into cloud reports. When time permitted, short-range (less than 6h) forecasts of these analyses were made at the Air Force Global Weather Central (AFGWC) and applied to military requirements. The van deployed to Vietnam provided essentially the same kind of products. The accuracy of the analysis was conceived, developed, and tested operationally.[17] To support this analysis, the DMSP image signal was digitized and inserted into the AFGWC computers. There the data were rectified,[18] adjusted for solar elevation (normalized), and mapped on to the standard AFGWC analysis grid. The final product, the three-dimensional (3D) Nephanalysis was a combined analysis of clouds and weather, incorporating the processed satellite image data as well as more conventional weather observations. Large variations on cloud brightness along with substantial specular reflection from snow, sand, and sun glint off water surfaces made the normalization process difficult.

With the evolution to Block 5, the quality as well as
the quantity of satellite imagery went up dramatically.
The two-dimensional distortion of Block IV was reduced to
one dimension by combining the spacecraft motion with an
across-track scan pattern. A solar aspect sensor on the
satellite allowed some image normalization to take place
in the raw data, the addition of infrared and higher-
resolution image channels more than quadrupled the amount
of data, and new ground processing equipment automatically
made other corrections which enhanced data use. Pictures
were now obtained both day and night and an improved version of the 3D Nephanalysis was developed to handle the new
data.[19] Corrections were made to the infrared data to account for look angle ("limb darkening") and for atmospheric
attenuation.

An example of the computer-processed imagery and the
corresponding 3D Nephanalysis is presented in Figs. 1 and
2. The area is the Pacific Ocean, so there is a minimum
amount of conventional data. There is good agreement between the two figures. The numbers on Fig. 2 are explained
in detail in Ref. 19. The 3D Nephanalysis was archived at

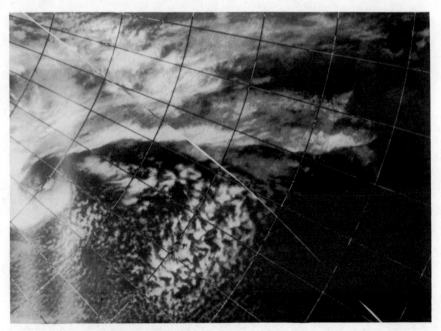

Fig. 1 Computer-processed DMSP 2.0 n.mi. visible imagery of north
central Pacific Ocean, Jan. 19, 1973.

Fig. 2   3D Nephanalysis of same area as Fig. 1, Jan. 19, 1973
(numbers are explained in Ref. 19).

the U.S. Air Force Environmental Technical Applications Center (USAFETAC) facility in Asheville, N.C., beginning in
1971, and the photographically processed imagery was stored
at the University of Wisconsin Space Sciences and Engineering Center beginning in 1972.

The Payoff

Because the DMSP began in a classified environment, it
was initially applied to military problems and, therefore,
its early value was almost exclusively oriented to selected
military operations. DMSP "first-light" cloud pictures (the
spacecraft was in a near-dawn sun-synchronous polar orbit)
were extensively used by the weather personnel in Saigon to
provide U.S. military commanders with crucial advice on
areas suitable to conduct aircraft operations. In many
cases, these data eliminated the need to use weather reconnaissance aircraft, thereby saving valuable men and planes
from exposure to enemy fire. This value was articulated by
Gen. William Momyer in 1967 during a nationally televised
interview, "As far as I am concerned, this weather picture
is probably the greatest innovation of the war. I depend
on it in conjunction with the traditional forecast as a
basic means of making my decisions as to whether to launch

or not launch a strike...The satellite is something no com-
mander has ever had before in a war."20

AFGWC's support requirements were increasing rapidly
during the late 1960s and many of these requirements were
very sensitive to clouds, especially over data-void and potentially data-denied areas. The 3D Nephanalysis was designed to be the primary tool in producing cloud forecasts
and climatologies in support of these needs. It wasn't
until the DMSP evolved to the Block 5 system that the satellite cloud data were of sufficient quality to be handled
in a semiautomated mode and reliable support to these cloud-
sensitive requirements became possible. Reconnaissance
flights needing clear weather were more accurately scheduled, long-haul transport flights were more efficiently
routed, and severe weather was monitored more precisely.
(The latter was aided immeasurably by the advent of the operational geostationary satellite in the mid-1970s, but in
the 1960s and early 1970s more frequent polar orbiters such
as the combined DMSP and TIROS had to suffice.)

One unique feature of the Block 5 imaging system is its
low-light-level visible detector, which has been described
by various authors.[3,21,22] In addition to the useful imag-

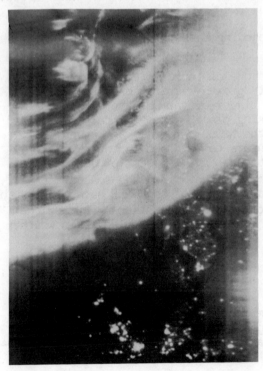

Fig. 3 DMSP 2.0 n.mi.
resolution visible imagery of
northern Europe, Nov. 22,
1972 (bright streaks make up
the aurora borealis).

ing of clouds at night (under moonlight) and the demographic novelty of the city lights, the display of the aurora
borealis (Fig. 3) was put to immediate use in assessing the
strength and character of solar stores.

The DMSP Declassifies

Near the end of 1972, the decision was made that the
DMSP should be declassified and made a national resource.
The reasons for this decision are beyond the scope of this
paper, but the result was dramatic in its impact on the
program. Image data from the DMSP were now a national asset and could be used to augment NOAA data in scientific
studies as well as in operational products. While the
DMSP continued to be driven by military needs and continued
to support military operations, it now had to contend with
a much larger and more diverse set of customers, both within DOD and on governmental and nongovernmental agencies.
The technology used in building the DMSP into "The most responsive operational system of its kind"[21] was available to
the entire community. As will be discussed in the next section, the benefits of declassification were many and varied.

The Expanding Years: 1973–1981

The late 1970s was one of incredible growth for the
DMSP. A portion of this growth was driven by the declassification, but an even bigger driver was the explosion in
technology that was taking place. Experimental sensors had
flown successfully on the Nimbus program[1] and paved the way
for new operational sensors to be flown on the DMSP. New
advances in microchip technology, computer processing, and
high-speed communication revolutionized the spacecraft and
the ground systems. Application of the DMSP data along with
exploitation of the Geostationary Operational Environment
Satellites (GOES) paid ever-increasing dividends in weather
research as well as in day-to-day forecasting.

The Hardware

The Block 5 system continued with only minor increases
in size, power, and capability until 1977. These minor
variations were known as 5A, 5B, and 5C. The changes were
made for two reasons: to increase the amount and types of

Fig. 4 DMSP 2.0 n.mi. visible imagery along the day/night terminator, August 1974.

data and to increase spacecraft life through redundant systems such as onboard tape recorders and data transmitters. Block 5B saw the first flight of a vertical temperature profiler on DMSP and was shortly followed by a precipitating electron spectrometer that provided data on energetic electrons in the ionosphere associated with the aurora borealis. The temperature sounder was an eight-channel infrared spectrometer based on the technology developed from the satellite infrared spectrometer and the temperature-humidity radiometer experiments flown on the Nimbus spacecraft. Details of the instruments are found in Refs. 16 and 22.

Block 5C added a fourth image channel, which provided infrared imagery at roughly the same resolution as the highest-resolution visible channel [0.5km (0.3n.mi.) at satellite nadir]. This allowed the DMSP to detect small cloud elements both day and night. In addition, an attempt was made to change the signal amplification along the visible scan in order to normalize the cloud reflectivity while scanning across the terminator. Figure 4 is an illustration of an early version of this capability.

During the mid-1970s, a new-generation DMSP spacecraft was being developed. Called the Block 5D, this DMSP space

system employed many new concepts and technologies. For
example, the spacecraft was controlled and operated by a
totally programmable onboard computer, the first of its
kind on an operational satellite. This proved to be invaluable as the computer was used to work around and overcome spacecraft anomalies, thereby extending the useful
lifetime of the Block 5D spacecraft considerably. The 5D
system was also unique in its attitude determination and
control system. It employed a celestial navigation system
and three orthogonal gyroscopes to maintain sensor attitude
to achieve a pointing accuracy of approximately 0.01 deg
[equivalent to approximately 0.4km (0.2n.mi.) on the ground
at nadir].

The greatly increased weight, stability, and communications capabilities of the Block 5D system were accompanied by new and greatly improved sensing systems. The old
four-channel rotating imaging radiometer was replaced by
a two-channel oscillating radiometer known as the operational linescan system (OLS). This system, described in detail
in Ref. 23, essentially preserves the ground resolution of
the image from spacecraft nadir to edge of scan at approximately 0.5km (0.3n.mi.). The nighttime visible channel is
improved in the Block 5D with a near constant resolution of
2.4km (1.5n.mi.). The spectral range of the imager is similar to that of the earlier Block 5 imagers. In order to
obtain global coverage, some of the high-resolution data
are smoothed on the spacecraft to a 2.4km (1.5n.mi.) resolution for subsequent recovery and processing on the ground.

The complement of additional sensors also grew with
the evolution to the Block 5D. The 8 channel infrared temperature sounder was replaced with a 16 channel infrared
temperature and water vapor sounder and a 7 channel microwave sounder. An improved energetic electron and proton
spectrometer and a plasma monitor to measure the in situ
plasma (electron and ion density) were flown as experimental sensors. For a description of the instruments, see
Refs. 1 and 23.

Data acquisition and processing systems were growing
at a rapid rate as well. Both DOD large environmental data
centers, AFGWC and the Navy's Fleet Numerical Oceanographic
Center (FNOC), were processing large amounts of both image
and nonimage data on a routine basis. The Navy, rapidly
becoming a full partner in the DMSP, installed a direct-
readout system on all its first-line aircraft carriers on
a one-per-year schedule. A new, more mobile self-contained
direct-readout terminal was designed and purchased by both
the Air Force and the Marine Corps to support tactical air
operations with exercise or battlefield weather pictures.

The Product

The dramatic increase in data quality and quantity that ensued with the Block 5 upgrades were exploited to the fullest. Data processing and enhancement techniques were developed and data analysis procedures were streamlined. Publications such as Refs. 3 and 22 described much of this work and showed in detail the full capabilities of the Block 5 system. Figures 5 and 6 illustrate the high quality of the high-resolution visual and infrared images of the Block 5D taken several hours after the eruption of Mount St. Helens in May 1980. Figure 7 is a high-resolution infrared picture highlighting the Gulf Stream rather dramatically.

The Block 5D upgrade, with its near-constant resolution across the picture, represented a technological breakthrough. The oscillating scanner, combined with an image motion compensation system, provided the most efficient duty cycle short of a string array. In addition, the data management system of the OLS provided a smoothed image for global coverage and processed data from many previously mentioned nonimaging sensors flown on the spacecraft.

Fig. 5 DMSP 0.3 n.mi. visible imagery of western United States, May 18, 1980 (---outlines the Mount St. Helens ash cloud).

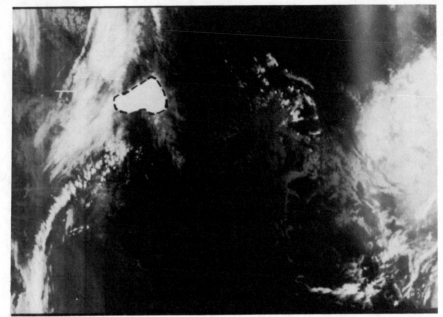

Fig. 6 DMSP 0.3 n.mi. infrared imagery of western United States,
May 18, 1980 (--- outlines the Mount St. Helens ash cloud).

Increased Value

The increased capability of the DMSP system, combined
with the increased availability because of declassification,
made DMSP a valuable resource during this period. For example, in the Pacific, the Selective Reconnaissance Program,
which had begun in 1971, was exploiting DMSP data fully with
very positive results. Substantial savings were achieved
by reducing the number of weather reconnaissance airplanes
and substituting satellite "fixes" on typhoons, especially
when the storms were in the formative stage.

The Navy at its Environmental Prediction Research Facility in Monterey, Calif. began extensive studies of the
application of DMSP data to various meteorological problems[24,25] The Air Force, at its Geophysics Laboratory near
Boston, performed a number of studies related to the characterization of clouds by the use of satellite imagery.[26]
The scientific community as well began to exploit the DMSP
imagery. Sheets and Grieman[27] showed that the positioning
accuracy of tropical storms increased with higher-resolution

Fig. 7 DMSP 0.3 n.mi. infrared imagery of Gulf Stream along U.S. east coast, date unknown (white areas are warm, black areas cold).

satellite imagery (such as that provided by the DMSP). Aka-sofu[28] described some of the advances made in understanding the morphology of the aurora borealis from DMSP nighttime photographs. Platz[29] compared the capabilities of various satellites to detect ocean surface features. Huh[30] did some analysis of ocean thermal fronts in the waters off the Korean peninsula. Croft[31] presented a survey of nighttime images from the DMSP. Issacs[12] modeled relative humidity and low-level maritime haze against the DMSP visible high-resolution data.

The 16 channel infrared sounder included six CO_2 channels (for temperature), five H_2O channels, and one channel on the ozone absorption band at $10\mu m$. Lovill[32] used these data to obtain a global distribution of total ozone and other investigators[33,34] examined the temperature and water vapor capabilities of this instrument. The other nonimaging sensors flown on the DMSP during this period also provided extremely useful data. Mizera et al.[35] compared data from the DMSP precipitating electron spectrometer with

similar data from a space test program research satellite.
Rich et al.[13] described the plasma monitor including a description of the obtained data. Liou et al.[36] developed a
radiative transfer program for cloudy atmosphere for the
DMSP microwave sounder. One experimental sensor flown was
a shortwave infrared imager called the snow-cloud discrim-
inator.[37] Its channel of 1.51 to 1.63μm allowed for the
separation of its images into those containing clouds versus those containing snow fields. Woronicz[7] describes the
results of this experiment, which was successful beyond anyone's expectation.

All in all, the contributions and uses of DMSP data
during this period were both many and varied. They reflected the general explosion in the capabilities of the DMSP
system. Unfortunately, the explosion was not without some
fallout, as described below.

The Challenges of Growth

The period of the 1970s saw the DMSP change from a
program with a single, rather straightforward mission and a
simple, rather low-cost satellite to a multimission, high-
technology, and accordingly high-cost satellite system.
These changes were not without a significant impact on the
program. The fact that DMSP now served many customers, including the scientific community, brought inquiries regarding the duplication of functions between the DMSP and the
civilian TIROS series of weather satellites. An extensive
study of the issues involved was conducted under the guidance of the Office of Management and Budget. The President's
Policy Review Committee (Space) reviewed the results of the
study and concluded that DOD and DOC should maintain and
coordinate dual polar-orbiting meteorological programs.
The study reaffirmed the decision of a prior study that the
two programs should combine technology as much as possible.
This decision resulted in DMSP and NOAA participating in a
common procurement for the DMSP 5D and the TIROS-N spacecrafts.

The rapid increases in the cost of space launches during the 1970s combined with the expanded mission responsibilities dictated a dramatic increase in the requirement for
reliability of the DMSP satellite and sensors. In order to
achieve the needed lifetime, considerable redundancy was
designed into the 5D system and higher quality parts were
used in critical components. The results, even though
costly, more than doubled the lifetime of the 5D system
over earlier systems.

The Mature Years: 1982–

During the late 1970s planning had begun for a new
generation DMSP spacecraft. A number of studies were performed for what was then called a Block 6 spacecraft. At
the same time, a number of improvements were identified for
the Block 5D and were being designed into a new version of
the series. One key element of these long-range activities
was the drive to transition the DMSP from an expendable
launch vehicle to the Space Shuttle in the mid- to late-
1980s. New sensors were also studied for inclusion on DMSP
and expanded requirements surfaced for additional direct-
readout terminals. Finally, decisions were made to incorporate the DMSP into the new Consolidated Space Operations
Center in Colorado Springs, Colorado. All these activities
have brought the program to full maturity, much like the
other military space programs, and has made DMSP a full
partner in the nation's weather programs.

Continued Growth

The highly successful Block 5D system now serves as the
system baseline. However, improvements and growth items
were identified almost as soon as the first 5D satellites
were launched. The push for increased reliability added to
changes to the system and increased the total weight of
the spacecraft. It was recognized that these changes would
result in exceeding the weight limit that the launch vehicle
(a Thor) could put into the DMSP's orbit and transition to
a larger Atlas booster was planned. In 1982, the first of
the new spacecraft, denoted the Block 5D-2, was launched on
an Atlas and successfully placed in orbit. It had greater
onboard power for the operation of an increased number of
sensors and its OLS had increased data processing capabilities so it could handle up to 12 other sensors.

The value of the precipitating electron and proton
data and the in situ plasma monitor flown on the earlier 5D
satellites required that these sensors be extended to this
new DMSP system. New versions of the sensors were flown
and/or procured to fly to gather more accurate and more comprehensive data on the character of the polar ionosphere and
on the electron and ion density at spacecraft altitude.
Each future 5D-2 is programmed to gather these data, virtually ensuring a long, reliable period of record of this valuable information.

Atmospheric temperature sounders which now supply much
of the thermal input to global analyses are also continuing
to be flown on each DMSP satellite. The problem of cloud

contamination on infrared sounders resulted in increased emphasis on microwave sounders for polar-orbiting spacecraft. Considerable study is underway to examine the cloud effects on these sounders as well (for example, see Ref. 38).

The infrared image channel on the OLS underwent a spectral change in 1979. Its spectral band was narrowed from $8-13\mu m$ to $10.5-12.6\mu m$ without seriously affecting the signal-to-noise ratio of the sensor. This narrowing was done to improve the sea surface temperature sensitivity in response to Navy needs. This narrower channel will be on all Block 5D-2 spacecraft.

A microwave imaging system based on the results obtained from Nimbus 6 and Seasat-A has been developed and built and will go into orbit in the mid-1980s. It is a seven-channel, four-frequency microwave radiometer utilizing a conical scan pattern. The sensor's data will be used to obtain values for ocean surface wind speed, ice coverage and age, areas and intensity of precipitation, cloud water content, and soil moisture. Hollinger and Lo[39] describe this instrument and its data applications.

In the late 1970s a concept was surfaced to use a spaceborne lidar to obtain an estimate of the three-dimensional wind field of the atmosphere.[40] The principle is based on using a pulsed coherent infrared or visible lidar in a conical scan mode and measuring the Doppler shift of the backscattered radiation to determine the radial wind component. Two measurements from different angles should allow computation of the vector wind. This concept is continuing to undergo evaluation for eventual flight on one of the future weather satellites.

To complement the network of ground-based inonosondes (devices that measure the high-frequency radio reflection heights of the ionosphere), a topside ionosonde has been suggested for the DMSP Block 5D-2. Such a device would be extremely useful for characterizing the ionosphere, but it is difficult to put on a multipurpose spacecraft because of radio frequency interference with and from other spacecraft systems. The concept is still under study.

Finally, the ground system has undergone a substantial transformation. The command and control element was completely revised to handle the increased redundancy of the Block 5D-2 spacecraft. Each redundant element required a complete set of backup procedures and dictated an extremely rapid telemetry analysis system. The new tactical data readout terminal procured in the late 1970s is now deployed around the globe and additional terminals are being procured to replace the older-generation terminals.

New Directions

The application of DMSP data to military problems and
to scientific endeavors remains high today and will continue in the coming years. Since early 1984, the imagery,
both visible and infrared, are being processed into an improved three-dimensional cloud analysis model at the Air
Force Global Weather Central. The imagery will also soon
be available in a graphically digitized form to the weather
analysts via an interactive data system similar in concept
to the man-computer interactive data access system (MCIDAS)
that has been successfully used on GOES data. The Navy has
installed an interactive satellite processing and display
system at its Naval Environmental Prediction Research Facility
at Monterey, Calif., and is using it operationally to support fleet activities. Fett et al.[25] describes the current
imaging weather satellite sensors, including sample pictures.
Studies of the auroral imagery were continued,[41]
many times comparing the results with data from other sources.[42]

The development of the microwave imaging system
was the first joint Air Force/Navy sensor procurement and as
such made the Navy a much more active partner in the DMSP.
The Navy also had entered into a concept development program with NOAA and NASA for a National Oceanic Satellite
System (NOSS) that was to have become an oceanographic
equivalent to the DMSP/TIROS-N meteorological satellites.
Budget cuts cancelled the NOSS program and an effort is
underway to meet many of the oceanographic requirements
through either the DMSP Block 5D-2 and/or the NOAA TIROS-N
follow-on systems. During the interim, the DMSP microwave
imager will at least partially fill a void in the gathering
of certain data over the broad ocean areas.

It is expected that the DMSP will also play an ever-
increasing, although not an exclusive, role in collecting
near-Earth geophysical data. With the establishment of
both an Air Force Space Command and a Navy Space Command
to better focus the needs for these data, the DMSP is certainly one candidate to collect them. In addition to the
presently operating sensors and the topside ionosonde
which has been studied, other sensors such as a magnetometer have been suggested for the DMSP. Such a diversity of
requirements and potential sensors may force the DMSP into
additional spacecraft, additional orbits, etc. In turn,
this will generate even more customers and responsibilities,
keeping DMSP one of the leading environmental data sources
in the world.

Summary

The DMSP is currently supplying products and information to many DOD and civilian agencies, meeting the needs of weathermen and nonweathermen alike. Data are also flowing to the scientific community, adding to the ever-growing volume of useful research on our planet's environment. The program has grown from a relatively simple "picture taker" to a highly sophisticated, long-lived, multimission space system. It has survived many challenges, technical, financial, and political, and has kept pace with the rapid advances in technology and data handling procedures. It accomplished a number of space firsts, from pictures of the aurora borealis to an onboard programmable computer. The pictures from DMSP complement those from the TIROS-N and GOES series and the nonimage data are used in operational and research versions of various atmospheric, oceanographic, and near-Earth models. Data application to specific DOD missions saves the department millions of dollars every year in either cost avoidance or resource planning.

References

[1]Allison, L.J., Schnapf, A., Diesen, B.C. III, Martin, P.S., Schwalb. A., and Bandeen, W.R., "Meteorological Satellites," NASA TM-80704, June 1980.

[2]Meyer, W.D., "The Role of the Meteorological Satellite in the Air Force Air Weather Service's Tailored Environmental Advice," Paper presented at the 12th Space Congress, Cocoa Beach, Fla., April 1975.

[3]Brandli, H.W., "Satellite Meteorology," HQ Air Weather Service, Tech. Rept. AWS-TR-76-264, Aug. 1976.

[4]Dash, E.R. and Meyer, W.D., "The Meteorological Satellite: An Invaluable Tool for the Military Decisionmaker," Air University Review , Vol.29, March-April 1978, pp. 13-24.

[5]Fett, R.W. and Mitchell, W.F., "Techniques and Applications of Image Analysis," Navy Tactical Applications Guide, Vol. 1, Naval Environmental Prediction Research Facility, Rept. NEPRF-AR-77-03, Jan. 1977.

[6]Ellis, J.S., Lovill, J.E., Luther, F.M., Sullivan, T.J., and Taylor, S.S., "DMSP/MFR Total Ozone and Radiance Data Base," NASA CR-170370, Jan. 1983.

[7]Woroncz, R.C., "Cloud/Clear/Snow Analysis Based on Satellite Data," Air Force Global Weather Central, Tech. Note AFGWC-TN-81-003, May 1981.

[8]Bunting, J.T. and D'Entremont, R. P., "Improved Cloud Detection Utilizing Defense Meteorological Satellite Program Near Infrared Measurements," Air Force Geophysics Laboratory, Tech. Rept. AFGL-TR-82-0027, Jan. 1982.

[9]"Positioning Tropical Cyclones in Satellite Imagery," First Weather Wing Tech. Note TN-81/002, 1981.

[10]Haig, T.O.,"The Role of Meteorological Satellites in Tactical Battlefield Weather Support," Air Force Geophysics Laboratory, Tech. Rept. AFGL-TR-82-0124, March 1982.

[11]Liou, K.N., Aufderhaar, G.C., Hutchinson, K., and Yeh, H., "Investigation of the Forward Radiative Transfer Problem Utilizing DMSP and Nimbus 6 Data," Air Force Geophysics Laboratory, Tech. Rept. AFGL-TR-80-0339, Sept. 1980.

[12]Issacs, R.G., "Investigation of the Effect of Low Level Maritime Haze on DMSP VHR and LF Imagery," Naval Environmental Prediction Research Facility, Rept. NEPRF-CR-80-06, Dec. 1980.

[13]Rich, F., Smiddy, M., Sagalyn, R.C., Burke, W.J., and Anderson, P., "In-flight Characteristics of the Topside Ionospheric Monitor (SSIE) on the DMSP Satellite Flight 2 and Flight 4, "Air Force Geophysics Laboratory, Tech. Rept. AFGL-TR-80-0152, April 1980.

[14]Fleming, H.E., "Determination of Vertical Wind Shear from Linear Combinations of Satellite Radiance Gradients: A Theoretical Study," Naval Postgraduate School, Rept. NPS63-79-004, Sept. 1979.

[15]Nichols, D.A., "DMSP Block-4 Conpendium," Space Div./DMSP Directorate of Engineering Report, Jan. 1975.

[16]Nichols, D.A., "DMSP Block 5A, B, C Compendium," Space Div./DMSP Directorate of Engineering Report, May 1976.

[17]Coburn, A.R., "Three Dimensional Nephanalysis," Air Force Global Weather Central, Tech. Memo AFGWC TM 70-9, March 1970.

[18]Roth, R.C., "A Data Selection Procedure for the Rectification and Mapping of Digitized Data," Air Force Global Weather Central, Tech. Memo. AFGWC TM 69-1, Dec. 1969.

[19]Coburn, A.R., "Improved Three Dimensional Nephanalysis Model," Air Force Global Weather Central, Tech. Memo., AFGWC TM 71-2, June 1971.

[20]Fuller, J.F., "Weather and War," Military Airlift Command, Histcrical Rept., Dec. 1974.

[21]Meyer, W.D., "Data Acquisition and Processing Program: A Meteorological Data Source," Bulletin of the American Meteorological Society, Vol. 54, 12, Dec. 1973, pp.1251-1253.

[22]Dickinson, L.G., Boselly, S.E. III, and Burgmann, W.S., "Defense Meteorological Satellite Program (DMSP) User's Guide," Air Weather Service, Tech. Rept. AWS-TR-74-250, Dec. 1974.

[23]Nichols, D.A., "DMSP Block 5D Compilation," Space Div./DMSP Directorate of Engineering Report, Jan. 1975.

[24]Fett, R.W., LaViolette, P.E., Nestor, M., Nickerson, J.W. and Rabe, K., "Navy Tactical Applications Guide, Volume II, Environmental Phenomena and Effects, "Naval Environmental Prediction Research Facility, Tech. Rept. NEPRF-TR-77-04, Jan. 1979.

[25]Fett, R.W., Bohn, W.A., Bates, J.J. and Tipton, S.L., "Navy Tactical Applications Guide Operational Environmental Satellites," Naval Environmental Prediction Research Facility, Tech. Rept. NEPRF-TR-83-02, June 1983.

[26]Bunting, J.T. and Fournier, R.F., "Tests of Spectral Cloud Classification Using DMSP Fine Mode Satellite Data," Air Force Geophysics Laboratory, Tech. Rept. AFGL-TR-80-0181, June 1980.

[27]Sheets, R.C. and Grieman, P., "An Evaluation of the Accuracy of Tropical Cyclone Intensities and Locations Determined from Satellite Pictures," National Oceanic and Atmospheric Administration, Tech. Memo. NOAA-TM-ERL-WMPO-20, Feb. 1975.

[28]Akasofu, S.I., "A Study of Auroral Displays Photographed from the DMSP-2 Satellite and from the Alaska Meridian Chain of Stations," Space Science Reviews, Vol. 16, Nov./Dec. 1974, pp. 617-725.

[29]Platz, B.W. Jr., "A Comparison of Satellite Images Capable of Detecting Ocean Surface Features," Thesis, Naval Postgraduate School, Monterey, Calif., Sept. 1975.

[30]Huh, O.K., "Detection of Oceanic Thermal Fronts off Korea with the Defense Meteorological Satellites," Remote Sensing of Environment, Vol. 5, 1976, pp. 191-213.

[31]Croft, T.A., "Nocturnal Images of the Earth from Space," Stanford Research Institute, Rept. SRI-5593-F, March 1977.

[32]Lovill, J.E., Ellis, J.S., and Weidhaas, P.P., "Global Observation of Atmospheric Ozone by Satellite," WMO Special Environmental Rept. 14, 1980, pp. 281-286.

[33]Valovcin, F.R., "DMSP Water Vapor Radiances, A Preliminary Evaluation," Air Force Surveys in Geophysics, No. 432, Oct. 1980.

[34]Nagle, R.E. and Clark, J.P., "Retrieval of Mass-structure Information from the Defense Meteorological Satellite Program (DMSP) Indirect Sounding Instrument," Proceedings of the 21st Plenary Meetings of COSPAR, 1979, pp. 161-164.

[35]Mizera, P.F., Cooley, D.R., Morse, F.A. and Vampola, A.L., "Electron Fluxes and Correlations with Quiet-Time Auroral Arcs," Space and Missile Systems Organization, Tech. Rept. SAMSO-TR-75-202, July 1975.

[36]Liou, K.N., Aufderhaar, G.C., and Nipko, P.T., "Some Examples of the Effects of Clouds and Precipitation on the Temperature Profile Retrieval for DMSP SSM/T Microwave Sounders," Journal of Applied Meteorology, Vol. 29, July 1981, pp. 821–825.

[37]Kimball, A.W. Jr., "DMSP Near IR Sensor for Cloud/Snow Discrimination," World Data Center A for Glaciology (Snow and Ice), Rept. GD-5, May 1979, pp. 43–47.

[38]Nipko, P.T., "Effects of Precipitating and Non-precipitating Cloud Layers on the Defense Meteorological Satellite Program," Master's Thesis, Air Force Institute of Technology, Wright-Patterson AFB, Ohio, June 1979.

[39]Hollinger, F.P. and Lo, R.C., "SSM/I (Special Sensor Microwave/ Imager) Project Summary Report," Naval Research Laboratory, Memo. Rept. NRL-MR-5055, April 1983.

[40]Huffaker, R.M., "Global Wind Monitoring by Satelliteborne Coherent LIDAR," Society of Photo-Optical Instrumentation Engineers, Vol. 183, 1979.

[41]Mizera, N.A., Gorney, D.J., and Roeder, J.L., "Auroral X-Ray Images from DMSP F-6," Geophysical Research Letters, Vol. II, March 1984, pp. 255–258.

[42]Saflekos, N.A. and Sheehan, R.E., "Estimates of Precipitating Electron Power Flux from Simultaneous DMSP Auroral Image and ISEE-1 AKR Observations," Proceedings of the Air Force Geophysics Laboratory Workshop on Natural Charging of Large Space Structures in Near Earth Polar Orbit, Jan. 1983, pp. 157–162.

The Development of the Geosynchronous Weather Satellite System

J.R. Greaves*

NASA Headquarters, Washington, D.C.

and

W.E. Shenk†

NASA Goddard Space Flight Center, Greenbelt, Maryland

Abstract

This paper traces the history of the U.S. geosynchronous weather satellite program. With the launch of NASA's first Applications Technology Satellite (ATS-1) in late 1966, the new dimension of time was added to the study and use of meteorological measurements from space. For the first time, continuous observation of almost one-third of the Earth's surface was possible. The evolution of this new capability through several generations of geosynchronous satellites is described. Also described are the many experimental and operational applications of the acquired data sets. The black-and-white and color imagery available from the ATS satellites in the late 1960s was supplemented in the 1970s by infrared imagery from NASA's Synchronous Meteorological Satellites, the predecessors of the first truly operational geosynchronous weather satellites. Other new capabilities included a data collection system that gathered information from remote Earth platforms, as well as instrumentation to monitor the near-Earth space environment. These satellites could also be used to retransmit processed meteorological information such as maps, charts, and annotated pictures back through the spacecraft to a large number of low-cost, Earth-based receiving stations. The first operational version, the Geostationary Operational Environmental Satellite (GOES-1), was launched in October 1975. Atmospheric soundings from geosynchronous altitude became a reality in 1980 with the launching of GOES-4. Future

---

*Program Manager, Operational Meteorological Satellites.
†GOES Project Scientist.

spacecraft in this series will feature independent sounding and imaging systems, improved spatial resolutions and location accuracies, as well as additional imaging channels.

Introduction

On April 1, 1960, the world's first meteorological satellite, Television Infrared Observation Satellite (TIROS-1), was successfully launched. The satellite was placed into a low Earth orbit at approximately 830 km with an orbital inclination of 48 deg. TIROS-1 was an immediate success, demonstrating the potential of meteorological observations from space. Over the next several years, the TIROS satellite series evolved into an increasingly more sophisticated and capable observational platform. By late 1966, 13 of these satellites had been flown. By that time, the operational configuration consisted of two polar-orbiting, sun-synchronous platforms, each providing twice daily observations of meteorological phenomena.

These satellites provided instantaneous "snapshots" of existing weather conditions. What was now desired was the ability to "hover" over selected areas to watch weather systems grow and develop. This capability was provided by geosynchronous (or geostationary) satellites that, flying in an equatorial orbit at an altitude of about 35,790 km, just kept up with the Earth's daily rotation. The first such satellite with meteorological instrumentation was the Applications Technology Satellite (ATS-1) launched in December 1966. For the first time, nearly continuous observations of the same area of the Earth could be made. The new dimension of time was added to the study of satellite meteorology.

This paper traces the development of the geosynchronous satellites over the past two decades and into the future. Like the TIROS series, the geosynchronous satellites have evolved into sophisticated multiparameter observational platforms. The introduction and use of the new data types that developed along the way are briefly described. A synopsis of our current capabilities in terms of parameter measurement and data application is also provided.

Applications Technology Satellites

During the middle 1960s, a NASA research program based on the use of geostationary satellites was implemented through the ATS series. Although primarily designed and

launched for the purpose of demonstrating improved
communications satellite technology, the basic spacecraft
bus provided sufficient excess capacity to permit the
flight of a number of experimental meteorological sensors.
The concept of using the spinning motion of the spacecraft
in concert with a telescope and photomultiplier tube
assembly to "paint out" an Earth image was pioneered and
developed by Prof. Verner Suomi of the University of
Wisconsin and implemented by the Santa Barbara Research
Center. The ATS spacecraft also provided a test bed for
experimental meteorological data relay systems.

ATS-1

On Dec. 7, 1966, ATS-1 was launched on an Atlas launch
vehicle and subsequently placed into a geostationary orbit
over the Pacific at 150° W longitude. The spin-stabilized
spacecraft was cylindrically shaped and measured 134 cm
long and 146 cm in diameter (see Fig. 1). It was equipped
with an electronically despun antenna that continuously
directed a cone-shaped beam at the earth. The on-orbit
weight was approximately 304 kg. Solar panels formed the
outer cylindrical walls of the spacecraft. Equipment
components and payload were mounted in the annular space
between the central thrust tube and the solar panels. In
addition to solar panels, the spacecraft was equipped with
rechargeable batteries to provide electrical power. Eight
vhf experiment antennas were mounted around the aft end of
the spacecraft, while eight telemetry and command antennas
were placed on the forward end. The prime contractor for
the spacecraft was the Hughes Aircraft Company.

SSCC. The ATS-1 spin-scan cloud cover camera (SSCC)
system provided for the first time nearly continuous
observations of cloud cover patterns over the whole sunlit
Earth disk. The optical system consisted of a two-element
cassegrain-type telescope. A photomultiplier assembly
could be tilted in discrete steps over a 15-deg range to
produce a north-to-south scan, corresponding to an earth
coverage from 52° N to 52° S. The east-to-west scan was
provided by the spin of the spacecraft itself. At the
nominal spin rate of 100 rpm, approximately 20 min were
required to scan the Earth, one line at a time. Two more
minutes were used to retrace the scanning assembly back for
the start of the next picture. Thus, a complete picture
was obtained approximately every 30 min (during daylight).
The camera had peak sensitivity in the green region of the
visible spectrum, permitting maximum information to be

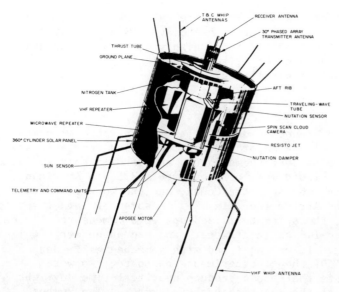

Fig. 1 Applications technology satellite configuration (ATS-1).

obtained when the signals were converted to black-and-white images. The spatial resolution at the satellite subpoint was about 3.2 km. The ATS-1 camera system operated successfully from a few days after launch until Oct. 15, 1972. The system was designed and built by the Santa Barbara Research Center under contract to the University of Wisconsin.

WEFAX. ATS-1 also included a meteorological data relay system intended to test satellite retransmission of weather facsimile (WEFAX) products to participating ground stations. Secondary objectives included 1) transmitting selected spin-scan camera pictures via satellite to automatic picture transmission (APT) ground stations and 2) exploring the feasibility of increasing the amount of data available to APT ground stations from other satellites. The experiment had no unique hardware on board. It was part a vhf experiment and used the vhf transponder to relay the data. The transponder transmitted at 135.60 MHz and received at 149.22 MHz. Weather facsimile charts were sent via land line from the National Oceanic and Atmospheric Administration (NOAA) in Suitland, Md., to the ATS WEFAX field station at Mojave, Calif. The charts and data were then transmitted to the spacecraft for relay to participating APT stations. Cloud cover photographs from

the ATS-1 spin-scan camera were retransmitted through the
spacecraft directly from the Mojave ATS ground station.
The experiment proved to be highly successful and has been
expanded and used on all subsequent geosynchronous
meteorological satellites.

ATS-3

ATS-3, launched on an Atlas launch vehicle on Nov. 5,
1967, was also a major success. From its geostationary
vantage point over the equator, at approximately 70° W, the
satellite viewed most of the North and South American
continents, the Atlantic Ocean, and the western edges of
Europe and Africa (see Fig. 2). A somewhat larger version
of ATS-1, the spin-stabilized spacecraft measured 180 cm in
length and 146 cm in diameter and had an on-orbit weight
of 365 kg. It was equipped with a mechanically despun
antenna. Of the 11 experiments on board, two were
experiments that could produce near real-time daylight
pictures of the earth-atmosphere system. The Hughes
Aircraft Company was the prime contractor for ATS-3.

MSSCC. ATS-3 was the first spacecraft to routinely
transmit full-disk Earth-cloud images in "living color."

NASA ATS III MSSCC 19 NOV 67 161257Z SSP 49.28°W 0.12°S ALT 22242.67 SM

Fig. 2 ATS-3 MSSCC image (November 19, 1967).

In that sense, the ATS-3 multicolor spin-scan cloud cover
camera (MSSCC) represented a significant advance over the
monochromatic spin-scan camera on ATS-1. Also built by the
Santa Barbara Research Center, the MSSCC was mounted with
its optical axis perpendicular to the spacecraft's spin
axis and viewed the Earth through a special aperture in the
spacecraft's side. The camera consisted of a
high-resolution telescope, three photomultiplier light
detectors (red, blue, and green), and a precision latitude
step mechanism. The telescope multiplier assembly could be
tilted in discrete steps to provide pole-to-pole coverage
in 2400 scan lines. As with ATS-1, the east-to-west scan
was provided by the spin of the satellite itself. A total
time of 24 min was required to scan one frame and 2.4 min
to retrace with a nominal satellite rotation of 100 rpm.
The camera had a ground resolution of better than 4 km at
nadir. Although the multicolor experiment was successful,
the red and blue channels failed approximately three months
after launch, and the system subsequently was limited to
producing black-and-white pictures using the remaining
green channel. Good quality black-and-white images were
received daily until Dec. 11, 1974, when operations were
reduced to three images a week. It should be noted that
the increased informational content of the color pictures
was not considered sufficient to warrent subsequent
attempts to fly a color imager. The ATS-3 camera system
was deactivated on Oct. 30, 1975.

IDCS. The ATS-3 spacecraft also carried an image
dissector camera system (IDCS) designed to test the
feasibility of using electrical scanning techniques in an
Earth-cloud camera. The camera was mounted with its
optical axis perpendicular to the spacecraft spin axis such
that the camera produced a scan line with each revolution
of the spacecraft. The direction of the scan, north to
south or east to west, was determined by ground command.
The image dissector tube consisted of a visible wavelength,
electrically scanning photocathode, a scanning aperture,
and a 12 stage electron multiplier. The image dissector
tube had a resolution capability of 1300 TV lines, which,
at nominal spacecraft altitude, corresponded to a ground
resolution of about 7 km at nadir. Successfully flown for
the first time, the IDCS system on ATS-3 served as a
prototype for similar experiments on NASA's Nimbus-3 and -4
research satellites. The camera performed normally until
May 1969, when the IDCS system was beset by erratic
spacecraft antenna performance. Routine data acquisition
ceased after May 30, 1969.

WEFAX. Like ATS-1, the ATS-3 included a WEFAX
experiment to test satellite retransmissions to
participating ground stations of facsimile products
prepared by NOAA. The ATS-3 system provided a somewhat
better data reproduction capability than was available on
ATS-1.

ATS-6

At the time of its launch on May 30, 1974, the ATS-6
spacecraft was the most versatile, powerful, and unique
communication spacecraft ever developed. ATS-6 carried
more than 20 technological and scientific experiments
focused primarily in the communications area. Experiments
included direct broadcast of health and education
television to remote receiving units, aeronautical and
marine communications, and spacecraft tracking and data
relay. Unlike its predecessors, the 930 kg ATS-6
spacecraft employed a three-axis stabilization system for
altitude control, rather than being spin-stabilized. As
may be seen in Fig. 3, the spacecraft consisted of four
major assemblies: 1) a 9.15 m dish antenna; 2) two solar
cell paddles mounted at right angles to each other on
opposite sides of an upper equipment module; 3) an
Earth-viewing equipment module connected by a tubular mast
to the upper equipment module; and 4) an attitude control
and stabilization system. Launched by a Titan III-C launch
vehicle, the ATS-6 spacecraft arrived at its initial
operating longitude of 94° W approximately 10 days after
liftoff. Fairchild Industries was the prime contractor

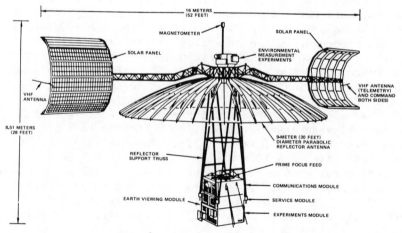

Fig. 3   ATS-6 configuration.

responsible for development, integration, and test of the
ATS-6 spacecraft.

GVHRR. The geosynchronous very high resolution
radiometer (GVHRR), housed in the ATS-6 Earth-viewing
equipment module, made measurements that were useful for
the study of meteorological events and the development of
techniques for extracting significant meteorological
variables. It was the first radiometer flown for
meteorological purposes that operated on a three-axis
stabilized geosynchronous spacecraft where the sensor
viewed the Earth rather than space the majority of the
time. The prime contractor for the GVHRR was ITT. The
major GVHRR objectives were: 1) to demonstrate that a
three-axis stabilized sensor could accurately determine
winds from cloud motions; 2) to study the life cycles of
severe local storms, tropical and extratropical cyclones,
and other important events; and 3) to improve techniques of
estimating surface temperature. The GVHRR was a
two-channel radiometer scanning in the visible
(0.55-0.75 μm) with a 5.5 km spatial resolution, and in the
i.r. (10.5-12.5 μm) with a 11 km resolution. Full-disk
(20 x 20 deg) scans were provided in 25 min, while sector
scans (5° N/S x 20° E/W) could be completed in 6.5 min.
For two months during the summer of 1974, several hundred
images were successfully taken. Data collection terminated
when the instrument chopper motor failed.

ATS Applications
    With the launch of ATS-1, the time domain could be
used for the first time in the analysis and interpretation
of meteorological satellite data. The first color imagery
was taken by ATS-3. Day and night, cloud and surface
temperature analyses were possible with the combination of
visible and i.r. radiances from the ATS-6 GVHRR. Cloud
motions (mostly for clouds wider than 3 km) could be
computed with the ATS-1 and -3 data. If the cloud type
could be recognized, then the motions would be assigned to
the normal height associated with that cloud type. The
ATS-6 data (with the i.r. channel) allowed a more direct
determination of height from the apparent cloud-top
temperature. The 6-30 min image frequency from the ATS
measurements provided adequate temporal coverage to
calculate thunderstorm horizontal expansion rates with the
visible channel, and vertical rise rates with the i.r.
channel. Applications such as these continued to evolve
and develop as technological advancements were made in the
next generation of geosynchronous satellites.

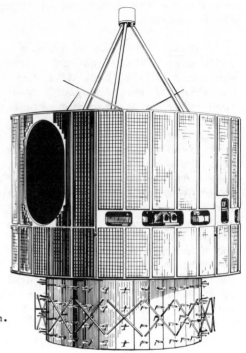

Fig. 4   SMS/GOES configuration.

SMS/GOES

The success of the meteorological experiments carried
onboard the ATS-1 and -3 satellites led to NASA's
development of a satellite specifically designed to make
atmospheric observations. Two operational prototype
satellites, designated Synchronous Meteorological
Satellites (SMS), were launched in 1974 and 1975. These
were followed by a series of operational satellites,
designated Geostationary Operational Environmental
Satellites (GOES), beginning in 1975. The first five of
these satellites (SMS-1 and -2, GOES-1, -2, and -3) were
essentially identical. They carried instrumentation for
visible and i.r. imaging, collection of data from automated
remote platforms, relay of weather products (WEFAX), and
measurement of a number of characteristics of the near
space environment. All five spacecraft were built and
integrated by Philco-Ford Inc. (now Ford Aerospace Corp.).

SMS-1 and -2, GOES-1, -2, and -3

These SMS/GOES satellites are spin-stabilized,
cylindrical in shape, and weigh approximately 260 kg

on-orbit. They measure 191 cm in diameter and are 231 cm high. As indicated in Fig. 4, the imaging telescope views the earth through a special aperture in the spacecraft's side. The solar panels form the outer walls of the spacecraft and provide the primary source of electrical power. Located in the annulus-shaped space between the thrust tube and the solar panels are stationkeeping and dynamics control equipment, batteries, and most of the space environment monitoring equipment. Proper spacecraft attitude and spin rate (approximately 100 rpm) are maintained by two separate sets of jet thrusters mounted around the spacecraft's equator and activated by ground command. The spacecraft used both uhf and S-band frequencies in their telemetry and command subsystems. A low-power vhf transponder provided telemetry and command during launch. The same subsystem served as a backup for the primary subsystem once the spacecraft had attained synchronous orbit. These spacecraft were launched from the Kennedy Space Center in Florida by a three-stage Delta launch vehicle. The launch dates extended from May 17, 1974 for SMS-1 to June 16, 1978 for GOES-3. Refer to Tables 1 and 2 for actual launch dates and duration of useful operations of the imaging system.

VISSR. The primary instrument on all five spacecraft was the visible/infrared spin-scan radiometer (VISSR), which (like the spin-scan cameras on the preceeding ATS satellite series) was designed and developed by the Santa Barbara Research Center. The VISSR was a true radiometer, providing day and night observations of clouds as well as data for the determination of cloud and surface temperatures, cloud heights, and wind fields (via cloud motion in successive images). The two spectral-channel instrument was able to take both full and partial images of the Earth's disk (see Fig. 5). The i.r. channel (10.5-12.6 μm) and the visible channel (0.55-0.70 μm) used a common optics system. The spinning motion of the spacecraft provided a west-to-east scan motion while the north-to-south scan was accomplished by sequentially tilting the scanning mirror at the completion of each spin. The angular position of the mirror was determined from redundant optical encoders using an incandescent light source. This determination provided essential feedback to the scan drive electronics. A full picture took 18.2 min to complete and about 2 min to retrace. During each scan, the field of view on the Earth was swept by a linear array of eight visible-spectrum detectors, each with a ground resolution of 0.9 km at zero nadir angle. The i.r. portion

Table 1   Geosynchronous weather satellites

Satellite	Launch date	Deactivated	Meteorological instruments/systems	Prime contractor
ATS-1	12/07/66	a	SSCC, WEFAX	Hughes Aircraft Co.
ATS-3	11/05/67	a	MSSCC, IDCS, WEFAX	Hughes Aircraft Co.
ATS-6	05/30/74	06/30/79	GVHRR	Fairchild Industries Inc.
SMS-1	05/17/74	01/29/81	VISSR, DCS, WEFAX, SEM	Ford Aerospace Corp.
SMS-2	02/06/75	08/05/82	VISSR, DCS, WEFAX, SEM	Ford Aerospace Corp.
GOES-1	10/16/75	b	VISSR, DCS, WEFAX, SEM	Ford Aerospace Corp.
GOES-2	06/16/77	b	VISSR, DCS, WEFAX, SEM	Ford Aerospace Corp.
GOES-3	06/16/78	b	VISSR, DCS, WEFAX, SEM	Ford Aerospace Corp.
GOES-4	09/09/80	b	VAS, DCS, WEFAX, SEM	Hughes Aircraft Co.
GOES-5	05/22/81	b	VAS, DCS, WEFAX, SEM	Hughes Aircraft Co.
GOES-6	04/28/83	c	VAS, DCS, WEFAX, SEM	Hughes Aircraft Co.

a Communications functions continuing.
b Limited operational support.
c Operational at 98° W.

SMS—1 IMAGES
FEB. 17, 1975
1730 GMT

VISIBLE (0.55-0.70 μ m)   INFRARED (10.5-12.6 μ m)

Fig. 5   SMS/GOES visible/infrared picture pair.

of the spectrum was sensed with a horizontal resolution of
approximately 8 km at zero nadir angle. The VISSR output
was digitized and transmitted at 28 megabit/s to the NOAA
Command and Data Acquisition (CDA) Station, Wallops Island,
Va. There the signal was fed into a "line stretcher" where
it was stored and time-stretched for transmission back to
the satellite at reduced bandwidth (1.75 megabit/s) for
rebroadcast to smaller data utilization stations for

processing and subsequent distribution. The entire process took place in near real-time, with the retransmissions of the stretched data occurring between the Earth-viewing portions of each scan.

The early SMS-1, SMS-2, and GOES-1 missions were highly successful, both in terms of data quality and useful lifetime of the primary imaging sensor. The GOES-1 VISSR is, in fact, still useable (visible channels only). Problems with bearing lubrication were experienced, but these did not seriously limit the usefulness of the imaging systems. Beginning with GOES-2 however, the encoder lamps began failing prematurely in orbit. By January 1980, a major investigation was begun to determine the causes of the lamp problems. These studies have led to a number of modifications in the bulb manufacturing process and in instrument design intended to alleviate the encoder problems in follow-on GOES missions.

DCS/WEFAX. The meteorological data collection system (DCS) was an experimental communications and data handling system designed to receive and process meteorological data collected from remotely located, Earth-based, data collection (observation) platforms (DCP). The collected data were retransmitted from the satellite to small, ground-based, regional data utilization centers. Data from up to 10,000 DCP stations could be handled by the system. The system also allowed for the retransmission of narrow-band (WEFAX-type) data to existing small, ground-based APT receiving stations from a larger weather-central facility. This communications system operated on S-band frequencies.

SEM. The space environment monitor (SEM) included a solar x-ray sensor, energetic particle detector, and a magnetometer. The SEM detected unusual solar activity (such as flares), measured the flow of electron and proton energy as well as the magnetic field strength and direction in the vicinity of the spacecraft. The SEM data were used by NOAA's Environmental Research Laboratory in Boulder, Colo., to monitor and predict sunspots and flares and their effects on the Earth's magnetic field.

SMS/GOES Applications

The same applications that were possible with the ATS-6 GVHRR could be accomplished with the GOES VISSR with some additions due to: 1) higher spatial resolution of the visible channel, 2) availability of simultaneous data from two GOES satellites separated by 60° of longitude, and 3)

Table 2 Geosynchronous satellite operations

GOES-East (approximately 75° W)			GOES-West (approximately 135° W)		
Start	Stop	Sat.	Start	Stop	Sat.
11/15/74	01/08/76	SMS-1	03/10/75	04/04/78	SMS-2
01/08/76	08/15/77	GOES-1	04/04/78	07/13/78	GOES-1
08/15/77	01/26/79	GOES-2	07/13/78	03/05/81	GOES-3
01/26/79	04/14/79	SMS-1	03/05/81	11/29/82	GOES-4
04/19/79	08/05/81	SMS-2	11/29/82	06/01/83	GOES-1
08/05/81	07/30/84	GOES-5	06/01/83	a	GOES-6

Other Applications

Start	Stop	Sat.	Location	Purpose
06/27/74	11/15/74	SMS-1	45 W	GARP[b] Atlantic tropical experiment (GATE)
12/01/78	11/30/79	GOES-1	60 E	First GARP[b] global experiment (FGGE)
10/08/80	03/05/81	GOES-4	105 W	VAS demonstration[c]
06/15/81	08/05/81	GOES-5	85 W	VAS demonstration[c]

[a] Operating at 98° W as of September 1984.
[b] GARP - Global Atmospheric Research Program.
[c] NASA/Goddard experiment exploring VAS capabilities.

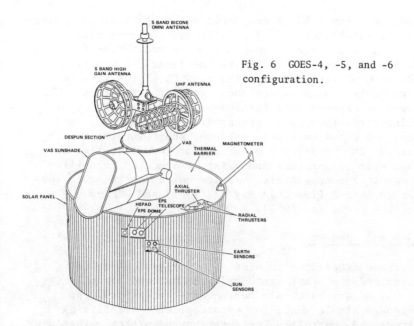

Fig. 6 GOES-4, -5, and -6 configuration.

higher temporal resolution of the imagery taken for research purposes. The higher visible channel and temporal resolution allowed much smaller clouds to be followed, thus increasing the resolution and accuracy of the wind fields derived from the cloud motions. These factors also lead to much better continuity in following the development and dissipation of the most active portions of strong convection (particularly the penetration of updraft cores into the lower stratosphere). The combination of the simultaneous data from two satellites separated by 60° longitude plus the high visible-channel resolution leads to accurate cloud height measurements from stereography. These stereographically derived cloud heights are primarily used in thunderstorm top analysis and in determining the levels for the cloud-motion winds.

GOES

Up until 1980, the geosynchronous satellites still dealt in only three dimensions: two in the horizontal and time itself. Other than some early work in stereo measurements of clouds using more than one satellite, the vertical dimension had yet to be explored from geosynchronous altitudes. The difficulties in achieving adequate spatial resolution and sensitivity had been a dominant factor in delaying the start of geosynchronous soundings. (By 1980, atmospheric soundings from the polar-orbiting satellites had already become commonplace.)

A major advance in geosynchronous weather observation occurred on Sept. 9, 1980, with the launch of the first VISSR atmospheric sounder (VAS) on GOES-4, the first of a new generation of geosynchronous weather satellites. The VAS was an experimental instrument capable of achieving multispectral imagery of atmospheric temperatures, water vapor, and cloudiness patterns over short intervals. In addition, the instrument provided for the first time an atmospheric temperature and moisture sounding capability from geosynchronous orbit. Follow-on VAS instruments were flown on GOES-5 (launched May 22, 1981) and GOES-6 (launched April 28, 1983).

GOES-4, -5, and -6

These satellites consist of a cylindrical spinning section and a despun, earth-oriented antenna assembly (see Fig. 6). Spacecraft spin motion at a rate of 100 rpm provides a simple means for gyroscopically stabilizing attitude and controlling orientation and orbit, maintaining temperature, and generating radiometric data by spin scanning. Despun S-band and uhf antennas provide high gain for efficient communications with GOES Earth stations. All three satellites were launched on a three-stage Delta 3914 launch vehicle. The prime contractor for GOES-4, -5, and -6 was the Hughes Aircraft Company.

Spacecraft length, from the S-band omni antenna to the base of the cylindrical main body, is 352 cm. The spinning solar panel section has an outside diameter of 215 cm. The spacecraft on-orbit weight is 396 kg. The spacecraft weight at launch, including apogee boost motor (ABM), is approximately 837 kg.

The primary structural member is the thrust tube located in the center of the spinning cylinder. The VAS instrument is located in the center of the spacecraft. The scanning mirror, located at one end of the thrust tube requires a clear field of view of the Earth. The radiation cooler mounted on the other end of the instrument requires a clear view of space with no sun impingement over the entire operational lifetime. The ABM is attached to the thrust tube and covers the radiation cooler area. Approximately 10 min after the spacecraft is boosted into a geosynchronous orbit, the expended ABM is ejected, exposing the radiation cooler.

VAS. The VAS is a radiometer with 8 visible channel detectors and 6 thermal detectors that detect i.r.

radiation in 12 spectral bands. A filter wheel in front of
the detector is used to achieve the spectral selection.
The spatial resolution is 0.9 km in the visible and 7 or 14
km in the i.r., depending on the detector used. Full
Earth-disk coverage is accomplished by spinning in the west
to east direction at 100 rpm and stepping a scan mirror
from north to south. SBRC was the primary contractor for
the VAS instrument. Additional VAS instrument
characteristics are summarized in Table 3.

The VAS has three operating modes:

1) The VISSR operating mode is the same as that of
the original VISSR system. Both day and night cloud cover
imagery are possible. One west to east raster line is
formed for each revolution of the satellite. A 20° N-S
frame results from a total of 1821 steps of the scan
mirror, one 0.192 mr step for each spacecraft revolution.
As in the VISSR, the visible channel 0.9 km resolution is
formed by a linear array of 8 detectors aligned so that
they sweep out a complete raster scan-line path. The i.r.
channel resolution is 6.9 km.

2) The multispectral imaging (MSI) operating mode is
intended to achieve relatively frequent (e.g., half hourly)
full Earth-disk imagery of the atmospheric water vapor,
temperature, and cloud distribution, as well as variations
in the surface skin temperature of the Earth. In order to
achieve full disk coverage at half-hour intervals, two
submodes of operation are possible: a) four spectral
channels can be observed (the visible at 0.9 km resolution,
the 11 μm window at 6.9 km resolution, and two others at
13.8 km resolution) or b) five spectral channels can be
observed (the visible at 0.9 km resolution and any four
i.r. spectral channels at 13.8 km resolution).

3) In the dwell sounding (DS) mode, up to 12 spectral
filters in a filter wheel can be positioned in sequence
into the optical train while the scanner is dwelling on a
single N-S scan line. The filter wheel can be programmed
so that each spectral band (filter) can dwell on a single
scan line for 0-255 spacecraft spins in order to build up
acceptable signal-to-noise levels. Either the 6.9 or 13.8
km resolution detectors can be selected for sounding
determinations. North-south frame size and position are
also programmable via ground command. An example of the
VAS sounding capabilities may be seen in Fig. 7.

A primary limitation of the current instrument is that
the DS mode cannot be used simultaneously with either the
VISSR or MSI mode. On an experimental basis, however, it
is possible to provide operational users with a 15-min
VISSR image every half hour and to provide research users

Table 3   VAS instrument characteristics

Spectral channel	Central wavelength, μm	Central wavenumber, cm^{-1}	Weighting function peak, mb	Absorbing constituent	Typical spin budget[a]
1	14.7	678	70	CO_2	2
2	14.5	691	125	CO_2	4
3	14.3	699	200	CO_2	7
4	14.0	713	500	CO_2	7
5	13.3	750	920	CO_2	4
6	4.5	2209	850	CO_2	7
7	12.7	787	surface	H_2O	3
8	11.2	892	surface	window	1
9	7.3	1370	600	H_2O	9
10	6.8	1467	400	H_2O	2
11	4.4	2254	300	CO_2	7
12	3.9	2540	surface	window	1

[a] Number of spins sensed by the same detector with filter and mirror positions fixed.

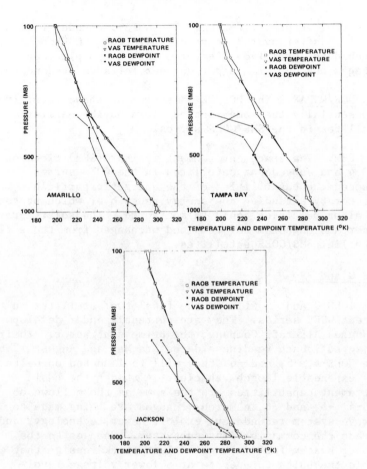

Fig. 7   GOES soundings at Amarillo, Texas, Tampa Bay, Florida, and Jackson, Mississippi.

with approximately 15 min of MSI data and 11 min of DS data during the same half hour. VAS unique MSI and DS data are relayed through a separate geosynchronous spacecraft to the research users. The operational users receive the VISSR imagery directly from the originating satellite. This so-called transparent VAS mode has been useful in demonstrating the capabilities of the VAS instrument and providing data sets in support of severe storms research. Occasionally, sounding data sets are acquired at the expense of one or more VISSR images.

The GOES-4 VAS system failed in November 1982 after over 2 years of operation due to a printed wiring-board anomaly. GOES-5 was the first in the series to use steppable encoder lamp voltages in an attempt to lengthen

the useful encoder lifetime. The GOES-5 encoder failed in
June 1984 after over 3 years of operation. GOES-6,
launched in April 1983, features both steppable lamp
voltages and dual lamps per encoder for added redundancy.

DCS/WEFAX. The DCS/WEFAX system on these satellites
is essentially the same as that flown on the earlier
satellites in the SMS/GOES series.

SEM. The space environment monitor (SEM) flown on
GOES-4 and subsequent satellites in the GOES series
enhanced the capabilities of the energetic particle
detector by extending the energy range over which proton
and alpha particles could be monitored. The solar x-ray
sensor and magnetometer remained unchanged from those flown
on earlier SMS/GOES satellites.

GOES-G and -H

GOES-G and -H will be the final two satellites in the
current GOES series. They are currently under development
by Hughes Aircraft Company, the prime contractor. Their
projected launch readiness dates are May and August 1986.
Like GOES-4, -5, and -6, they will be launched on Delta
3914 expendable launch vehicles. Although the basic
instrument capabilities are the same as those flown on
GOES-4, -5, and -6, numerous changes are being made to
improve system redundancy, exploit newer technology, and
upgrade the communications subsystem. Changes to the
encoder system include a new "clear-track" design that will
enable the bulbs to operate at a lower voltage level
(thereby significantly lengthening projected bulb
lifetimes) as well as the use of light-emitting diodes as a
light source. The GOES-G and -H spacecraft design is
described in detail in the article by Louis Fermelia in
this volume.

GOES Applications

In addition to the VISSR applications described above
for the SMS/GOES satellites, the VAS instrument flown on
GOES-4, -5, and -6, with its 11 additional i.r. channels,
provides a number of new quantitative measurement
capabilities. The most significant is the derivation of
temperature and moisture profiles. Higher spatial
resolution, low-level moisture estimates are possible with
the combination of the data from two or three of the i.r.
channels. Instability calculations can be made from the

temperature and moisture data. Accurate surface
temperature estimates are possible using the visible and
upper tropospheric water vapor channels for cloud detection
and several i.r. channels for the surface temperature
estimates and for correcting for water vapor absorption. A
nighttime cloud height determination technique looks
promising using some of the temperature profiling channels.
With simultaneous VAS data from the two satellites viewing
along different slant paths, it may be possible to further
improve water vapor results and the vertical resolution and
accuracy of temperature profiling.

The Current Operational System

As seen earlier, the geostationary satellite program
began in 1966 as an experiment in which the imaging and
weather broadcast systems of NASA's ATS-1, -3, and -6 were
tested. NASA's SMS-1 and -2 satellites, launched in 1974
and 1975, were the prototypes for the current operational
GOES series. NOAA routinely operates a two-satellite
system, one at $75^{\circ}W$ longitude ("GOES-East") and the other
at $135^{\circ}W$ longitude ("GOES-West"). With the failure of
GOES-5 on July 30, 1984, GOES-6 has been moved from its
$135^{\circ}W$ operating position to midcountry at $98^{\circ}W$. This is
the first time since March 1975 that the United States has
not had access to data from two geosynchronous satellites.
The remaining satellites (GOES-1 through -5) provide
limited operational support for data collection, weather
facsimile services, and relay of data from the VAS
instrument. The principal products derived from the
geostationary satellites are: full-disk and sectorized
cloud cover images, observations of wind speed and
direction, assessments of hurricane motion and intensity,
severe thunderstorm and tornado detection and monitoring,
and warnings of potential flash flooding.
    The routine imaging schedule calls for images to begin
on the hour and half-hour for GOES-East, and at quarter to
and quarter past the hour for GOES-West. The signals
obtained from the visible and i.r. detectors are digitized
and transmitted to the NOAA CDA station at Wallops Island
at the rate of 28 megabit/s. At Wallops, the raw data
bursts are "stretched" in time to 1.7 megabit/s for
retransmission to the spacecraft and broadcast to simpler
and less costly receiving stations in the field.
Latitude-longitude grids are also implanted at this time.
    The stretched data are received at a central computer
facility in Maryland where VISSR data products are
prepared. The VISSR data are forwarded to a central data

distribution facility, also in Maryland, where the data are
"sectorized" into a form suitable for transmission over
telephone lines to six satellite field service stations.
At these stations, which were established to support the
National Weather Service on a regional basis, analyses and
interpretations of the imagery are performed. This imagery
is distributed to television stations, universities, state
governments, industries, and to other U. S. government
agencies.

     NOAA is responsible for setting the observational
requirements to be met by the geostationary satellite
system. Under a basic agreement between NASA and NOAA for
the operational satellite system, NASA is responsible for
designing, engineering, and procuring the GOES spacecraft,
selecting and procuring the launch vehicles, overseeing
launch operations, and on-orbit checkout before turning the
satellite over to NOAA. The responsibility for carrying
out these activities has been delegated to the Metsat
Project at the NASA Goddard Space Flight Center. NOAA is
responsible for the actual operation of the satellites and
ground systems, for replacement decisions, and for
acquiring, processing, distributing, and archiving the
satellite data. Operational control and management of the
satellite program has been delegated to the National
Environmental Satellite, Data, and Information Service.

Use of Geosynchronous Satellite Measurements

     The initial attempts to work with data obtained from
the geosynchronous satellites focused primarily on the use
of imagery. A wide range of operational users monitored
the growth and movement of cloud systems, while researchers
mostly used the imagery to give them a general concept of
the cloud systems or surface temperature to augment their
other data sources. During the past decade, however, the
emphasis has gradually changed to a more quantitative
utilization of the data. Interactive systems developed at
the University of Wisconsin, NASA, and NOAA permit the time
lapse display of enhanced images where the system operators
can select what will be measured and have immediate access
to the digital data to make the calculations. Quantitative
estimates of temperature and moisture profiles, surface
temperature, cloud properties, and winds can now be made.
In this section, results from the major parameter
extraction methods are presented first, followed by short

discussions of how these parameters are employed in mesoscale analysis or used for other purposes.

Parameter Measurement

Temperature and Moisture Profiles. The methods used for the determination of temperature and moisture profiles in clear and partly cloudy areas from the VAS are similar to those used to obtain profiles from the low-orbiting satellites. The radiances from several channels in the 4.3 and 15 μm CO_2 absorption regions are mathematically inverted to determine the temperature profile. A similar process is used for water vapor profiles with two channels in the 6.7 μm water vapor absorption region and another channel around 12 μm which is slightly removed from the most transparent portion of the 10-12 μm atmosphere window. The accuracy of the tropospheric and lower stratospheric temperature profiles is about ± 2 K, with the best results in the middle troposphere. The water vapor profiles are taken in the troposphere and their accuracy is $\pm 25\%$ relative humidity. Profile horizontal spatial resolutions of 30-100 km are possible, with the best resolution occurring in clear conditions. In the lowest portion of the troposphere, the water vapor can be determined with 15 km resolution in clear conditions to within 0.75-1.00 precipitable cm, essentially using the radiance difference between the 11 μm and window channel and the 12 μm channel mentioned above.

Surface Temperature. Accurate surface temperature measurement from the VAS requires data from several channels. The visible and 3.8 μm (at night) channels are used to determine the cloud cover conditions, whereas the 3.8, 11, and 12 μm channels all help estimate the water vapor correction that is applied to the 3.8 or 11 μm temperature measurements. By far the most accurate measurements are made over water, where the clear-column water vapor corrected, equivalent blackbody temperature (T_{BB}) is very close to the water surface temperature. The accuracy demonstrated thus far is less than or equal to 1 K, and the potential exists for spatial resolutions of around 10 km in clear areas, with less than or equal to 0.5 K accuracy. Over land, the wide variations in soil type and vegetation preclude similar results to those over water. However, the diurnal temperature cycle is very useful, and radical changes from the normal cycle provide valuable information on certain types of mesoscale phenomena. (Some examples will be discussed later.)

Cloud Properties. One of the most direct measurements
that can be made from satellites is the basic properties of
clouds (type, amount, and height). Multispectral and
spatial reflectance properties are the primary indicators
used for determining cloud types, since the spatial
resolution is usually insufficient to identify the cloud
type uniquely. Considerable success has been achieved
using the VAS channels for separating the basic cloud types
(cumulus, stratus, and cirrus). Some subgrouping can be
achieved, especially where the altitude range is large
(i.e., cumulus through cumulonimbus).

Cloud amounts are generally estimated through
brightness and/or T_{BB} thresholding above or below a
background level. For large clouds (average cloud size $\geq$
20 km) this produces $\leq$ 5% overestimation errors for the $\overline{VAS}$
visible channel and $\leq$ 10% overestimation errors for the 11μm
channel. The smaller clouds (e.g., cumulus) can produce
overestimation errors of up to 30% with the visible channel
with an actual cumulus coverage of about 30%. However, the
potential exists to substantially reduce the errors for the
smaller clouds using multispectral techniques.

Cloud-top heights are obtained from radiation and
stereographic methods. The radiometric methods include the
traditional technique of comparing the 11 μm T_{BB} at the
cloud top with a nearby radiosonde to estimate the height.
With VAS data, a more sophisticated multispectral method
has been developed using some of the profiling channels.
The accuracy of these techniques depends on the complexity
of the cloud situation, cloud size, and where in the
troposphere (or lower stratosphere) the cloud is located.
The accuracy is as good as 250-500 m for simple large cloud
areas in the lower 80% of the troposphere, degrading to
several kilometers for small semitransparent cirrus where
the most simple 11 μm channel-only method is employed. The
stereographic approach, which uses synchronized images from
two geosynchronous satellites surveying a common area,
produces consistent 250-500 m accuracies for all cloud
situations where the visible channel is used. Stereo is
also possible with the i.r. channel, but the accuracies are
greater than 1 km due to the relatively low spatial
resolution.

Winds. The primary method of estimating winds from a
series of geosynchronous images is to trace the motions of
small discrete clouds that are assumed to represent
atmospheric motion. Most of the winds are near the top of
the boundary layer near the bases of the plentiful cumulus
and stratocumulus clouds. A secondary peak of useful cloud

motions is at the cirrus level near the tropopause. While
middle-level clouds can be used, they often occur in more
complex cloud situations, and it becomes difficult to trace
individual elements. Stereo is a possible way of
increasing the number of useful middle clouds since the
altitude separation between layers is better than with the
radiometric methods.

Wind measurement accuracies of 3-4 m/s have been
operationally demonstrated for cumulus clouds and 7-8 m/s
for cirrus clouds. Since a large portion of this error is
the proper assignment of cloud height, the stereographic
cloud height technique could reduce these errors
considerably. Aircraft flights have shown that the cloud
motion/wind relationship is 1-2 m/s for cumulus clouds over
water (and it is probably close to that over land).
Therefore, a better knowledge of cloud type and height
should result in improved accuracies. High image
frequencies of $\leq$ 5 min have also been shown to improve the
accuracy, spatial resolution, and coverage of the cloud
motion fields because it is much easier to consistently
identify the clouds being followed. This image frequency
is absolutely essential for cumulus cloud tracking over
land since their lifetimes are usually around 10-15 min.

Meteorological Applications

Severe Storms and Other Mesoscale Phenomena. The
geosynchronous satellite capability to measure over large
areas with very high spatial and temporal resolution makes
it the principal satellite system for studying and
monitoring mesoscale and/or rapidly changing meteorological
events. These include severe local storms, tropical and
extratropical cyclones, frost and freeze conditions, fog,
and dust storms. The major contributions of geosynchronous
measurements to each of these events is presented below.

1) Severe local storms. Prior to storm formation,
the favorable atmospheric areas for development need to be
identified. The most favorable regions contain an
approaching middle and upper troposphere trough, an
unstable lower and middle troposphere, copious lower
tropospheric moisture, and converging winds in the lower
troposphere. Often the convergence regions are associated
with former boundaries (e.g., warm fronts, prior
thunderstorm outflows in the lowest layers) or fresh
boundaries created by new storms or the interactions
between the storms and the environmental flow.

Fig. 8 SMS-1 image of Hurricane Carmen (September 1, 1974).

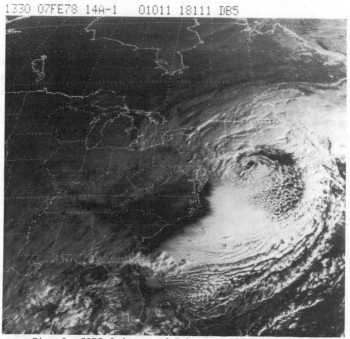

Fig. 9 GOES-2 image of February 1978 snowstorm.

Parameters calculated from the GOES VAS contribute to detecting all of these potentially favorable conditions for storm development. The temperature profiles and the cirrus cloud motions help to delineate the middle and upper tropospheric circulation features. Instability trends are followed using stability indices calculated from the temperature and moisture profiles. The low-level moisture is estimated from the radiance difference between the i.r. channels mentioned above. If several images are taken at $\leq$ 5-min intervals, then winds determined from cumulus and stratocumulus cloud motions provide mesoscale convergence estimates. These convergence fields are especially valuable starting 1-3 h before potential storm development, and that usually is when the small trackable cumulus begin to form. Boundaries are often detected through the location of cumulus cloud lines shaped like an arc. These lines are often produced by the relatively cold air outflow from thunderstorm gust fronts.

Once the thunderstorms are occurring, the position, movement, and growth of individual cells can be monitored, principally with the visible and the 11 μm i.r. channels. Relationships have been determined among thunderstorm intensity and cell growth rates, upper cloud boundary thermal patterns, and the amount of cloud-top penetration into the stratosphere. These types of cloud-top measurements have also been found useful for locating areas of excessive rainfall.

2) Tropical cyclones. The early stages of tropical cyclone formation can be identified and studied with satellite imagery and the quantitative meteorological parameters. Characteristic cloud patterns reveal the cyclonic structure in the earliest stages. Thus, the center can be located and, if appropriate, reconnaissance aircraft can be flown to the area to provide a more complete description of the cyclone. A comprehensive range of intensity estimates can be made from the cloud pattern configurations. A well-defined cyclonic circulation of an intense hurricane is seen in the SMS-2 image in Fig. 8, which shows Hurricane Carmen near the Yucatan Peninsula in the summer of 1974. A less intense cyclone would show a less organized cloud pattern near the center, and it would usually have a more asymmetrical shape.

Theories concerning the conditions most favorable for the intensificaton of incipient vortices can be investigated with a combination of temperature and moisture profiles plus the wind fields. Subsidence in the upper troposphere above the center of the low-level vorticity associated with a weak vortex is a favorable circumstance to lower the pressure near the vortex center and produce a more intense circulation. Besides the determination of the upper and lower tropospheric circulation for research studies from the cloud motion-derived winds, the lower tropospheric winds can be used to determine the radius of potentially dangerous winds.

Fields of temperature, moisture, and clouds have considerable potential to contribute to forecasting cyclone motion. The temperature and moisture profiles can be used in numerical and statistical models. Cloud estimations and heights derived from Nimbus satellite data have already been used in combination with conventional cyclone parameters to statistically estimate cyclone motion with forecast accuracies at 24-48 h that are about the same as the current operational forecast. At 72 h, this statistical method shows a 20% improvement over current operational methods. Since GOES has the same type of data, it could be used in a similar manner.

3) Extratropical cyclones. The most significant measurements of extratropical cyclones are those concerned with the cyclogenesis process. The VAS temperature and moisture profiles can be used to define the middle and upper tropospheric circulation features that contribute to the initial formation of these storms. Another contributing factor is lower tropospheric heat and moisture fluxes. The wind, low-level moisture, and surface temperature measurements from the VAS all contribute to assessing the lower tropospheric role in storm formation. A major extratropical cyclone field experiment is planned for the winter of 1985-86, and the geosynchronous satellite measurements are expected to make a significant contribution to determining the relative importance of these types of cyclone formation processes for storms that develop along the central portion of the U.S. east coast. The cloud pattern associated with an intense northeastern U.S. snowstorm in the winter of 1978 is shown in a GOES-2 image in Fig. 9. This storm produced 2-3 ft of snow and hurricane-force wind gusts over portions of New England. It is worth noting the appearance of a cloud configuration similar to the shape of a tropical cyclone at the center of the circulation near 40° N, 71° W.

4) Other mesoscale phenomena. A very successful use of geosynchronous satellite measurements has been the monitoring of frost and freeze conditions through the diurnal cycle of surface temperature measurements. Following the position movement and growth of clouds that could affect radiational cooling with the geosynchronous satellite imagery has also helped to improve the frost and freeze forecast.

Fog is easily detected during the daytime with the combination of the visible and 11 μm imaging channels since the fog clouds are bright, have characteristic patterns that do not change rapidly, and the T_{BB} values are high because the cloud tops are low. The visible imagery has shown that the fog usually dissipates inward from its edges. At night, radiation fog often appears as relatively warm areas because the surrounding surface skin temperatures are higher than the fog cloud-top temperatures. Another potential use of the low-level moisture measurements could be to help determine at what temperature fog would start to form. Finally, the nightime knowledge of the distribution of other clouds and their movements from the time-lapse i.r. imagery provides an indication of the clear areas where radiation fog could form.

Dust storms can be detected and followed with both the visible and 11 μm i.r. imaging channels. The i.r. channel is especially effective for the onset during the latter half of the daytime hours since the lifted dust causes a sudden drop in the radiating temperature from the skin (surface) temperature, which is often 5-15° C above the shelter temperature (measured 1.3 m above the surface), to at or below the shelter temperature. Stereo is useful for calculating the height of the dust using the visible channel.

<u>Synoptic Scales and Climate</u>. Some of the derived parameters from geosynchronous satellite measurements are important for larger spatial and time scales. For the synoptic scale, perhaps the most significant contributions come from the cloud-motion derived winds and the monitoring of convectively driven events (e.g., in the intertropical convergence zone). The winds were very important to the Global Atmospheric Research Program (GARP) implemented in 1979 and were calculated from five different geosynchronous satellites placed around the globe. The winds were used in the global dynamic models. They are currently part of the data base for the NOAA operational dynamic model run by the National Meteorological Center. Temperature profiles from the VAS over the eastern Pacific area are being inserted into the operational model to see if they will contribute sufficiently to the forecast to become part of the routine data base. Both of these parameters plus moisture profiles can be inserted into smaller-scale models and some testing is already underway.

For climate, the primary focus is on the measurement of cloud cover and top heights. The geosynchronous satellite data provide the diurnal cloud changes. These data are part of the core data base of the International Satellite Cloud Climatology Project (ISCCP), which is estimating cloud parameters for the 5 year period from 1983-88.

Future Potential of Geosynchronous Satellites. Major new observing capabilities are possible in geosynchronous orbit. Microwave sounding and imaging could provide temperature and moisture profiles in cloudy areas, improve the profiles in other areas, and determine precipitation parameters. Higher vertical resolution i.r. temperature profiles are feasible by sharply increasing the spectral resolution of the profiling channels. Ozone measurements can further improve the temperature profiling by estimating the tropopause height. These data could also assist in delineating strong upper tropospheric circulation features (e.g., jet streams). Increasing the spatial and temporal resolution of the imager could lead to substantial improvements in convective cell monitoring, wind determinations from cloud motion, measurements of surface temperature, and low-level moisture estimation. Earth resource oriented measurements could also be initiated. Other possible sensor candidates include lightning mapping, regional radiation budget surveys where diurnal changes are important, and higher-frequency solar measurements, which would contribute to the climate program.

GOES-Next

In order to ensure that spacecraft are available for launch when they are needed, extensive lead time is required. The time from issuing a request for proposal (RFP) to availability for launch can easily be 6 years or more. The establishment of observational requirements must begin earlier still. In the case of the next generation of geosynchronous weather satellites (designated GOES-Next), efforts to establish these requirements began late in 1980. The RFP for GOES-Next satellites was issued in the summer of 1984. Launch of the first of the new satellites is unlikely before 1990. That represents a ten year interval from concept to reality!

Some of the improvements being sought in the GOES-Next satellites are 1) independent imaging and sounding capabilities to avoid the current limitation of having to perform either imaging or sounding at a particular time, but not both; 2) increased location accuracy for analysis and forecasting of small-scale meteorological phenomena;

3) additional imaging channels to improve capability of
monitoring moisture and atmospheric stability for severe
storm forecasting; 4) improved imaging and sounding spatial
and temporal resolution; 5) improved vertical resolution
and accuracy in soundings; 6) independent WEFAX
transmission to permit WEFAX transmission during imaging
and/or sounding operations; and 7) expanded data collection
system capabilities to include search and rescue
frequencies (for detection only, location will be provided
by the polar orbiters). Details of these improvements are
covered in L. Heacock's paper, appearing elsewhere in this
volume.

Data Availability

The periods of operation for the primary
imager/sounder instrument on all the geosynchronous weather
satellites from ATS-1 to GOES-6 are depicted in Fig. 10.
The satellite locations during periods of operation are
indicated. Standby times are also shown. Due to the need
to drift these satellites into operating position,
instrument start times are typically a few weeks after
launch date. The last date indicated for any particular
satellite designates either the instrument failure date or
the deliberate deactivation date.

The operational use of SMS-1 through GOES-6 as either
GOES-East or GOES-West is summarized in Table 2. Also
shown are the periods and locations of special applications
of these satellites.

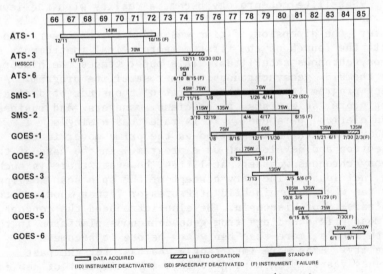

Fig. 10 Imager/sounder operating times/locations.

Both NASA and NOAA maintain archives of geosynchronous
weather data. For the early ATS and SMS satellites, the
NASA holdings are more extensive. Researchers should
direct their requests to: National Space Science Data
Center, NASA Goddard Space Flight Center, Greenbelt, MD
20771. Telephone: (301) 344-6695.

For the GOES satellite, the NOAA holdings are more
extensive. Researchers should direct their requests to:
NOAA/NESDIS, Satellite Data Services Division, Washington,
DC 20233. Telephone: (301) 763-8111.

Conclusion

Geosynchronous satellite meteorology is fast
approaching its twentieth anniversary. We have progressed
from relatively low-resolution single-channel visible
imagery to high-resolution multichannel imaging and
sounding. A data collection system has been added to
permit the gathering of environmental data from thousands
of remote Earth platforms. Transmission of weather maps,
charts, imagery, and other information has become routine.
Day and night images of temperature and water vapor
patterns are now possible. In the next decade we can look
forward to continued improvement and expansion of our
observational capabilities.

Acknowledgment

Satellite meteorology became a reality with the launch
of the first TIROS low-Earth orbiter in 1960. Some six years
later, the dimension of time was added to the observations
with the launch of the first meteorological instruments on
geosynchronous satellites. This paper traces the history
of the U.S. geosynchronous weather satellite program. Any
such program involves the efforts of thousands of dedicated
engineers, scientists, technicians, managers, and business
and clerical personnel. It is rare that a single
individual can be identified as the prime mover in the
creation and development of a program. In the case of the
geosynchronous weather satellites, however, there is such
an individual. The very concept of the spin scan imaging
system was the brainchild of Professor Verner Suomi of the
University of Wisconsin. He also introduced the concept of
atmospheric soundings from geosynchronous platforms in the
late 1960's, more than ten years before it became a
reality. Even more importantly, he has, for the past
twenty years, been a pioneer in the development of new and
increasingly sophisticated applications of the data from

the sensors that he brought into being. We are pleased and honored to dedicate this paper to Professor Suomi, whose drive and vision have contributed so much to the success of this program.

The GOES-G and -H Spacecraft Design

Louis R. Fermelia*
Hughes Aircraft Company, Los Angeles, California

Abstract

The design of the Geostationary Operational Environmental Satellites (GOES) uses newer technology and has expanded capability relative to the predecessor GOES series of satellites. The satellite directly transmits day and night observations of hemispheric-scale weather, hurricanes, and other more localized severe storms and relays processed high-resolution observation data along with weather facsimile (WEFAX) data. Weather observations are generated in the visible and infrared spin scan radiometer (VISSR) atmospheric sounder (VAS). The VAS performs visible and infrared imaging as well as multispectral imaging (MSI) and temperature sounding of the atmosphere. The satellite provides direct interrogation and simultaneous relay transmission between the command data acquisition station (CDAS) and the multiple, widely dispersed data collection platforms (DCP). The satellites also monitor the condition of the Earth's magnetic field, energetic particle flux, and x-ray emissions from the sun. The satellite performs all communications functions by means of a multifunction communications system that operates on S-band and uhf frequencies at rates varying from 100 bit/s to 28 megabit/s. An experimental capability for the detection of the emergency locator transmitter beacons is included in the GOES-GH design as a part of the international satellite-aided search and rescue system.

Introduction

The Geostationary Operational Environment Satellite (GOES) provides a wide variety of meteorological satellite services as a part of the network of satellites for the world weather watch program planned by the World Meteoro-

---

logical Organization (WMO). The primary satellite mission is the transmission of visible and infrared observations of hemispheric-scale weather, hurricanes, and other localized severe storms to an Earth-based processing center; then it performs time-shared relay of the processed high-resolution observation data along with weather facsimile (WEFAX) data to the field stations. Weather observations are generated in an advanced instrument, the VISSR atmospheric sounder (VAS). GOES also provides direct interrogation and simultaneous relay transmission between the command data acquisition station (CDAS) and multiple widely dispersed data collection platforms (DCP). The GOES-GH spacecraft configuration includes the search and rescue (SAR) repeater, an advanced part of the COSPAS-SARSAT Project (Soviet), the international joint venture in satellite-aided search and rescue. Compatibility with the NASA Deep Space Network (DSN) has been incorporated into the command and ranging communications system that will be used to support the launch and transfer orbit operations. The condition of the Earth's magnetic field and energetic particle flux in the vicinity of the spacecraft and x-ray emissions from the sun are also monitored. These measurements are made through instruments collec-

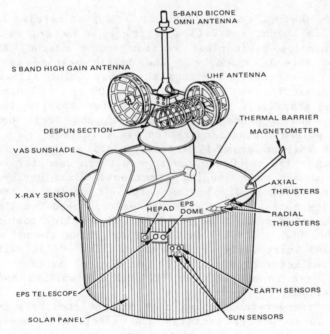

Fig. 1 GOES.

tively called the space environmental monitor (SEM) and transmitted directly to a central processing center.

The spacecraft provides an operational capability for temperature sounding of the atmosphere with the VAS. The VAS performs all of the operational visible and infrared imaging functions of its VISSR predecessor as well as operational multispectral imaging (MSI) and temperature sounding of the atmosphere by processor control of the 12 infrared spectral bands.

Other important design features include a fully channelized communications system that meets the multicarrier intermodulation performance requirements. Light weight and high performance are achieved with the hybrid microcircuit implementation in the VAS digital multiplexer. The satellite structural design employs beryllium members and a graphite composite apogee motor adapter to achieve weight efficiency. The latest design solar cells (K-7) provide efficient lightweight power system performance. The use of these weight-efficient materials and high-efficiency solar cells has enabled the satellite design to provide sufficient fuel and solar panel and battery capacity for a 7 year design life.

Spacecraft Design Configuration

The GOES (Fig. 1), which is approximately 3.66 m (12 ft) in height and 2.13 m (7 ft) in diameter, consists of a spinning cylindrical section and a despun, Earth-oriented antenna assembly. The despin bearing assembly and the noncontacting tricoaxial rotary joint allows the spinning section to spin freely at 100 rpm. Therefore, attitude stability, a simple means for passive thermal control, and a means for orientation and orbit control through pulsed thruster operation are effected.

The antenna assembly includes: 1) a bicone antenna providing a ±50 x 360 deg coverage pattern used for telemetry, command, and ranging functions; 2) a north-south linearly polarized dipole fed parabolic reflector providing ±9 deg conical Earth coverage pattern used for the VAS downlink and for the S band uplink and downlink portion of both the DCP and the multifunction channel; and 3) a right-hand circularly polarized bifilar helix with a cupped reflector providing a ±9 deg conical Earth coverage pattern used to support the DCP and SAR uplinks and the DCP downlinks.

The spacecraft spinning section, enclosed by a cylindrical solar panel, contains the electronics equipment shelf, the VAS and SEM instruments, and the propulsion system hydrazine tanks and thrusters. The Earth and sun sensors provide timing references to the despin control electronics, which in turn maintain the antenna pointing as well as timing references for VAS operation, SEM, and time multiplexing of the communications signals in the multifunction transponder. The GOES significant performance parameters are listed in Table 1.

The spacecraft spinning structure consists of seven major assemblies: 1) the apogee boost motor (ABM) adapter; 2) the primary thrust tube, which supports the VAS instrument, the reaction control subsystem (RCS), and the electronics equipment shelf; 3) the solar panel substrate; 4) the despin bearing support assembly; 5) the VAS sunshade/cover; 6) the electronics equipment shelf; and 7) the magnetometer boom assembly. The structural configuration is illustrated in an exploded view in Fig. 2. The ABM adapter is constructed of 10 ply graphite fiber composite material for lighter weight. The magnetometer boom, designed to accommodate the magnetometer sensor,

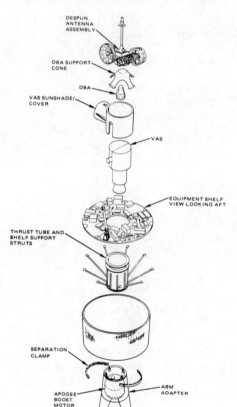

Fig. 2 Exploded view of GOES.

Table 1 Spacecraft performance characteristics

Parameter	Value
Weight	
At launch	835 kg (1841 lb)
7 year	350 kg (770 lb)
Solar panel power	
At launch	400 W
7 year	320 W
Communications	
UHF	
Frequencies	402 and 468 MHz
EIRP	45 dBm
G/T	22 dB/k
S band	
Frequencies	1681 and 2034 MHz
EIRP	55 dBm
G/T	-16 dB/K
VAS	
Visible	
Channels	8
Resolution	0.93 km (0.5 n.mi.)
Response	0.55 to 0.72 μm
Infrared	
Channels	12 (VAS)
Resolution	6.86 and 13.7 km (3.7 and 7.4 n.mi.)
Response	3.9 - 14.7 μm
Energetic particle sensor	
Protons	
Range, energetic particle sensor (EPS)	0.8 - 500 MeV
Range, HEPAD	>370 MeV
Alphas	
Range, EPS	3.2 - 400 MeV
Range, HEPAD	>640 MeV
Electrons	
Range, EPS	$\geqq$2.0 MeV
X-ray sensor	0.5 - 3 A 1 - 8A
Magnetometer	DC -1200 to 1200 γ

consists of a 76 x 6.3 cm (30 x 2.5 in.) diameter graphite tube deployed by the spacecraft centrifugal force. A spring damper limits the deployment loads on the magnetometer instrument sensor and boom mounting structure.

The thrust tube is a riveted assembly of machined aluminum rings and rolled magnesium alloy conical skins. The remaining structural elements use aluminum honeycomb sandwich construction with facesheets of appropriate material: the equipment shelf has aluminum facesheets, the solar panel has Kevlar facesheets, and the remaining assemblies employ epoxy fiberglass facesheets.

The uhf and S-band antennas are one integrated structure composed of polyamide impregnated paper honeycomb core sandwich materials. Multiple layers of preimpregnated figerglass cloth form the facesheets. Weight reducing holes are cut in this sandwich consistent with structural integrity to reduce weight and solar pressure exerted on the antenna. The bicone antenna assembly uses a beryllium mast to support the aluminum fiberglass bicone radome structure.

Communications Subsystem

The GOES communications subsystem consists of the despun antenna array connected to the electronics on the spinning side of the spacecraft through a noncontacting rotary joint as illustrated in Fig. 3. For reliability, the subsystem has full redundancy (except for the rotary

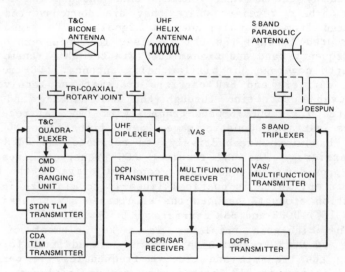

Fig. 3   Communications subsystem block diagram.

joint and antenna elements) and cross strapping of all
active electronics and filter units; the redundancy
details are omitted from Fig. 3 for clarity. The subsystem can be divided into individual systems according to
their mission function: the multifunction S-band system;
the uhf system; and the telemetry, command, and ranging
system.

The multifunction S-band system contains the
communication equipment for transmission and relay of VAS,
stretched VAS (SVAS), WEFAX, and trilateration mission
functions. Analog VAS data are multiplexed and converted
to pulse code modulation (PCM) in the VAS digital multiplexer (VDM). The VAS PCM is then quadraphase shift key
(QPSK) modulated at 28 megabit/s in the S-band receiver
and directly transmitted via the 20 W S-band transmitter
and the dipole-fed S-band parabolic antenna. The multifunction relay signals (SVAS, WEFAX, and trilateration)
are received by the S-band antenna and coupled via the
same S-band transmit path as the direct VAS signal for
time-multiplexed transmission. Time-multiplexed transmission between the VAS and SVAS signals occurs every 360 deg
of the spacecraft spin revolution, with direct VAS transmission during the 20 deg of VAS imaging and SVAS relay
during the remaining 340 deg. WEFAX or trilateration
relay services are operated by means of ground control
during periods when VAS imaging has been completed (e.g.,
during the VAS north-south scan mirror retrace).

The DCP interrogation (DCPI) signals are also
received by the Earth coverage S-band antenna and routed
to the S-band receiver where they are downconverted and
separated from the multifunction signals. The signal is
then routed through the uhf receiver for upconversion to
uhf frequency band and transmitted via the uhf transmitter
and Earth coverage uhf bifilar helix antenna. DCP report
(DCPR) carriers and SAR carriers transmit and receive in
the reverse direction through the uhf antenna and the
dedicated 0.5 W DCPR S-band transmitter. The uhf receiver
employs surface acoustic wave (SAW) filters at 80 and
40 MHz bandwidth, respectively, to separate the DCPR and
SAR carriers. The uhf receiver AGC preserves linearity
while providing an essentially constant drive to the DCPR
transmitter, which is operated linearly to minimize intermodulation products between the simultaneously transmitted
(up to 188) DCPR and SAR carriers.

The high-gain triplexer is a key element of the
S-band and DCPR transmission systems. In addition to separating the transmit and receive frequencies, it permits
channelization of the high-power, time-multiplexed, VAS/

multifunction transmission link and the low-power continuous DCPR link. The triplexer is required to 1) minimize
the delay variation and distortion in the VAS transmission
band, 2) suppress the VAS and SVAS power flux density in
the adjacent radio astronomy band (1660-1670 MHz) to less
than -240 dB • W/m^2/Hz, and 3) diplex the VAS and DCPR
carriers to the S-band antenna with minimum insertion
loss.

To meet these somewhat conflicting requirements, the
design uses an eight-section VAS transmit filter to band
limit the VAS spectrum and provide out-of-band suppression
necessary for radio astronomy protection. The VAS filter
was tuned to give a quasielliptic function response with a
3 dB bandwidth of 22 MHz and sharp band edge transitions,
which give large out-of-band rejection. The large rejection at the band edges also provides the isolation
required to efficiently sum the DCPR signal in the
triplexer.

VAS and VDM Design

Visible and infrared two-dimensional cloud mapping
data of high resolution [0.93 km (0.5 n.mi.) visible and
6.86 km (3.7 n.mi.) infrared] originate in the VAS. The
VAS also obtains radiometric data in 12 infrared bands,
including the Earth's atmospheric water vapor and CO_2
absorption bands, to help determine the three-dimensional
structure of the atmospheric temperature and water vapor
distribution.

The VAS image mapping raster is formed by the
combination of the satellite spin motion (spin scan) and
the step action of the scanning optics. One raster line
in the Earth's west-east (W-E) direction is formed for
each revolution of the spinning satellite at each north-
south (N-S) angular scan step position of the VAS scan
mirror. Each 0.192 mr (0.93 km or 0.5 n.mi. ground track)
N-S axis scan step corresponds to the total field of view
of the eight visible channel detectors. The 0.93 km
(0.5 n.mi.) resolution in the visible spectrum is obtained
by using a linear array of eight photomultiplier tube
(PMT) detectors aligned so that they sweep out the complete scan line path. The Earth is covered in the N-S
direction with 1820 successive latitude steps until 20 deg
coverage is obtained.

The VAS has six infrared detectors; two are used primarily for imaging and four for atmospheric sounding
information. Two infrared detectors are in use during any
satellite spin period. The detectors are automatically
switched into the VAS digital multiplexer (VDM) by the VAS

processor depending upon the selected mode of operation. The processor also controls the VAS filter wheel, which can selectively position spectral filters into the optical train to provide infrared response in 12 different spectral bands for multispectral imaging (MSI) and atmospheric sounding.

The redundant, cross-strapped VAS digital multiplexer provides high-accuracy multiplexing of the VAS visible and infrared data. Implemented primarily with hybrid microcircuits, it features differential signal detection and employs four visible and two infrared analog to digital (A/D) converters operating in parallel for relatively low-speed operation and reduced power consumption. Figure 4 is a block diagram of one of the redundant VDM units.

Each of the eight visible channels from the VAS is processed through a differential input receiver, a five-pole Bessel filter, and a dedicated sample and hold circuit. The use of four A/D converters instead of a single high-speed converter provides better timing margins and allows the use of a conservative, simple A/D converter design. The A/D converters are a successive approximation type, operating at 500,000 samples/s, with autoranging capability using a switchable gain for higher resolution of low-level inputs. The gain mode is controlled by a comparator that determines whether the input signal falls above or below 1/8 full scale. If above, the A/D converter operates as a normal 6 bit linear converter. If below, the signal is multiplied by eight, which provides the required high resolution for low-level signals.

The VDM is designed with a visible channel input/output signal transfer function in which the output signal approximates the square root of the input signal.

The A/D output includes the 6 bits from the converter and a single-gain indication bit from the comparator. These 7 bits are processed by a programmable read-only memory that, for each of the 128 possible input words,

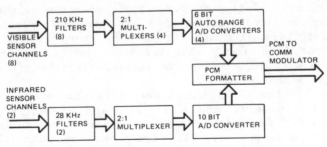

Fig. 4 VAS digital multiplexer block diagram.

produces the appropriate 6 bit output approximation to the square root function.   A single PROM performs the square root conversion for all visible A/D converters.

Infrared (i.r.) channel processing also uses different input buffers, active five-pole Bessel filters, and sample and hold circuitry similar to the visible channel. The i.r. A/D converter used mode configuration that initially performs the four most significant bit conversions, followed by a second conversion that forms the six least significant bits.   This implementation allows the use of slower and lower power components for the 4 bit conversion with its attendant advantages of conservative design margins and lower power operations.

The i.r. A/D converter also features an individual offset correction for each input chain.   Once per satellite revolution, during preamble transmission, a calibrated voltage is applied to the input filters.   An integrating circuit within the A/D converter is driven to a value that nulls the combined offsets of the filter, track and hold, and the converter itself.   This offset correction is held for the ensuing Earth scan.

SEM Design

The space environmental monitor (SEM) performs three functions with three sets of instruments that are depicted in Fig. 1:

1)   The magnetometer measures the magnetic field strength and direction in the vicinity of the spacecraft. The sensor is a biaxial flux gate magnetometer with one axis parallel to the spacecraft spin axis and a transverse axis normal to the spin axis.   The two coils in the magnetometer are mounted on a 76 cm (30 in.) boom deployed by spacecraft centrifugal force after separation from the launch vehicle upper stage.

2)   The x-ray sensor monitors solar flare activity in the soft x-ray spectrum.   The x-ray radiation travels at the speed of light and is advance warning that slower moving energetic particles may follow.   A geared stepper motor can adjust this sensor to track the seasonal relative movement of the sun in steps of 0.125 deg.   The step size corresponds to an average of two steps per day.

3)   The energetic particle sensor is designed to detect alpha particles, protons, and electrons resulting from solar flare-associated particle injection events. This instrument has three detector assemblies to cover the broad energy spectrum of penetrating radiation.   These units are:

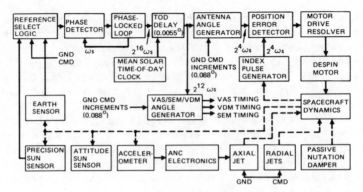

Fig. 5 Control subsystem block diagram.

a) Telescope: The telescope uses two silicon surface barrier detectors to detect low-energy protons
(0.8-15 MeV) and alpha particles (3.2-60 MeV) with a half-
angle field of view of 35 deg.

b) Dome: The dome uses three groups of paired silicon surface barrier detectors (SSBD) to detect electrons
(greater than 2 MeV), protons (15-500 MeV) in seven channels, and alpha particles (60-400 MeV) in six channels
within a field of view of 130 deg.

c) High-energy particle detector: The HEPAD is a
Cerenkov counter telescope combining a photomultiplier
tube and solid-state detectors to measure protons
(350 to > 850 MeV) and alpha particles (640 to > 900 MeV)
within a field of view of 68 deg.

Controls Subsystem Design

The controls subsystem performs antenna pointing
VAS/SEM timing and nutation, attitude, and orbit control
as shown in Fig. 5. The heart of the system is the phase-
locked loop (PLL), which generates timing that is accurately phase controlled to the spacecraft rotor spin rate
as defined by the sensor reference. The sensor reference
supplies a pulse train at spin frequency ω_s with pulse
positions carrying rotor inertial phase information. The
pulse train is then processed by the PPL, which has three
functions: 1) to quantize the spin cycle into 2^{16}
(0.0055 deg) parts, 2) to increase the output phase sample
rate to $2^4 \omega_s$, and 3) to filter noise from the input sensor pulse train. The PPL output pulse train is delayed by
the Earth-to-sun angle by means of the time-of-day (TOD)
delay, whose delayed output is at $2^{12} \omega_s$. The TOD delay
output is then counted down and delayed in two angle gene-

rators to provide an independent control reference for antenna pointing and VDM/VAS/SEM angle reference timing.

The antenna angle generator counts the 2^{12} ω_s input train down to 2^4 ω_s and provides for ground commanded pulse additions or subtractions that step the antenna reference in ±0.088 deg increments. Its output then contains rotor phase information, which is compared with the despin bearing assembly generated by the index pulse generator rotor-to-antenna relative phase to produce an estimate of the antenna pointing error. The resulting error signal is applied as the pointing torque command.

The VAS/SEM angle generator uses the 2^{12} ω_s output of the TOD delay to generate a stream of eight timing signals each spin period to synchronize the required mission line scan operations with rotor spin phase. This signal stream can be advanced or retarded in phase by ground command in increments of ±0.088 deg over the full ±180 deg range.

The fully redundant automatic nutation control unit consists of sensing accelerometers, control electronics, and axial thrusters to provide control torque during the transfer orbit when the spacecraft spin-to-transverse-inertia ratio is less than 1. After apogee boost motor firing and the achievement of geosynchronous orbit, the ABM/adapter combination is jettisoned, the inertial ratio becomes greater than 1, and the active nutation control (ANC) is disabled. Orbit control ΔV maneuvers and spin axis attitude precision maneuvers are accomplished by ground commanding axial and radial thrusters in appropriate continuous and pulsed modes. The orbit is controlled to maintain the satellite on station within 0.1 deg in both north-south and east-west directions. To meet these requirements, the satellite/ground control system maneuvers are performed with a resolution of 0.006 m/s (0.020 ft/s) and a predictability of 3%. Spin axis attitude determination is implemented by ground processing of telemetered Earth chord width and sun aspect angle data. The attitude determination allows computation of pulsed axial jet control maneuvers that meet the requirement for maintenance of the spin axis within ±0.5 of normal to the orbital plane. Maneuvers are performed with a resolution of 0.01 deg and a predictability of 3%.

The control system includes a passive nutation damper consisting of a 1.9 cm (3/4 in.) diameter aluminum alloy toroid with a 10% fraction-fill of alcohol fluid. The damper provides a time constant of less than 1 min and is effective at damping north-south scan mirror induced transients as small as 2 μrad.

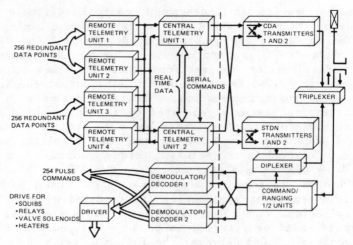

Fig. 6 Telemetry and command block diagram.

Telemetry and Command

The telemetry and command subsystem (Fig. 6) monitors
the health of the spacecraft, multiplexes and transmits
operational SEM data and spacecraft attitude data, and
controls the subsystems via ground command. Commands are
received by the bicone antenna and downconverted for baseband processing by the demodulator/decoder. Telemetry is
transmitted by both the CDA (1694 MHz) and the NASA Spacecraft Tracking Data network (STDN) (2214 MHz) telemetry
transmitters through the bicone antenna.

The central telemetry unit (CTU) contains the basic
timing and control functions required to sample and multiplex spacecraft diagnostic and operational analog and
digital measurements. It organizes the data into a composite PCM format for transmission to the ground network.
The CTU also time and frequency multiplexes attitude,
nutation sensor, and control operatinal data for transmission in real time. These real-time sensor and control
data are priority gated or command selected to frequency
modulate two interrange instrumentation group (IRIG) channels. The PCM and both real-time data streams are routed
to the CDA and STDN telemetry transmitters for downlink
transmission. The CTU has been designed with processor
control, which provides flexibility for accommodating
changes in payload configuration and telemetry monitoring
requirements.

Each remote telemetry unit (RTU) is capable of
sampling 256 totally programmable combinations of analog

and bilevel data sources. Sampling of the sources is under control of the CTU via a supervisory bus. When interrogated, the RTU samples the selected data points, multiplexes, and encodes; formats the data into PCM-RZ data; and returns it to the CTU via a data bus.

The demodulator/decoder unit alternately samples the redundant STDN ranging/command receivers and automatically selects one of two on the basis of baseband frequency shift keying (FSK) tone signal level. The demodulator recovers the baseband FSK/AM signal, and the decoder, upon receipt of the execute tone, completes the command execution. Both demodulator/decoders have the capability of executing all 254 pulse commands.

Power and Propulsion Subsystems

The power subsystem comprises solar panel and battery energy sources, solar panel limiters and battery controllers, and a preregulator that furnishes controlled voltage to the VAS. The spacecraft summary power is provided by a cylindrical solar panel 216 cm (85 in.) in diameter by 147 cm (58 in.) long. The 6138 2.2 x 6.2 cm solar cells distributed in 99 groups of 62 series cells form the main array while 408 2 x 2 cm cells distributed in 12 groups of 34 series cells form the battery charge array. The high-efficiency K-7 solar cells are $10 \, \Omega \cdot cm$, shallow diffused N-on-P configuration with a front sculptured surface, a back surface field, and an aluminum infrared surface reflector. Each cell provides approximately 19.2 mW/cm^2 power density at 25°C, while the main array provides a minimum of 350 W at the end of mission life (7 years). Two batteries consisting of 27 series connected nickel-cadmium battery cells provide 6 A $\cdot$ h of beginning of life capacity to handle the spacecraft 150 W eclipse loads with ample margin. The solar panel harness design has been tailored to minimize the spacecraft-induced magnetic environment and its potential interference with the magnetometer sensor measurements.

The spacecraft propulsion subsystem consists of an apogee boost motor and a hydrazine reaction-control subsystem (RCS). The solid-fuel Thiokol Corporation TE-M-616 apogee boost motor provides an effective specific impulse of 288 s and a total impulse of approximately 97,000 kg/s (213,800 lb/s). The RCS system includes redundant axial thrusters for spacecraft attitude and north-south station-keeping. Redundant pairs of radial thrusters arranged to perform east-west stationkeeping and spin rate control completes the thruster complement. Three monopropellant hydrazine (N_2H_4) tanks provide the 227 lb of propellant capacity in a pressure blowdown mode to operate the 4.45 N (1 lbf) thrusters.

The spacecraft is launched from the Eastern Space and Missile Complex (ESMC) by a Delta 3914 launch vehicle. Synchronous transfer orbit is achieved by utilizing the Delta launch vehicle third stage, and the apogee boost motor is ignited nominally on the second apogee (approximately 24 h after launch vehicle liftoff). The residual longitudinal drift velocity will bring the spacecraft on station within the required 14 days.

Summary

The GOES-G and -H spacecraft design combines proved design concepts with newer technology to provide a system with improved performance and more capability than its predecessors. The SAR repeater, an important spacecraft advanced capability, has the promise of expanding the effectiveness of the COSPAS-SARSAT international joint venture in satellite-aided search and rescue. The improved design command and ranging transponder provides compatibility with the NASA STDN, the NASA Deep Space Network (DSN), and the National Oceanic and Atmospheric Administration command and data acquisition (CDA) stations. Upgrade of the communications subsystem to nearly all microwave integrated circuits (MIC) technology have been added to improve the spacecraft operational reliability. While the atmospheric sounding and multispectral imaging was experimental in previous GOES spacecraft, this operational requirement for GOES-G and -H has been implemented by redundancy and reliability improvements in the VAS subsystem. The use of hybrid microcircuit technology in the VAS digital multiplexer and telemetry subsystems contributed to the reliability and weight efficiency of the spacecraft. Incorporation of K-7 solar cells provides solar panel power sufficient for mission lifetime in an efficient manner. The microprocessor design in the telemetry subsystem provides flexibility for changes in payload or mission requirements during the program development. The weight efficiency afforded in these areas and the use of lightweight graphite composites and beryllium in the structure enable hydrazine fuel capacity to support the 7 year mission lifetime. In conclusion, the GOES-G and -H spacecraft configuration is a sound design that promises more capability and a high probability of meeting the mission lifetime goals.

Acknowledgment

Programmatic and operational responsibilities for the GOES system are assigned to the NOAA within the U.S. Department of Commerce. Procurement and advance developments for GOES are managed for NOAA by the National Aeronautics and Space Administration at the Goddard Space Flight Center. The GOES-G and -H spacecraft are being built by Hughes Aircraft Company, Space and Communications Group, under Contract NAS 5-27316.

NOAA's Environmental Satellite Data Processing and Derived Products

Russell Koffler* and William M. Callicott†

National Oceanic and Atmospheric Administration, Suitland, Maryland

Abstract

Data from the geostationary and polar satellite systems are received and processed at the National Environmental Satellite, Data, and Information Service (NESDIS) processing facilities at Suitland, Md. The flow of geostationary data is constant and concurrent with the spacecraft spin where the polar data are collected onto tape on-board the spacecraft throughout the orbit and transmitted from the Command and Data Acquisition (CDA) Stations in bulk to Suitland. The culmination of both processes is a data base of complementary data-supporting operations and research serviced by NESDIS. This paper presents a description of the products produced and the processing involved in deriving these products.

Polar Satellite Ingest System

The contents of the recorders on-board the TIROS-N/NOAA polar satellite are collected at the Command and Data Acquisition (CDA) Station and retransmitted to Suitland via a domestic satellite link at a rate of 1.34×10^6 bits/s. At Suitland, the data are passed through a data acquisition and control system (DACS) computer, which strips out the spacecraft telemetry

---

This paper is declared a work of the U.S. Government and therefore is in the public domain.

*Director, Office of Satellite Data Processing and Distribution, National Environmental Satellite, Data, and Information Service.

†Deputy Director, Office of Satellite Data Processing and Distribution, National Environmental Satellite, Data, and Information Service.

portion of the data before passing the
instrument data to the data processing and
subservices system (DPSS) computer for data
ingest. The DACS computer convert the telemetry
information into engineering units for
monitoring and command and control operations.
The DPSS computers ingest the data and perform
the preprocessing functions necessary to prepare
the instrument data into a format suitable for
data processing.

Geostationary Satellite Ingest System

Where polar data are delayed and
transmitted in bulk after CDA acquisition, the
geostationary visible infrared spin scan
radiometer (VISSR) data are transmitted to the
Wallops Island, Va., CDA where grid information
is added and the combined data retransmitted at
a slower rate during a single spin period for
receipt on a dedicated 8 m antenna at the
processing center in Suitland. At Suitland, the
data are directed to two separate processing
systems, one in the Suitland processing center
and the other in nearby Camp Springs, Md. The
processing system at Suitland ingests and
prepares the data for further computer
processing. At the Camp Springs location,
multiple partial-image "sectors" are written to
the computer tapes in facsimile format for
retransmission over telephone lines to the seven
principal National Weather Service Satellite
Field Service Stations around the country.

Data Processing

After the raw satellite data are converted
into discrete instrument data files with the
appended calibration and Earth location
parameters, a variety of computer and analytical
products can be generated and distributed over
various user links. All of the products require
computer processing steps. Analytical products
are manually or interactively derived on remote
computer terminals. Scientist or technicians
subjectively analyze these data using a
combination of imagery and quantitatively
derived values. Most quantitative products are

processed on the large-scale NOAA central
computer systems.

Quantitative Products

The basic quantitative or numerical
products produced are atmospheric soundings, sea
surface temperatures, global radiation budget,
low-level wind vectors, composite mapped
imagery, image data bases, and atmospheric
ozone. The products are disseminated through
computer data bases, off-line media for archives
(usually computer-compatible tape), facsimile
for telephone-circuit transmission for receipt
on standard facsimile recorders, global
telecommunications system (GTS) teletype
transmission, and point-to-point digital
transmission of data of up to 50,000 bit/s
(circuit rates depend on the modem capacity,
usually at 300-9600 bit/s rates).

Soundings. Atmospheric soundings are
extracted from measurements made by the
TIROS operational vertical sounder (TOVS). A
TOVS system is comprised of a high-resolution
infrared radiation sounder (HIRS/2), a microwave
sounding unit (MSU), and a stratospheric
sounding unit (SSU). The SSU instrument is
provided by the United Kingdom. The TOVS
soundings provide three-dimensional observations
of the atmosphere from the surface to
approximately 65.5 km. The TOVS processing
software system combines and converts the raw
radiance retrievals of the three atmospheric
sounders into operational products consisting
of:

1) Layer mean temperatures for 40
pressure levels surface, 100-0.10 mbar
(up to 65.5 km).

2) Layer precipitable water
amounts for three layers of surface to
700, 700-500, and above 500 mbar.

3) Clear radiance values for the
twenty HIRS/2 channels, for MSU channels
and three SSU channels.

4)   Numerical sounding coefficients used in the statistical sounding approach.

Soundings are produced at a spatial density of 250 km in a global array. Approximately 600 sounding retrievals are generated from each orbit. The two polar-orbiting satellites provide a total of 16,000 soundings/day. The TOVS soundings are transmitted over the GTS at a spatial resolution of 500 km. Derived soundings are also copied to the NOAA computer data base in a conventional radio atmospheric observation balloon (RAOB) format for direct input to the National Weather Service forecast models.

There are over 200 worldwide users of TOVS sounding data. The principal user is the National Weather Serivce's National Meteorological Center (NMC), which utilizes the data to supplement conventional sounding data input to both the hemispheric and global numerical weather models. Of particular importance are those satellite soundings collected over the northeastern Pacific Ocean during the primary 1200 and 0000 Greenwich time observation periods.

Special users of sounding data include NASA, the University of Wisconsin, and Department of Defense agencies. Also, near real-time, Earth-located and calibrated intermediate radiance values are provided to the British Meteorological Office over the DPSS communications system. Raw data, quality control information, and Earth-located calibrated data are provided to the research community. All of the data input, intermediate products, and processed soundings are retained in the NESDIS archive.

Sea Surface Temperatures. Observations of sea surface temperature (SST) are obtained from the advanced high-resolution radiometer (AVHRR) sensors flown on the polar satellites. Multichannel techniques employing the two visible and three infrared channels of the AVHRR are used to produce SST observations for both day and night coverage. Global observations are produced in the computer at a spacing of 25 km. In coastal United States regions, the SST resolution is processed at 8 km to improve the depiction of the ocean thermal gradients vital to the fishing industry. Also, the high-resolution sea surface temperature values are used to determine the edge boundaries of currents such as the Gulf Stream and to detect sea ice.

During the SST processing steps, detection of clouds is accomplished using visible channels during the day and the thermal infrared (IR) window-channel relationships at night. Atmospheric attenuation correction is done using multiple IR window channels. Between 20,000 and 40,000 SST observations are produced each day and stored along with the time, latitude, and longitude in a user-accessible data base. The number of observations collected each day varies because of the variability of cloud cover.

A file containing grid points at every 1° latitude/longitude intersection between 70° south and 70° north is used as the principal source for producing analyzed contour fields. There are three 50 km mesoscale analyzed fields covering the United States 200 mile coastal conservation and management zone. These fields cover the Atlantic and Pacific coasts and the waters between Hawaii and Alaska. A global 250 km monthly mean field of satellite temperature observations is maintained in the NESDIS archive. A 100 km analyzed filed is produced daily and stored on the NOAA computer data base for access by computer terminal users.

Observations of SST are placed in an accessible observation data base within 8 h of satellite data transmission. Sea surface temperature values for every 2.5° of latitude/longitude are transmitted twice per day via GTS at 0900 and 2100Z. All of the analyzed data fields are averaged to generate weekly contour charts. Monthly contour charts are produced for distribution on a subscription

basis to users by the Satellite Data Services
Division.

Satellite sea surface temperature
observations augment ship and buoy observations
used by the National Weather Service (NWS) and
the Navy Fleet Numerical Oceanographic Center.
SST data are used by the National Hurricane
Center in Miami, Fla., for monitoring conditions
conducive to hurricane formation and, in some
cases, the probable storm track. Private
fishing companies use the analyzed fields to aid
in the location of tuna and salmon fishing
grounds. In addition, the isotherm contour
charts are used in weather forecasting and
physical and biological oceanographic and
meteorological applications by universities,
corporations, and private individuals.

Low-Level Wind Vectors. Measurements
of low-level winds over the ocean are obtained
three times a day for the region 50° north
to 50° south, 20° - 180° west using
data from the GOES-east and west satellites
Approximately 1200 low-level wind measurements
(picture-pair winds) are automatically
calculated each day. These are quality
controlled manually before being stored in the
data base along with high-level wind
measurements. Middle (10-20,000 ft) and high
(above 30,000 ft) wind vectors are computed
manually using an interactive computer system to
compare successive half-hourly images.

The low-level picture-pair winds are
derived from 8 km resolution infrared images
stored in a computer data base. The pair of IR
images 30 min apart are selected by analyzing
the picture quality and the proximity of picture
times to the synoptic observation times. The
selected pair is precisely registered using
cross correlation applied to landmark features
and prominent surface thermal features. Low-
level winds are extracted at preselected
locations spaced 250 km apart. Clouds having
equivalent blackbody tempertures greater than
the 700 mbar air temperature are examined for
motion using cross correlation and cloud

displacements obtained from the correlation
matricies which are translated into Earth-
location wind estimates. Automatic wind
editing is accomplished by comparing the wind
estimates with the latest 850 mbar wind analysis
from NMC and rejecting those winds that deviate
substantially from the NMC field. A smoothed
wind field is constructed from the remaining
satellite winds. A facsimile map is produced
showing the composite of winds derived from both
satellites.

Wind measurements are used in numerical
weather and ocean analyses and in forecast
models operated by the National Meteorological
Center, the Air Force Global Weather Center, and
the Navy Fleet Numerical Oceanographic Center.
Wind vectors are computed to coincide with the
0000, 1200, and 1800 Greenwich mean time
observation periods. Users worldwide receive
the data via the GTS and retrospective users can
access the data through the NESDIS archive
service.

Heat Budget. The global radiation
budget is analyzed from polar-orbiting satellite
AVHRR data. Measurements of daytime and
nighttime outgoing long-wave flux and incoming
available and absorbed solar radiation are made
using infrared and visible radiances averaged
for 50 km regions. These measurements are
combined with time, Earth-location, angular
measurements of satellite, and solar attitude to
form an initial data base for analysis.
Radiation budget parameters for one complete day
are composed to derive daytime and nighttime
long-wave flux. The absorbed solar energy is
measured from the difference between the solar
constant and the reflected radiation obtained
from the visible data. Radiation budget
measurements are then mapped into 2.5°
latitude/longitude fields (250 km resolution)
and stored on a monthly archive file. The
global radiation budget fields are important to
long-range forecasting and climate research.
They are used by the Long-Range Prediction Group
of the National Weather Service.

Ozone. One channel of the high-resolution infrared sounder (HIRS) is sensitive to total ozone. A regression technique uses this and other TOVS channels to produce a total ozone value (dobson units) as part of the routine temperature retrieval process. A total ozone value is produced along with the TOVS temperature retrieval (about 600/orbit) and is available on the NOAA central computer data base. The Climate Analysis Center in NWS accesses the total ozone values daily to produce analyses of total ozone for climate studies. The polar satellite launched in December 1984, carries the solar backscatter ultraviolet radiometer to monitor ozone directly.

Images

Satellite image products are produced for dissemination over facsimile networks in near-real time. The image products are derived from visible and infrared sensor data input from both the geostationary and polar operational satellite systems. The data from the polar-orbiting satellites are transformed to polar stereographic and mercator map projections to form global orbit composites. Sectors of mapped polar satellite data, as well as sectors of the geostationary VISSR data, are merged with the appropriate Earth grids and coastlines and formated as facsimile output for dissemination. Users can receive the data through a GOESTAP facsimile circuit or over the Weather Facsimile Communication System (WEFAX) operated on-board the GOES satellites. Over 435 sectors are broadcast on a fixed schedule each day over the WEFAX system. There are over 200 GOESTAP users in the system. The major image product users include the Department of Defense and associated agencies, National Weather Service, Department of Agriculture, and numerous private sector users in the media, aviation, and weather consulting. The polar stereographic and mercator mapped data composites from the polar satellite data and 8 km infrared VISSR images from the three hourly synoptic times are retained on computer tapes in the NESDIS archive facility.

Fig. 1   Thermal gradients along the Atlantic coastline.

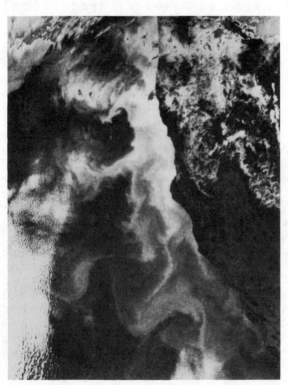

Fig. 2   Cold water
upwelling along
the U.S. Pacific
coastline.

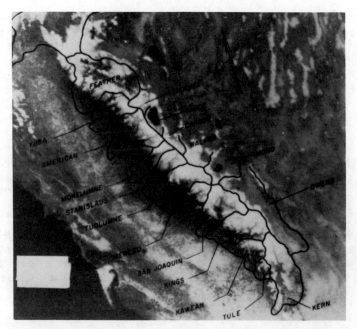

Fig. 3   River basin boundaries in California.

Polar   Satellite   Imagery.   Polar
satellite infrared imagery is used to observe
gradients in   sea   surface   temperatures   and
specifically to monitor ocean currents, thermal
boundaries, and upwelling. The NOAA-7 AVHRR
image (Fig. 1) is enhanced to show sea surface
temperature gradients over the northeastern
United States. In this image, the warmest
waters of the Gulf Stream show up as the darkest
tongue of water in the Atlantic. Several large,
darker swirls represent warm eddies north of the
main current. The lighter shading along the
coast is colder continential shelf water. The
western enhanced image (Fig. 2) shows cold water
upwelling along the northern California
coastline, indicated by the almost white
shading. Numerous thermal boundaries can be
identified by the image. Ocean navigation,
commercial fishing,   and many associated
industries benefit from satellite sea surface
temperature analyses.

Snow cover over North America and the
Northern Hemisphere is mapped using visible

imagery from the NOAA polar-orbiting satellites.
Accurately estimated snow cover can be
quantified for use by hydrologists, utilities
planners, climate researchers, and agricultural
interest. Individual river basins can be mapped
for the extent of snow cover (Fig. 3 illustrates
typical coverlays showing river basin boundaries
in California).

The visible channel 1 and the near-infrared
channel 2 of the NOAA satellites AVHRR
instrument can be combined to produce an image
that is a measure of "greenness" called the
vegetation index. The diferenceinresponse
between the two channels increases with
increasing chlorophyll activity. The darkest
areas on an image are regions of most active
biomass, where this response difference is
greatest.   The lightest areas are where

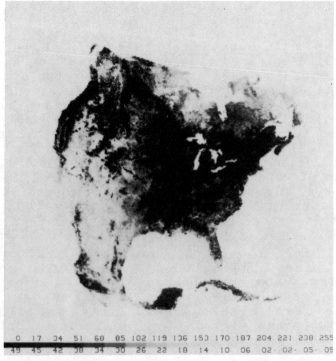

Fig. 4 Normalized vegetative index greenest 6 day composite.

chlorophyll activity is lower.   Figure 4 is a
6 day composite of vegetation index over the
U.S. (1982, days 194-199 or June 12-17). Using
imagery such as Fig. 4 allows analysts to
monitor the health of crops on a worldwide
basis.

          Both civilian and military marine
interest are highly concerned about position
and movements of ice and ice boundaries in polar
regions and over inland navigable waters.   The
NOAA series polar-orbiting satellites provide
high-resolution 1 km imagery used in ice
monitoring. Oceanographers in NESDIS and the
NOAA/Navy Joint Ice Center provide ice analyses
derived from these images over the Great Lakes,
the northwest Atlantic, the Gulf of Alaska, and
the Bering Sea. Figure 5 shows ice in the
Bering sea and western Alaska.

          GOES Satellite Imagery. Multiple sectors
from the visible and infrared imagery relayed

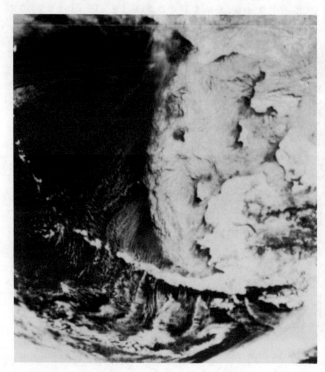

Fig. 5 Ice
extent in Bering
Sea.

from the GOES east and west spacecraft are produced at the NESDIS Central Data Distribution Facility. The National Weather Service uses the imagery to incorporate satellite-observed changes in synoptic and mesoscale weather features into its analyses, forecasts, and warning cycles. Private users tap the same imagery via telephone line facsimile circuits from distribution points at seven National Weather Service Satellite Field Service Stations.

GOES imagery is used for monitoring the formation, growth, and position of extreme or severe weather phenomena that may be hazardous to life and property. Also, repeated satellite views of hurricanes and lesser tropical disturbances has improved our knowledge and ability to more accurately determine their movement and strength. Figure 6 is a visible sector showing superhurricane Allen in the Gulf of Mexico in August 1980.

In the spring and summer, GOES imagery is used to detect the onset of rapidly developing

Fig. 6 Hurricane Allen in the Gulf of Mexico.

thunderstorms that can produce tornadoes and
other severe weather.   Figure 7 shows a late
evening view of the V-shaped cloud wedge with
overshooting cloud turrets of convection that is
a signature of such devastating storms.   This
satellite view of April 10, 1979, was recorded
when violent tornadoes were on the ground
causing widespread destruction in the north
Texas city of Wichita Falls.

Special enhancement curves can be
implemented on GOES digital infrared data to
highlight cloud or surface features of varying
temperatures, a method called thermal slicing.
This scheme enables meteorologists to isolate
intense convective activity for estimating heavy
precipitation.   The enhanced GOES imagery is
used operationally by NESDIS meteorologists to
support the National Flash Flood Program.   The
areas of most-rapidly increasing enhancement in
a thunderstorm complex indicate the coldest,
highest, and most active convection.   In Fig. 8,
a massive convective complex that produced

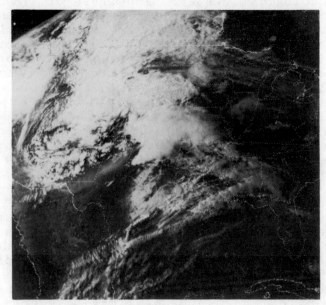

Fig. 7   Violet thunderstorm development over
Texas.

widespread flooding in Tennessee and Kentucky is clearly outlined by the special enhancement curve. The most active areas are under the brightest white shading superimposed over the dark outline of the storm cloud boundaries.

By using a different enhancement curve that accentuates surface temperatures near freezing, GOES imagery can be used to monitor the movement of the freeze line over Florida during cold waves (Fig. 9). The timing of the southward progression of freezing temperatures by satellite imagery for fruit-frost forecasting can mean big economic savings to the citrus industry.

Analytical Products

Quantitative data are used in conjunction with image products to provide a number of analytical services to enhance the value of the satellite data delivered to the user community. A staff of meteorologists, expert in satellite data interpretation, work around the clock to provide analytical support to the National Meteorological Center. The areas of principal support include aviation forecasting, upper air analysis (particularly in areas devoid of conventionally observed data), quantitative precipition estimates, issuance of tropical storm bulletins, warning to the aviation industry of detected volcanic ash clouds, jet stream analysis, and detection of rapidly developing coastal winter storms. Interactive computer systems are used to superimpose numerical or analyzed fields on satellite cloud imagery, mutually enhancing the utility of both information forms.

Time-Critical Operations. Satellite products and services are used in support of near-real-time activities. There often are tight and rigid deadlines to be met where delays in data processing result in the loss of the utility of the satellite data. For example, the forecast models run by the National Meteorological Center have rigid synoptic cut off times for data input covering specific

Fig. 8 Image enhancement used to detect corrective intensity.

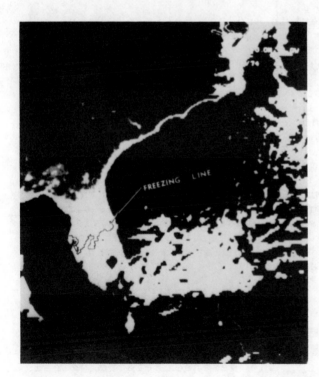

Fig. 9 Freeze line detection using GOES IR data.

geographic areas. The limited fine mesh (LFM)
model is scheduled to run for 1-1/3 h after the
1200 and 0000 Greenwich synoptic cutoff times.
The spectral hemisphere model runs at 4 h after
the same synoptic time periods. Since the LFM
confines the forecast to the continental United
States and adjacent ocean areas, data over the
northeastern Pacific is extremely critical to
the forecast. This area is almost devoid of
conventional observations and thus dependence on
satellite data is high. Similar deadlines must
be met in the preparation of the
satellite/derived wind and moisture data fields
used in the initial analysis for the principal
forecast models.

All of the facsimile and WEFAX sector
broadcasts are transmitted on a fixed-time
schedule where as little as a 30 s delay results
in data loss. The satellite image data products
rapidly lose value with time, as most of these
products are used in near-real-time event
monitoring functions.

Improvement in Product Delivery. Polar
satellite orbit times coupled with data
processing delays make it impossible to provide
the necessary data coverage over the
northeastern Pacific in time for the critical
LFM data cutoff. Beginning with NOAA-G, the
polar spacecraft will be configured to fly an
orbit nearer noon so that the spacecraft will
orbit over the northeastern Pacific Ocean in
time for the 0000Z and 1200Z LFM forecast runs.
At the same time, NESDIS is upgrading the ingest
and preprocessing computers with more advanced
systems to enable the preprocessing and archive
cycles to be run in better than half the time of
the current systems. The goal is to provide the
satellite products to the direct users and to
the NMC data bases in less than 60 min after
receipt of data from the CDA station.

Future

Software is being prepared to include
(along with the aforementioned satellite
products) the VISSR atmospheric sounder (VAS)
data processing, the Defense Meteorological

Satellite Program (DMSP) microwave thermal and image sounding data, and the ultraviolet backscatter radiometer and Earth radiation budget instrument data from the advanced TIROS-N system. In addition, initial support is being added to the search and rescue system operations to our array of processing. NOAA recently upgraded their central computer facilities to include a Class VI vector processing system and have replaced the older large-scale systems with more advanced technology. The NESDIS upgrade will centralize the direct ingest and data preparation steps from both the polar and geostationary satellites into a single operating system to better meet forecast deadlines and increase the effectiveness of the data collection mission.[‡] This system will include real-time data base management system to service interactive users and provide an archive data base.

Conclusion

Over the past 24 years the quantity, quality, and reliability of satellite coverage has improved greatly. Since 1966, the entire Earth has been photographed at least once daily on a continuous basis. The data are now being used routinely by meteorologists and environmental scientists throughout the world. NOAA-next and GOES-next specifications have been issued and the procurements are proceeding to assure a continuity and improvement of the present service.

[‡] NOAA's three IBM 360/195 central processing units are being replaced with NAS 9040 processors. At NESDIS, SEL32/55 (polar ingest) and GTE IS1000 (GOES ingest) mini-computer systems being replaced by interconnected multiple IBM 4381 systems.

The Economic Benefits of Operational Environmental Satellites

W. John Hussey*

National Oceanic and Atmospheric Administration, Washington, D.C.

Abstract

Satellite observations of the atmosphere on a global scale began 25 years ago. In the intervening period, satellite sensors and operational techniques for the use of the data have evolved to a high degree of proficiency. This paper identifies and attempts to quantify, to the extent possible, many of the current benefits and uses derived from the United States' operational environmental satellite system. Since the initial paper on this subject was published in 1978, there has been considerable interest in the evolving benefits of environmental satellites and the primary benefits discussed in the 1978 and 1983 papers have been updated and included here. In addition, several other unique uses of environmental satellite data are discussed. The benefits discussed herein are evidence that the operational environmental satellite has become an irreplaceable weather and ocean observing tool. These satellites are making major contributions toward the saving of lives and property from natural disasters and improving the efficiency of many sectors of our national economy.

Introduction

Operational Environmental Satellite Program Mission Objectives

The U.S. environmental satellites are operated by the National Oceanic and Atmospheric Administration's (NOAA) National Environmental Satellite, Data, and Information

This paper is declared a work of the U.S. Government and therefore is in the public domain.

*Chief, Satellite Services Division, National Environmental Satellite, Data, and Information Service.

Service (NESDIS). The mission objectives of this
operational satellite program include:
1) Monitoring the atmosphere regularly and reliably on
a global basis, day and night, with direct readout to
local ground stations around the globe within radio range
of the satellites.
2) Sounding the atmosphere regularly on a global basis
and providing quantitative data for numerical weather
prediction services.
3) Continuous monitoring of environmental features in
the western hemisphere and the collecting and relaying of
environmental data from remote platforms such as buoys,
ships, automatic stations, aircraft, and balloons.
4) Applying environmental satellite data for the
purpose of improving environmental services.

Geostationary Satellite System

NOAA's Geostationary Operational Environmental
Satellite (GOES) system includes two satellites, the
ground data acquisition station and a centralized data
distribution system. The first satellite in this system,
NASA's Synchronous Meteorological Satellite (SMS-1), a
prototype for GOES, was launched May 17, 1974. The
operational system consists of two satellites: GOES-West
located over the equator at 135°W longitude and GOES-East
located at 75°W longitude. GOES-West observes North
America and the Pacific Ocean west of Hawaii and GOES-East
observes North and South America and most of the Atlantic
Ocean. These geostationary spacecraft are in circular
orbits at an altitude of approximately 35,800 km (22,240
miles).
The primary instrument carried by GOES is the visible
infrared spin-scan radiometer (VISSR) atmospheric sounder
(VAS). This instrument, first carried into space on
GOES-4, provides the traditional visual and infrared
imagery of cloud cover and the Earth's surface. In
addition, VAS provides measurements of the infrared
radiation that can be used, with known atmospheric
properties, to calculate the atmospheric temperature
profiles over selected geographic areas. It can also
produce images in multiple infrared (i.r.) spectral bands
instead of the single band produced by the VISSR. This
new capability is called multispectral imaging and has
proved very useful in depicting the amount, distribution,
and movement of water vapor at various levels.
The United States normally operates a GOES-East
spacecraft at 75°W and a GOES-West spacecraft at 135°W.

The GOES-East spacecraft visible and infrared spin-scan radiometer atmospheric sounder (VAS) failed on July 29, 1984. The spacecraft redundant optical encoder lamps failed after various cross-strapping configurations had been implemented. Thus, GOES-5 does not have image/sounder capabilities, but the weather facsimile data (WEFAX), data collection system (DCS), and space environmental monitor (SEM) systems are operational.

As a result of the failure of GOES-5, GOES-6 was moved from 135°W to a central location of 98°W to provide coverage for hurricane forecasting during the Atlantic hurricane season (June to October). During the nonhurricane season (October to June), the GOES-6 spacecraft was moved to 108°W to provide coverage of the fast-moving synoptic-scale systems moving into the U.S. west coast, the Alaskan coast, and Hawaii.

Two additional spacecraft in the current GOES series, GOES-G and -H are under construction. Improvements are being made with respect to operational reliability, including optical encoder bulbs designed to operate at lower voltages, parallel wiring paths added to critical VAS circuits, and redesigned data transmitters. GOES-G is scheduled for launch in early 1986 and GOES-H is planned to be launched in late 1986.

The United States is planning for the next generation geostationary system called GOES-Next to be launched in the 1989-90 time frame. The GOES-Next procurement includes three satellites with associated ground operations support equipment and an option for two additional satellites. A contractor is expected to be selected in the summer of 1985. The GOES-Next system is expected to have several major technical improvements over the current GOES series, some of which include:

1) Independent imaging and sounding by separate instruments. The two data sets would be available simultaneously.

2) Independent weather facsimile (WEFAX) transmission capability. WEFAX transmissions will not preempt the acquisition of imager/sounder data.

3) Earth location accuracy for imager and sounder data will be improved from 5 to 2 km.

4) Number of imaging channels will be increased to 5, which will improve the monitoring of atmospheric stability for severe storm forecasting.

5) Infrared channels will have improved their resolution (from 8 to 4 km) and their sensitivity to assist in monitoring location and development of severe storms.

6) Number of sounding channels will be increased from 12 to 14, permitting better temperature profile definition.

7) Spatial resolution of sounder channels will be improved from 14 to 7 km.

8) Channel sensitivity of the sounder will be improved.

9) Timeliness of sounding data will be improved because the sounder operations will be independent of the operation of other instruments on the satellite.

10) The space environment monitor (SEM) and data collection system (DCS) will remain essentially unchanged.

The VAS provides a full-disk view of the Earth every 30 min. More frequent images can be obtained at the sacrifice of spatial coverage. The visible channel provides high-resolution (about 1 km) daytime images. The infrared channel provides lower-resolution (about 8 km) day and night images. The GOES images are processed through the NESDIS Central Data Distribution Facility, either as a full-disk image or a sector of this full-disk image. These products are routed to the National Weather Service (NWS) Satellite Field Services Stations (SFSS) for analysis with further routing to NWS Forecast Offices (WSFO) and other users.

The SFSSs are located at Washington, D.C., Miami, Fla., Kansas City, Mo., San Francisco, Honolulu, Anchorage, and Slidell, La. Each SFSS provides regional analysis, interpretation, and distribution of the VAS images to meet a wide variety of environmental needs. An important service is the near-continuous viewing of the development and movement of severe weather systems such as hurricanes and thunderstorms. An extension of the GOES image distribution service is the "GOES-TAP" system. Established by NESDIS in 1975, "GOES-TAP" enables Federal, state, and local agencies, television stations, universities, and private industry to receive an inventory of GOES satellite images directly from the nearest SFSS. In addition, the GOES satellites broadcast environmental products to remote locations using the weather facsimile system (WEFAX). Over 200 stations in 34 countries receive the WEFAX broadcasts.

The GOES satellites also carry a data collection system (DCS) that collects and relays environmental data obtained by remotely located sensing platforms, such as river and rain gages, seismometers, tide gages, buoys, ships, aircraft, and automatic weather stations. Each operational GOES spacecraft can accommodate data from 12,000 platforms each hour. The data are normally transmitted in a self-timed mode or upon interrogation by the satellite. The data may also be transmitted under emergency conditions in which the platform transmitter is triggered whenever an observed parameter exceeds a predetermined threshold value. About 4800 platforms now provide environmental data to users in the United States and Canada. The geostationary satellite DCS provides a near-instantaneous source of information for many applications, such as river level and flood monitoring and forest fire index measurements.

Also included in the GOES instrument complement is a space environment monitor (SEM) that provides measurements of solar activity for detecting solar flares, the intensity of the solar wind, and the strength and direction of the Earth's magnetic field. The SEM data included in the satellite telemetry data stream are received at the NOAA Space Environment Services Center (SESC) in Boulder, Colo. These data are separated from the telemetry stream and processed in the SESC data base. When significant solar events are detected, the SESC issues warnings to a number of users throughout the United States. Routine forecasts of solar activity and its implications (such as interference with high-frequency radio transmissions) are also distributed by SESC.

Polar Orbiting Satellite System

NOAA's operational polar-orbiting environmental satellite (POES) system is called the TIROS-N/NOAA series and consists of two satellites and the ground data acquisition and processing systems. The first spacecraft in this current series called TIROS-N was launched on Oct. 13, 1978. There are two polar-orbiting satellites currently in operation providing global coverage at different times of the day. NOAA-6 is in a morning orbit (0700 local equator-crossing time descending) and NOAA-9 is in an afternoon orbit (1420 local equator-crossing time ascending). These satellites are in sun-synchronous orbits at altitudes of 806 and 852 km, respectively. Their orbital period is 102 min, which equates to 14.2 orbits/day. NOAA-8, a morning orbit spacecraft, failed in June 1984.

NOAA-8, the first of the advanced TIROS-N (ATN) series, was the first American meteorological satellite designed to help international search and rescue missions. The second NOAA SARSAT-equipped satellite, NOAA-9, was launched in December 1984 and is functioning normally. The ATN/SARSAT satellite can detect distress signals from downed aircraft or ships in trouble and relay accurate information to ground stations that then alert

rescue teams. The satellite search and rescue system can
pinpoint the emergency site within 2-5 km. The search and
rescue capability is the result of an international
agreement between the United States, Canada, France, and
the Soviet Union.

Five additional NOAA spacecraft are either built or
being built by RCA Astro-Electronics. These five
spacecraft (NOAA-D, -G, -H, -I, and -J) are planned to be
launched at a rate of about one per year through 1989. A
continuation of the advanced TIROS-N series is planned
with the procurement of NOAA-K, -L, and -M to provide
polar-orbiting services through 1992.

Some technical improvements under consideration
include:

1) A 1.6 μm channel will be added to the imager. This
channel will be used in a time-share mode with the 3.8 μm
channel and will provide a capability to discriminate
between snow and clouds for snow cover mapping.

2) The stratospheric sounding unit (SSU) and the
microwave sounding unit (MSU) will be replaced by an
advanced microwave sounder unit (AMSU) to be developed by
the United States with the contribution of a major
component by the United Kingdom. The 20 channel AMSU will
improve the capability for determining temperature
profiles in cloudy areas.

Other systems such as the space environment monitor
(SEM), ozone monitor (SBUV), search and rescue system and
the high-resolution and automatic picture transmission
(HRPT and APT) systems will essentially retain the
capabilities utilized today. The spacecraft command and
telemetry system currently utilizing the vhf spectrum may
be shifted to the S-band spectrum.

The TIROS-N/NOAA series utilizes four primary
instrument subsystems. These are the advanced very-high-
resolution radiometer (AVHRR), TIROS operational vertical
sounder (TOVS), data collection system (DCS), and space
environment monitor (SEM).

The AVHRR provides visible and infrared image data for
real-time transmission to direct readout users and for
storage on the spacecraft tape recorders for later
playback. The AVHRR consists of five channels providing
data on daytime cloud cover, snow and ice coverage,
nighttime cloud cover, and sea surface temperatures. The
direct readout high-resolution picture transmission (HRPT)
has a resolution of 1 km in all spectral channels. The
automatic picture transmission (APT) provides an
undistorted resolution of 4 km. There are over 1000 APT
receiving stations located in approximately 123 countries

throughout the world. At least 80 HRPT receiving stations
are operating in 50 countries.

Also available is onboard recording of the 4 km
resolution data that provides global area coverage (GAC).
Selected onboard recording of the 1 km resolution data is
available as local area coverage (LAC). The recorded data
are played back to the NOAA command and data acquisition
(CDA) stations located near Fairbanks, Alas. and Wallops
Island, Va. The data are subsequently transmitted via a
domestic communications satellite to the NOAA central data
processing facility in Suitland, Md.

The TIROS operational vertical sounder (TOVS) includes
three complementary sounding instruments. These are:
high-resolution infrared sounder (HIRS/2), stratospheric
sounding unit (SSU), and microwave sounding unit (MSU).

The HIRS/2 provides data that permit calculation of
temperature profiles from the surface to 0.1 mb
(~215,000 ft), the water vapor content of the atmosphere,
and the total ozone content. Data from the TOVS
instruments are also broadcast via the direct readout
transmission links. The SSU instrument is provided by the
United Kingdom.

The data collection system (DCS) is provided by
France. It is called the ARGOS data collection and
platform location system. The ARGOS system provides a
means to locate and collect data from moving platforms.
The platform data are stored and relayed to the Suitland
center where it is separated and relayed to the CNES
Toulouse Space Center in France. There, the data are
processed, Earth located, and relayed to the ultimate user.

The TIROS SEM includes three detectors that measure
solar proton flux, alpha particle and electron flux
density, energy spectrum, and total particulate energy
distribution at spacecraft altitude. The data from the
SEM are stripped out of the spacecraft telemetry stream
and transmitted to NOAA's Space Environment Services
Center (SESC) in Boulder, Colo. These data are used to
monitor the state of solar activity, which has a
significant effect on terrestrial communications,
electrical power distribution, etc.

Activities Benefiting From Operational Environmental Satellite Programs

Following is a synopsis of several specific examples
of the economic benefits and also intangible benefits,
such as lives saved, that are derived directly from
operational environmental satellite data or from a

combination of satellite and "conventional" weather data.
It should be recognized that many of these benefits are
possible because of the <u>operational</u> nature of the NOAA
environmental satellites. In other words, users can
depend on the availability of these satellite-derived data
today, tomorrow, and in future years. Therefore, users
can afford to invest in special data handling and
processing equipment, software, and applications
techniques with confidence that these satellites will be
available to provide the data they require year after year.

Ocean Current Navigation for Fuel Savings

Use of the swift Gulf Stream currents to increase a
ship's northbound steaming speed is an old idea, but
utilizing that idea has not been easy. The swiftness and
great variability of the Gulf Stream position creates many
uncertainties and hazards to navigation. Much of the
uncertainty is created by eddies and meandering of the
Stream. The meanders can be 250 miles across and the
stream axis can move as much as 60 miles in a week.
A 1975 Gulf Stream navigation experiment conducted
jointly by the Exxon Company and NOAA showed that
significant fuel savings could be realized by using timely
satellite analyses of the Stream position for oil tankers
navigating along the eastern seaboard. An improved NOAA
satellite capability, operationally available with the
launch of NOAA-2 in 1972, was infrared measurement of sea
surface temperatures. Enhanced infrared images
representing sea surface temperature differences clearly
delineated the warm Gulf Stream in contrast to the colder
shelf water. The joint Exxon/NOAA experiment was
conducted to test whether using satellite-derived Gulf
Stream analyses could improve navigation enough to realize
significant fuel savings. NOAA analyzed the satellite
infrared images of the Gulf Stream's western boundary
(called the "western wall") and estimated the axis of
maximum current velocities relative to it. Exxon arranged
for radio broadcast of the information to their tankers at
sea.
Eleven Exxon tankers, steaming from the Gulf of Mexico
to east coast ports and returning, participated in the
experiment. Five were instructed to follow the usual
navigational practices, which used or avoided the Gulf
Stream in a relatively random manner. The other six were
to use the NOAA satellite analyses for their navigation.
In other words, the tankers were to transit within the
Gulf Stream northward and avoid the Gulf Stream on their
southbound journey.

The seven-month study showed a very definite fuel
savings for the six vessels using the NOAA data. Exxon,
assuming a total of 15 tankers navigating by satellite
data, projected savings amounting to 31,500 barrels of
fuel oil. Using a 1975 cost of $11.50/barrel, the Exxon
study reported a potential annual fuel savings of around
$360,000 for their company alone. Assuming a 1982 cost of
$30/barrel, the estimated annual savings would be around
$945,000 for 15 tankers navigating the Gulf Stream
effectively. The use of satellite-derived Gulf Stream
position data is now standard navigating procedure for
ships of the Exxon fleet. Applications of this
information by all coastal traffic of the U.S. Merchant
Marine is possible and could result in significant savings
of U.S. fuel resources. The analyses are made available
by automatic telecopier and radio broadcasts.

A similar product is available for Gulf of Mexico
navigation. A clockwise flow of warm water from the
Yucatan Straits, around the Gulf, and out through the
Florida Straits is quite strong. The coastward edge of
the warm water in this "loop current" is marked by a
thermal gradient that is great enough in the cold winter
months to be discerned in the satellite infrared imagery.
The NOAA Miami Satellite Field Services Station produces a
Loop Current Bulletin (November to May) that aids ships in
the Gulf of Mexico to use the loop current for assistance
in a manner similar to the use of the Gulf Stream
described above. These analyses are also available by
automatic telecopier.

The Crowley Towing and Transportation Company of
Jacksonville, Fla., operates 60 vessels in the West Indies
and Gulf of Mexico and has stated that accurate knowledge
of the Gulf Stream and loop currents is vital to their
operations. An on-going fuel conservation program has
been enhanced by this satellite information with fuel
savings of 20-40% obtainable when their 9000 hp tugs are
able to reduce engine rpm by 18%, with only a small
reduction in speed. They are experiencing savings of up
to $2000 per steaming day on their line-haul tugs. Other
Crowley barge sailings, returning north from Cuba via the
Santaren Channel and utilizing the Gulf Stream to the
utmost, are improving their average speed from 9.5 to 12.0
knots, which on a biweekly basis saves 8 h/voyage. This
totals 192 h/year or 8 days/year at an average equipment
operating cost of $15,000/day.

Commercial Fishing Industry

The NOAA Satellite Field Services Station (SFSS) in
San Francisco produces charts derived primarily from the

polar orbiting satellites' AVHRR infrared imagery
depicting the location of thermal boundaries or "fronts"
as part of an operational sea surface temperature
analysis. It has been well documented by marine
biologists and fishermen that certain species of fish are
temperature sensitive. Albacore (blue fin tuna) and coho
(silver) salmon, the principal commercial fish found along
the west coast, tend to congregate in nutrient-rich waters
in the vicinity of thermal fronts. Albacore are found at
temperatures of 16°-20°C, while salmon prefer temperatures
of 11°-13°C.

Since 1975, NOAA has been issuing sea surface
temperature (SST) frontal charts from the San Francisco
SFSS to aid fishermen in locating these "productive"
areas. In 1981 the SFSS began producing a sea surface
thermal analysis incorporating satellite-observed thermal
features. Geographically, the area originally covered by
the charts extended from 34°N to 49°N and from the coast
to 128°W. Since 1981, only one area has been charted and
that extends from 28°N to 40°N and west to 136°W. It is
known that the food chain is often concentrated along
these fronts, usually as a result of the seasonal
upwelling process that takes place along the west coast of
the United States. Charts produced when skies are cloud
free have greatly assisted commercial albacore and salmon
fishermen in locating fish productive areas. The results
were so encouraging that the program was expanded to cover
most of the west coast.

The infrared images, received up to four times daily,
are enhanced using computerized tables to assist in the
identification of the thermal gradients. The changes in
temperature are represented by changes in the tones of
gray in the enhanced satellite image. The frontal
positions are analyzed directly on the image and then
transferred to a marine navigational base chart. These
analyses are produced twice a week. The latest chart is
transmitted twice daily by radio facsimile from Point
Reyes, Calif., and by automatic telephone telecopier.

Satellite images are also transmitted twice per day to
the Seattle Northwest Ocean Service Center (NOSC) of the
National Ocean Service. This unit produces a
satellite-derived thermal boundary and sea surface
temperature analysis extending from 40°N to 52°N that is
distributed to Pacific Northwest fishermen via a
telecopier system, mailing list, and direct telephone
briefings.

An example of how the fishing community has received
this product is indicated in a quote from Ref. 1 prepared

by the Pacific Marine Fisheries Commission as their input
to the nationwide "Eastland Fisheries Survey," a report to
Congress dated May 1977.[2] This report states
(underscore added):

"Commercial salmon and albacore trollers emphasized that
the federal government should not be involved in
developing new equipment and methods for locating fish
with one exception. They support the use of satellite
pictures which display temperature gradients and
indicate that the federal government should continue to
use existing satellites to provide this information.
Present methods for developing and providing advisories
are adequate and existing advisories for the albacore
fleet should continue. More emphasis should be placed
on provision of practical information such as water
temperature, weather, and currents...."

The commercial fishermen are beset with a number of
problems that include changing and more stringent
regulations and increasing fuel costs. By delineating
those areas that are often fish productive through the use
of infrared satellite imagery, a fisheries management tool
is available whereby commercial fishing can become more
efficient and thus more cost effective. Fishermen can
disperse over larger areas when productive frontal
locations are known, thus helping to avoid overfishing
small areas.

During the initial experiment in 1975, it was
estimated that approximately 200 salmon and albacore
fishing vessels were able to save $580,000 in fuel costs
as a result of using satellite data. The albacore fishery
has the most direct benefit from the satellite data since
they are very temperature oriented. The salmon industry
benefits to a lesser extent. Fred Jurick, of the Marine
Advisory-Extension Service at Humbolt State University in
Arcata, Calif., was a pioneer in the use of satellite data
to directly support fishermen. Mr. Jurick correlated
catches of albacore and salmon of $2000-14,000 directly to
the use of the satellite-derived thermal front charts.
One commercial salmon troller stated that he caught an
extra $10,000-12,000 of fish (which was about one-third of
his total seasonal catch) as a direct result of using the
thermal front charts.

If one uses the estimates of the National Marine
Fisheries Service and places a modest savings of 10% on
the fuel bill for each of 1000 fishing vessels in
operation off the west coast, the annual fuel savings for
the fleet is $440,000. If one then adds a "catch
advantage" of $2000 worth of fish per vessel (approxi-

mately 2 tons of albacore) due to time saved and improved
location of the fish, one has an annual benefit of
$2,440,000 to the fishing industry on the west coast.
This figure is conservative since there are more than 1000
vessels fishing off the west coast.

In Alaska, the weekly sea surface temperature (SST)
charts are distributed by the Anchorage Satellite Field
Services Station (SFSS) to approximately 200 users of
which 65% are commercial fishermen/processors, 15% Federal
and state agencies, 10% oil industry, and 10% research
organizations. These SST charts provide guidance to
commercial fishermen and fisheries researchers concerning
the expected arrival of commercial species to Alaskan
waters: herring (SST 4°C), red salmon (SST 7°C) in
Bristol Bay, silver salmon (SST 11-13°C) in Southeast
Alaska, and pink salmon (SST 11°C) near Kodiak Island,
thus saving travel time, labor, and fuel costs. This
information is being used for local fish inventory and
migration studies and fish harvest forecasting.

NOAA sea surface temperature and ice condition charts
derived from polar-orbiting satellite data have saved an
Alaskan herring processing plant an estimated
$7000-8000/day in wages and fuel costs. Using these data,
the company determines where it should send its floating
processing plant for herring runs. Multiplied by 8-10
processors over a month's time, the savings are
substantial. Commercial fishing for silver salmon around
southeast Alaska has also been enhanced by the location of
the 11°C isotherm. The catch increased from 50 to 200
salmon a day; again trolling costs (fuel, equipment, and
time) are significantly reduced.

Other Alaskan users are the king crab fishermen in the
southern Bering Sea and Bristol Bay. In 1980, the king
crab fishermen lost more than $3 million in crab pots due
to untimely ice formation. These fishermen now use the
satellite-derived ice charts to determine when to retrieve
their pots prior to ice formation.

On the east coast, the swordfish is one of the few
temperature-sensitive fish in the Atlantic. Swordfish
prefer areas with temperatures of 13-25°C. The east coast
fishermen supplement satellite-derived data with
information on water depth and the migration routes of the
swordfish. The president of the Swordfishermens'
Association stated: "Receiving these charts has resulted
in a tremendous savings of time. We used to spend up to
five days looking for the fish, and now we can go right to
the place where the fish are located. When you figure
that most boats will use from 20 to 50 gallons of fuel an

hour, you can recognize the savings involved. There are about 500 vessels in the swordfish fishing fleet."

For completeness and comparative purposes, the dollar value of all pelagic and benthic fish species caught in the major fishing regions within U.S. waters in 1981 are shown in Table 1. Note that 62% of the dollar value of these species were caught in Alaskan and Californian waters. It is interesting to note that satellite data support to the fishing industry is utilized to a greater extent in Alaska and California than in any other major U.S. fishing area.

Internationally, NOAA satellite-derived sea surface temperature data are used to aid commercial tuna fishing by the Portuguese near the Azores and by a consortium of New Zealand companies and the Star-Kist Tuna Company fishing around northern New Zealand.

General Agriculture Industry

A study published in 1973 by the Space Science and Engineering Center of the University of Wisconsin showed that improved weather information and forecasting could provide large economic benefits to the agriculture industry. The purpose of the study was to determine the value of improved weather information and weather forecasting to farmers and agricultural processing industries in the United States. The study, funded by NASA, was undertaken to identify the production and processing operations that could be improved with accurate and timely information on changing weather patterns. Estimates were then made of the potential savings that could be realized with accurate information about the prevailing weather and short-term forecasts for up to 12 h. Improved weather information was defined to mean that a satellite observation not more than 1 h old was available and was the basis for a current weather description and an accurate 12 h forecast.

Table 1 Value of all pelagic and
benthic fish species caught in 1981

State	Value, $	Percent
Alaska	639,797,000	43
California	275,196,000	19
Maine	196,854,000	13
Louisiana	193,549,000	13
Texas	174,787,000	12
	1,480,183,000	100

The growing, marketing, and processing operations of the 20 most valuable crops in the United States in 1971 were studied to determine those operations that are sensitive to short-term weather forecasting. Agricultural extension specialists, research scientists, growers, and representatives of processing industries were consulted. Statistics from the U.S. Department of Agriculture (USDA) Crop Reporting Board show that the value for farm crops produced in the United States was more than $26 billion in 1971. The total value for crops surveyed in this report exceeds $24 billion and represents more than 92% of total U.S. crop value.

A detailed study was made of the operations in the production and processing of vegetable crops to obtain precise estimates of the value of improved weather information. Vegetable processing industries of the North Central Region (Wisconsin and Minnesota) were contacted through the Wisconsin Canners and Freezers Association and a special weather forecasting subcommittee was established. Meetings were held with industry personnel representing six large processors in these states to determine aspects of their operations that could be improved with more precise weather information and to develop procedures for estimating the value of this information. The company representatives utilized their field and processing plant records to determine losses resulting from unfavorable weather and to provide estimates of the savings that could have been realized with accurate short-term weather information. The entire agricultural process was considered in the survey from soil preparation and pesticide spraying operations to the harvesting of crops and the delivery of field products to consumers or food processors.

This survey of agricultural crops has indicated that improved weather information would have saved crop growers and processors $74,000,000 in 1971. Short-term forecasts utilizing satellite data are of particular value for crops that yield perishable products and require very precise production practices in order to ensure marketability. The annual weather related loss in agriculture in the U.S. is estimated to be $12 billion. It is estimated that protectable losses through improved 3-5 day weather forecasts average about $5 billion per year. Regional agricultural advisories issued by the National Weather Service (NWS) are responsible for saving approximately $400 million per year in the NWS Western Region alone. These regional savings include:

1) Raisin crop drying - harvest vs cover - California ($800 million/year potential loss).

2) Water removal from ripe cherries using helicopters ($124 million/year protectable loss).

3) Grape harvest - Monterey County, Calif. ($79 million/year bonus).

4) Frost protection - Arizona ($500/acre savings).

5) Planting impact in Washington state ($70 million/year savings).

6) Weed and pest control - cost to respray due to rain washoff ($8-$10/acre).

Scientists at the University of Kansas are using NOAA satellite data as input to a model that is used to forecast world grain yields. The satellite data used is the mean Eurasian and North American snow-covered area as derived from the satellite-based NOAA Northern Hemisphere Weekly Snow and Ice Cover Chart. They have found that by incorporating the snow cover into their index, the reliability of their model is increased. In their opinion the model reliability increases because Northern Hemisphere snow covers many of the grain producing areas, thus significantly impacting grain yield. The model has generated considerable interest in the commodity and farming markets where knowledge of future world grain yields can influence major investment decisions.

In 1980, specially enhanced AVHRR data were used in a novel way to solve an agricultural problem in California. A local bee breeder, with the intention of relocating and expanding his operations, asked the San Francisco SFSS for help in determining the warmest daytime areas during the months of January through March. Warmer daytime temperatures increase bee activity. TIROS-N/NOAA-6 AVHRR infrared images over the three-month period were enhanced to accentuate afternoon ground temperatures. Persistent warm areas were then located in the desirable counties and these data were superimposed on maps detailing favorable bee habitats. Once an optimum correlation was made, the bee breeder contacted the land owners for possible rental space for the beehives.

Citrus Industry

When frost is expected in Florida on cold winter nights, the SFSS in Miami, Fla., provides specially enhanced GOES infrared images and interpretations for the National Weather Service, which has responsibility for fruit frost forecasting. This capability was first successfully demonstrated in January 1976 and became an operational program during the winter of 1976-1977.

The enhanced satellite images show surface temperatures, which are critical to freeze predictions.

These ground temperatures, derived from images taken every 30 min over the entire southern citrus belt, are accurate within ± 1°C. Thus, the movement southward of the cold winter air and associated "freeze line" can be monitored and tracked every half hour. The Weather Service provides the observations and forecasted movement of the cold air to the citrus growers as soon as it is available.

The Florida citrus grower must decide whether or not to protect his crop upon receiving a forecast for temperatures below about 28°F. These protective actions usually include the firing of diesel heaters and/or the use of electrically operated wind machines. The grower must decide when to call in work crews, when to activate heaters and/or wind machines, and how many heaters must be used. All of these decisions affect their operating costs and losses incurred from inadequate protection.

Protecting citrus groves is a very expensive operation and needless heating can produce an exorbitant waste of fuel. There are approximately 750,000 citrus-bearing acres in Florida. On "cold" nights, an average of 6 h of heating protection is needed at a cost of approximately $830,000/h for fuel. This amounts to a potential $5,000,000/night cost for the State of Florida if smudge pots and other frost prevention devices are operated because of expected temperatures near the freezing mark. The cost to have labor on duty waiting for specific satellite-aided fruit frost warnings before lighting smudge pots and operating frost prevention devices is about $0.42/acre or $315,000/h. Thus, the net potential savings for timely and accurate satellite freeze line forecasting is $515,000/h.

It is estimated that 1–2 h of heating protection per "cold" night could be saved as a result of the use of the frequent satellite imagery. Assuming a reduction of 1.5 h average heating protection, the savings could amount to $770,000/cold night. During the winter of 1976–1977, a total of 64 cold nights and, during the winter of 1977–1978, 54 cold nights were experienced in the State of Florida. The average number of cold nights in Florida each winter is 35–40. The enhanced satellite images are used routinely to observe the movement of the "freeze line" to warn citrus growers via NOAA weather radio and a telephone communications network via county agricultural agents. The satellite enables a greater amount of temperature information to be acquired more frequently and passed on to the citrus growers in a timely manner.

The NOAA SFSS at San Francisco prepares a daily satellite image interpretation narrative tailored to the

needs of the NWS fruit frost forecasters. Frost sensitive
agricultural products grown in California amount to $3.7
billion/year. Advisory committees have estimated that the
frost forecasts provided by the NWS are responsible for
savings of 5-20%. The fruit frost forecasters have
estimated that the satellite contribution to this savings
of harvests would be 0.5-1.0%, or $15-40 million annually.

Hawaii Sugar Cane Industry

The harvesting of sugar cane is a process that is very
dependent upon local weather conditions and benefits
greatly from satellite-derived forecasts. The Waialua
Sugar Company on the island of Oahu has been using
satellite imagery provided by the NOAA SFSS in Honolulu,
Hawaii, to plan their harvesting schedule.

When a cane field is ready for harvest (about 2 years
after planting), it is first deliberately set on fire and
burned; the remains are then gathered and hauled to the
mill. Weather is an important factor in this complex
operation. Convection and trade wind showers are the main
weather hazards to the harvesting process. Burning must
abide by state and Federal air pollution regulations.
Tactical procedures for burning a particular field depend
heavily on wind direction and speed. After burning, the
remains must be harvested within 24-36 h to avoid
spoilage. Any significant rainfall during this critical
period interferes with the movement of heavy harvesting
vehicles in and out of the field. Typically, 50-100 acres
are burned at one time, leaving burned cane worth $250,000
lying in the field at the mercy of the weather.

The production manager of the Waialua Sugar Company,
who is responsible for making the daily harvesting
decisions, has said, "I look at the weather maps and
listen to what they are saying on the broadcasts, but when
I look at the satellite pictures, I can really see what's
coming." Their company has about 15,000 acres under
cultivation. Over a typical harvest season from September
to December, the daily weather-related decisions must be
based on the most accurate information available if costly
mistakes are to be avoided. The availability of satellite
pictures helps to reduce the odds in an operation where
mistakes are measured in millions of dollars. The
estimated savings of the Waialua Sugar Company alone as a
result of using satellite data is $1,000,000/year.

Crop Monitoring

The polar-orbiting NOAA satellite's AVHRR channel 1
and 2 data are used by a variety of national and

international agencies for crop monitoring purposes.

U.S. Department of Agriculture Commodity Condition
Assessment Division (CCAD) uses AVHRR data to monitor crop
conditions internationally including USSR, Australia,
Argentina, Brazil, Mexico, and India. Crop production in
these nations can have a direct impact on commodity prices
in the United States. CCAD has been receiving about 16
AVHRR tapes per week from NOAA since May 1981. These are
sent via courier from NOAA/NESDIS in Suitland, Md., to the
South Agriculture Building in Washington, D.C. The data
generally arrive at USDA for operational analysis within
48 h of a satellite overpass. Annual cost to CCAD is
about $80,000. CCAD receives Landsat data for these same
areas on a daily basis by courier from the NOAA/Goddard
facility. In 1984 CCAD received the Landsat data within
7-14 days of observation and at a cost of almost
$1000/scene. Prior to 1981, CCAD used 15,000 Landsat
scenes yearly. Users must balance their budgetary
resources, need for geographic coverage, and need for the
highest resolution data available to obtain the proper
Landsat MSS (multispectral scanner) vs NOAA AVHRR mix.

The United Nation's Food and Agriculture Organization
(FAO) uses NOAA AVHRR data in several projects, some of
which are:

1) The Sud area in Sudan - monitor agriculture
development activities in an area that experiences yearly
flooding from the Nile.

2) Kenya - country-wide agricultural land use
assessment.

3) Zambia and Botswana - monitor grazing lands and
large-scale land use changes.

4) Lake Chad area (Niger) - monitor agricultural
activity surrounding the lake.

Search and Rescue Operations

Satellite pictures provided by the National
Environmental Satellite, Data, and Information Service
(NESDIS) assist in search and rescue (SAR) planning
throughout the United States' inland SAR area. The
satellite data are coordinated through the U.S. Air Force
Rescue Coordination Center (AFRCC) located at Scott Air
Force Base, Ill. The USAF Aerospace Rescue and Recovery
Service (ARRS) provides coordination of air searches
throughout the United States. When an aircraft is
overdue, the ARFCC must obtain the routing of the
aircraft, determine if weather might be a factor, check on
the missing pilot's qualifications, and have a knowledge
of the performance capabilities of the missing aircraft.

Most search and rescue missions conducted over the
enroute phase of flight have shown that missing general
aviation aircraft encountered unexpected weather along
their route. Pilots who obtained weather briefings prior
to departure in which good VFR (visual flight rules)
flight conditions were forecast, encountered narrow bands
of unreported weather that could be seen on the satellite
image. If an aircraft is reported missing, areas of
severe weather can be located with satellite imagery
showing conditions at the time the pilot was in distress.
These pictures assist in determining if certain preferred
mountain routes were open or blocked by hazardous
weather. The height of the cloud tops can be estimated to
determine if the missing pilot could fly over the storm
system or was faced with staying at lower altitudes and
trying to get through the weather.

The statistics for missing general aviation aircraft
that were lost on the enroute phase of flight over 3 years
are discussed below. These are incidents in which the
USAF ARRS responded with search and rescue service.
During the period 1975-1977, a total of 747 aircraft were
lost. A total of 1679 persons were aboard these aircraft
of which 1008 were killed and 671 survived. Based on the
analysis of satellite imagery of the crash sites, the ARRS
and the California Wing of the Civil Air Patrol (CAP)
believe that weather was a factor in more than 85% of
these aircraft accidents. A 10 year study of aircraft
accidents by the National Transportation Safety Board
(NTSB) for the period 1964-1974 without analysis of
satellite imagery, indicated that weather was a factor in
only 25% of the accidents.

The California CAP began utilizing satellite photos
obtained from the NOAA SFSS in San Francisco for search
and rescue operations in October 1974. By mid-1975, it
was apparent that satellite data were a new time-saving
aid in locating missing aircraft. During this test
period, 58 search missions were conducted and only two
searches exceeded 48 h. During the previous year, 46
search missions were conducted and CAP pilots averaged
more than a week searching for the crash sites. Search
missions of 10-15 h are now common as opposed to several
days to two weeks without satellite data.

During the period 1975-1977, a reduction of 32% in
total SAR flying hours was realized by the USAF ARRS and
the CAP. However, at the same time, the number of SAR
missions actually increased by 14%. Following the
introduction of satellite image data to SAR operations,
for the first time in the history of rescue service, the

number of flying hours actually decreased. Table 2 lists
the number of CAP missions, hours flown, and average hours
per mission for a 13 year period.

Satellite image support to search and rescue
operations was introduced in 1974, tested in 1975, and has
been used extensively since 1976. Table 2 shows a marked
decrease in average hours flown per mission. This
decrease is especially noticeable during the period
between 1974, before the launch of the first SMS/GOES
satellite and 1977 after routine geostationary satellite
operations began. Between 1974 and 1977 the average
number of hours flown per mission decreased by 45% and has
remained relatively constant through 1982. The average
cost of a CAP mission is $60 per hour for fuel, oil, and
maintenance. CAP manpower is entirely voluntary. These
reductions result in an annual savings of about $360,000
for CAP search and rescue operations. USAF ARRS C-130
search and rescue mission hours have also been
significantly reduced. A C-130 costs about $1250 per hour
to operate, thus major savings can be realized by reducing
mission hours.

Since the mid-1970's, several countries have been
evaluating the concept of using satellites equipped with
special receivers to detect and locate emergency
transmissions from aircraft and ships in distress. This
mutual interest led to the formation of the COSPAS/SARSAT
Project, an international joint venture in satellite-aided
search and rescue. The partners in this joint venture
were Canada's Department of Communications (DOC), France's

Table 2   Civil Air Patrol mission summary (1971-1983)

Year	No. of missions	Hours flown	Average hours/mission
1971	389	30,909	79.5
1972	348	27,391	78.7
1973	429	27,284	63.6
1974	460	21,773	47.3
1975	694	24,500	35.3
1976	817	17,064	21.6
1977	896	16,004	17.9
1978	892	24,800[a]	27.8
1979	1000	18,340	18.3
1980	1175	14,424	12.3
1981	1160	17,878	15.4
1982	1194	16,960	14.2
1983	1745[b]	16,725	9.6

[a]Significant increase in hours flown in Alaska and California.
[b]Increase due to input from COSPAS/SARSAT operations.

Centre National d'Etudes Spatiales (CNES), the United
States' National Aeronautics and Space Administration
(NASA), and the U.S.S.R.'s Ministry of Merchant Marine
(MORFLOT). The objective of the COSPAS/SARSAT Project is
to demonstrate that detection and location of distress
signals can be greatly facilitated by the use of a global
monitoring system based on low-altitude, polar-orbiting
spacecraft. The U.S., Canada, and France have jointly
developed the SARSAT system, which is flying on the NOAA
satellites. The COSPAS system was developed by the Soviet
Union.

One of the characteristics of a satellite in a low
polar orbit is that it will observe the entire globe once
every 12 hours, but the contact time with any one area is
relatively short. The waiting time between the activation
of a distress transmitter and its detection by a satellite
is significantly reduced by having more than one satellite
operating. For a constellation of four satellites, the
mean waiting time is approximately one hour at
mid-latitudes. At higher latitudes where the weather is
more hostile, waiting time is less than 30 minutes,
improving survival chances where time is most critical.

The COSPAS/SARSAT system involves the use of multiple
satellites "listening" for distress transmissions. The
signals received by the satellites are relayed to a
network of dedicated ground stations, where the location
of the emergency is determined by measuring the Doppler
shift between the satellite, with a precisely known orbit,
and the distress signal. This information is then relayed
to a Mission Control Center (MCC) that alerts the
appropriate Rescue Coordination Center (RCC). The RCC
then begins the actual search and rescue operation in
accordance with conventional practice.

The first satellite of the joint COSPAS/SARSAT
activity was launched by the Soviet Union in June 1982.
In March 1983, the second COSPAS satellite and the first
SARSAT-equipped satellite, NOAA-8, were successfully
launched. NOAA-8 suffered a catastrophic failure in June
1984 rendering it inoperable for SARSAT needs. At about
the same time, the Soviet Union launched its third COSPAS
spacecraft. The second NOAA SARSAT-equipped spacecraft,
NOAA-9, was launched in December 1984 and is functioning
normally.

It is estimated that the majority (could be as much as
80%) of private flights are not under an FAA-approved
flight plan. Prior to SARSAT, the average notification
time to alert search and rescue resources to begin
searching for a missing aircraft was 36-48 hours. The
highest lifesaving probability, however, is within 24

hours of the time of crash. If the crash beacon
(Emergency Locator Transmitter--ELT) is activated on
impact (approximately 1/3 of ELTs do not activate), the
SARSAT system will provide a location within about two
hours. It should be noted that emergency locator
transmitters are installed on 200,000 U.S. civil aircraft
and 6000 U.S. vessels. In a given year, there may be from
4000 to 5000 aircraft crashes--of which some 1400 to 1500
require a search. The U.S. Coast Guard responds to 3000
to 4000 distress calls per year from the region more than
25 miles off shore.

The COSPAS/SARSAT system contributed to the saving of
272 lives during the period January 1984 to September
1984. To date, the system has contributed significantly
to saving about 350 lives in Canada, the U.S., Western
Europe, and their associated ocean areas. In some cases,
the only alert was provided by the COSPAS/SARSAT system.
In other cases, where an aircraft or vessel was known to
be missing, the satellite data provided the precise
location of the incident, which was crucial to the rescue.

Increased detection of beacons by satellites has
improved the probability that search and rescue
authorities will become aware of distress incidents. At
the same time, however, it has increased the number of
incidents these authorities must handle, including false
alarms that are detected and must be screened. As shown
in Table 2, the precise location information from the
COSPAS/SARSAT system has reduced the average search time.
For example, prior to the SARSAT program, the Civil Air
Patrol (CAP) in 1977 conducted 896 missions expending
16,004 flying hours. In 1983 the CAP participated in 1745
missions with about the same number of flying hours
(16,725). The average hours per mission was reduced from
17.9 in 1977 to 9.6 in 1983.

As indicated in Table 2, there has been a relatively
constant annual rise in the number of missions flown and a
gradual decrease in the average hours per mission. This
is indicative of the value of new technology in search and
rescue operations. Thus satellite data, available on an
operational basis, has annually saved hundreds of
thousands of dollars in tangible benefits and has produced
untold intangible benefits in reductions of human suffering
and death through the faster location of downed aircraft.

Ice Monitoring

Shipping operations in the Arctic, Great Lakes, and
St. Lawrence Seaway are obviously greatly affected by sea,

lake, and river ice. The NESDIS operational satellites
provide support during the ice season to the U.S. Coast
Guard International Ice Patrol. The satellite ice
analyses are also extremely valuable to ice reconnaissance
aircraft in Canada as an aid in preflight planning and in
locating areas of improved visibility. This has resulted
in increased efficiency in the visual reconnaissance
missions producing a savings of about 1500 aircraft flight
hours and related cost reductions of about $5,000,000
annually.

The Canadian Centre for Remote Sensing (CCRS),
Department of Energy, Mines, and Resources has shown that
imagery indicating the presence and extent of sea ice has
been very useful and cost effective to geophysical survey
ships engaged in seismic surveying off the north coast of
Canada in the Arctic Ocean. AVHRR images are routinely
received by the Atmospheric Environment Services Receiving
Station at Downsview, Ontario.

Seismic operations for oil and gas exploration in the
Bering Sea, Norton Sound, Chukchi, and Beaufort Seas have
relied heavily on satellite observations. Because of the
competitive nature of this activity, the information is
proprietary, but exploratory companies involved indicate
that the satellite data are used as a planning tool to lay
out cruise tracks that save time and fuel and minimize
damage by ice to nonice-reinforced ships and testing
equipment. The presence of any floating ice makes seismic
sounding impossible. In one instance, an area scheduled
for survey was found to have free-floating ice fragments.
Advice was sought from the CCRS by a geophysical survey
ship and the CCRS redirected the ship to a nearby area
(100 n.mi. away) where ice-free conditions were
interpreted from the daily satellite imagery. As a
result, the ship was able to acquire twice the amount of
data normally gathered. In this instance, the single
image saved $250,000.

In another example, the ARCO Oil Company used NOAA
satellite imagery in 1979 to monitor ice conditions near
Alaska. ARCO was using a drilling ship designed for use
in the Gulf of Mexico for exploratory ice drilling in the
lower Cook Inlet. By using the satellite data, ARCO was
able to save $45,000 in insurance premiums on this
project. A more recent example of the use of satellite
data to monitor ice conditions in support of offshore
drilling operations occurred in January 1983. The ARCO
Oil Company was using the "Gulf of Mexico" jack-up rig to
drill an exploratory well north of Port Heiden in the
Aleutians. Extremely cold temperatures and a strong north

wind began moving the ice front toward the rig at 25-30 miles/day. NOAA satellite imagery and analyses of the ice were provided daily by the Anchorage SFSS to the Minerals Management Office, U.S. Coast Guard, ARCO, and the media. The rig was eventually evacuated and towed to safety based almost entirely upon the real-time analysis of the polar satellite imagery. Satellite ice observations also play an important role in the Arctic regions for the U.S. Fish and Wildlife Service monitoring of marine mammals' (walrus, whales, seals, and polar bears) migration patterns.

In the Great Lakes, satellite imagery is used to find navigable waters for shipping as long as possible into the winter season. The high-resolution satellite images show small ice-free areas that can be used by ships to continue operations longer than previously possible. It is estimated that the extension of the shipping season by this method results in a cost benefit of $1,000,000/day for each day extended. Before the use of satellite data, the Great Lakes were closed to shipping for about 2 months each winter. In the winter of 1976-1977, which was exceptionally bad, the Lakes were closed to shipping for only 1 month and during the 1977-1978 winter, they were never completed closed. In this case, however, it is incorrect to attribute all of the savings to satellites alone, since the use of side-looking radar (SLR) on reconnaissance aircraft was introduced in the same time period. Nevertheless, satellites could contribute to annual benefits of as much as $30 million.

Satellites are also used to provide early warning of river ice melting and breakup, which could cause ice jams and flooding. Hydrologists require timely information on the progress of river ice breakup during spring thaws. Ice jams often cause severe flooding and threaten hydroelectric plants, bridge piers, and ship navigation. As an example, in 1977, NOAA scientists closely monitored the Ottawa River in Canada using visible images from NOAA's polar-orbiting satellites. They were able to view the day-to-day changes in the breakup and melting of the ice.

Snow Cover Mapping

The use of satellite acquired data for mapping snow cover has proved valuable in water resource planning and flood forecasting. Snow-covered area estimates from operational NOAA satellites have proved to be much faster and more economical than conventional aerial surveys.

Snow and ice cover a significant portion of the Earth's
surface. For example, snow covers 30-50% of the land
area, ice covers about 25% of the oceans, glaciers cover
about 10% of the land area, and permafrost covers 10% of
the land area.

Frequent observations of the extent and
characteristics of snow and ice are needed to assist many
industries in their day-to-day operational requirements.
Some operational requirements that are especially affected
by snow are flood warning systems, municipal and regional
water supply management, irrigation systems management,
hydroelectric power management, energy requirements,
transportation systems operations, and food supply
requirements.

For example, satellite snow cover analyses were used
in 1976 while a storm was still in progress to determine
that it would not be necessary to spill the Verde River
reservoir system in Arizona as had been previously
planned. Spilling of the reservoirs would have put water
into the normally dry Salt River channel above Phoenix,
which causes road closings and local flooding in the
Phoenix metropolitan area and results in the loss of
valuable irrigation water. The dollar savings were
considerable. In addition, continental snow cover has
important climatic impacts on surface and air temperature,
radiation balance, soil moisture, cloudiness, and
precipitation.

Donald R. Wiesnet, former hydrologist with NESDIS, has
shown that satellites have made a significant contribution
in snow-cover mapping where the cost ratio between the
satellite and conventional aerial survey is as much as
200:1 in favor of the satellite. For example, it takes
about 40 h of flying at $500/h to map 20 river basins in
the Sierra Nevada mountains. Thus, it costs about $20,000
per aerial mapping operation, which is done several times
during the winter and spring, funds permitting. When
cloud-free conditions are available, this job can be
accomplished using satellite data in about two man-days at
a cost of $200. Thus, annual savings in mapping the
Sierra Nevada basins alone could be as much as $1,000,000.

In the mountainous regions of the United States,
millions of dollars are spent each year to measure the
snowpack at fixed locations for forecast purposes. In
1969, a panel of scientists from the National Academy of
Sciences stated, "The changing extent, surface
temperature, thickness, water equivalent, and liquid water
content of seasonal snowpack are necessary for engineering
design and operation and planning of water projects large

and small. In the mountain areas of the United States, millions of dollars are spent each year at fixed locations to measure snowpack for forecast purposes. Improved forecasts are estimated to be worth $10,000,000 to $100,000,000 per year to water users in the western United States alone." Operational environmental satellites contribute greatly to improved hydrological forecasts.

Seventy percent of the runoff in the western United States is derived from melting snow. In a study funded by the National Science Foundation, it was found that increased cloud seeding in the upper Colorado River basin could result in snowpack augmentation with $12.8 million in annual benefits.

NESDIS began operationally producing satellite snow-cover maps for 30 selected western U.S. river basins in the spring of 1974. The snow-cover data are used in river runoff models, dam and reservoir release decisions, and are input to seasonal water supply forecasts to determine how much water is available for irrigation, hydroelectric power generation, municipal consumption, and recreation. About 600 river basin snow maps are produced annually; data are relayed to users via teletype, telecopier, or through the mail. Agencies subscribing to this satellite service include the U.S. Forest Service, Soil Conservation Service, Army Corps of Engineers, Bonneville Power Administration, Bureau of Reclamation, Bureau of Land Management, and the U.S. Geological Survey.

In the late 1970s, NASA initiated a four-year (1975-1979) effort to evaluate the usefulness of satellite snow-cover information for water resource managers. The project was identified as the snow mapping Applications Systems Verification Transfer (ASVT) project. Volume VII of the project's final report addressed cost/benefit aspects of the snow study. It was found that:

1) The improvement in runoff prediction due to the addition of satellite information is 6-10%.

2) Benefit models developed for irrigation and hydroenergy uses revealed savings of $36.5 million yearly when satellite snow-cover data were supplied for river basins throughout the western United States. The cost of such a satellite snow mapping program was determined to be $505,000 thus yielding a benefit/cost ratio of 72:1.

During the last 25 years, climatologists and meteorologists have become more interested in the role of continental snow cover in climatic processes and weather forecasting. Continental snow cover can also impact energy requirements, transportation systems, food supplies, and the economies of areas dependent on winter

recreational activities. In order to study and understand
the climatic/economic impact of snow cover, it is
necessary to have long time-period data bases of various
snow-cover parameters, such as snow-covered area. To
answer this need, a satellite-based atlas of Northern
Hemisphere snow cover has been prepared covering the
period 1967-1981. The atlas presents 15 years of NOAA
satellite-based snow-cover data in the form of monthly,
midmonthly, and seasonal snow-cover frequency maps. At a
glance, the user of the atlas can determine the
probability of snow cover occurring for any part of the
Northern Hemisphere during any time of the year.

An unusual use of the atlas occurred when a movie
company wanted to film a snow-covered scene in New England
during April. A quick glance at the atlas enabled them to
determine the location in New England that had the highest
probability of snow cover occurring in April. It also
turned out that the satellite-based atlas was the only
source of this information.

Natural Disaster Warning

Environmental satellites have been very effective in
providing data for improved natural disaster warnings. It
is, however, very difficult to correlate lives and dollars
saved during a disaster directly to improved forecasts and
warnings. NOAA satellites provide environmental data to
forecasters and government officials regarding tornadoes,
severe thunderstorms, hurricanes, tropical storms,
flooding, severe winter storms, and other less destructive
environmental phenomena. Satellite data are transmitted
around-the-clock, 7 days/week to the various national
centers for environmental warning including: the National
Severe Storms Forecast Center (NSSFC) in Kansas City, Mo.,
the National Hurricane Center (NHC) in Miami, Fla., the
Eastern Pacific Hurricane Center in San Francisco, and the
Central Pacific Hurricane Center in Honolulu.

Hurricane Warning. Satellite imagery is used
extensively in monitoring tropical storms and hurricanes.
Several years ago, aircraft reconnaissance was the primary
method of finding and tracking dangerous tropical storms
in the oceans. Increasing costs of petroleum,
maintenance, and manpower have caused a significant
cutback in tropical storm reconnaissance by the U.S. Air
Force and NOAA. Satellite observations have practically
replaced aircraft storm reconnaissance except when a
hurricane is approaching land. The cost of aerial
reconnaissance is about $2500/h, and the average mission

requires at least 10 h. Thus, there is a potential
savings of $25,000/flight for every reconnaissance flight
avoided by the use of satellite data. In addition, the
satellite imagery has enabled the aircraft storm
reconnaissance to be more efficient and cost effective in
plotting flight tracks for data gathering due to improved
navigational information about the location of tropical
cyclones.

Since the inauguration of the operational satellite
system, no tropical storm goes undetected, even in the
most remote areas of the world. The GOES-East spacecraft
acquires an image every 30 min around-the-clock of the
North Atlantic Ocean, the Caribbean Sea, and the Gulf of
Mexico, providing excellent tropical storm detection and
monitoring capabilities. Hurricane reconnaissance
aircraft no longer have to fly random search patterns over
the vast tropical oceans to locate storms that may be
developing there. Estimated savings from using satellite
storm detection and monitoring in midocean in place of
expensive aircraft reconnaissance are about $1,800,000
annually.

The information in Table 3 illustrates the magnitude
of hurricane destruction in terms of dollars and
fatalities. The most damaging individual hurricanes by
name and year are listed in Table 4.

The damage estimate of $2.3 billion makes Hurricane
Frederic in 1979 the costliest hurricane ever to hit the
United States, exceeding the $2.1 billion cost estimated
for Hurricane Agnes in 1972. Five deaths were attributed
directly to Hurricane Frederic in the United States, only
one of which occurred along the coastal region when a
person was swept off a boat near Pensacola, Fla. The
insurance industry estimated insured losses of $750
million for Hurricane Frederic. Approximately 250,000
persons were evacuated in advance of Frederic.

A 1975 NOAA Technical Memorandum[3] noted that until
1974 the initial position error for storms within 500 n.mi
of the coast averaged 22 n.mi and landfall forecasts were
made from distances no more than 300 n.mi. A positioning
error is defined as the difference between the
forecaster's assumed initial position of a storm and the
actual position as determined from a postanalysis.

The issuance of hurricane warnings along a portion of
the United States coastline is generally accomplished
18-24 h prior to the expected arrival of the storm at the
coast. This particular time interval has been found to be
an optimized tradeoff between the desire to provide
maximum warning lead time and the ability to keep the size

Table 3 Hurricane fatalities and damage (1900–1983)

Year (period)	U.S. Fatalities	U.S. Damage, $ millions
		Adjusted to 1957–1959 construction costs:
1900–1904	6000	N/A
1905–1909	2200	N/A
1910–1914	100	N/A
1915–1919	983	541
1920–1924	9	15
1925–1929	2114	357
1930–1934	80	164
1935–1939	1026	850
1940–1944	149	495
1945–1949	67	480
1950–1954	217	918
1955–1959	675	1331
1960–1964	173	1156
		Unadjusted annual cost:
1965	75	1420
1966	54	15
1967	18	200
1968	9	10
1969	256	1455
1970	11	454
1971	8	213
1972	121	3097
1973	5	18
1974	1	150
1975	21	550
1976	9	100
1977	0	0
1978	35	20
1979	22	3050
1980	2	300
1981	0	25
1982	1	350 [a]
1983	22	2000

[a]Primarily Hurricane Iwa damage. Hawaii had not been struck by a hurricane in 23 years.

of the warning area within reasonable limits. With such a lead time, the length of the warning zone averages nearly 300 n.mi. Inasmuch as the swath of damaging winds is generally less than 100 n.mi, the public could expect a minimum overwarning area of about 200 n.mi.

The study includes an economic analysis of potential changes in the size of hurricane warning areas. It is estimated that protection costs (including losses due to temporarily curtailed production) for a typical 300 n.mi.

Gulf of Mexico coastal hurricane warning zone total
$25.1 million. A 10 n.mi increase in positioning error
will increase this economic loss by about
$5 million/storm. A 10 n.mi decrease in positioning error
will decrease protection costs by about
$2.75 million/storm. Since an average of about two
hurricanes annually move inland on the continental U.S.,
using these figures, $50 million is the average annual
cost of protection. As a conservative estimate, a
reduction of only 5% in the coastal warning area would
mean an average annual savings of about $2,500,000/year.
Satellite observations play a major role in keeping the
warning area to a minimum.

Global Tropical Storm Monitoring. NOAA polar-orbiting
satellites are used to monitor tropical storms worldwide
in addition to those near or endangering the United
States. Table 5 lists the number of named tropical
cyclones monitored and tracked by NOAA satellites in three
remote ocean areas of the world.
When these storms are detected and tracked by polar
satellites a Satellite Weather Bulletin is sent directly
to the meteorological agency of the countries that could
be affected by the storm. These bulletins are transmitted
daily throughout the life of the tropical storm, which
averages 8-10 days. In the highly populated countries of
southeast Asia, this satellite tropical storm warning
service could save many lives if the capabilities to
disseminate the warning to the general public were
available. Unfortunately, in many cases, the populace
does not receive the warnings due to the lack of adequate

Table 4   Costliest United States hurricanes of record

Name	Year	Damage, $
Frederic	1979	2,300,000,000
Agnes	1972	2,100,000,000
Alicia	1983	2,000,000,000
Camille	1969	1,420,700,000
Betsy	1965	1,420,500,000
Diane	1955	831,700,000
Eloise	1975	550,000,000 [a]
Carol	1954	461,000,000
Celia	1970	453,000,000
Carla	1961	408,000,000
Donna	1960	387,000,000
David	1979	320,000,000

[a] Includes $60,000,000 in Puerto Rico.

communications facilities and the death toll has not
reflected the availability of these timely warnings.

Severe Thunderstorm and Tornado Warning. Satellite
imagery is a primary data source for the National Severe
Storm Forecasting Center (NSSFC) in Kansas City, which has
severe thunderstorm and tornado forecasting responsibility
for the continental United States. In 1972, the NESDIS
established a Satellite Field Services Station (SFSS)
collocated with the NSSFC. The Kansas City SFSS has been
instrumental in developing new techniques in applying
satellite imagery to severe storm forecasting. The use of
high-resolution GOES visible and enhanced infrared imagery
taken at frequent intervals (as often as every 15 min) has
been extremely useful in monitoring the development of
severe thunderstorms. This satellite capability has
enabled NSSFC forecasters to pinpoint areas with a high
probability of a tornado so as to reduce the area of
warning. By reducing the area of warning, the "cry-WOLF!"
attitude that sometimes exists toward tornado alerts will
be lessened. The satellite has been instrumental in
accurately defining the tornado watch areas, which are
provided to the news media and NWS forecast offices.

Table 6 lists the fatalities and property loss
statistics due to tornadoes for the period 1972–1983. As
shown, the cost of damage has risen significantly in
recent years due to more populated areas being hit by
tornadoes and increased building costs due to inflation.
Because tornadoes and severe thunderstorms are relatively
small scale and short lived, it is difficult to prepare to
protect property in a manner similar to that done with the
larger-scale and slower-moving hurricanes. It is

Table 5   Satellite-monitored named tropical cyclones (1974-1983)

Year	West Pacific Ocean	South Pacific Ocean	Indian Ocean
1974	38	12	26
1975	27	8	33
1976	27	10	27
1977	21	10	23
1978	27	7	23
1979	27	6	20
1980	27	8	20
1981	28	12	19
1982	27	9	21
1983	24	14	20

currently impossible to predict the exact time and
locations these severe storms will arrive, but satellite
images provide an early indication of the development of
the type of meteorological conditions in which these
storms occur. Unfortunately, satellite observations of
tornadoes and severe thunderstorms can do little to aid in
reducing the amount of property damage sustained. It is
significant, however, that there has been a notable
reduction in the average number of deaths since 1975.

Beginning in 1975, GOES data have been a significant
and heavily used input to the NSSFC. It seems clear that
there is a correlation between the lower number of lives
lost since 1975 and the introduction of operational
geostationary satellite data into the severe storm
forecasting and warning process. Even excluding the
April 3rd calamity of 1974, an average of 84 fatalities
per year occurred between 1968 and 1974. The average
number of deaths since satellite data have been
extensively utilized is 48/year.

The New Orleans SFSS plays an important role in
reducing the element of surprise of severe weather
sweeping in from the Gulf of Mexico and overtaking
mariners, offshore oil workers, and coastal residents.
During this century alone, 21 hurricanes have come ashore
from the Gulf killing hundreds of persons and causing

Table 6   Tornado summary (1972–1983) property loss frequency[a]

Year	No. of tornadoes	Fatalities	Category[b]		
			5	6	7 and over
1972	741	27	100	28	1
1973	1102	87	219	67	9
1974	947	361	166	82	25
1975	920	60	189	31	11
1976	835	44	145	41	5
1977	852	43	173	40	6
1978	788	53	153	53	6
1979	852	84	169	62	11
1980	866	28	205	79	13
1981	782	24	144	43	12
1982	1047	64	237	77	12
1983	931	32	211	85	10

[a]Number of times property losses were reported in storm
damage categories 5–7 and over. Losses are based on estimated
values at time of occurrence.

[b] Property loss category definitions: 5) $50,000–500,000,
6) $500,000–5 million, 7)$5–50 million, 8) $50–500 million,
9) $500 million and over.

billions of dollars in damage. In addition, scores of
tropical storms and winter cyclones have hit the Gulf
coast areas. Although not as severe as hurricanes, these
storms cause extensive damage and threaten the lives of
those individuals who use the Gulf for their livelihood
and recreation.

With the advent of the energy crisis, emphasis has
been placed on offshore oil drilling and production
activity. The magnitude of this effort is reflected in
the following statistics. There are 1249 production
platforms with heliports, approximately 240 drilling rigs
on location, and 28,000 individuals working offshore. To
support this vast and complex industry, approximately 700
helicopters (flying an average of 25,000 h/month)
transport 150,000 passengers each month from bases located
along the Texas and Louisiana Gulf coasts.

The New Orleans SFSS focuses on small-scale
meteorological events in an area extending from 90 miles
onshore to 200 miles offshore. Special attention is given
to the thunderstorms and squall lines that develop rapidly
throughout the Gulf with little advance warning. When
these storms are detected, the SFSS issues advisories to
National Weather Service Offices and other government
agencies along the coast.

Flood Warning. Satellite data also have been valuable
in providing early warning for floods. An example is the
Sept. 13, 1977, flood disaster in Kansas City.
Information provided by the NESDIS SFSS in Kansas City to
National Weather Service forecast units prior to and
during the Kansas City flood was timely and accurate. The
early recognition of the precipitation boundary that had
been left by the previous night's thunderstorm activity in
northern Missouri identified a meteorological condition
that had potential for initiating new thunderstorm
development over an area where the ground was already
saturated. This satellite information, when incorporated
with other data, contributed to the NWS decision to issue
a local forecast early in the day for heavy rain. Later
satellite data provided information that was instrumental
in the issuance of a severe thunderstorm watch for the
Kansas City metropolitan area. The satellite evaluation
gave new information concerning the southward shift of the
axis of thunderstorm development, and coupled with
supporting evidence from the NWS radar, suggested the
potential for heavy rain in the Kansas City area.

An example of satellite contributions to international
flood warnings occurred in August 1977 when United States

satellite assessments of snowpack were used as an
indicator of flood potential in Pakistan. NOAA-5 VHRR
coverage was especially programmed to include the Himalaya
Mountains. Two large river basins in the Himalayas were
monitored: the Indus River above Besham (162,100 km^2)
and the Kobal River above Nowshera (88,600 km^2). A late
snow melt in the Himalayas could have greatly increased
the potential for flooding in Pakistan. The percent of
snow cover as derived from the satellite was compared with
historical data and transmitted to the Pakistani
Ambassador in Washington, D.C.

Satellite data are very beneficial in flash flood
forecasting. During the period Oct. 12-13, 1981,
excessive rainfall occurred over Texas and Oklahoma. The
primary ingredient for this episode was a dying tropical
storm (Norma) that was moving out of Mexico. Numerical
forecast models, due to the scarcity of data over Mexico,
were unable to forecast its movement. The first hint of
this feature moving toward Texas came from
satellite-derived data. This information prompted the
issuance of 20 flash flood watches in various parts of
Texas. As the system moved into Texas, triggering copious
rains, quantitative precipitation estimates based on
satellite images were provided to numerous NWS offices.
There were four major floods during 1982. Flooding in
Fort Wayne, Ind., New England, Louisiana, and the central
Mississippi valley claimed 150 lives and caused damage in
excess of $2 billion.

Large-Scale Weather Forecasting

NOAA operational environmental satellites contribute
greatly to the National Weather Service's National
Meteorological Center (NMC), the central weather analysis
and prediction facility for the United States. At NMC,
which is also a World Meteorological Center, observations
from all over the globe including satellite data are
collected, processed by computer, and used to produce maps
of existing and predicted weather conditions. In a 24 h
period, the NMC receives approximately 50,000 satellite
observations. Maximum benefits from satellite data are
realized when this information is effectively used to
bridge the gap in time and space between conventional
meteorological observations. A synthesis of all types of
meteorological data such as satellite, surface, upper air,
radar, etc., results in a more complete and accurate
understanding of atmospheric processes.

Dr. Robert M. White, former Administrator of NOAA,
discussed the role of satellite data in large-scale

weather applications in an article[4] in 1973 as follows:
"The World Meteorological Center, Washington, D.C. (the
other World Centers are in Moscow and Melbourne) uses
photographs, temperature soundings, and wind
measurements acquired by satellite to improve the
accuracy of large scale weather analyses and forecast
weather charts. These charts are communicated by
facsimile circuits to civil and military weather
stations in the United States and become part of the
guidance material given to field stations for use in
weather forecasting. Air Force and Navy weather
centrals receive both direct and processed data for use
in similar ways. Analysis centers, which provide
special services to agricultural, hydrological,
engineering, maritime, and other interests, use
satellite data routinely in the preparation of their
products. Several factors make satellite data unique in
comparison with data acquired from other sources. A
major characteristic is that, because of its vantage
point above the atmosphere and its broad field of view,
the satellite can provide information regularly for vast
areas of the globe where data from other more
conventional sources are sparse or unobtainable. This
coverage of the large data gaps over oceans and remote
land areas is one of the basic and most important
contributions of satellites to improved weather
forecasts. Also important is the immediacy of data
transmitted directly from satellites to ground
stations. Such data frequently are received and put
into use some hours before routine data are received
through normal communications channels. The third
characteristic is the broad view of Earth and
atmospheric features that can be obtained only from
satellite altitude. Large-scale weather systems can be
seen in a single view, whereas the definition of
atmospheric or sea surface conditions obtained from
aircraft or ground based observation is incomplete."

The environmental satellite is an excellent global
observational platform and the United States freely
contributes data from its satellites to the world
meteorological community. Satellite data are an important
part of the World Weather Watch program of the United
Nations' World Meteorological Organization. The direct
readout systems (APT and HRPT) from the polar-orbiting
spacecraft and the WEFAX transmissions from the
geostationary spacecraft are used by more than 123
countries around the world.

Thus, large-scale weather observation and forecasting benefit greatly from the contributions of environmental satellites. Deriving the actual cost benefits of such services is extremely difficult, if not an impossible task. The weather and satellite service activities have never performed controlled, quantitative experiments to investigate in a completely unambiguous manner questions such as the benefits. Such experiments are extremely expensive in terms of computer and personnel resources, because they require a period of dual operation—one real and one experimental—that differ only in the particular element being evaluated. However, research studies have shown that global temperature soundings from the polar satellites have had a positive effect on numerical modeling activities. Results obtained by NASA and NOAA on the quality of numerical weather analyses and forecasts produced with and without satellite data indicate a positive contribution from satellite data for forecasts over the northern Pacific Ocean, North America, and Europe. The average reduction of error in the majority (60%) of the 5-day forecasts is near 10%.

Studies conducted with wind and temperature data derived from both polar and geostationary satellites indicate improved upper air analyses and forecasts. Forecast guidance issued to the NWS field offices from the NMC containing data derived from satellites has greatly improved over the past 15 years. This improvement results from a large number of advances in technology and science. Forecasts produced from this guidance have improved to the point that forecasts of temperature and precipitation valid for 18-30 hours are as accurate today as forecasts for only 6-18 hours were a decade ago. Similarly, within the last decade, the reliability originally obtained with 2 to 3 day forecasts is now attained at 4 to 5 days. A significant fraction of that improvement is due to satellite observations. The value of satellite-acquired observations to global-scale forecasting is certainly several millions of dollars annually.

Miscellaneous Uses of Environmental Satellite Data

There have been many uses of environmental satellite data, some of which are significant and others of which have no measurable economic benefit at present, but may have in the future. This section discusses some of these activities with respect to the utilization of environmental satellite data.

Airline Fuel Savings. The NASA Lewis Research Center
completed a 20 month study in 1981 regarding the value of
improved upper air wind and temperature forecasts to the
worldwide commercial airline industry. In a paper
discussing this study,[5] Steinberg reviews the
meteorological basis for the present method of airline
flight planning and analyzes its impact on current flight
operations. He suggests a new approach for developing a
weather base for flight planning that has the potential of
providing fuel savings of 2-3% on long-distance flights.

Steinberg suggests that a meteorologist, using
man/computer interactive techniques, could develop an
accurate upper air nowcast (3-12 h) using the NWS synoptic
numerical forecast, satellite data, rawinsonde, and pilot
reports. Satellite data are the most timely and also
provide information on the location of jet streams, which
is very important. This nowcast would provide the basis
for automated flight planning by the airline.

Steinberg estimates that an interactive system with
satellite data input to provide upper air tuned forecasts,
including manpower for a 24 h operation, would cost about
$600,000/year after a one-time capital investment for
equipment of about $1,000,000. An international carrier
with a present fuel bill of $1 billion could expect to
save at least $20 million/year on trip fuel alone. When
one considers the potential for optimizing reserve fuel
requirements, the savings could even be considerably
higher.

Game Bird Management. The Office of Migratory Bird
Management of the U.S. Fish and Wildlife Service has used
NOAA polar-orbiting AVHRR pictures to help determine the
reproductive success of several species of arctic nesting
geese. The Wildlife Service is responsible for annually
adjusting hunting regulations to conform with the
estimated population of particular species of waterfowl.
The waterfowl managers must know well before the hunting
season what the supply of game birds will be, because
their existence could be threatened by overharvesting.

The most important factors affecting the reproductive
success of arctic nesting geese are the timely
disappearance of snow, ice, and the availability of melt
water to allow for the production and rearing of young.
Late seasons or adverse weather conditions can result in
the geese not nesting, reduced brood sizes, or failure to
renest. Any of these adversely affects the population.
Waterfowl managers, using NOAA's polar-orbiting
satellites, can monitor habitat snow and ice conditions in
the remote arctic nesting areas in a timely and economical

manner. The satellites provide visual and infrared images
twice daily to help identify areas of catastrophic or
outstanding goose production, permitting the wildlife
service to establish appropriate hunting regulations.

Dust Storm Monitoring. Both the geostationary (GOES)
spacecraft and the polar-orbiting (NOAA) spacecraft have
been used to monitor the development and dissemination of
dust storms in the Plains states. For example, in
February 1977, these operational satellites detected dust
clouds originating in New Mexico and Colorado and tracked
them across Kansas, Oklahoma, Mississippi, Alabama, and
Georgia out into the Atlantic Ocean. The major dust storm
was considered among the worst since the "Dust Bowl" days
of the 1930s.

Major dust storms can often go undetected in regions
(e.g., the Middle East) where there are few local
meteorological stations. In these areas, NOAA satellite
imagery may provide the only information on these storms.
Detection of such storms in the Middle East is important
because of their impact on oil field operations, shipping,
and military activities.

Monitoring the development and movement of dust storms
is important to the aviation industry, soil erosion and
agriculture experts, scientists conducting solar energy
research, pollution monitoring specialists, etc.
Satellites can be used effectively by meteorologists to
monitor major dust storms.

Locust Plague Control. Agricultural crops and
rangeland resources estimated to be worth $30 billion over
some 30×10^6 km^2 in 60 countries with more than a fifth
of the world's population are prone to the ravages by the
desert locust, Schistocera gregaria. The primary factors
that influence the growth and movement of the locust are
the temperature and moisture content of the air and ground
and the standing crop. These factors can be measured
using NOAA environmental and Landsat satellites. NOAA
polar-orbiting satellite images have been used by the
United Nations Food and Agriculture Organization (FAO) to
monitor areas of probable rainfall in countries such as
Algeria, Somalia, India, and Pakistan. The NOAA satellite
images are examined in detail with Landsat images of these
areas, enabling U.N. FAO scientists to locate areas of
emergent vegetation essential for desert locust
development. The location coordinates of potentially
dangerous areas are relayed to locust control teams in the
countries involved. These teams then examine the area and

determine if insecticide spraying is necessary to inhibit
the development of migratory swarms.

Building further on the results obtained during the
Desert Locust/Remote Sensing Pilot Project, carried out by
FAO in northwest Africa in 1976/77, techniques were
developed and initially tested for quantitative rainfall
monitoring over large areas using environmental satellite
data, e.g., METEOSAT and TIROS-N/NOAA, and vegetation
biomass activity detection and monitoring with Landsat
digital data. Vegetation monitoring for the entire desert
locust region with Landsat 80 m resolution data (MSS
bands 5 (visible) and 7 (near infrared)) requires the
processing of huge amounts of data at an extremely high
cost. Analysis has shown that Landsat data often have
excess resolution for FAO purposes and can be reduced by a
factor of 35 and still be used effectively.

With the launch of TIROS-N in October 1978 and NOAA-6
in June 1979, five-channel AVHRR data (including the near
infrared) at a resolution of 1.1 km became operationally
available for the first time. Previous NOAA
polar-orbiting satellites (the ITOS series) had sensors
that imaged only in the visible and thermal infrared
regions of the spectrum. FAO began exploring the use of
AVHRR data in desert locust studies in the summer of 1980
with promising results. Locust breeding grounds in
southern Algeria were successfully identified for the
first time on AVHRR data of Aug. 31 and Sept. 10, 1981.
The data were analyzed on the NASA/GSFC HP-1000
interactive system. Ground confirmation was supplied
through FAO headquarters in Rome.

Volcano Monitoring. Ash spewed out from erupting
volcanoes often poses a threat to commercial aircraft. In
addition, the ash and dust may remain in the atmosphere
for many months and affect the Earth's radiation balance
and surface temperature and, in turn, crop and vegetation
growth. The five-channel AVHRR data have been used in
recent studies to determine height of volcano plumes,
plume dispersal, plume composition, as well as to map the
extent of lava flows and the distribution of volcanic ash
and dust on the ground. Information gleaned from the
satellite data is provided to the Smithsonian Institute
for inclusion in the Scientific Event Alert Network (SEAN)
Bulletin published each month to pass needed information
to scientists and government officials.

The AVHRR satellite data are analyzed on the HP-1000
interactive system at the NASA Goddard Space Flight
Center. Information on the volcanic plume height is

obtained by reducing the thermal data in channels 4 and
5. The extent of the lava flow can be mapped (while the
lava is still hot) by using channel 3. The distribution
and amount of dust covering the regional vegetation can be
inferred using channels 1 and 2. The volcanoes listed in
Table 7 have been studied extensively by NOAA/NESDIS
during the past several years.

A team from the Australian Commonwealth Scientific and
Industrial Research Organization (CSIRO) and the Western
Australian Institute of Technology have developed a method
of tracking volcanic clouds. The Australian team
recognized that the volcanic ash would contain a large
amount of silica that the infrared radiation band would
detect. When the clouds begin to disperse, they consist
of particles only a few microns across and they attain
very high altitudes where they pose a threat to jet
aircraft. The ash also merges with other clouds and
becomes undetectable in the visible spectrum. The
silicates in the ash provide a thermal emission pattern
different from other clouds.

Currently, NOAA and the Federal Aviation
Administration are working on a plan to use NOAA satellite
data as a primary source for providing volcanic hazard
warning information to airline pilots. In two separate
incidents, Boeing 747 commercial aircraft flew into
eruption clouds from the Galunggung volcano in Java. Both
planes suffered multiple engine failures and had to make
emergency landings. Neither plane had any warning of the
erupting volcano. In the near future, NOAA satellite data
may help to prevent such incidents.

Metropolitan Planning. The heat emitted from
metropolitan areas is measured by high-resolution infrared
sensors aboard NOAA's polar-orbiting satellites. The
sensing of urban "heat-islands" by environmental

Table 7 Volcanoes studied by NOAA/NESDIS

Location	Volcano	Dates
Hawaii	Mauna Loa	April 1–April 10, 1984
Sicily	Etna	1981–present (various dates)
Celebes	Una Una	July 28–Aug. 26, 1983
Celebes	Soputan	Aug. 26–Sept. 18, 1982
Mexico	El Chichon	March 29–April 4, 1982
Java	Galunggung	June 24–July 15, 1982
Soviet Union	Alaid	April 28–May 1, 1981
Iceland	Krafla	Feb. 4, 1981
Iceland	Hekla	April 1981
USA	St. Helens	May 18, 1980

satellites is used by metropolitan planners to monitor
population growth and industrial development. Planners
are able to monitor the urban growth by comparing greatly
enlarged computer-enhanced satellite images with urban
census maps. The satellite imagery supplements and in
certain cases may be more cost effective than aerial
photographs as a tool in determining the amount and
direction of growth of a metropolitan area and for
delineating boundaries for future census surveys.

The pattern of a city's heat can be quantified from
satellite measurements and monitored annually or on a
season by season basis. Even small urban areas can
produce noticeable thermal anomalies or heat islands when
compared to their surrounding rural environment. A NOAA-5
image of New Hampshire, Massachusetts, and Rhode Island
acquired on May 23, 1978, was digitally enhanced by NOAA
scientists to study urban heat islands. A total of 17
heat islands were detected ranging from Norwood, Mass.
(pop. 32,000) to Boston (pop. 625,000).

Hydroelectric Power Production. Temperature changes
of 1°C or more at customer locations are reflected in
electric power demand variations at the servicing
hydroelectric facility within 4-8 h. The hydroelectric
operator must regulate water flow or bring thermal power
units on-line to compensate for these demand variations.
Because it requires about 4 h to make major water flow
adjustments or to add thermal power, large hydroelectric
operators invest substantial amounts in establishing
well-instrumented surface observation networks
(temperature, wind, humidity, and precipitation) over
their service regions. Both ground-based and
satellite-acquired data are used as the basis for specific
area forecasts by the meteorologists supporting the
hydroelectric operator.

In 1973, a major hydroelectric operator, the Tennessee
Valley Authority, investigated the potential benefit of
using satellite data every 1-2 h to increase the density
of surface temperature observations in order to improve
the accuracy of their 4-8 h forecasts. It was concluded
that operational efficiencies could be achieved that would
result in savings "in excess of 1% of operating costs."

Forest Fire Prevention and Detection. The National
Weather Service maintains Fire Weather Offices (FWO) at 17
locations in the western United States: Billings and
Missoula, Mont.; Boise, Idaho; Wenatchee and Olympia,
Wash.; Eureka, Fresno, Los Angeles, Redding, and

Sacramento, Calif.; Medford, Pendleton, Portland, and
Salem, Ore.; Phoenix, Ariz.; Reno, Nev.; and Salt Lake
City, Utah. The "official" fire weather season varies by
FWO district, but can begin as early as April 1 and end as
late as Nov. 15. The FWOs release a daily fire load index
(defined on a scale of 1-100) for regions throughout the
western United States. The higher the index number, the
greater the number of man-hours needed to contain a fire.
With millions of acres to be monitored in the western
region and limited resources to accomplish the task, the
fire load index serves as the most important tool in
determining how these resources will be distributed over
the next day, week, or even month. Poor weather forecasts
can mean thousands of dollars lost when a
misrepresentative fire load index is distributed.

The NWS SFSS in San Francisco releases a daily fire
weather satellite interpretation message (SIM) to aid the
FWO in deriving the proper fire load index. The fire
weather SIMs include information on rapidly developing
thunderstorms, surface wind speed and direction,
precipitation duration and type (layered or convective),
cloud cover, variations in temperature and humidity,
extent of surface inversions, and amount of solar
insolation.

Also of interest to fire weather forecasters are the
changes in plant biomass or chlorophyll density in forest
plant life and cultivated fields. The plant biomass is
directly related to its moisture level and thus to its
susceptibility to burning. The Bureau of Land Management
(BLM) and the EROS Data Center (EDC) have initiated a
program to utilize NOAA AVHRR channels 1 and 2 data to
determine fuel loading conditions in wildfire hazard
areas. The AVHRR data are analyzed to make estimates of
standing green biomass loading within previously
Landsat-mapped wildfire fuel types. These estimates
(high, medium, low) are incorporated as part of the BLM
initial attack wildfire system data base. Initial spring
1982 test areas were located in southeastern Oregon,
northwestern Arizona, and the Fairbanks region of Alaska.
If the experiment is successful, this technique will be
used operationally in fuel loading models for the entire
western United States and Alaska.

Another application of NOAA AVHRR data is to monitor
the actual outbreak of fires. The third channel on the
AVHRR (3.5-3.9 μm) is extremely sensitive to high-heat
sources. These data have been used to identify oil
flares, mine smelts, factories, powerplants, lava
flows--and wildfires. Some of these targets have been

found to occupy an area that is less than 1% of the AVHRR
pixel size, thus effectively giving "subpixel resolution"
for high-heat sources in this channel. The NOAA San
Francisco SFSS ran a test in the summer of 1981 that
involved locating "hot spots" on the channel 3 imagery and
sending out precise locations to the FWOs. As many as 30
fires were spotted on a single day. The overwhelming
majority of fires detected on the data proved to be
controlled timber or agricultural burns. However, in
several cases, the satellite data were used to give first
notice of a fire. Field verification was supplied by the
U.S. Forest Service, timber companies, and in several
cases the local police.

The NOAA AVHRR channel 3 data is also being used to
study deforestation in Brazil. On some satellite images
over 100 fires related to timber cutting and
slash-and-burn agriculture have been detected. Some
scientists believe that burning of the tropical forests
may lead to increased global carbon dioxide. The
increased carbon dioxide can trap heat emitted from the
Earth's surface, thus possibly increasing global
temperatures. The increased temperatures may have a
direct impact on growing seasons in agricultural areas.
Knowing the number, size, and temporal variability of
fires in Brazil as detected by AVHRR channel 3 provides
important data to scientists studying the carbon dioxide
problem.

Bowhead Whale Monitoring. The NOAA SFSS in Anchorage
supports several agencies with respect to the annual
bowhead whale migration. Direct briefings and blowups of
polar satellite visible imagery of the area from
St. Lawrence Island to Prudhoe Bay are provided to the
National Marine Fisheries Service. Polar satellite
imagery of the coastal sea ice is provided to the Bureau
of Land Management Outer Continental Shelf Program. The
imagery is used to determine where aircraft observers
should fly to count and observe the whales. In addition,
ice imagery is supplied to the nine Eskimo Whaling
Commissioners of the Alaska Eskimo Whaling Commission who
use the imagery as a management tool.

Water Quality Monitoring. The effectiveness of NOAA
geostationary satellites in water quality monitoring was
demonstrated in a recent study of Pyramid Lake. The lake,
located northeast of Reno, Nev., is the largest desert
water body in North America with a surface area of
440 km^2 and a mean depth of 40 m. During the summers of

1978 and 1980, the lake experienced massive precipitations
of calcium carbonate (whitings). In each case, the lake
surface became entirely covered with calcium carbonate
within two weeks of the onset of whiting, and it would
take several months to regain its normal appearance. GOES
data were used daily to map the entire whiting sequence:
the growth, distribution pattern, intensity, and finally
cessation of the phenomenon. As more and more water is
diverted for agricultural, industrial, and municipal use
in the western United States, lakes will become
increasingly susceptible to such events. The NOAA
satellites provide a timely source of data for monitoring
such events on inland waters.

    Recreational Boating. Satellite data have been used
as a major data source to brief sailboat cruising races
for several years. The 1982 Newport-to-Bermuda Yacht Race
was postponed 48 h based on forecasts of a subtropical
storm being monitored by NOAA satellites and conventional
data. Unfortunately, one of the racers ignored the
warnings and sailed on the original starting day. The
yacht suffered considerable damage and one crew member was
lost at sea in the storm. The satellite-based weather
support was responsible for preventing considerable
property damage and additional loss of life in this
particular sailboat race.

Conclusion

    The use of operational environmental satellite data is
well established in weather forecasting. Forecasting and
warning of severe storms and large-scale (global)
forecasting are activities that derive special benefits
from satellites. In addition, operational satellite data
are used effectively in a variety of activities as diverse
as ocean navigation, agricultural industry management,
search and rescue, and radio communications frequency
selection.
    Operational environmental satellites have established
their value and benefit in support of many public warning
functions and economic activities. Beyond all value are
the lives that have been saved because environmental
satellites have made it possible to improve natural
disaster warnings to the public with respect to
hurricanes, tornadoes, severe thunderstorms, and
flooding. The environmental satellite has earned its
distinction as an irreplaceable weather and ocean
observing tool.

Thus, it is fair to say that the operational environmental satellite is the most significant advance to occur in the history of environmental monitoring.

References

[1]"Summary of Pacific Input to the Eastland Fisheries Survey," Pacific Marine Fisheries Commission, Report 1977.

[2]"Eastland Fisheries Survey," Report to Congress, May 1977.

[3]Neumann, C. J., "A Statistical Study of Tropical Cyclone Positioning Errors with Economic Applications," NOAA Tech. Memo NWS/SR 82, 1975.

[4]White, R. M., "Environmental Satellites -- A Progress Report," The Military Engineer, July-Aug. 1973.

[5]Steinberg, R. "Airline Flight Planning -- The Weather Connection," Paper presented at Symposium on Commercial Aviation Energy Conservation Strategies, Washington, D.C., April 1981.

Earth Radiation Budget Satellite

Joseph A. Dezio*
NASA Goddard Space Flight Center, Greenbelt, Maryland
and
Clarence A. Jensen†
Ball Aerospace Systems Division, Boulder, Colorado

Abstract

As part of the National Climate Program, the National Aeronautics and Space Administration (NASA) has established the Earth Radiation Budget Experiment (ERBE) Research program to study the Earth radiation budget, which describes the thermal equilibrium that exists between the sun, the Earth, and space. The data collected will serve as a foundation from which to validate climate and long-range weather predictive models. The Earth Radiation Budget Satellite (ERBS) is a mid-inclination satellite of the Earth Radiation Budget Experiment Research Program and was launched from the Space Shuttle Orbiter (Mission 41-G) on October 5, 1984. The research program will also include two National Oceanic and Atmospheric Administration (NOAA) satellites (NOAA-F and NOAA-G) in near polar, sun synchronous orbits. All three satellites will carry an identical, two instrument package --ERBE-- to provide the basic data on the Earth radiation budget. The ERBS is a three-axis momentum-biased spacecraft that contains the operational subsystems for attitude control and determination, electrical power generation and storage, thermal control, orbit adjust propulsion and communications, as well as data handling. The satellite is capable of transmitting and receiving data through the NASA Spacecraft Tracking and Data Network (STDN) and the Tracking and Data Relay Satellite System (TDRSS). The ERBS was successfully launched from the Shuttle Challenger using the Remote Manipulator System (RMS). The satellite propelled itself to its current orbit ($\approx$610 km) using the on-board hydrazine system.

This paper is declared a work of the U.S. Government and therefore is in the public domain.
*ERBS Spacecraft Manager.
†ERBS Program Manager.

All subsystems and experiments have been activated and the total system is operating very successfully. The satellite is operated from the Multi-Satellite Operations Control Center at the NASA Goddard Spaceflight Center in Greenbelt, MD.

Introduction

Our land, air, and waters are engaged in a perpetual cycling of energy, absorbing solar radiation, emitting and reflecting thermal radiation into planetary space, and transporting energy in an endless attempt to balance temperatures around the globe. The interactions of this energy cycle determine our weather and shape our climate. To better understand the components and dynamics of the energy cycle, analogously referred to as the Earth radiation budget, the National Aeronautics and Space Administration (NASA) has established the Earth Radiation Budget Experiment (ERBE) Research Program, which includes the Earth Radiation Budget Satellite (ERBS) as the dedicated, mid-inclination orbiting element of that program.

The program will produce data sets of reflected and emitted energy at various spatial scales. Observations for one year will produce useful studies of geographical-seasonal variations of the Earth radiation budget. Concurrent data from Earth Radiation Budget Experiment instrument sets on two of the National Oceanic and Atmospheric Administration (NOAA) polar-orbiting satellites is also planned to be collected.

The Earth Radiation Budget Experiment Research Program is managed by NASA's Goddard Space Flight Center (GSFC) and Langley Research Center (LaRC). The Ball Aerospace Systems Division (BASD) of the Ball Corporation designed and built the ERBS spacecraft bus, integrated the scientific instruments, tested the satellite, and will support launch operations of the Space Shuttle Orbiter. BASD will also support the satellite for its orbital lifetime from the Project Operations Control Center located at GSFC.

The ERBS will be launched in the fall of 1984 from the NASA Space Shuttle Orbiter. This paper discusses the ERBS program in detail.

Program Background

During the 1960s, man's increasing awareness of his environment led him to study the phenomena that shape his habitat. In the late 1970s, the U. S. Congress enacted legislation establishing a National Climate Program to focus federal efforts aimed at understanding and responding to changes in climate.   In 1980, the government issued a five year plan for the National Climate Program. One of its major elements concerns the study of the Earth radiation budget.

Definition of the Earth Radiation Budget and Its Variables

The quantity known as the Earth radiation budget describes the thermal equilibrium existing between the sun, the Earth, and space. Measurements have shown that on an annual and global average, the Earth is nearly in thermal equilibrium; the annually averaged, global shortwave solar radiation absorbed balances the annually averaged global longwave thermal radiation emitted.   The excess in energy absorption in the tropics and deficit at the polar regions, which are due to differences in solar angle, cloud distribution, and surface reflectivity - are balanced by poleward transport of energy by the atmosphere and oceans.

In the atmosphere, several factors affect the transfer of radiant energy. Clouds and aerosol reflect and scatter radiation, while many trace gases (such as water and carbon dioxide) absorb radiation, giving rise to the so-called "greenhouse effect."   Other important factors include changes in surface reflectivity due to the seasonal snow cover and the extent of sea ice.

The amount of absorbed solar radiation during the day--varying for seasonal, latitudinal, and atmospheric conditions--has been estimated at 100-1000 W/m^2. Nevertheless, the heat is so well distributed over the globe that annually averaged emitted radiation is only about 140-300 W/m^2, depending on latitude. Given all the variables, the Earth radiation budget for a selected area may be determined by the equation:

Amount of solar radiation absorbed-amount of radiation emitted = net Earth radiation budget

Scientific Monitoring of the Earth Radiation Budget

Scientific investigation of the Earth radiation budget and related phenomena was facilitated by space-based monitoring. From the late 1960s, instruments flew on sounding rockets, balloons, and weather satellites to measure the variables of the atmosphere/hydrosphere/biosphere interaction that determines our climate and weather. Most notably, instruments to measure the Earth radiation budget flew on the TIROS/NOAA series and Nimbus satellites, as did instruments to study the radiation energetics of the atmosphere.

Concurrent with this research, NASA and other national and international groups sought to coordinate study of phenomena determining climate and weather.

NASA, in consultation with the National Academy of Science and the National Science Foundation, developed a long-range program designed to provide complete readings on the Earth radiation budget on a global, zonal, and regional scale. The multi-satellite, multi-instrument concept is now known as the Earth Radiation Budget Experiment Research Program. Its objective is to contribute to a comprehensive, long-term data base on the components of the Earth radiation budget that will serve as a foundation from which to validate climate and long-range weather predictive models. Such models will help us in adapting to changes in our environment that might otherwise undermine our economic and national security stances or those of the world itself.

Scope of Data Collection

To accumulate the appropriate data base, scientists recommended measurements at different spatial scales. Thus, observations will be made from a series of satellites carrying identical instruments over several years. Data will be taken continuously and integrated to provide variations over monthly, seasonal, annual, and interannual time scales. The geographical distribution for data collection will include four areas: 250 x 250 km (155 x 155 mile) regions, 1000 x 1000 km (622 x 622 mile) regions determined by the orbits of the multi-satellite system, ten degree latitudinal zones, and the entire planet.

At the smallest regional scale, it is necessary to measure such interactions as: the development of sea-surface temperature anomalies, the effects of ice and snow cover on atmospheric circulation, and Earth albedo variations in desert-vegetation boundary areas. On larger scales, the data returned will encompass: equator-to-pole gradients of the net radiation budget; average diurnal variations of the net radiation budget, measured monthly; and the time series of the solar constant.

In addition to measuring the solar-absorbed radiation
and terrestrial-emitted radiation, the program will monitor
the radiation energetics of the atmosphere, which include:
1) the amount of, and global distribution of, stratospheric
aerosols, and constituents such as nitrogen dioxide and
ozone; and 2) the natural background formed by ambient
constituents.

Space Segment Mission Plan

The Earth Radiation Budget Experiment Research Program
will begin its extensive, long-range monitoring in late
1984 when NASA and NOAA orbit the first satellite series
for these studies. The system will include two NOAA-class
satellites in near polar, sun-synchronous orbit (NOAA-F and
NOAA-G) and the mid-inclination ERBS satellite. All three
satellites will carry an identical, two-instrument package,
called the Earth Radiation Budget Experiment (ERBE).

Additional atmospheric physics and weather instruments
will be flown on the NOAA satellites. The ERBS will also
carry an instrument for monitoring the vertical distribution of stratospheric aerosols, ozone, and nitrogen dioxide
called the Stratospheric Aerosol and Gas Experiment II
(SAGE-II). This first satellite series is planned to operate for one year and its measurements will be analyzed and
archived as the data base for all users.

The Earth Radiation Budget Satellite Program

The ERBS is the mid-inclination satellite of the Earth
Radiation Budget Experiment Research Program and will be
deployed by the NASA Space Shuttle Orbiter in late 1984.

The three scientific instruments are the ERBE scanner
(ERBE-S), the ERBE nonscanner (ERBE-NS), and the Stratospheric Aerosol and Gas Experiment II (SAGE-II). The data
returned by the instruments will be analyzed and interpreted by LaRC and then combined with data taken by ERBE instruments aboard the NOAA satellites. GSFC and NOAA will
share the reduced, combined data. Scientific investigators
will also have access to the final data through the National Space Science Data Center.

ERBS Technical Description

The ERBS, as shown in Fig. 1, is a three-axis,
momentum-biased spacecraft carried in the Space Shuttle
Orbiter cargo bay and deployed by the Orbiter's Remote

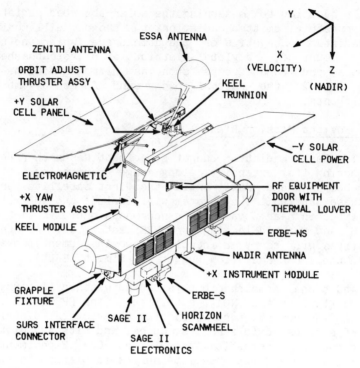

Fig. 1   ERBS configuration, on-orbit.

Manipulator System (RMS). The satellite contains the operational subsystems for attitude control and determination, electrical power generation and storage, thermal control, orbit-adjust propulsion, and communications and data handling through the NASA Spacecraft Tracking and Data Network (STDN), including the Tracking and Data Relay Satellite System (TDRSS). The spacecraft also houses the three scientific instruments and their associated electronics. Table 1 summarizes the parameters for the ERBS.

Spacecraft Structural/Mechanical Subsystem

The spacecraft structure, illustrated in an exploded view in Fig. 2 and in an assembled configuration in Fig. 3, is composed of three basic modules: keel, base, and instrument.

The keel module is a torque box design consisting of two removable honeycomb panels, riveted sheet metal side structure, and internal honeycomb bulkheads It provides

Table 1   ERBS operations summary

Spacecraft Type	3-axis momentum biased
Launch System	Space Shuttle/Remote Manipulator System
Orbit Altitude	610 km (379 miles)
Orbital Inclination	57°
Orbit Knowledge	± 250m (820 ft) altitude; 500m (1640 ft) along and cross track
Attitude Control	1° pitch and roll, 2° yaw; 0.01° per sec max rate
Attitude Knowledge	0.25° all axes at <0.005°/sec rate
Power Capability	470W orbit average to loads
Data Rate	1.6 and 12.8 Kbps (2 data streams); 32 Kbps and 128 Kbps tape recorder playback transmission
Timing	UTC ± 20 msec
Communications	S-band using NASA Spaceflight Tracking and Data Network and TDRSS — single and multiple access
Launch Configuration	4.6m (15 ft) wide × 3.8m (12.5 ft) high × 1.6m (5.2 ft) (length in bay)
Weight	2250 kg (4960 lbs)

structural support for the orbit-adjust propulsion system, the deployable solar array panels, and the Electronic Switching Spherical Array (ESSA) and zenith omni antennas. The basic ERBS X-axis loads (Orbiter Y axis) are carried by this structural module.

The base module is the core structural member of the spacecraft and houses or supports the remaining subsystem hardware and components. It is also a torque box structure that provides direct structural interface with the Shuttle through longeron trunnions on either end of the module.

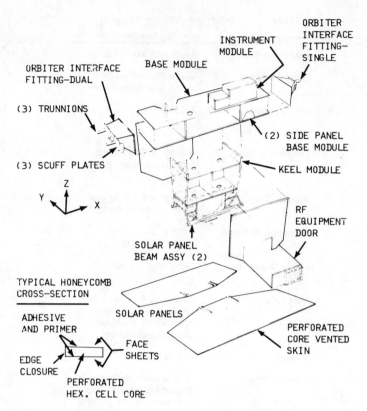

Fig. 2   ERBS spacecraft structure.

This structural element must also be stiff enough to provide and maintain the required alignments between the instruments and the attitude determination hardware components. The ERBE-NS instrument and its electronics mount
directly to the deck of the base module.

The instrument module is made up of honeycomb panels
that provide a stable optical bench for the ERBE-S and
SAGE-II instruments and the horizon scanners. This structure is mounted directly to the base module deck and provides the integrated alignment requirements necessary to
correlate the spacecraft position and attitude with the
instrument data scans.

The solar array substrates are aluminum honeycomb
panels which are 3.8 cm (1.5 in.) thick with 0.05 cm (0.020
in.) face sheets. They provide the mounting base for the
power system solar cells.

The ESSA antenna structure is an aluminum tube that interfaces with the antenna on one end and with the deployment mechanism on the other end. The antenna structure is secured to the keel module by a single release mechanism during launch.

The deployment and release mechanisms used on the solar arrays and the ESSA antenna contain redundant Non-Explosive Initiators (NEI) and are identical, except for the geometric changes required to interface with the different structures. The solar arrays and the ESSA antenna each have deployment mechanisms that use torsion springs to provide the deployment force. The deployment mechanisms also lock the appendages in a fixed position at the end of deployment.

Thermal Control Subsystem

The ERBS Thermal Control Subsystem (TCS) accommodates the large variations in thermal environments and internal heat dissipation that can occur during launch, in-bay checkout, RMS release, orbit injection, normal orbit operations, and potential mission abort. This is accomplished by using a combination of Multi-Layer Insulation (MLI), heaters, louvers, and thermal control finishes as illus-

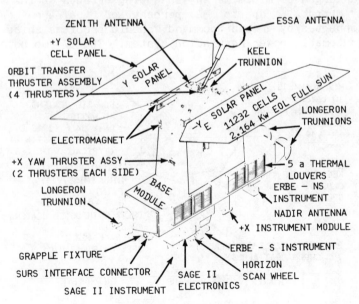

Fig. 3   ERBS spacecraft components.

trated in Figs. 4 and 5.   Except for the solar arrays and
ESSA antenna, the spacecraft is covered with 10-layered MLI
blankets inside Kapton covers.   Five louvers (totaling 15
ft^2) and a radiator (measuring 3.2 ft^2) interrupt the MLI
blankets on the anti-sun side. An 180 degree yaw maneuver
(required to keep the sun illumination on the solar arrays)
prevents the sun from ever illuminating the anti-sun side
of the spacecraft. The five louvers on the anti-sun side
reduce the day-night swing and handle the fully sunlit
orbits occurring when the beta angle (angle between the sun
line and orbit plane) exceeds 66 degrees.

Electrical Power Subsystem

The Electrical Power Subsystem (EPS) generates,
stores, controls, and distributes all electrical energy
required by the ERBS.   It utilizes proved, reliable hardware designs supplied by the same manufacturers that have
demonstrated successful orbital performance on previous
spacecraft. The operation of the EPS is illustrated in
Fig. 6 and the component locations in Fig. 7.

The electrical power is generated by two solar arrays
that, when deployed, are fixed with respect to the spacecraft body coordinates. The details of the key features of
the solar array are shown in Table 2. The cell circuits
are arranged to minimize any shadowing effects on the total
array output.   Up to 32 percent of the array can be
disconnected by ground command should problems arise with
the automatic power regulation system. The 50 amp-hour, 22

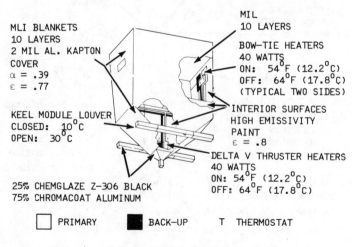

Fig. 4   Keel module thermal control.

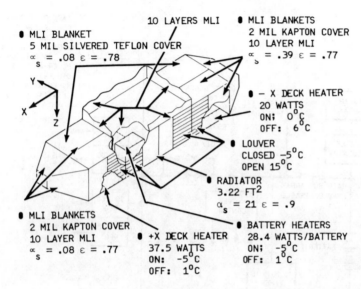

● MLI BLANKET
5 MIL SILVERED TEFLON COVER
$\alpha_s = .08$ $\epsilon = .78$

10 LAYERS MLI

● MLI BLANKETS
2 MIL KAPTON COVER
10 LAYER MLI
$\alpha_s = .39$ $\epsilon = .77$

● − X DECK HEATER
20 WATTS
ON; 0°C
OFF: 6°C

● LOUVER
CLOSED -5°C
OPEN 15°C

● RADIATOR
3.22 FT^2
$\alpha_s = 21$ $\epsilon = .9$

● MLI BLANKETS
2 MIL KAPTON COVER
10 LAYER MLI
$\alpha_s = .08$ $\epsilon = .77$

● +X DECK HEATER
37.5 WATTS
ON: -5°C
OFF: 1°C

● BATTERY HEATERS
28.4 WATTS/BATTERY
ON; -5°C
OFF: 1°C

Fig. 5   Base module thermal control.

cell nickel-cadmium batteries provide the energy storage
for the Electrical Power Subsystem.

The current from the array passes through the Standard
Power Regulation Unit (SPRU) where solid-state,
series-switching circuitry controls the array voltage and
thereby optimizes the current delivered to the common battery and load bus for battery charge control. The SPRU, in
response to the measured battery temperature and bus voltage, controls the charging current through three different
generating modes: 1) automatic tracking of the array characteristics to deliver maximum power to the spacecraft load
bus; 2) constant voltage (taper) charging at one of eight
command-selectable, temperature-compensated V/T (voltage/
temperature) levels; 3) trickle charging at a fixed current
in response to a charge completion signal from an
amphere-hour meter. The amphere-hour meter contains integrating logic and scaling circuitry for determining the
battery state-of-charge and also circuitry to develop temperature-compensated charge/discharge thresholds. The
output of the SPRU is connected directly to the essential
bus supplying subsystem components (such as the command
system) that are absolutely necessary to the survival the
spacecraft and cannot, therefore, be interrupted by
load-shedding circuitry. Other loads are supplied from the
essential bus via load-shedding relays.

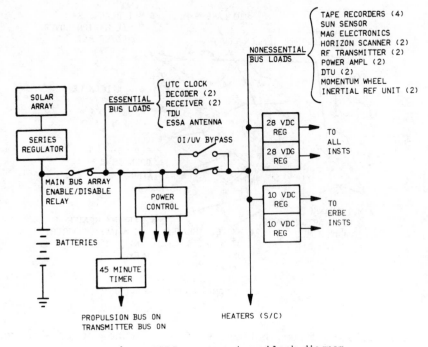

Fig. 6   ERBS power system, block diagram.

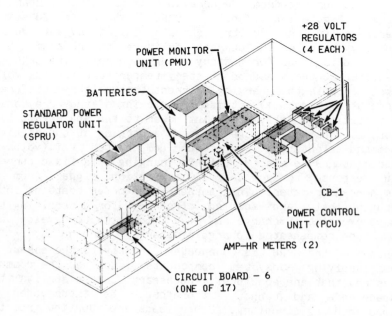

Fig. 7   ERBS power system components.

Table 2   Solar cell array key features

- Cells — Type K6.75 — Laid-Down Size — 2.08 × 6.25 cm (0.818 × 2.459 inches) — 10 ohm-cm

- Cell — Circuit Configuration — 144 Series Cells; 78 Strings

- Total Laid-Down Circuit Area — 14.57 meters² (157 ft²)

- Min. End of Life Current (At Max. Power Voltage of 63.2) 0.965 Sun — Normal Incidence, 28°C — 34.1 Amps

- Cover Slips — 0.03 cm (0.012 inches) Thick Fused Silica

- Interconnects — Silver-Plated Molybdenum

- Substrate Insulation — Micaply Type EG-802 — 0.0012 cm (0.003 inches) Thick

- Adhesive — McGhan Nusil R2568

- Conformal Coating — DOW-6-1109

- Isolation Diodes — Redundant Pair Each Pair of Strings
    Type — JANTX-IN5552 — Inverse Peak Rating — 600 Volts (M5)

The Power Control Unit (PCU) contains the load-shedding main bus and battery isolation relays, plus all of the current meters and the power and ground bus terminations. This unit is being used on ERBS without design changes from its application on the Solar Maximum spacecraft. The Power Monitor Unit (PMU) contains load-shedding and battery monitoring circuitry, relay drivers for the power relays in the PCU, and the command backup logic and interface circuitry required to accommodate the operation of the PCU and the SPRU.

Regulated power is supplied to the three experiments by four +28 Volt switching regulators, each rated at 60 Watts. Command-driven selection relays allow connection of either of two regulators to any individual experiment, thereby protecting against first and second level failures in the regulator complement. All regulators are equipped with a fold-back circuit that limits the output current to 1 ampere in case of a short on the output.

The EPS component description is given in Table 3.

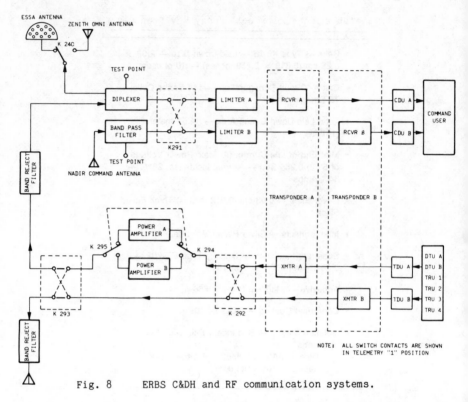

Fig. 8   ERBS C&DH and RF communication systems.

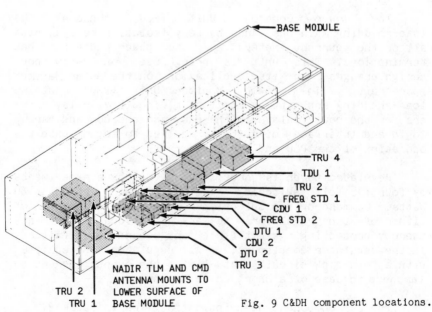

Fig. 9 C&DH component locations.

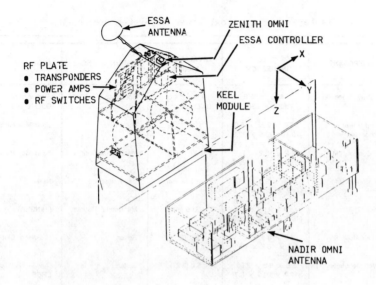

Fig. 10   ERBS communications subsystem.

Command and Data Handling Subsystem

Data collected by the scientific instruments and generated by the operational subsystems are processed by the
Command and Data Handling (C&DH) subsystem for real-time
transmission by the communications subsystem or storage
into four Tape Recorder Units (TRU) for later playback.
The C&DH subsystem, as illustrated in Fig. 8, uses redundant, cross-strapped components with backup modes to eliminate single-point failures. The subsystem includes two
Digital Telemetry Units (DTU), two Telemetry Distribution
Units (TDU), and two Command Decoder Units (CDU) as well as
the four TRUs. The placement of these components is shown
in Fig. 9.

The TDUs process information from the data sources,
generating signals compatible with the DTUs. The DTUs
create a serial data stream from these signals. The DTUs
have four formats available with 200 words /minor frame and
8 bits/word. The units include a maximum subcom depth of
32 frames and three format bit rates of 1.0, 1.6, and 12.8
kilobit/second. Words common to all formats are: major
frame counter, minor frame counter, format and bit rate
flags, and a 40 bit truncated Julian date with 1.0 millisecond resolution. A 24 bit synchronization pattern and a
command accept/reject count are also common to the units.

Table 3   Electrical power subsystem components

COMPONENT	SIZE INCHES (CM)	TOTAL WEIGHT LB (KG)	MANUFACTURER	FLOWN ON
Solar Array Panels (2)	143.0 × 92.0 (363.0 × 234.0)	119.0 (54.0) (W/O Substrate)	Specrolab	Similar to SME, OSO-H, and E-28
Standard Power Regulator Unit	27.6 × 9.25 × 8.0 (70.1 × 23.5 × 20.3)	41.0 (18.6)	Gulton	Solar Max Mission
Power Control Unit	35.5 × 10.2 × 11.7 (90.2 × 25.9 × 29.7)	53.6 (24.3)	MacDonnell-Douglas	Solar Max Mission
Power Monitor Unit	17.6 × 9.0 × 9.0 (44.7 × 22.9 × 22.9)	25.1 (−1.4)	Ball Aerospace	New
Batteries (2)	18.9 × 11.7 × 9.0 (48.0 × 29.7 × 22.9)	231.5 (105)	MacDonnell-Douglas	(LANDSAT–D)*
Amp-Hour Meter (2)	3.5 × 6.6 × 4.3 (8.9 × 16.8 × 10.9)	6.2 (2.8)	Gulton	Lockheed, Block V
+28 Volt Regulators (4)	5.0 × 8.0 × 2.65 (12.7 × 20.3 × 6.7)	5.0 (2.27)	Gulton	New — Qualified on ERBS
Circuit Bd. Assy's (17)	7.0 × 12.0 × 2.4 (17.8 × 30.5 × 6.1)	69.7 (31.1)	BASD	New — Qualified on ERBS

The Frequency Standard Unit (FSU) provides a highly stable oscillator to synchronize data handling and allow experiment and spacecraft "events" to be correlated to universal time to within 20 milliseconds. This limit is maintained without need of ground-commanded adjustment more often than once every six days. A synchronous countdown chain in the TDU provides twelve unique timing signals of 0.031-2.048 Hz for experiment and spacecraft functions. The output of only one clock and countdown chain is in control at any given time.

The TRUs have an input rate of 1.6 and 12.8 kilobit/second of real-time data and 32 and 128 kilobit/second playback data. Input data are formated at the "non-return-to-zero" level and output data are either convolutionally encoded over the four ranges for compatibility with TDRSS or encoded and filtered for GSTDN. Each of the four TRUs is capable of recording approximately 19.5 hours of 1.6 kilobit/second data and approximately 2.5 hours of 12.8 kilobit/second data for science data storage. This capability will allow twelve continuous orbits without a data dump with no loss of data. The TRU dumps are downlinked at one of two selectable data rates (32 or 128 kilobit/seconds) and are nominally planned to occur 7-8 times per day. Uplink commands are decoded and executed by

Table 4   C&DH and communication subsystems component summary

COMPONENT	MASS KG (LBS)	SIZE WIDTH/ LENGTH/HGT CM (INCHES)	POWER (WATTS)	SUPPLIER	HERITAGE
Zenith Omni Antenna	0.3 (0.66)	3 dia × 2 H (1.2 dia × 0.79 H)	—	Ball	Single ESSA Element
ESSA Hi-Gain Antenna	29.9 (65.9)	76 dia (29.9 dia) 4/5 Sphere	10.0 (Driver)	Ball	New — Qualified on ERBS
ESSA Controller	4.1 (9.0)	33.0/22.9/21.6 (13.0/9.0/8.5)	8.3	Ball	New — Qualified on ERBS
NADIR CMD and TLM Antennas (on common ground plane and pedestal)	1.0 (2.2)	34.3/25.4/1.9 (13.5/10.0/0.75)	—	Ball	SME
NASA Standard TDRSS/ GSIDN Transponder	6.4 (14.1)	25.4/35.5/10.7 (10.0/14.0/4.2)	10.2 RCV 15.0 Trans.	Motorola	MMS, Landsat D, SME
28 Watt S-Band Power Amplifier	6.6 (14.6)	12.7/19.1/3.6 (5.0/7.5/1.4)	168 Watts	Loral/Conic	New — Qualified/TDRSS tested on ERBS; adapted from a higher power transmitter; used on missile applications
Telemetry Distribution Unit (TDU)	7.1 (15.7)	22.9/20.3/15.4 (9.0/8.0/6.1)	5.7	Ball	Similar to unit qualified and flown SME
Command Decoder Unit (CDU)	4.5 (9.9)	16.5/12.7/8.9	5.0 Operate 1.5 Standby	Gulton	Qualified for HCMM and SAGE and used on SME
Digital Telemetry Unit (DTU)	4.5 (9.9)	20.6/12.7/8.9 (6.5/5.0/3.5)	13.0	Gulton	Qualified for HCMM and SAGE and used on SME
Tape Recorder Unit (TRU)	8.9 (19.6)	30.5/22.9/15.3 (12.0/9.0/6.0)	9.8 Record 15.4 P/B 2.2 Standby	Odetics	Developed/flown on many USAF satellites; requalified for ERBS; comparable unit on P-78-1, DE
Frequency Standard Unit (FSU)	0.77 (1.7)	7.3/19.5/8.0 (2.9/7.7/3.2)	3.0 Watts — Operate	Gulton/ Frequency Electronics, Inc.	New application for a standard product line; qualified on ERBS

the CDUs. The CDUs receive the commands at a rate of 125 bit/s bps or 1.0 kbps from the transponder. The units use a nonreturn-to-zero level format with three types of commands: high-level discrete at 28 V, 200 mA, 45 ms pulse; low-level discrete, ground closure 20 mA sink, 45 ms pulse; and serial digital at 16 bits, TTL compatible, 10 kHz rate. The CDUs have a memory capability of 48 hours with a 2 s resolution.

The C&DH and communications subsystem components are shown in Table 4.

Communications Subsystem

The Communications Subsystem (CS), as shown in Figs. 8 and 10, interfaces with the C&DH subsystem using redundant, cross-strapped components. The subsystem includes two NASA TDRSS/GSTDN standard transponders, two RF power amplifiers, an Electronically Steerable Spherical Array (ESSA) antenna, and a nadir and zenith omnidirectional antenna system. The transponders detect and demodulate the uplink commands and then route them to the CDUs. The transponders also accept and modulate signals from the DTUs or TRUs for the return-link transmission. One transponder can be connected to the ESSA or zenith omnidirectional antenna by command. The second is linked with the nadir antenna. The transponders may be switched to either antenna system at ground command in the event of a failure. The power amplifiers boost the 2.5 Watt output from the transponder to the 28 Watt used to drive the ESSA antenna.

The ESSA provides the main TDRSS interface for both the command and telemetry links. Its high gain beam is pointed by a microprocessor-driven ESSA antenna controller to maintain the RF illumination of the TDRSS satellite. The zenith and nadir omnidirectional antennas provide backup for the TDRSS and GSTDN interfaces in the event of an ESSA failure. Both antenna systems are tuned to the defined S-band frequencies. The zenith and nadir antennas are mounted to fixed masts but the ESSA is deployed while the ERBS is attached to the Shuttle's Remote Manipulator System (RMS).

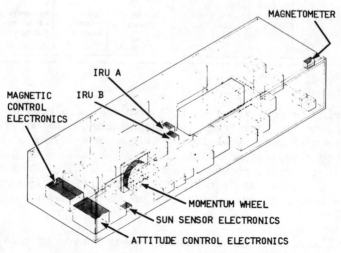

Fig. 11   ACDS base module components.

Attitude Control and Determination Subsystem

The Attitude Control and Determination Subsystem (ACDC) is a three-axis, momentum-biased, closed-loop system to be used for attitude pointing, maneuvers, and thruster control. The subsystem consists of a momentum wheel, two scanwheels, four electromagnets, a magnetometer, magnetic control electronics, attitude control electronics, two inertial reference units, and sun sensor heads and electronics. Figure 11 shows the ACDS components in the base module. The scanwheels are shown in the orbital configuration previously illustrated in Fig. 1.

For most of the mission, the satellite maintains a nadir-pointing attitude. The momentum bias is provided by the Momentum Wheel (MW) that spins about the pitch axis. Control of the pitch attitude is effected by slowing or decelerating the MW, which has a torque capability of 0.4 N·m. The gyroscopic stability resulting from the MW limits roll and yaw attitude motions that result from internal and external disturbances. Electromagnets react against the Earth's field and apply control torques of 0.003 N·m to the observatory to keep the MW speed in the operating range, correct roll errors (and, indirectly, yaw errors) by precessing the observatory/MW combination, and damp nutation of the observatory. The Earth-pointing mode uses earth horizon scanners to detect attitude errors and the magnetometer to determine appropriate electromagnet commands based on the sensed Earth's field. Due to the scanner design, this system can also maintain attitude in the 90 degree pitch and 180 degree pitch orientations.

The ACDS executes a 180 degree yaw reorientation to get the proper solar array illumination each time the orbit

Table 5   ACDS operating modes

MODE	FUNCTION
Earth Pointing	Pitch control, roll/yaw control (precession), nutation damping, and wheel desaturation.
Stabilization for Orbit Transfer	Hold observatory Z axis along velocity vector to within 6° based on a pitch of 90° for velocity change.
Yaw reorientation	Uses thrusters and inertial reference unit to rotate about the Z axis.
Pitch Maneuvers	Two used: 90° for velocity change thrusting and one 180° for the ERBE-NS calibration.
Acquisition	Reacquires coarse three axis local vertical orientation using only elecromagnets if normal mode is interrupted.

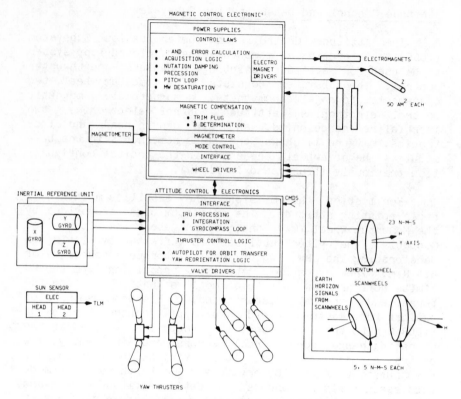

Fig. 12   ACDS functional block diagram.

precesses through the sun line. During orbit adjust thrusting, the ACDS performs as an autopilot controlling the on-times of the four ΔV thrusters. To achieve this, a three-axis, Inertial Reference Unit (IRU) provides signals to the Attitude Control Electronics (ACE) that controls the thrusters. Three-axis stabilization of the observatory is also accomplished with this system for operating modes that do not use the momentum biased magnetic system.

Attitude determination is accomplished onboard in the control electronics using the IRU in a gyrocompass configuration. The IRU is updated in pitch and roll by the horizon sensors. The IRU data filters noise such as cold clouds and thus improves accuracy.

Figure 12 shows a functional block diagram of the ACDS. The narrow field of view of the scanwheel generates a 45 deg cone as it rotates about the pitch axis and thus provides the Earth-space and space-Earth transitions for use in computing pitch and roll attitude The operating modes of the ACDS are summarized in Table 5.

Attitude determination is performed continuously on-board in the ACE using IRU and horizon scanner signals. The scanwheels measure the observatory pitch and roll attitude. The IRU measures rates about all three axes. The ACE integrates these rates to maintain an attitude reference. The roll and pitch angles are updated continuously from the horizon scanners to remove the effects of uncompensated gyro drifts. A gyrocompass loop is used to minimize the effects of the yaw gyro drift. The sun sensors provide data to the ground for periodic adjustment of the ACE by ground commands. The ACDS components are shown in Table 6.

Orbit Adjust Propulsion Subsystem

The ERBS Orbit Adjust Propulsion System (OAPS) is a monopropellant hydrazine propulsion system which uses ni-

Table 6   ACDS components

COMPONENT	UNIT MASS KG (LBS)	SIZE CM (INCHES)	POWER (WATTS)	VENDOR	HERITAGE
Momentum Wheel	8.3 (18.2)	14 × 31 dia (5.5 × 12.2 dia)	8.9	Bendix	ATS, SEASAT
Electromagnets (4)	1.6 (3.6)	64 × 2.5 dia (25 × 1.0 dia)	1.0	Ithaco	AEM, SEASAT, SME
Earth Horizon Scanner (2)	6.8 (15.1)	14 × 20 dia (5 × 8 dia)	6.0	Ithaco	AEM, SEASAT
Magnetic Control Electronics	8.1 (17.8)	37 × 16 × 19 (15 × 6 × 7)	10.0	Ithaco	AEM, SEASAT, IUE, SME
Magnetometer	0.3 (0.7)	7 × 7 × 12 (3 × 3 × 5)	0.7	Ithaco (Schonstedt)	AEM, SEASAT, P78-1, SME
Inertial Reference Unit	2.6 (5.7)	11 × 16 × 18 (4 × 6 × 7)	21.0	Northrop	P80-1
Sun Sensor	1.0 (2.2)	3 × 16 × 21 (1.2 × 6 × 8)	1.6	Adcole	IUE
Attitude Control Electronics	11.2 (24.8)	23 × 23 × 38 (9 × 9 × 15)	7.4	BASD	New — Qualified on ERBS

trogen pressurant operating in a blowdown, or nonregulated,
mode for maximum reliability.   The propellant is stored in
two 72 cm (28 inch) diameter.   Shuttle APU tanks separated
from the pressurant by standard AF-E-332 positive displacement diaphragms. The propellant is directed first through
a system filter, then through a series of latching isolation valves with integral filters, and finally through dual
series control valves having integral filters before reaching any thruster. The control valves are operated by the
Attitude Control Electronics (ACE), while the latching
valves are controlled directly by ground command. The
block diagram for the OAPS is shown in Fig. 13.

     When the system is serviced on the ground, propellant
is pressurized up to the latch valves, which are not opened
until the observatory is clear of the Orbiter. The latch
valves, which can also be used to isolate a malfunctioning
thruster, represent an additional level of safety over and
above the already redundant series of propellant control
valves. The probability of leakage of hydrazine through
any thruster is extremely remote.

     The four ΔV thruster quad-assembly is roughly aligned
with the observatory X axis as depicted in Fig. 14. Each

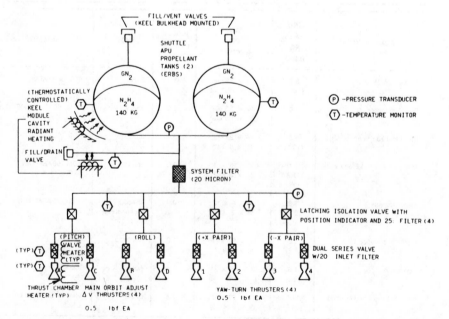

Fig. 13 Orbit adjust propulsion subsystem, block diagram.

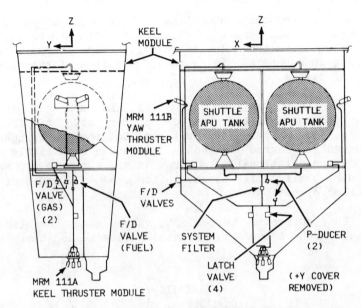

Fig. 14   OAPS component locations.

thruster is canted 12 deg , thus creating moment arms of 50 cm (20 inch) about the observatory center of mass. These moment arms permit the OAPS to generate X and Y (yaw and pitch) attitude torques during ascent and orbit sustenance maneuvers. This is accomplished by systematically reducing slightly the 100% duty cycle of a particular thruster as required. The thruster cant angle is selected to guarantee more than adequate control authority with worst-case center-of-mass shifts and thruster misalignments, while sacrificing only a 2% reduction in the ΔV impulse. The quad-assembly as a unit is also canted very slightly to symmetrically encompass the computed observatory center of gravity location. To minimize "pinwheel" disturbance torques about the Z axis due to thrust vector misalignments, nozzle throats are clustered in a tight 5 cm (2 in.) diam circle about the Z axis. This ΔV thruster configuration provides orbit adjustment without any catastrophic failure modes. Failure of one thruster merely requires shutdown of the opposing thruster via the appropriate isolation latch valve.

ERBS orbit raising is expected to take approximately 15-18 hours of operationally segmented continuous thrusting, depending upon the propellant temperature and pressure. The ΔV thrusters are also used for orbit maintenance maneuvers, normally operating while in a 90 degree pitched-over spacecraft orientation, which is parallel to the velocity vector. The ΔV thrusters also act as a backup for attitude control in case of failure of the magnetic control system.

The four yaw-turn thrusters are arranged in two "bow-tie" assemblies, one on either side of the keel module. Their principal use is to provide torques for required 180 degree yaw-around maneuvers with little or no induced translational ΔV. They also serve to oppose any residual small roll pinwheel torques produced during ΔV thruster operation.

The subsystem propellant valves and thrusters are fitted with integrally mounted heaters and temperature

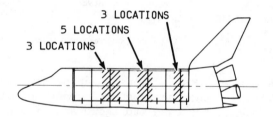

COMPATIBLE LOCATIONS IN
THE CARGO BAY

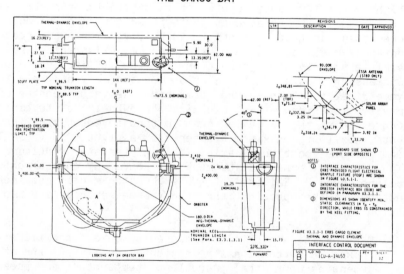

Fig. 15   ERBS cargo bay location.

sensors. Tanks and lines are radiatively heated by continuously enabled, thermostatically controlled panel-type
heaters located within the thermally insulated keel module.

Flight Support Equipment

The ERBS mounts directly to the Orbiter's cargo bay,
using one keel and three longeron fittings. The ERBS position in the cargo bay is illustrated in Fig. 15. An
Orbiter Interface Box (OIB) provides the electrical interface between the Orbiter's electrical and data system and
the spacecraft while the spacecraft is attached in the bay.
The OIB contains the necessary circuitry for battery
charging and interface data conditioning. The OIB mounts
to the Orbiter's bridge fitting on the port side just forward of the longeron trunnion. The Orbiter Standard
Mixed-Cargo Harness (SMCH) cables are connected directly to
the bottom side of the OIB. These cables connect the OIB
to the Orbiter avionics in the aft flight deck and to the
T-0 umbilical connectors. Orbiter direct current power is
connected to the OIB by cable from the aft payload power
bus.

The OIB is electrically connected to the ERBS through
the dematable umbilical called the Standard Umbilical
Release Retract System (SURS). The spring-loaded SURS arm
contains the connector plug and is mounted on the port
Orbiter bridge fitting between the OIB and the longeron
fitting. The umbilical receptacle is mounted on the ERBS.
The SURS cables on the arm mate to the interface connectors
on the OIB. The SURS connectors are mated manually. The
SURS release solenoids are controlled by the Orbiter crew
through the deployment and pointing panel in the Orbiter
aft flight deck.

The Electrical Flight Grapple Fixture (EFGF) provides
the electrical and mechanical connections between the
Shuttle Orbiter Remote Manipulator System (RMS), Standard
End Effector (SEE) and the ERBS spacecraft. The EFGF
mounts to the ERBS spacecraft through an Extra-Vehicular
Activity (EVA) dematable grapple fixture pedestal. This
pedestal is a two-piece structure that incorporates the
capability for EVA separation in case of malfunction in the
RMS/EFGF interface. The grappling action by the EFGF
mechanically attaches the ERBS to the RMS and engages the
EFGF connector with the SEE connector. The RMS is used to
remove the ERBS from the cargo bay, configure the ERBS for
deployment, and then release the ERBS from the Orbiter.

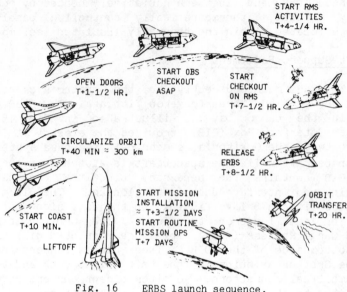

Fig. 16   ERBS launch sequence.

The original EFGF was designed and developed by SPAR Aerospace Products, Ltd. of Canada for the University of Iowa's Plasma Diagnostic Package contract with NASA/MSFC (Marshall Space Flight Center). This design has been modified to meet the ERBS requirements.

The ERBS contains thermal sensors, accelerometers, and microphones to monitor the thermal, dynamic, and acoustic environment of the shuttle launch. The data is recorded on the Orbiter payload recorder for postflight evaluation.

Deployment Sequence and Orbit Injection

The Orbiter is launched into a 350 km (190 n. mi.) circular orbit. The ERBS is released from the Orbiter by the Remote Manipulator System. After separation from the RMS, the spacecraft's Orbit Adjust Propulsion System (OAPS) is fired in a programmed sequence to raise the orbital altitude to 610 km (330 n. mi.). The launch and deployment sequence is shown in Fig. 16.

Scientific Instruments

The three scientific instruments aboard ERBS are directed by scientific investigative teams from the NASA Langley Research Center. The ERBE dual-instrument package

is provided by TRW Systems, Inc., and includes nonscanner
and scanner sensors that will measure the radiation budget
and solar constant. The third instrument, SAGE II, was
built by Ball Aerospace Systems Division (BASD) and monitors concentrations and distributions of stratospheric
aerosols, nitrogen dioxide, and other constituents affecting the radiation energetics of the Earth's atmosphere.

Earth Radiation Budget Experiment

The ERBE dual instrument will provide the measurements
required to determine the Earth radiation budget on several
spatial scales and a multitemporal scale. Both ERBE instruments will return data in the 0.2-50 μm range, providing
readings of solar-absorbed radiation and emitted thermal
radiation monthly on regional, zonal, and global scales.
Analysis of the data will also derive: the equator-to-pole
energy transfer gradient; average diurnal variations,
monthly and regionally, of the radiation budget; and the
solar output constant. The data will also be analyzed to
ascertain instrument engineering integrity, calibration
procedure effectiveness, and the efficiency of sampling and
analysis to derive "top-of-the-atmosphere" fluxes.

The ERBS instrument contains a total of eight channels
distributed in two sensor packages: the ERBE nonscanner
(ERBE-NS) and the ERBE scanner (ERBE-S).

ERBE Nonscanner. The ERBE-NS instrument, as illustrated in Fig. 17, includes five channels with cavity
radiometer detectors. Four of the channels are primarily

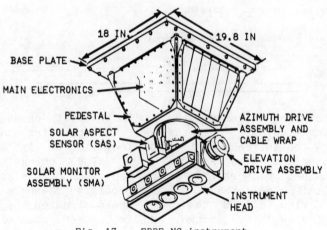

Fig. 17   ERBE-NS instrument.

Table 7 Instrument physical characteristics

SAGE-II

Size: 24.0 cm x 24.86 cm x 22.5 cm
             (9.4 x 9.8 x 8.9 inches) — electronics module
             38.7 cm (diameter) x 68.5 cm (length)
             (15.2 x 27.0 inches) — instrument module

Weight: 33.6 kg (74.1 lbs.)

Power: 14W (average); 45W (peak)

Data Rate: 6.3 kbps

ERBE SCANNER

Size: 54 cm (diameter) x 59 cm (length)
             (21.3 x 23.2 inches)

Weight: 29 kg (63.9 lbs.)

Power: 28W (orbit average)

Data Rate: 960 bps

ERBE NON—SCANNER

Size: Envelope with Contamination Cover closed —
             45.7 cm x 50.3 cm x 62.4 cm (length)
             (18.0 x 19.8 x 24.6 inches)

Weight: 32 kg (70.5 lbs.)

Power: 22W (orbit average)

Data Rate: 160 bps

nadir-pointing (Earth viewing), with the fifth channel used
for solar viewing.   Of the four nadir-pointing channels,
two view the entire Earth's disk from limb to limb and are
designated the Wide Field-of-View (WFOV) channels. One
WFOV channel measures the total radiation of the Earth at
0.2-50 μm. The other two nadir-pointed channels have a
field of view of 88 deg and are designated the medium
field-of-view (MFOV) channels. Like the WFOV channels, one
MFOV channel measures the total radiation of the Earth and

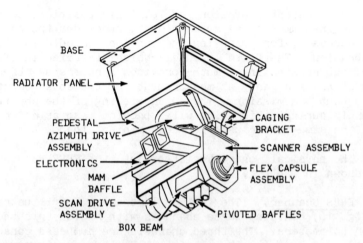

Fig. 18   ERBE-S instrument.

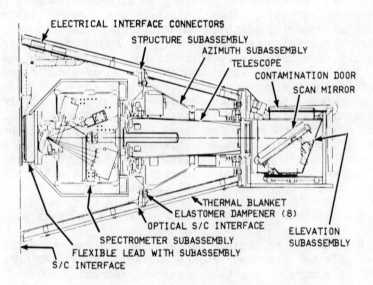

Fig. 19   SAGE-II instrument.

the other channel measures the shortwave radiation. For
both WFOV and MFOV, the Earth-emitted, longwave radiation
component is determined by subtracting the shortwave
Earth-reflected radiation channel measurement at 0.2-5.0 µm
from the total radiation channel measurement of 0.2-50 µm.

The four Earth-viewing detectors are mounted on an
elevation gimbal that, when commanded, rotates the detec-

tors to a present elevation angle. This position, coupled
with an instrument's azimuth gimbal, provides the net motion necessary for observing the sun for periodic in-flight
calibration. The fifth channel--which is fixed in elevation, but rotates in azimuth--provides a reference observation of the sun and a measurement of the solar constant
throughout the mission. The solar viewing of the shortwave
channels during calibration will provide a solar reference
with the same sensor used for determining albedo.

The physical characteristics of the ERBE Nonscanner
are shown in Table 7.

ERBE Scanner. The ERBE-S instrument, as illustrated
in Fig. 18, contains three channels with radiometric thermistor bolometers. The three channels are numbered consecu-
tively 6, 7, and 8. Channel 6 isolates the shortwave radiation at 0.2-5 µm, channel 7 covers the longwave radiation
at 5-50 µm; and channel 8 provides total radiation measurements at 0.2-50 µm. These channels are located within a
continuously moving scanhead assembly that is oriented to
perform cross-track scanning with a rapid retrace. A
two-point, in-flight calibration is provided for each channel. For one point, each channel views space during each
scan for zero radiance. For the shortwave and total radiation channels, the second calibration point is obtained
periodically when the sun is in position for viewing. The
second calibration point for the longwave channel is provided by a precision, onboard blackbody. There is an additional precision onboard blackbody for the total radiation channel to view, and a shortwave internal calibration
source for the shortwave channel to view.

The physical characteristics are shown in Table 7.

In addition to flying as a dual instrument on ERBS,
ERBE-S will be launched aboard NOAA-F (1984) and NOAA-G
(1986) as a part of the ERBE Research Program.

Stratospheric Aerosol and Gas Experiment II

The SAGE-II is a seven-channel radiometer designed to
map aerosol, nitrogen dioxide, and other constituent concentrations in the atmosphere at 10-150 km. Readings will
be taken in the 0.385-1.020 µm range over latitudes of 70°N
and 70°S. Such measurements will provide insights into
constituent distribution patterns and their effect on climate; the influences of transient phenomena, such as vol-

canic ejecta, on constituent transport patterns and circulation; and tropospheric-stratospheric exchange.

The SAGE-II instrument, as shown in Fig. 19, is a sun-scanning radiometer constructed of a Cassegrain telescope and a Rowland circle spectrometer. An external scan mirror reflects solar radiation into the telescope, scanning the solar image over the entrace slit of the spectrometer, which then disperses it into seven wavelength bands. The seven channels and their spectral ranges are given in Table 8. The detectors are silicon photodiodes. Channels 1, 2, 3, 4, and 7 use neutral density filters. Channels 2, 5, and 6 use bandpass filters.

SAGE-II operates at orbital sunrise and sunset. Its instantaneous field of view is 0.5 x 2.5 arcmin, corresponding to an latitudinal coverage of 0.4 km measured at the horizon of the Earth. The mirror scans across the sun through the vertical field of view of 5 degrees.

The instrument's solar intensity measurements, along with spacecraft and solar ephemeris data, provide extinction altitude profiles as a function of latitude and longitude with a vertical height resolution of 1 km (0.6 miles). The instrument takes calibration readings on an unattenuated solar disk just after orbital sunrise and just before orbital sunset.

The physical characteristics are shown in Table 7.

SAGE-II is the fourth in a series of stratospheric aerosol monitors. earlier models of the remote sensor have flown on the Apollo/Soyuz test projects (1975), Nimbus (1978), and Applications Explorer Mission 2 (1979).

Table 8 SAGE-II spectral characteristics

Channel	Central Wavelength (m)
1	1.020
2	0.940
3	0.600
4	0.525
5	0.453
6	0.448
7	0.385

Project Operations Control Center

The Project Operations Control Center (POCC) is the controlling facility for all spacecraft mission operations. The POCC contains all of the processing resources, switching, control consoles, and testing facilities to operate the mission assigned. All spacecraft operations will be conducted by Bendix Field Engineering Corporation personnel under the direction of Ball Aerospace Systems Division.

The POCC for the ERBS mission is the Multi-Satellite Operations Control Center (MSOCC-1). MSOCC-1 Operations and Maintenance personnel (O&M) will provide support for operations of the various hardware and software systems. Routine support under this program includes the following:

1) Mission planning/terminal scheduling interface.

2) Generation of MSOCC-1 computer schedules.

3) Operation of TACs and PDP-11/70 systems.

4) Configuration interface for data lines.

5) Data line test and troubleshooting interface.

6) Hardware maintenance.

7) Software maintenance (program maintenance library).

8) Distribution of data products and messages.

9) Off-line processing per project request.

All services will be coordinated with the ERBS Flight Operations Team (FOT) on a routine or as-required basis. MSOCC-1 computers will generally be set up, verified, and turned over to the FOT approximately 20 minutes prior to schedule data Acquisition-Of-Signal (AOS). Data line interfaces through the Network Control Center and NASCOM will be verified and turned over to the FOT 5 minutes prior to AOS. MSOCC-1 data operations controllers will be debriefed postpass and the systems released for other support. The MSOCC-1 will support approximately 8-12 real-time passes of 25 minutes each per day with a 22 minute 32 kilobit/s tape recorder dump on each TDRSS pass. If the GSTDN is used, the MSOCC-1 will support 8-12 real-time passes of 10 minutes each per day with a 6 minute 128 kilobit/s tape recorder dump on each pass. Off-line processing and POCC command memory management is estimated at approximately 80-160 minutes of support time per day in MSOCC-1.

The Upper Atmosphere Research Satellite

P.T. Burr* and C.A. Rebert†

NASA Goddard Space Flight Center, Greenbelt, Maryland

Abstract

The Upper Atmosphere Research Satellite (UARS) will provide, for the first time, data on a global basis for the study of the physical processes acting within and upon the stratosphere, mesosphere, and lower thermosphere. Specifically, the areas of scientific study to be addressed are energy input and loss, photochemistry, dynamics, and the coupling among processes and between atmospheric regions. The UARS is a single observatory consisting of a multimission modular spacecraft (MMS) and an instrument module containing 10 scientific instruments. The satellite will be Shuttle launched and placed in a 57 deg inclined orbit at 600 km altitude. A Central Data Handling Facility (CDHF) will receive data from the satellite and process these data into atmospheric quantities for use by the science team. The "processed" data will be stored at the CDHF and will be available via communication lines for analysis by the investigators at their home laboratories using remote computers. Together with other satellite programs, balloons, sounding rockets, and laboratory efforts, UARS will make available the opportunity for extensive coordination of data devoted to solar terrestrial study.

Introduction

Background

There has been increasing concern in recent years about the sensitivity of the Earth's atmosphere to external influences associated with natural phenomena and the changes arising as by-products of various human activities. Long-standing curiosity about atmospheric evolution and the factors influencing climate and weather has been sharpened and refocused by the discovery of technological threats that introduce the possibility of inadver-

---

Presented as Paper 84-0482 at the AIAA 22nd Aerospace Sciences Meeting, Reno, Nevada, January 9-12, 1984. Copyright © 1981 by the American Institute of Aeronautics and Astronautics, Inc. All rights reserved.
*Project Manager, Upper Atmosphere Research Satellite Project.
†Project Scientist, Upper Atmosphere Research Satellite Project.

tent atmospheric modification. Such changes, occurring in both the troposphere and the upper atmosphere, have far-reaching consequences for the
terrestrial habitat and may eventually set the basic constraints governing
man's life on this planet. These potential threats, and other possible changes
that may occur in the atmosphere, highlight the need for a long-term program of scientific research directed toward improving our knowledge of the
physical and chemical processes occurring in the Earth's atmosphere.

The Upper Atmosphere Research Satellite (UARS) is an important new
mission aimed at improving our knowledge of the atmosphere above the
troposphere, including those regions that are known to be especially susceptible to substantial change by external agents. The UARS will provide a
focus for the resolution of scientific questions relating to the chemistry,
dynamics, and overall energy balance of these regions, particularly with regard to the stratosphere and mesosphere. Through a balance between measurements, theoretical studies of basic processes, and model analysis, it
seems likely that substantial progress will be made in solving the outstanding
physical and chemical problems of these regions. Since its inception, the use
of extensive theoretical activity coupled to data and mode analyses is an
integral part of the program.

Coupling among Radiative, Dynamical, and Photochemical Processes

The energetics, chemistry, and dynamics of the upper atmosphere cannot be treated in isolation from each other, but must be viewed as highly
coupled processes with both positive and negative feedbacks among them.
Variability in the ozone induced photochemically by perturbations in
chemically active trace species will lead to variability in the distribution of
radiative heating due to the absorption and emission of radiation by ozone.
In turn, this will lead to variations in the temperature distribution. Since the
temperature and wind in the upper atmosphere are closely coupled (they
both depend on the pressure distribution), temperature variability implies
variability in the winds and hence in the transport of trace species. Such
temperature and wind variability will itself generate changes in the ozone
distribution due both to the temperature dependence of photochemistry
and the redistribution of various trace gases by the winds. The net effect
of these couplings may be to either enhance or decrease the original ozone
change. A full understanding of possible anthropogenic perturbations to the
ozone layer requires that the energy sources and sinks, photochemical and
dynamical processes be treated as a coupled system for the global upper
atmosphere.

In addition to the coupling processes mentioned above, it is essential
to consider the radiative, dynamical, and chemical coupling between the
upper and lower atmospheres. The budget of the ozone layer depends critically on the transfer of trace species between the troposphere and the
stratosphere. The distribution and magnitude of such transfer is itself believed to be sensitive to variations in the tropospheric circulation. Such
variations, which may be associated with natural or anthropogenically in-

duced climate variability, provide an important link between the problems of ozone change and climate change. An example of one aspect of this linkage is the role of water vapor. It is believed that the observed extreme aridity of the stratosphere is due to the "freeze drying" of air entering the stratosphere through the tropical tropopause. Any climate change that significantly altered the temperature of the tropical tropopause could substantially change the water budget of the upper atmosphere, with profound consequences for the photochemistry of the region.

In addition to the links provided between the troposphere and stratosphere due to radiatively active gases and to other chemical transport, there are dynamical links related to the vertical propagation of planetary-scale meteorological waves. The behavior of such waves is sensitive to the distribution of mean winds in the upper atmosphere. Under some conditions, it is believed that irregularities in the circulation of the upper atmosphere may cause anomalous reflection of such waves and thus significantly affect short-term climate variability at the ground. Global observations of the upper atmosphere and its dynamical links to the troposphere and extensive theoretical work are required to definitely establish the role of the upper atmosphere in weather and climate. However, the fact that current forecast models which include the stratosphere provide better forecasts of the weather than do models which omit the stratosphere suggests that significant links exist.

Mission Characteristics

Scientific Measurements

The measurement requirements for the UARS mission and the scientific justification for those requirements were delineated by the UARS Science Working Group (SWG) and published in their final report in 1978. In general, these requirements reflect the need for measurements of those parameters related to the study areas of the previous section: energy inputs and vertical profiles of temperature, species concentrations, and winds. The SWG also defined the baseline requirements for the spatial and temporal extent and resolution of the measurements. To implement the scientific studies envisaged for the UARS, the measurements should be of a global nature and be essentially continuous in time. Given the characteristics of remote sensing from low-orbiting satellites, this essentially implies a global map every 24 h. The data should also allow the detection of local (solar) time effects from the background of latitude and seasonal effects. The spatial resolution requirements were half a scale height in the vertical (2.5-3 km) and 500 km latitude, while requirements on longitude resolution range from 1000 km to zonal means, depending on the specific study and the time scale of the measurement. The 500 km latitude resolution translates into about 1 min time resolution along the satellite track, given the spacecraft velocity of 7.6 km/s. This defines the basic requirement for the atmospheric sensors to be capable of making vertical profile measurements in 1 min or less.

Tables 1-4 list the investigators, their institutions, and their contributions to the UARS.

The observatory will be launched in the fall of 1989 from the Eastern Space and Missile Center, using the NASA Space Transportation System (Shuttle). The Shuttle will deliver the spacecraft directly to the operational circular orbit at 600 km and inclined 57 deg to the equator. At this altitude and inclination, the remote sensors looking 90 deg to the spacecraft velocity vector can see to 80 deg latitude, providing nearly global coverage. This inclination also produces a precession of the orbit plane such that all local solar times can be sampled in about 33 days, thus allowing resolution of the diurnal atmospheric effects in a period that is short relative to seasonal effects. The planned operational life of the satellite is 18 months, while the observatory design life (excluding instrument expendables) is a minimum of 30 months. The fall launch, combined with the 18 month lifetime, will provide coverage of two Northern Hemisphere winters. (Northern Hemisphere winters were identified by the Science Working Group as times and locations of particularly interesting atmospheric phenomena and they recommended enhanced coverage of these periods.)

Observatory

The UARS observatory will consist of the 10 scientific instruments, an instrument module including mission-unique equipment, and the multimission modular spacecraft (MMS). The MMS will provide attitude control, communications and data handling, electrical power storage and regulation, and propulsion. Mission-unique items include the solar array, a high-gain antenna for communication through the Tracking and Data Relay Satellite (TDRS), additional attitude sensors, and a solar/stellar positioning platform.

Table 1 UARS energy input measurements

Instrument	Description and primary measurements	Investigator, institution
SOLSTICE – Solar-stellar intercomparison experiment	Full disk solar irradiance spectrometer incorporating stellar comparison Solar spectral irradiance: 115-500 nm	G. J. Rottman, University of Colorado
SUSIM – Solar ultraviolet spectral irradiance monitor	Full disk solar irradiance spectrometer incorporating onboard calibration Solar spectral irradiance: 120-400 nm	G. E. Brueckner, Naval Research Laboratory (NRL)
PEM – Particle environment monitor	X-ray, proton, and electron spectrometers In-situ energetic electrons and protons; remote sensing of electron energy deposition	J. D. Winningham, Southwest Research Institute

Table 2 UARS species and temperature measurements

Instrument	Description and primary measurements	Investigator, institution
CLAES – Cryogenic limb array etalon	Solid-hydrogen cooled spectrometer sensing atmospheric infrared emissions T, CF_2Cl_2, $CFCl_3$, $ClONO_2$, CH_4, O_3, NO_2, N_2O, HNO_3, and H_2O	A. E. Roche, Lockheed Palo Alto Research Laboratory
ISAMS – Improved stratospheric and mesospheric sounder	Mechanically cooled spectrometer sensing atmospheric infrared emissions T, O_3, NO, NO_2, H_2O, HNO_3, H_2O, CH_4, and CO	F. W. Taylor, Oxford University
MLS – Microwave limb sounder	Microwave radiometer sensing atmospheric emissions ClO, H_2O, and O_3	J. W. Waters, Jet Propulsion Laboratory (JPL)
HALOE – Halogen occultation experiment	Gas filter/radiometer sensing sunlight occulted by the atmosphere HF and HCl	J. M. Russell, NASA Langley Research Center (LaRC)

Table 3 UARS wind measurements

Instrument	Description and primary measurements	Investigator, institution
HRDI – High resolution doppler interferometer	Fabry-Perot spectrometer sensing atmospheric emission and scattering Two-component wind: 10-110 km	P. B. Hays, University of Michigan
WINDII – Wind imaging interferometer	Michelson interferometer sensing atmospheric emission and scattering Two-component wind: 70-300 km	G. G. Shepherd, York University, Canada

Table 4 Instrument of opportunity

Instrument	Description and primary measurements	Investigator, institution
ACRIM – Active cavity radiometer irradiance monitor	Full disk solar irradiance radiometer Continuation of solar constant measurements	R. C. Willson, Jet Propulsion Laboratory (JPL)

The UARS instrument module structure will be designed to house the instrument and mission-unique equipment. The configuration will be designed to meet the combined fields of view requirements of the instruments, solar array, attitude sensors, and high-gain antenna. The thermal control design will allow operation of any instrument at any duty cycle independent of the operational duty cycle of other instruments.

Two of the more important requirements on the observatory design are to provide Earth-referenced control of instrument pointing to an accuracy of 0.1 deg and to include attitude sensors that can support ground determination of instrument boresight pointing to an accuracy of 0.03 deg. These requirements will be met by the MMS attitude control subsystem and additional star trackers on the instrument module structure.

The UARS power subsystem will consist of a solar array, the MMS power module, and power distribution electronics. The solar array will be sized to provide sufficient power for a period of 36 months.

Communications with UARS will be achieved through the Tracking and Data Relay Satellite System (TDRSS). Compatibility with TDRSS will be provided by a steerable high-gain antenna operating in conjunction with the MMS communications and data handling subsystem. This subsystem will also provide the command, telemetry, data storage, and computational functions. The UARS telemetry data rate will be 32 kilobits/s with a tape recorder playback rate of 512 kilobits/s.

The UARS design will include a hydrazine propulsion module that will have sufficient capacity to perform 180 deg yaw attitude maneuvers approximately every 34 days for the duration of the mission. These maneuvers will orient the observatory with respect to the sun as needed to meet instrument thermal and viewing requirements. The propulsion system will also be used, if necessary, to maintain a nominal orbit altitude of 600 km.

Instruments

The flight instruments are described below. The principal investigator is noted with each instrument (Tables 1-4).

Wind Imaging Interferometer (G. G. Shepard)

This instrument will make measurements of temperature and winds in the high mesosphere and low thermosphere utilizing a wide-angle Michelson interferometer that analyzes atmosphere emission lines in the spectral range 5500-7000 Å. The instrument views the Earth's limb in orthogonal direction (±45 deg with respect to the direction of motion) to derive the vector wind component. Use of charge couple device (CCD) array detector permits simultaneous viewing in both directions over an altitude range of 70-300 km with a resolution of 3 km vertical by 20 km horizontal. Small-scale wave structures can also be observed using the array detector. Wind measurement accuracy is 5 m/s.

High-Resolution Doppler Imager (P. B. Hays)

The objective is the measurement of the temperature and vector wind fields from the upper troposphere into the thermosphere. The instrument uses a triple-etalon Fabry-Perot interferometer which analyzes the O_2 absorption features of scattered light at lower altitudes and emission features at higher altitudes. The instrument telescope is gimballed to view the horizon at two orthogonal directions and scan in the zenith direction for altitude coverage. Instrument spectral range is 3000-8000 Å, with a spectral resolution of 8 m/Å. Wind measurement accuracy is 5 m/s or better in the lower atmosphere. The instrument field of view provides a height resolution of better than 5 km.

Solar-Stellar Irradiance Comparison Experiment (G. J. Rottman)

The instrument will measure solar irradiance in the spectral range of 1200-4400 Å with an absolute accuracy of 6-10% and directly compare the solar irradiance with the ultraviolet flux from stellar sources. It consists of a small grating spectrometer mounted to a spacecraft-provided scan platform that provides solar or stellar tracking. The spectrometer has three optical channels and three photomultiplier tube detectors with resolutions of 0.12-0.25 Å for solar observations and 5-10 Å stellar observations. Stellar observations should permit determination of the day-to-day solar variations to an accuracy of 1%.

Cryogenic Limb Array Etalon Spectrometer (A. E. Roche)

The objectives are to obtain synoptic measurements of the concentrations of:

1) The source, radical, and sink species of the ozone-destructive nitrogen family (N_2O, NO, NO_2, and HNO_3).

2) Some of the ozone-destructive chlorine family species (CF_2Cl_2, $CHCl_3$, HCl, ClO, and $ClONO_2$).

3) Temperature over the same stratospheric altitude range.

The instrument consists of a cryogenic limb array high-resolution etalon spectrometer operating in the 3.5-12 μm spectral range. Detectors, spectrometer, telescope, and baffles are cooled by a cryogenic cooler using solid hydrogen with a design lifetime goal of 2 years at a 50% measurement duty cycle. An 18 element detector array provides a profile over the 10-60 km range, with resolution of better than 3 km. Time required for a complete spectral sequence is 64 s, corresponding to about 500 km of ground coverage.

Particle Environment Monitor (J. D. Winningham)

The objective is to determine the global input of charged-particle energy into the Earth's stratosphere, mesosphere, and thermosphere and the predicted atmospheric responses. Direct in situ measurements of precipitating electrons in the energy range of 5 eV to 5 MeV and of protons in the energy range of 5 eV to 150 MeV will be made with a medium-energy particle spectrometer (MEPS) and a high-energy particle spectrometer (HEPS). In addition, global images and energy spectra of atmospheric x-rays produced by electron precipitation of 2-150 keV will be performed over the energy range with an atmospheric x-ray imaging spectrometer (AXIS).

The MEPS instrument uses parabolic electrostatic analyzers with channel electron multiplier detectors. The HEPS instrument is a solid-state silicon detector spectrometer mounted in a plastic scintillator that serves as an anti-coincidence shield. The particle detectors are mounted on zenith and nadir booms. The zenith boom has five MEPS and six HEPS detector units; the nadir boom has three MEPS and two HEPS units. The AXIS instrument is a series of 16 collimated solid-state detectors oriented to measure x-rays that are produced in the atmosphere by impinging high-energy electrons.

Solar Ultraviolet Spectral Irradiance Monitor (G. E. Brueckner)

The objective is to measure the solar stellar irradiance in the 1200-4400 Å region with two spectral resolutions, 1.5 and 5 Å, with an absolute accuracy of 6-10%.

The instrument consists of two double-dispersion scanning spectrometers, seven detectors, and four deuterium calibration lamps. The spectrometers and detectors are sealed in a canister filled with 1.1 atm of argon gas. Solar flux enters through a MgF1 window. One spectrometer is used for continual measurements; the second is used infrequently to track stability of the first. The deuterium lamps serve as secondary standards for in-flight calibration.

Halogen Occultation Experiment (J. M. Russell)

The objective is to measure the vertical distributions of HCl, HF, $O_3 CH_4$, NO, NO_2, H_2O, and CO_2 over an altitude range of 10-65 km, with a height resolution of 2 km.

The instrument contains a four-channel gas filter correlation radiometer and a four-channel filter radiometer mounted on a two-axis gimbal system that provides solar tracking through occultation. Measurements are in the near-infrared band of 2-10 μm.

Improved Stratospheric and Mesospheric Sounder (F. W. Taylor)

The objective is the measurement of the vertical distributions in the 15-80 km region of CO_2, H_2O, CO, NO, N_2O, NO_2, O_3, HNO_3, and CH_4 with a height resolution of 4 km and a horizontal resolution of 400 km. The instrument is an infrared radiometer observing thermal emission and resonance fluoresence of radiation from the atmospheric limb using gas correlation spectroscopy. Measurements are in the range 4-15 μm in a total of 11 channels with 8 pressure modulator cells. Observations are made on either side of the spacecraft normal to the direction of flight. Solid-state detectors are cooled to 80 K by a closed-cycle refrigerator.

Microwave Limb Sounder (J. W. Waters)

The objective is the measurement of thermal limb emission in several millimeter wavelength bands to obtain global maps of O_3, ClO, H_2O, and pressure in the 15-50 km region with a vertical resolution of 3-6 km. The instrument consists of a 1.6 m antenna and three radiometers operating at 63, 183, and 205 GHz. The antenna is gimballed to provide the altitude scan of the Earth's limb.

Active Cavity Radiometer Irradiance Monitor (R. Willson)

The objective is the measurement of the total solar irradiance with state-of-the-art accuracy and precision. This experiment is part of a long-term program of extra-atmospheric observations to determine the magnitude and direction of variations in the output of total solar optical energy. The instrument measures solar output from the far-ultraviolet through far-infrared wavelengths using three electrically self-calibrated cavity detector pyrheliometers, each capable of defining the absolute radiation with an uncertainty of ±0.1% and resolution of ±0.02%.

Theoretical Investigations

In addition to the investigators who have been chosen to provide flight instruments, 10 investigators have been selected to provide analytical and interpretive support to the UARS program. Their contributions include chemical and dynamical modeling, meteorological and empirical modeling, and the application of these techniques to the organization and geophysical interpretation of the UARS measurements. The investigations, principal investigators (PI), and their institutions are given in Table 5.

Following completion of observatory activation and checkout, normal mission operations will commence as follows:

1) The Science Team will meet every few weeks to generate long-term science plans.

2) The mission planning group, located at GSFC, will generate daily event sequences based on the long-term science plan.

3) The Project Operations Control Center (POCC) will uplink prepared commands, monitor instrument health and safety, and provide the remote terminals with all user-selectable POCC displays in real time.

Table 5 Theoretical investigations

Investigator	Institution	Investigation
J. Chang	Lawrence Livermore Laboratory	Chemical, radiative, and dynamic processes
D. M. Cunnold	Georgia Institute of Technology	Impact of ozone change on dynamics
A. Gadd	United Kingdom Meteorological Office	Three dimensional/stratospheric model
M. A. Geller	NASA/Goddard Space Flight Center	Dynamics
W. L. Grose	NASA/Langley Research Center	Transport, budgets, and energetics
J. R. Holton	University of Washington	Wave dynamics and transport
J. London	University of Colorado	Response to solar variations
A. J. Miller	National Oceanic and Atmospheric Administration	Meteorological interpretation
C. A. Reber	NASA/Goddard Space Flight Center	Analytic-empirical modelling
R. W. Zurek	Jet Propulsion Laboratory	Radiative-dynamic balance

Data Processing System

UARS telemetered data will flow through a facility for data capture, de-communication, and data quality functions to the Central Data Handling Facility (CDHF) for processing of the scientific data. The CDHF will be a dedicated UARS facility. The scientific investigators will have access to these data electronically, using their remote terminals. The UARS Science Team, composed of all the PIs, will be responsible for coordinating the measurement program, optimizing the scientific analysis of the data, providing appropriate theoretical models, and disseminating the results in the open scientific literature and the National Space Science Data Center (NSSDC).

The CDHF will perform data processing (calibration, extraction of geophysical units, and interpolation onto a common grid) and maintain a data base of processed data. The levels of data processing correspond to the levels of data defined in the following:

Level 0: Raw telemetry from instruments (time tagged, quality checked, correct chronological sequence).

Level 1: Calibrated instrument data (e.g., radiances for most UARS remote sensors).

Level 2: Geophysical data (e.g., temperature, minor species mixing ratio) at the temporal and spatial resolution associated with the specific instrument scan/sweep/sampling rate (to be stored with the temporal and spatial location tags appropriate to the instrument).

Level 3: Smoothed/gridded geophysical data. Geophysical data to be smoothed and/or interpolated to a common grid spacing (to be stored with the appropriate temporal and spatial location tags).

In addition to the scientific data, supporting data such as time, orbit, and attitude information will be available to the users.

The CDHF data management system will perform all bookkeeping, library, and data archival functions. On-line and off-line data storage will be available. Other major supporting activities provided within the CDHF are communications, scheduling, reporting, and logging. The CDHF communications processor will support two-way intercommunications to the remote terminals. The communications software will channel requests for data products, support the transfer of data sets to and from the remote terminals, accept requests for nonroutine processing functions, and provide reports on processing status. In addition, the PIs will be able to transmit updated software modules to the CDHF for incorporation into the processing library.

Although routine production processing of UARS science data will occur at the CDHF, PIs will be provided with their own remote facilities suitable for analysis of the processed data. The main functions supported by the remote facilities are: 1) development and refinement of production processing algorithms to be installed at the CDHF; 2) accessing the UARS central data base; 3) interactive analysis of UARS data; and 4) transmission of instrument operating mode requests and microprocessor loads to the mission support facilities.

Complementary Measurements

Since the UARS will rely primarily on remote sensing for its sampling of the stratosphere, it is important that methods of confirming the deduced results should be available.

For example, measurements to confirm the accuracy of the deduced geophysical parameters are crucial to establishing confidence in the inversion techniques applied to radiance profiles used to obtain these specie and temperature profiles. These experiments will involve a number of expeditions using sounding rockets and balloons to establish that the deduced results are truly representative of atmospheric conditions.

The concept of the UARS is such that relatively low-data-rate instruments will be used for the measurement of a variety of selected species. There will be times when it will be desirable to obtain much more comprehensive sets of measurements, for example, with significantly higher spectral resolution or using active techniques. Payloads that involve extensive measurement capabilities, such as those that will be available on some of the Spacelab payloads, will be used in coordination with UARS.

Certain laboratory studies are extremely important to the scientific output of the UARS program. The two major areas in which these studies will have an impact are: 1) spectroscopic data, i.e., wavelengths and line intensity information, for use in interpreting the remote measurements, and 2) the rates and energetics of reactions to be used in the geophysical interpretation of the data. In addition, the UARS data and their interpretation will be closely coupled with model predictions (e.g., three-dimensional circulation models) developed by theoretical groups not necessarily associated with the UARS.

Some Possibilities on an Observing System for the World Climate Program

Verner E. Suomi*

University of Wisconsin, Madison, Wisconsin

Abstract

A climate observing system that can be used immediately is proposed. However, in many instances, it is unsatisfactory. It is hoped that, in the proposal outlined, the reader gets a better appreciation of the need for an entire system -- instruments, spacecrafts, orbits, and above all a viable data processing system. Success must be measured not by the elegance of the instruments or complexity of the spacecraft, but by the throughput of data needed by the climate modelers on Earth. Illustrating the current opportunities and problems should lead to a better understanding of what is needed in the future. There are many studies and proposals of what might be added to new spacecraft. The goal should be a <u>system</u> with sufficient performance and reasonable cost, so we can get on with the task of trying to predict climate.

Objectives

The major objectives of the World Climate Research Program are to determine to what extent climate can be predicted and the extent of man's influence on climate.

These objectives are very different from those of classical climate studies. For example, the climate of a region describes the overall character of the daily weather over a defined time period. It might be that which occurs from season to season, year to year, decade to decade, or century to century. Indeed, it could extend to the time scales of the major advances of the glaciers. We can speak of many climates—warm, cold, marine, continental, mountain,

---

* Director, Space Science and Engineering Center.

desert climates, and so on, depending on the main factors
controlling a particular climate.

These classical climate studies can be described as
"weather history." The World Climate Research Program
(WCRP) is an attempt to learn what can be done with "climate
prophecy".

In this volume on remote sensing, it is important to
differentiate the factors influencing our climate from those
controlling our weather, even though one is the average of
the other. The weather prediction problem is basically an
initial value problem. That is, given a well-described
present state of the atmosphere, what will it be at various
future times and in different places? The problem is made
very complex by the wide range of time and space scales of
important meteorological phenomena.

Figure 1 illustrates the time and space scales of a
variety of meteorological phenomena, together with an
estimate of the total global kinetic energy that can be
assigned to each scale. It should come as no surprise that
our ability to make extended deterministic weather
predictions is directly related to the scale and kinetic
energy embodied in that particular feature of the weather. A
further complication is the fact that important weather

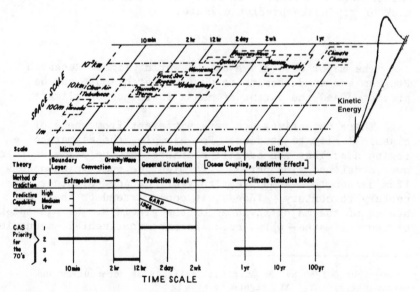

Fig. 1   Space-time and kinetic energy scales of atmospheric
phenomena and their prediction.

means different things to different people. The ordinary
citizen is concerned largely with small-scale weather,
especially if it is wet or severe, whereas the meteorologist
is more interested in large-scale weather -- which is what
he can best predict.

Lorenz[1] put it best when he remarked that there are
three important meteorological questions before us: 1) What
would we like to predict? 2) What are we able to predict?
and 3) Is there anything in common between questions 1) and
2)?

That that ability varies depending on scale is clearly
evident in Fig. 2. The information, provided by Bengtsson[2]
using the European Center for Medium-Range Weather
Forecasting (ECMWF) numerical model of the general
circulation, shows that even with the excellent global
weather data set gathered during the Global Weather
Experiment (GWE), a more rapid decay of the height anomaly
correlation (a measure of the accuracy of the forecast)
occurs at the higher wave numbers representing the smaller
scales. Indeed, even at the largest wave numbers, the decay
is too great to be useful at time scales approaching two
weeks. Stated another way, the atmosphere simply "forgets"

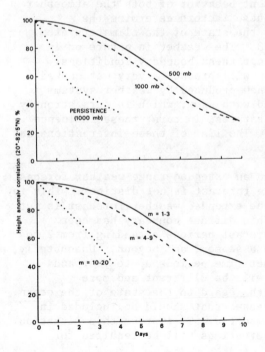

Fig. 2   Height anomaly vs
decay with time. Wave
numbers are indicated by m
(from Bengtsson[2]).

its inital state much sooner than the time scales we might
consider for climate prediction scale, say, a month or a
season -- not to mention a year or a decade.

While a longer-range forecast might be useless when
assessed as a determinist forecast, it can be much more
useful when considered statistically. Good numerical
weather prediction models can be made to operate for
extended periods without "blowing up." They produce
synthetic weather, which while not the same as the actual
weather that will occur in the future, could have similar
statistical properties. This is the key notion behind the
WCRP's attempt at "climate prophecy."

On long time scales, the general circulation model
(GCM) is no longer influenced by the initial state of the
atmosphere. However, it is profoundly affected by the
boundary conditions. These boundary conditions include the
atmosphere's interaction with the bottom surface (land,
ocean, ice, or snow, and living things thereon), as well as
"external" influences, such as the amount of solar energy
and the variations in the optically active gases or aerosols
within the atmosphere that control the radiative heat loss
to space. Since three-fourths of the surface of the Earth
is ocean, the air/sea interactions have an important
influence on the subsequent behavior of both the atmosphere
and the ocean. All of these factors determine the
parameters that describe the state of the climate system.
These are shown in Fig. 3. The weather in nature or in
numerical models can change these boundary conditions.
Over time, excessive rain will produce a very wet soaked
land surface. Copious snow produced by weather systems
controls the area covered with snow, which in turn strongly
influences surface temperatures; in turn, these influence
atmospheric temperature. The list of these interactions and
feedbacks can go on and on.

The boundary between an extended-range weather forecast
and a short-range climate forecast is not distinct. This is
particularly true when the extended weather forecast is put
in statistical terms. This diffuse boundary has been
described in terms of forecast periods extending from 2 to
20 days, from 20 days to a season, and beyond. Undoubtedly,
the requirements for other time periods up to year and
extending beyond a year will be different and more
inclusive, especially with regard to the state of the ocean.
All of the physical processes that should be included in
GCMs cannot yet be accommodated. To improve this situation,
still another set of observations will be required for

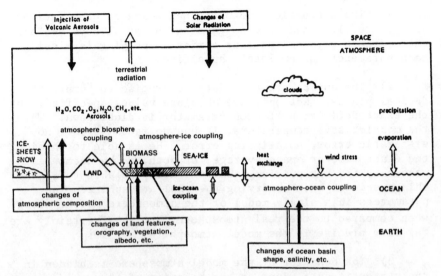

Fig. 3   Schematic illustration of the components of the
climate system. The full arrows are examples of
external climate processes and the open arrows
are examples of internal processes.

diagnosis and parameterization. These sets of experimental
observations may need to be very intensive, but it is not
expected that they will need to continue for long time
periods. On the other hand, the data requirements
previously mentioned, which describe the initial state of
the atmosphere and the climate state, must be continued on
an <u>operational</u> basis into the foreseeable future.

Before we describe in any detail the requirements and
the means by which they might be acquired using space-based
remote sensing systems, it might be helpful to first view
them as a whole to gain a better appreciation of the
magnitude of the task. This comparison has been discussed
previously in a document outlining the needs for observing
the global atmosphere[3]. Although it was written almost
twenty years ago, parts of it deserve repeating, and the
following paragraphs have been extracted from that document,
revised as appropriate to fit the needs for climate.

Properties of a Model Atmosphere
and Boundary Parameters

The task is to provide real observations for the
"synthetic" observations used in numerical climate
prediction models.

1)   The synthetic atmosphere has a log of observations that is total. There are no gaps in the areal coverage and there are no gaps in the time series -- nothing is missing. Each parameter is completely specified.

2)   The entire array of data is precise to "umpteen" decimal places. Not only are absolute values specified, but the exact definition of each parameter is also known. When the modeler says temperature, it has no random error, no systematic error, no aliasing error. He is able to obtain the exact time or space average, or both, as he deems necessary for his problem. We will never be able to reach this precision when observing the real atmosphere. The parameters in a simple model of the atmosphere may be wrong when compared to the real atmosphere, but they certainly are far more precise in the model atmosphere.

3)   The behavior of the model atmosphere is hidden in the synthetic data, just as the behavior of the real atmosphere is hidden in the real data. The modelers have indicated that a greater programming effort has been expended trying to diagnose what the model is doing than was expended in programming the model itself. Even so, they are able to be far more precise about processes and fluxes than will ever be obtained by measurements in the real atmosphere. This point will be expanded later.

4)   The modeler can find his data by looking at a specific location in the computer memory and in a few microseconds retrieve his "observation." In the real atmosphere, we must collect observations from all over the world, give the location and time of observation, insert the appropriate calibrations, etc.

These illustrations indicate the formidable task facing us. They should both warn technologists who are anxious to get at the task and gain some sympathy and understanding from modelers who are anxious for data from the real atmosphere with which to test their models. Clearly, the dialogue to date encouraged by the planning sessions of the WCRP must be continued. The interface between what technology can provide and what the models require is not sharp; rather it is a "grey zone." Each group must make the effort to reach some distance into the other's area. Only if effective "bargaining" goes on between the two basic groups will there evolve a system that both meets the needs of the program and remains within the bounds of the available resources and personnel.

Data Requirements

Basically, we need three groups of observations: 1) the thermodynamic and dynamic properties of the atmosphere; 2) the parameters at the Earth's surface (the ocean/atmosphere interface); and 3) the ocean heat content and motions below the surface. Not all prediction time scales require the same amount of information. Indeed, the shorter time scales do not even require global information.

As stated by the World Meteorological Organization:[4]

"The observational fields of information which are required to form the initial conditions from which numerical deterministic forecast models evolve include those which describe the dynamical and thermodynamical properties of the atmosphere and the forces that drive it. These fields of information include: (i) three dimensional fields of temperature, winds and relative humidity, (ii) sea surface temperature (SST) and other ocean variables in the mixed layer which ultimately determine the evolution of SST (the latter are only required for the ocean-atmosphere coupled models predicting in the 20-day to seasonal forecast range as described further below), (iii) other variables which are important in describing forcing terms (e.g. those components of diabatic heating that are a part of the radiation and hydrological cycle)."

Several of the fields of information mentioned in this statement are detailed in Table 1.

Research is continuing on a detailed specification of the observational requirements. The following quote from Bengtsson[2] at the ECMWF states the specification as follows:

"It seems logical to assume that as the forecast interval is extended, observations from remote areas are successively becoming more important and a global model is certainly required for long range prediction. Furthermore, observations about the surface conditions and the ocean mixed layer are successively required when the forecast length is extended."

"We have tried to summarise the data requirements. The forecast interval has been given in three intervals: (i) 2-20 days, (ii) 20 days-1 season, (iii) >1 season. The data requirements are for the initial data only. Special data sets are needed for parameterization and diagnostic studies to be used for model development. These

Table 1   Fields of information needed for deterministic
                    forecast models

Temperature	
Horizontal resolution	500 km
Vertical resolution	4 levels in troposphere
	3 levels in stratosphere
Wind	
Horizontal resolution	500 km
Vertical resolution	4 levels in troposphere
	3 levels in stratosphere
Relative humidity	
Horizontal resolution	500 km
Vertical resolution	2 degrees of freedom in
	troposphere
Pressure	
Temporal resolution	at least 2 times per day,
	but 4 times per day is
	preferred
20 Days to seasonal	
Measure ocean surface energetics	
Heat content of upper mixed layer	
Vector wind stress	
Net radiation at the surface	
Ocean currents, conventional	
and satellite alternately	

requirements are very much the same as has previously been
proposed for the so-called first stream of the Climate
Research Programme, such as cloud/ radiation interaction,
land-surface processes and the hydrological cycle."

Table 2 is the summary of the data requirements
mentioned in the previous paragraph.

In Tables 1 and 2, it should be noted that there is no
request for rainfall information as an initial condition.
Presumably, the model will be able to predict the rainfall
and thus there is no requirement for precipitation data. As
will be shown later, the measuring systems have
deficiencies. In order to remove, or at least reduce, the
errors due to these deficiencies, there is a need to include
rainfall as an initial condition. The heat released during
the condensation produces atmospheric forcing and cannot be
ignored. Of course, if one had an error-free set of

Table 2   Estimated data requirements for long-range
prediction

Pred. Int.	Integration domain	Atmospheric parameters[a] $T, \underline{v}, p_s, q$	Surface parameters[a] T_s, w_s, snow, ice	Ocean parameters surface & mixed layer (except T_s)
2-20day	$\leq$Global	x	x[b]	
20 day 1 season	Global	x	x	x[b]
>1 season	Global	c	x	x

Resolution and accuracy:

Horizontal resolution	200-500 km
Vertical resolution	1-3 km
Time resolution	1-2 times/day
Accuracy	$T \sim 1°C$, $\underline{v} \sim 3$ ms^{-1}, $p_s \sim 1$ mb

[a] T = temperature, $\underline{v}$ = horizontal wind, p_s = surface pressure, q = specific humidity, T_s = sea surface temperature, w_s = soil moisture.

[b] Not required in full for the first part of prediction interval.

[c] Possibly not required.

observations, the effects of the heat release would be captured by the error-free data set. Unfortunately, this is not the case at present. In view of this, the rainfall rate and amount should be included in the data on a space scale commensurate with the specific needs of the modelers. Such specifics include adequate resolution -- not for today's numerical models, but for global models likely to be available in the future (say, having a resolution of 50 km, especially in the tropics). This point will be discussed more fully in a later section.

A Climate Observing System Feasible Now -- March 1985

Thanks to the World Weather Experiment and the World Weather Watch, several key elements of the climate observing system are already in place. Therefore, our highest priority is to insure that this basic system does not

<u>degrade in capability, but instead is improved</u> . Several
improvements can be added now -- the technology is well in
hand; definitive designs have been prepared; and
implementation plans prepared. Let us examine what is
possible with what is now available.

It will be helpful to divide the observations into two
groups: 1) those made indirectly, or remotely, such as
measurements of the atmosphere made from a satellite and
2) in-situ observations where the sensor is immersed in the
atmosphere or is at its boundary. It may be wise to <u>collect</u>
these observations with a satellite and to <u>locate</u> the point
where the observation was taken using a satellite, but this
is not absolutely necessary. In some instances (for
example, in studies of limited areas), use of satellites for
data collection and location may make the data far more
accessible for both operations and research than it is at
present.

A proposed system satisfying many of these requirements
is shown in Fig. 4. The figure depicts the area from the
pole to the equator, although what is required is pole-to-
pole coverage. Figure 4 attempts to include the boundary
conditions describing the climate state and, where feasible,
indicates in a schematic way that the subsystems can provide
the required observations.

The height scale is roughly divided into the boundary
layer, troposphere, stratosphere and space. The observing
requirements differ over land and sea and from region to
region. The ability to provide these observations will also
differ for each region.

Our comments here are limited to the possible role of
the technique in the observing system and do not include
descriptions of the hardware and software produced by the
efforts of those who brought this technique to reality. We
now know it can be done and how well it will work -- we also
know its limitations. Many are described in considerable
detail in other sections of this volume. The objective here
is to view the whole as an integrated system.

Remote Measurements from Spacecraft

<u>Temperature and Moisture Profiles</u>

The temperature and moisture sounders now in operation
on both polar-orbiting and geosynchronous satellites have
been carefully evaluated as part of the first Global
Atmospheric Research Program (GARP) and on a continuing

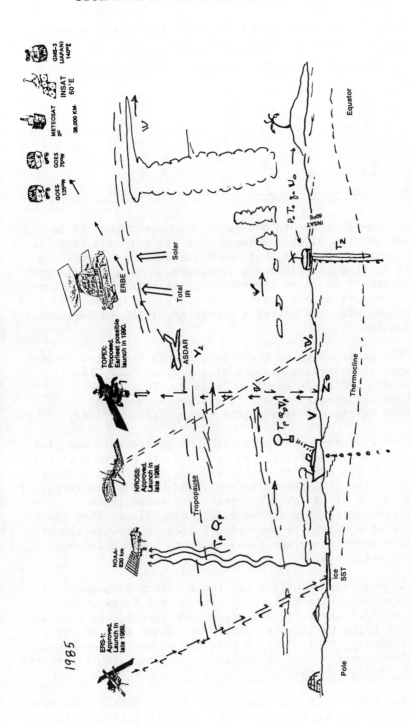

Fig. 4   A proposed climate observing system.

Table 3   RMS difference K between satellite retrievals and
radiosondes during FGGE

Layer, mb	Clear	Partly cloudy	Overcast cloudy
100- 70	2.2	2.2	2.2
200-100	2.1	2.2	2.3
300-200	2.3	2.5	2.8
400-300	2.3	2.4	3.0
500-400	2.3	2.4	3.0
700-500	2.0	2.1	2.7
850-700	2.4	2.7	3.4
1000-850	2.8	3.1	3.8

basis. The instruments now being used are described in
another section of this volume. For our purposes here, it
is sufficient to state that the polar orbiters carried
HIRS/2 (a broadband infrared instrument having a horizontal
resolution of 30 km at the subsatellite point) and a four-
band microwave sounder unit (MSU) operating in the 50.3-57.7
GHz oxygen band and having a footprint of 150 km horizontal
resolution.

The performance of these instruments evaluated during
the special observing periods of the First GARP Global
Experiment (FGGE) is shown in Table 3. This table
represents a special effort to extract as many and as
accurate retrievals as possible during these periods.

Table 3 shows that even with the instruments now aloft
and with special efforts, the requirements stated have not
been met. The error is double what is considered desirable,
even when the atmosphere is clear, and becomes progressively
worse as the cloud cover increases. Despite these
limitations, it has now been firmly established that the
ability of a satellite observing system to provide almost
complete global coverage does, in fact, lead to improved
weather forecasts.

We must also consider how these errors propagate. If
error can be cut in half, the forecast can be extended
another 2-2.5 days. If the errors are random, the forecast
accuracy might be improved simply by taking more of them.
Unfortunately, Table 3 shows that the errors increase with
the cloud cover -- but clouds are associated with the storms
we are trying to predict!

The errors are not random, but show a spatial coherence
with the traveling storm systems. To make matters worse,

there is little or no data about areas with extensive cloud cover. Data is available around a storm center, but not at the storm center. The latter is of much higher value. The impact of these errors is not so large in the Northern Hemisphere in which there exist a network of radiosonde data over the land surfaces, aircraft observations over the oceans, and forecasts extending to 2-3 days. These errors have their greatest impact for the extended range forecast where they propagate to degrade the prediction. Clearly, if our weather predicting capability is to be extended beyond a few days into and beyond the two-week interval, we must remove the gaps in the data and improve the accuracy. This should be the first step.

Infrared vs Microwave Sounding Techniques

As already noted, the IR sounding techniques fail in regions of extensive cloud cover. Microwave sounding techniques do not suffer this limitation, at least under most cloud conditions. So why is more accurate data not available from microwave sounders?

Figures 5a and 5b show the weighting functions for a number of IR channels (not all of them) and a number of microwave sounding channels. Figure 6b is the typical plot of temperature on a log p (height) scale. Figure 6c shows the same information plotted as a linear pressure scale. The sigma coordinate in typical numerical models is more directly related to a linear pressure scale than to a linear height scale as shown in 6a. Clearly, one can see from Fig. 5a that the IR weighting functions have better vertical resolution than the microwave in the lower troposphere, but the microwave has better resolution than the IR function in the upper troposphere and stratosphere. Both are needed.

The microwave sounders have another important purpose -- the identification of poor IR soundings. It has been stated that there are three kinds of data: good, poor, and none. "No data" is preferable to erroneous data and, since the atmosphere has some "memory," the model can supply a limited amount of synthetic data that is preferable to poor data. The task is to identify the poor data. In cloudy regions where IR retrieval errors are likely to occur, it is possible to degrade an IR sounding in terms of the vertical resolution to simulate the sounding retrieval of the microwave sounder. If the two agree, the IR sounding

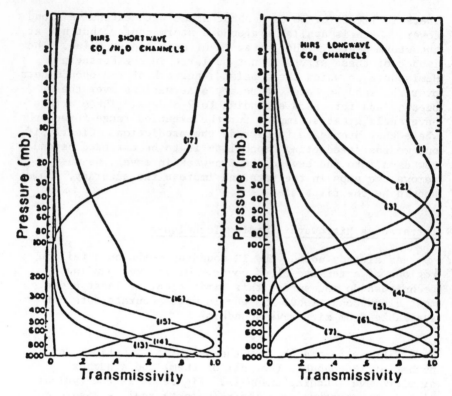

Fig. 5a Normalized weighting functions for the
high-resolution infrared radiation sounder (HIRS).
Channels 1-7 are located near 15 μm, channels 13-17
near 4.5 μm.

is likely to be a good one, but if they disagree, there is a
basis for quality control and thus elimination of the poor
IR retrievals.

Can the retrieval procedures be improved? The answer
is, probably, yes. There are several temperature and
moisture retrieval techniques discussed in some detail in
another chapter. Basically, the information content in the
upwelling radiation, be it IR or microwave, is insufficient
to obtain a retrieval. The problem is underdetermined.
Rodgers[5] has described the problem as having two sources of
errors. The first is in the real data from instrument noise
or interference from clouds. In order to obtain a solution,
one must provide some virtual data, usually the first guess
as to the structure of the atmosphere. These virtual data
have errors as well, and both sets of errors propagate into
the retrieval calculation. Table 3 shows the errors using

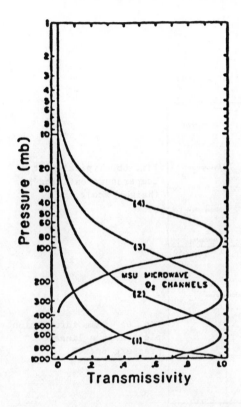

Fig. 5b Normalized weighting
functions for the microwave
sounding unit (MSU). Channels
1-4 are located between 50-60
GHz.

the operational procedures then in current use. Several
researchers[6-8] have demonstrated improved retrieval
techniques that reduce the errors. However, these
techniques do not reduce them as much as desired.

Figs. 7 through 8 show typical retrieval errors for
different atmospheric structures. Inspection of these
figures shows that the greatest errors occur near the
surface and near the tropopause. If one had additional
information -- for example, on the height of the tropopause
-- it could be used to constrain the retrieval solution more
satisfactorily.

It may be possible to use the total ozone in the
stratosphere for additional information. The ozone content
obtained by backscattered ultraviolet observations is highly
correlated with the depth of the stratosphere, which is
another way of saying it is negatively correlated with the
height of the tropopause. The author has no knowledge that
this approach has been put to practical use.

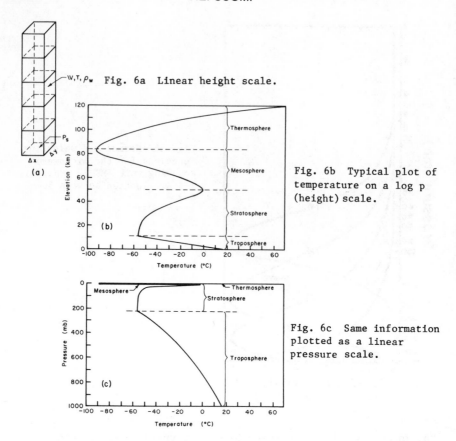

Fig. 6a Linear height scale.

Fig. 6b Typical plot of temperature on a log p (height) scale.

Fig. 6c Same information plotted as a linear pressure scale.

Near the surface, it would also be very useful to have information on the height of the boundary layer, since this too would help constrain the solution. Unfortunately, there are no operational satellite observations that will yield this information directly. Over the ocean, there is only a small diurnal temperature range and that should make the task easier. One can almost guess at the shape of the boundary layer temperature profile in different regions of a traveling storm or under the large subtropical high-pressure areas. The shape of the boundary-layer profile should also help to constrain the solution. Both visible and IR satellite images show where these areas are located. Again (to the author's knowledge), no operational use of this information is being made, although the Australian and Brazilian weather services have used such images to generate synthetic weather maps over the open ocean where there is no other source of weather information.

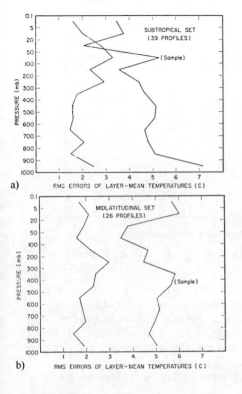

a)

Fig. 7a   Temperature residuals
("sample" curve) and
retrieval rms errors.

Fig. 7b   Temperature residuals
as in Fig. 7a but for a
mid-latitudinal set of 26
profiles.

b)

There are no operational satellite instruments being planned for the next decade that will be able to provide this vital information, although the remote sensing feasibility of such observations does not seem unduly difficult. Perhaps we have labored the topic of the accuracy of temperature and moisture retrievals unduly. However, although the effort expended so far has been great, the accuracy has not met the requirements. Improving this accuracy remains as one of the key challenges to the technology of remote sensing of the atmosphere. The requirements are very demanding indeed.

Surface Temperature, T_o

The techniques for measuring surface temperature remotely, particularly sea surface temperature, are well established. Certainly, the accuracy is good enough to establish the surface temperature, T_o, of the soundings and to establish whether or not the sea surface temperature has departed significantly from climatological means, as it did during the 1983 El Niño episode.

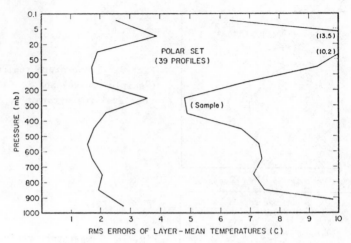

Fig. 8   Temperature residuals for a polar set of 39 profiles.

The desired accuracy of 0.25°C has not yet been met
operationally, not because of instrument limitations
(providing there is an onboard accurate and continuing
calibration procedure), but because of the effects of the
intervening atmosphere. There are three sources of error:
water vapor, clouds whose size is smaller than the
resolution of the images, and particulates released from
large volcanoes.

When one has information on the total water content and
uses procedures to ensure that the observations are not
contaminated by cloud, accuracies to 0.6° have been reported
by McLain,[9] using the NOAA Advanced Visible High Resolution
Radiometer (AVHRR). However, during the eruption of the El
Chichon volcano, large errors were evident downwind from the
volcano and extended over a large area. Even this effect
could be removed if one had several views of the same point
on the surface from different angles. The European ERS-1
will carry an along-the-track scan instrument with which the
same location will be observed from several angles.
Simulations show that the accuracy should be better than
the projected 0.2°C, but that is for the future.

At present, it should be possible to improve the
accuracy, using a combination of geostationary and polar-
orbiting spacecraft. The polar orbiter has the advantage of
higher resolution (1 km IR) over the geostationary satellite
IR images (4-16 km), but the large nadir angle needed to
obtain coverage requires a much larger atmospheric
correction from low orbit than from geosynchronous orbit.

Since there is a significant overlap in coverage from five geostationary satellites (GEO), the nadir angle is smaller. Of course, the nadir angle is large at high latitude, but there the total water vapor burden is much less than in the tropics, so the correction is not as large. At high latitude, the overlap from low Earth orbit (LEO) satellites is very large, so only small nadir angles are required for coverage there. Thus, a combination of LEO and GEO SST observations should yield higher accuracy.

Why all this effort to obtain SSTs to better than 0.25°C? Studies of the 1984 El Niño by Rasmussen et al.[10] show that, if one can detect that an El Niño event is about to occur, almost a year's forecast of regional climate variations can be made. Such a forecast can be worth billions of dollars. The maximum temperature departure in the SST anomaly is about 5°C and the precursors are, of course, more like 1.0°C. One definitely needs the 0.25°C accuracy to predict such an event with confidence. Also, the vapor pressure exerted by the sea surface increases rapidly at tropical SSTs, so change in the SST gives rise to an important change in surface vapor pressure, a parameter needed to estimate the evaporation from the ocean.

We have not yet mentioned observations of SST using microwaves. At microwavelengths, the emissivity of the ocean surface varies strongly with wind speed. Using multifrequency microwave observations, it is possible to remove most, but not all, of these emissivity variations. Under ideal conditions, given the choice of microwave or IR SST, the IR observations will win on the accuracy account. However, there are areas of persistent cloudiness and in these regions the microwave technique wins. The observations are not as good -- more like 1.0°C. However, beggars cannot be choosers; we need both.

Winds

So far, no method of obtaining wind information as a function of height directly from satellite observations has been available on meteorological satellites. Wind information is vital, especially in the equatorial regions where the mass field, obtained from temperature observations, cannot be used to infer the air motions because the coriolis parameter is near zero.

Winds can be inferred using successive visible and IR images obtained from all the GEOs in the World Weather Watch

system by tracking cloud displacements. Considerable effort
has been made to measure cloud displacement winds by the
operating agencies and such information is now available on
a routine basis. It does not, however, meet the accuracy
requirements and there is incomplete coverage. Where there
are no clouds, there can be no cloud winds. They are not
available at all altitudes at all locations. By and large,
upper clouds tend to hide lower clouds, but not completely.

Assignment of wind vector heights based on data from
the heights of clouds (determined by measuring their top
temperatures) are not sufficiently accurate because the
emissivity, especially of high cirrus clouds, is not known.
As a result, the largest source of error is in the cloud
height assignment.

Coverage can be improved by a more dedicated effort, as
has been demonstrated in research studies, but these
techniques have not yet been adopted by the operating
agencies. At present, the rms wind error from all sources
is about 6.0 m/s, about three times worse than what is
desired; but the information is still very useful over the
large ocean areas where no other data are available.

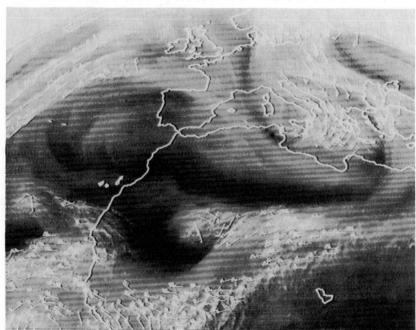

Fig. 9   Meteosat closeup high-level water vapor winds.

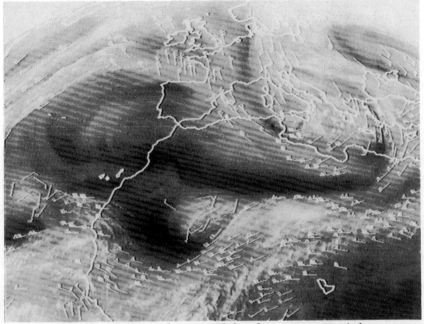

Fig. 10 Meteosat closeup mid-level water vapor winds.

Using present spacecraft or those in the foreseeable future (those that are now included for planned operations satellites), what can be done to improve the situation? Several things can be done:

1) Improved accuracy of the cloud displacement. An intercomparison of wind observations provided by the operating agencies has been made by the ECMW[2]. The study shows that there are significant differences in the coverage and accuracy in the data from the various agencies. Presumably, if one agency can do well, the others can too -- simply by adopting the successful techniques. It is an institutional problem, not a technical one.

2) Improved coverage - water vapor tracking. As stated earlier, one cannot obtain cloud wind information where there are no clouds. Studies by Johnson[11], and more recently by Stewart[12] show that an enormous increase in coverage is possible, using the 6.7 μm water vapor images available from two U.S. GOES satellites and the European Meteosat. Surprisingly, the height assignment of these water vapor winds is better than the height assignment now available for cloud winds. The error is 6-7 m/s, not too different from the accuracy for cloud winds.

The Japanese Himiwara satellite and India's Insat do
not yet have a water vapor imaging capability. Action is
being taken by the Joint Scientific Committee (JSC) of the
WCRP to urge these nations to include this capability on
their next satellites. While this will require an addition
to the present imaging camera system, it does not require a
new satellite or a new instrument -- only a new filter.
Thus, we have included it in this outline of a climate
observing system, using already available operational
satellites.

Figures 9-16 show the additional winds that it would be
possible to measure using water vapor tracking. Figures
13 and 14 show the combination of all levels. The amount of
added coverage is fantastic and should be included in the
climate observing system.

Improved Height Accuracy Using CO_2 Slicing
_____

Menzel and Smith[13] have shown that it is possible to
obtain much more satisfactory cloud height estimates using
the "CO_2 slicing" technique. Here images are made in

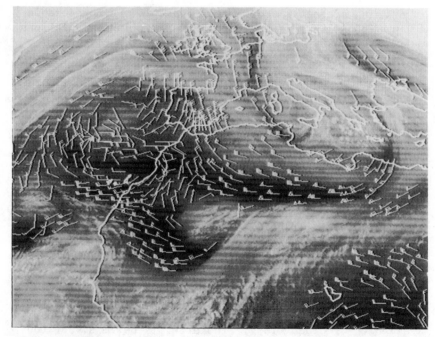

Fig. 11 Meteosat closeup low-level water vapor winds (350-550 mb).

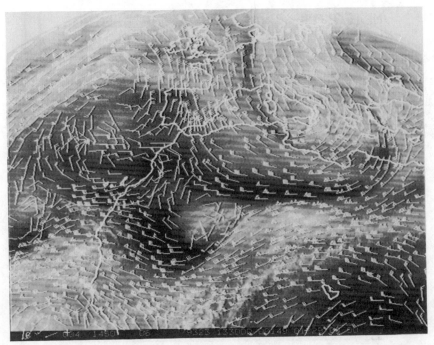

Fig. 12 Meteosat closeup all-level water vapor winds.

several bands of the CO_2 channels ordinarily used to obtain
temperature soundings on the VISSR (Visible Infrared Spin
Scan Radiometer) Atmospheric Sounder (VAS). Only the higher
clouds appear in the more opaque channels and, as one uses
more transparent regions of the spectrum, one "sees" further
down. Figures 15 and 16 show high, middle, and low clouds
using this technique. Actually, one sees high, medium, and
low clouds in the last figure, but one already knows which
are the high and middle clouds, so the low ones are selected
by subtraction. Table 4 shows height intercomparisons using
the radiosonde, stereo, and CO_2 slicing techniques.

These observations can be obtained only from the two
U.S. GOES satellites, since it requires the VAS or a similar
instrument. The technique is not as accurate as the stereo
technique, but it has an important advantage in that only
one spacecraft is required and the method is relatively
simple computationally. One can obtain much needed climate
data on cloud extent, height, and emissivity using this
technique, all vital for studies of the cloud radiation
parameterization physics needed for improved climate models.

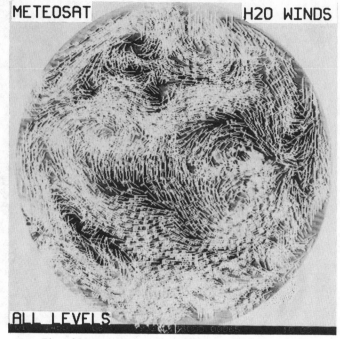

Fig. 13 Meteosat all-level water vapor winds.

Winds at the Surface

Using microwave backscatter techniques, the Seasat
satellite was able to measure wind speed and direction on
the sea surface. Wind at the ocean surface is the primary
force behind the ocean currents. This basic scheme will be
used in the operational satellite of the future, the Navy
Remote Ocean Sensing System (NROSS), to be launched in 1989.
However, a world climate program element, TOGA (the Tropical
Ocean Global Atmosphere program), is underway -- and where
will it get its winds?

The report of the Workshop on Ocean Surface Wind Data
Sets[14] proposed a scheme to infer the winds at the surface
using low level cloud winds as the data source. The
correction to be provided is obtained from an
intercomparison with ship observations when available. Two
methods were proposed: one by Sadler[15] using a wind shear
climatology obtained from six years of ship and satellite
data obtained earlier, and a second by Wylie and Hinton[16]
using available ship data to provide dynamically the shear
to the surface correction. It remains to be seen whether
either method will suffice for the stringent requirements
set forth by the modeling oceanographers.

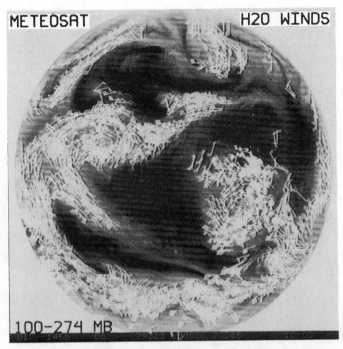

Fig. 14 Meteosat high-level water vapor winds.

Wind <u>speed</u> information is available (through its effect
on emissivity and reflectivity) in microwave images and
radar altimeters. Some additional information is available
from sun glitter. Table 5 and Fig. 17 show the sources of
lower atmospheric wind information in the past and near
future for climate studies.

Surface Parameters: The Hydrological Cycle

The surface parameters listed in Table 2 include the
extent and depth of the snow cover, soil moisture, and
surface albedo. One could add the type of vegetative cover
because, through plants, we get coupling to soil moisture in
the root zone. One can get some indication of the soil
moisture using microwave techniques, but it is only a thin
surface layer and not too useful. We need to know the
moisture in the root zone. Through evapotranspiration
processes, plants partition the net radiation available at
the Earth's surface into sensible and latent heat added to
the atmosphere. The question is, what is the fraction?

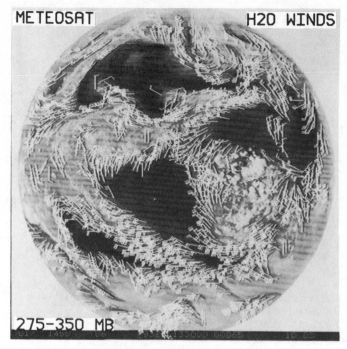

Fig. 15 Meteosat mid-level water vapor winds.

Over the ocean, latent heat added to the atmosphere by
evaporation predominates, so only estimates of the sensible
heat will probably be possible.

These moisture fluxes, together with rainfall, form
part of the hydrological cycle. Without a full assessment
of the hydrological cycle, no climate prediction is
possible.

The approaches over the ocean and over land must be
different. Over land, we can (at least on a 24 h basis)
ignore the heat stored in the soil. What goes in during the
daytime by and large comes out at night. The net effect is
zero. Thus, if one has a measure of the net radiation at
the surface and the partitioning ratio (the Bowen ratio),
the problem is solvable.

Over the ocean, the situation is different. The well-
mixed surface layer of the ocean can absorb vast amounts of
solar energy and can also give up large amounts of heat,
depending on the behavior and condition of the overlying
atmosphere.

Fig. 16   Meteosat low-level water vapor winds.

Over land, we can use the heat budget approach.   Over
the ocean, we are obliged to use a bulk aerodynamic
approach.   The bulk aerodynamic relationship is

$$E = LC_D U(e_s - e) \qquad (1)$$

where L is the latent heat of evaporation; C_D the drag
coefficient, a parameter that depends on the atmospheric
stability near the surface; U the wind speed; e_s the vapor
pressure of the ocean surface; and e the vapor pressure of
the atmosphere at about 10 m above the surface where the
wind speed is assigned. Using ship observations, Esbensen[17]
has shown that monthly average values of evaporation can be
obtained by using monthly values of u and of e. Liu[18] has
shown that the value of e above the ocean surface can be
estimated from an observation of the total water in the
atmospheric column above the ocean. Liu was able to obtain
the latent heat of evaporation accurately to about 20 W/m^2.
The modeler's wish is for 10 W/m^2. While we cannot now meet
the modeler's requirements for evaporation over the ocean,
we do have the odd situation that over the ocean we can
measure evaporation more satisfactorily than we can measure
the rainfall!

Table 4   Height intercomparison using radiosonde, stero, and CO_2

Station	Radio-sonde	Bi-spectral	Stereo	CO_2	Cloud type
LIT	760	570	710	700	Stratus
OMA	--	420	670	670	Strato cumulus
TOP	570	400	560	500	Strato cumulus
UMN	680	510	700	700	Strato cumulus
SLO	350	410	335	350	Cirrus
BNA	--	--	420	400	Cirrus
CKL	630	--	680	700	Stratus
BVE	420	550	390	430	Cirrus
JAN	570	550	560	570	Cirrus
LCH	820	680	740	780	Cumulus
OKC	830	570	720	780	Stratus
GGG	830	550	810	780	Strato cumulus
IAD	400	410	--	350	Cirrus
HAT	475	410	--	430	Cirrus

Station	Radio-sonde	Bi-spectral	Stereo	CO_2
LIT	890	810	870	850
OMA	820	550	--	780
TOP	640	410	--	620
UMN	750	610	780	780
PIA	--	200	250	250
BNA	--	840	--	920
CKL	--	740	790	780
BVE	--	810	--	850
JAN	--	810	740	850
LCH	590	610	720	620
OKC	620	610	--	620
GGG	690	510	690	670
IAD	440	410	--	400
HAT	560	470	--	570

Satellite Tropical Rain Data Set

There are two problems in obtaining the global coverage of rainfall desired for climatic studies: sampling and measurement.

The traditional source of rain data, a rain gage network, is unavailable over the tropical oceans and, because of the convective nature of the rainfall, island stations are not representative of the surrounding ocean.

The following section illustrates some of the products from the remote sensing research and development as well as operational systems in space. A number of the photographs have been computer processed to enhance special features for the user community. It should be noted that there is a loss in quality of the data since these have been reproduced from photographs many generations removed from the original.

Plate 1   ESA METEOSAT: March 26, 1982; 11.55 GMT artificially colored visible channel received and processed at ESOC Darmstadt; Copyright ESA.

Plate 2   The clean-room assembly area for the NOAA advanced TIROS-N spacecraft at RCA Astro-Electronics, Hightstown, N.J.

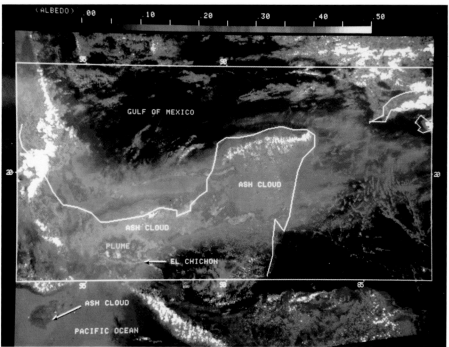

Plate 3　NOAA-7 satellite picture: El Chichon Volcano, Mexico; March 29, 1982 (AVHRR visible channel).

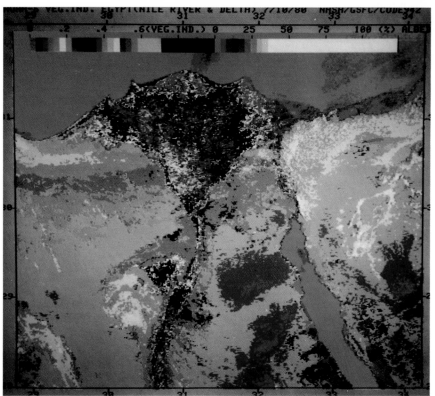

Plate 4　Egypt, Nile Delta, Sinai Peninsula; NASA/GSFC computer processed (AVHRR 1R image) from NOAA-6 satellite: mapping vegetation.

Plate 5   Landsat thematic mapper image of Greater New York.

Plate 6   San Francisco Bay Area: Landsat-4 thematic mapper; image depicting urban buildup in San Francisco Berkeley and neighboring communities.

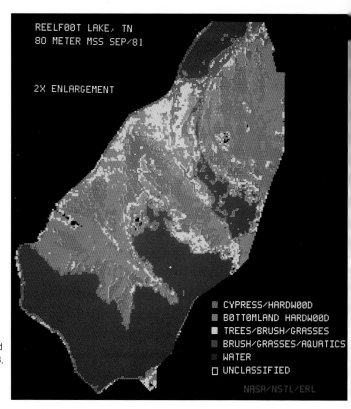

Plate 7 Multispectral scanner forested wetlands classification. (See Chapter 3, Conner & Mooneyhan, Section "Renewable Resource Inventory and Monitoring.")

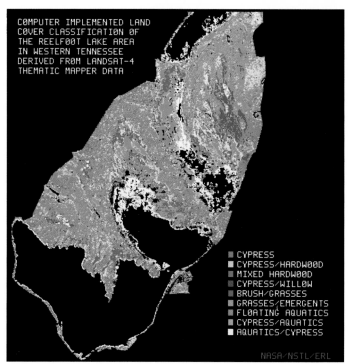

Plate 8 Thematic mapper forested wetlands classification. (See Chapter 3, Conner & Mooneyhan, Section "Renewable Resource Inventory and Monitoring.")

Forest fire hazard assessment of Olympic National Park in Washington illustrates the utility of geographic information system (GIS) technology. The data base for the assessment is constructed from Landsat MSS-derived land cover classification and elevation, slope, and aspect calculated from National Cartographic Information Center (NCIC) digital terrain data. Geographic units were mapped from climatic information representing differences in annual rainfall occurring within the park. Each data plane was geographically registered to a common map base, overlaid, and analyzed to derive the fire hazard classification.

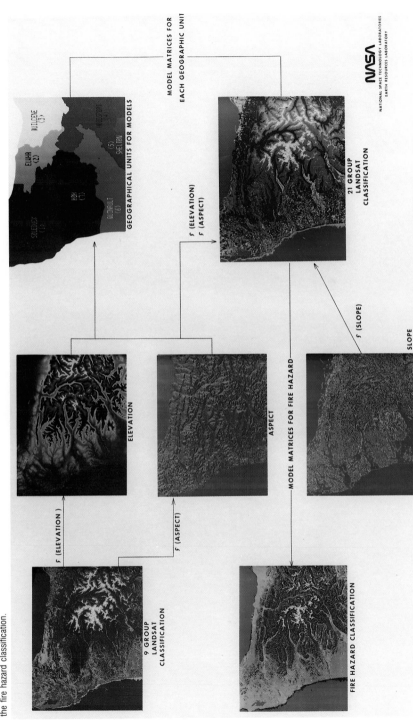

Plate 9 Olympic forest fire hazard assessment. (See Chapter 3, Conner & Mooneyhan, Section "Renewable Resource Inventory and Monitoring.")

Plate 10 Multispectral scanner color composite of Mount St. Helens: pre-eruption. (See Chapter 3, Conner & Mooneyhan, Section "Geologic Applications.")

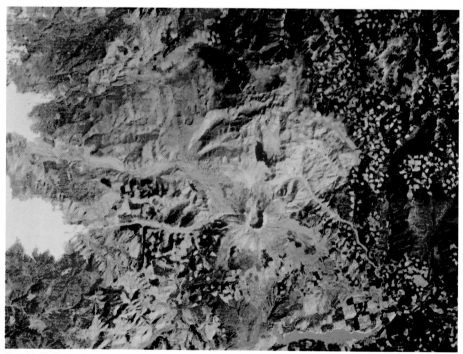

Plate 11 Multispectral scanner color composite of Mount St. Helens: post-eruption. (See Chapter 3, Conner & Mooneyhan, Section "Geologic Applications.")

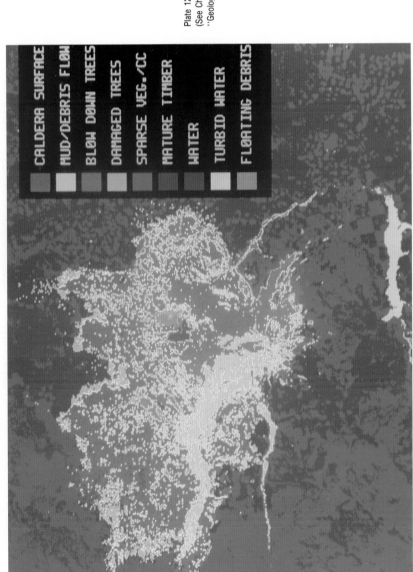

Plate 12 Multispectral scanner damage classification.
(See Chapter 3, Conner & Mooneyhan, Section
"Geologic Applications.")

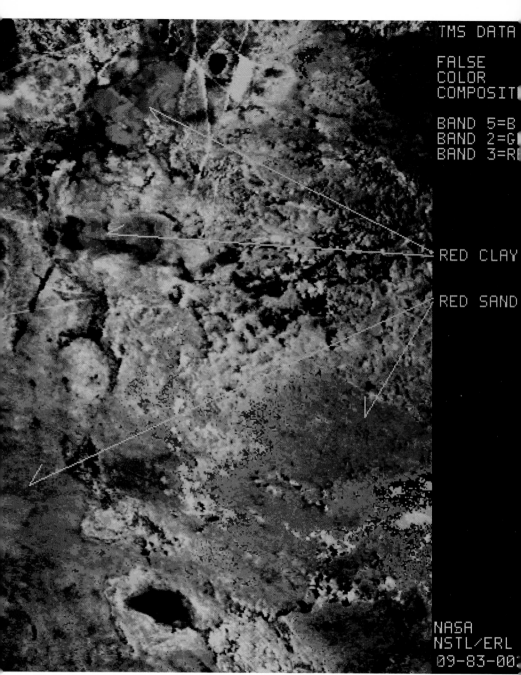

TMS DATA

FALSE
COLOR
COMPOSIT

BAND 5=B
BAND 2=G
BAND 3=RI

RED CLAY

RED SAND

NASA
NSTL/ERL
09-83-00

Plate 13   Thematic mapper scanner soils delineation color composite of bands 2, 3, and 5. (See Chapter 3, Conner & Mooneyhan, Sectio "Geologic Applications.")

Plate 14(inset) SPAS photographed from the Shuttle during deployment and retrieval maneuver (STS-7). In the foreground is the Canadarm manipulator arm with which SPAS was deployed and retrieved. (See Chapter 5, Bodechtel et al., Section "MOMS-01 Missions on STS-7 and STS-11/41-B.")

Plate 15   During STS-11 orbit 28, MOMS imaged a sequence over central Saudi Arabia approximately 50 km southeast of Riyadh. Modern irrigation technology enables man to grow vegetation, which is displayed in this false color composite in red colors. The fields are irrigated by self-propelled sprinkling devices drilled into geological formations containing fossil water resources. The radius of the computer-controlled systems comes to about 0.5 km (scale 1:300 000). (See Chapter 5, Bodechtel et al., Section "MOMS-01 Missions on STS-7 and STS-11/41-B.")

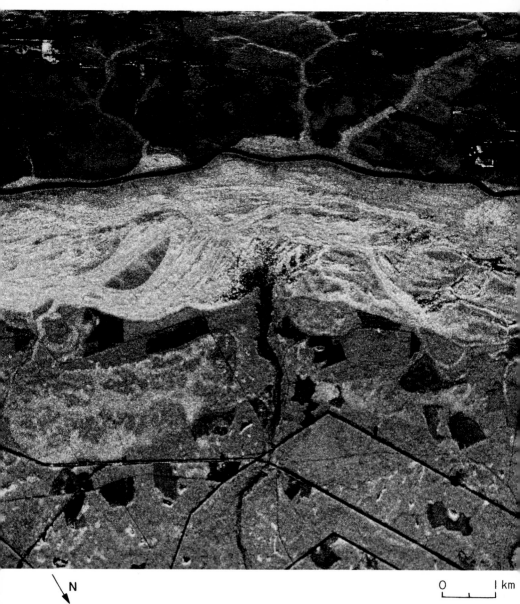

N

0 ____ 1 km

Plate 16   NASA/JPL airborne L-band SAR multipolarization false-color composite image of Savannah River Swamp, SC: centered on 33°08′N, 81°43′W (HH=red, VV=green, VH=blue). See text for further detail. (See Chapter 6, Elachi et al., Section ''Future Development and Conclusions.'')

Plate 17   In-flight photo of the Orbiter cargo bay showing the Orbiter camera payload system large-format camera/attitude reference system installed in the aft end of the bay. (See Chapter 6, Schardt & Mollberg, Section ''Flight Performance Report.'')

Plate 18(inset)   Final close-out of the Orbiter cargo bay showing the large-format camera and attitude reference system installed in its flight position. (See Chapter 6, Schardt & Mollberg, Section ''Flight Performance Report.'')

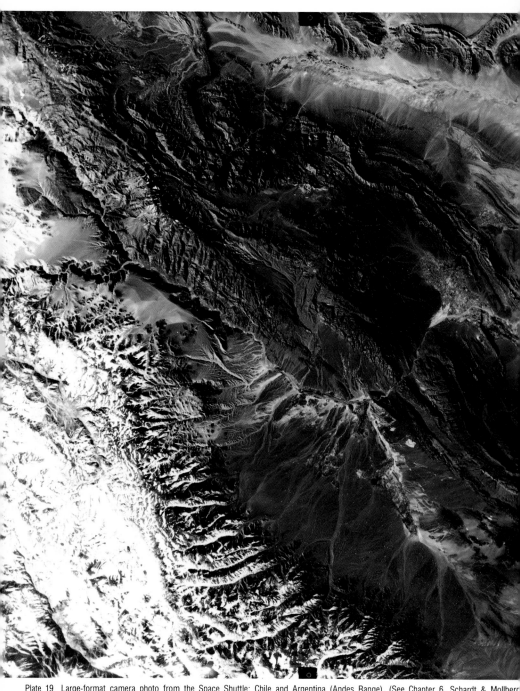

Plate 19 Large-format camera photo from the Space Shuttle: Chile and Argentina (Andes Range). (See Chapter 6, Schardt & Mollberg

Plate 20   Large-format camera photo from the Space Shuttle: Eastern Australian Coast and the Great Barrier Reef. (See Chapter 6, Schardt & Mollberg.)

Plate 21 Large-format camera photo from the Space Shuttle: Eastern Florida Coast; Kennedy Space Center pictured at top, left of center. (See Chapter 6, Schardt & Mollberg.)

Table 5   Methods of monitoring winds from satellites

Type of Satellite

Method	Geostationary	Polar	Instrument used	Wind direction
Cloud motions	Yes	No	Visible & IR images	Yes
Sun glitter reflections	Yes	Yes	Visible images	Maybe
Thermal microwave	No	Yes	Multichannel microwave radiometer (3-37 GHz)	No
Radar backscatter	No	Yes	Altimeter	No
Radar backscatter	No	Yes	Bidirectional scatterometer	Yes

Ship station rainfall observations are notoriously unrepresentative and, moreover, do not sample much of the tropical ocean.

Using radar data, Laughlin[19] showed that, if the averaging area is much larger than the size of the rain cells, the fractional error does not depend strongly on the area, but rather only on the number of samples per averaging period. Using his findings, the sampling error for daily average rain should be about 13% for _four_ samples per day in a 2 x 2° latitude box.

During the GARP (Global Atmospheric Rearch Program) Atlantic Tropical Experiment (GATE), it was shown that the Electrically Scanning Microwave Radiometer (ESMR) data from the Nimbus Satellite correlated with the calibrated ship radar data by better than 0.8 when both were observing the same area. Unfortunately, the Scanning Multifrequency Microwave Radiometer (SMMR) on Nimbus is turned on only every other day and has a swath width less than the interorbit gap. Thus, while microwave multifrequency radiometers onboard polar-orbiting satellites meet the measurement accuracy criteria, they fail on adequate sampling.

Geosynchronous satellites sample much of the Earth continuously and the tropical belt completely. They provide

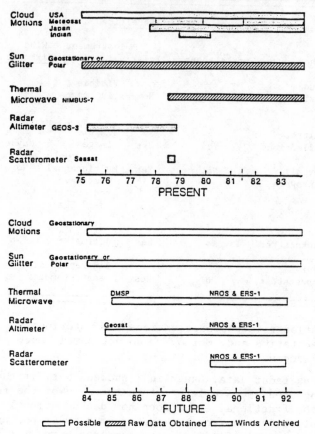

Fig. 17 Past and future of satellite sensors for measuring
winds over oceans.

information on where it is raining, but not on how much.
Several rain estimation schemes have been devised. Evidence
is quite convincing that the factor available from
geosynchronous satellites most closely related to the rain
rate for convection rain is cloud height. Actually, cloud
top temperature is the observable. Additional factors, many
of which are determined by an analyst, add less and less to
the accuracy. Stout et al.[20] modeled rain rate by a
relation of the form

$$r = a_0 A + a_1 \frac{\delta A}{\delta t} \tag{2}$$

where a_0 and a_1 are empirically determined constants and A
is the cloud area with a temperature colder than a suitably

chosen threshold (usually about 235 or 240 K). If this
relation is averaged over a time long compared to the life
of a cloud (e.g., less than one day) it reduces to

$$r = a\bar{A} \qquad (3)$$

Other researchers have found similar relationships.
Unfortunately, the threshold value is variable, depending on
the location and season. So while the geosynchronous
satellite data satisfy the sampling requirement, these data
do not satisfy the measurement criteria.

It appears feasible to use the SMMR (and after 1986 the
Special Sensor Microwave Imager [SSMI] on the Defense
Meteorological Satellite Program [DMSP]) to calibrate (or
update) a threshold scheme. Because the method is otherwise
simple, a machine can apply it several times each day, and
thus solve both the sampling and measurement problems.

Additional Rainfall Possibilities
Using Experimental Satellites

The measurement schemes using microwave observations
follow two schemes, scattering or absorption. The scattering
scheme, useful at the higher microwave frequencies, is
largely empirical. On the other hand, the theory of
microwave attenuation due to rainfall is in much better
order. These are applicable to centimeter scale microwave
radiation instead of millimeter scale wavelengths. Here,
the key uncertainties remaining are the thickness of the
rain layer and the presence or absence of the ice phase. A
satellite equipped with suitable radar can remove this
uncertainty and greatly improve the measurement accuracy of
microwave observations. However, adequate sampling from a
polar-orbiting satellite would still be a problem.

Plans for future U.S. space programs now include large
manned and unmanned platforms in polar and tropical coverage
orbits. These large platforms, or the new experimental
platforms that will be available, could be equipped to
provide a much improved measurement capability. The near-
equatorial orbit would greatly improve the sampling. These
experimental satellites cannot be counted on to provide a
long-duration uninterrupted data set, but they would be
extremely valuable for improving our ability to use the
operational systems likely to be available.

The requirements for accurate rainfall measurement are
very demanding. The accuracy should improve with the more

advanced microwave radiometers and active systems likely to
be available later in the decade. We cannot realistically
configure a system based on a Nimbus satellite operating
beyond its design lifetime. After 1986, when the DMSP
satellite and its microwave radiometer instrument are
operational, the scheme outlined above will have to serve
for at least 5 years.

Evaporation over Land

The task of measuring evaporation over land surface is
complicated by the heterogeneous nature of the surface.
Different croplands have different roughness, albedo, depth
of the root zone, and different stomatal behaviors. When
the moisture supply is ample, most of the net radiation is
converted to latent heat; but when the moisture supply is
low, sensible heat dominates. The surface temperature rise
due to the solar energy absorption depends on the wind speed
and atmospheric stability. Many researchers have investigated the use of remote sensing techniques to estimate the
evapotranspiration and, under special circumstances, have
indeed succeeded quite well. For our purposes, we need a
more general approach that is independent of the terrain as
much as possible.

Since the solar energy received at the Earth's surface
can be estimated from satellite observations, even in the
presence of cloud cover, and because the solar radiation is
the major term of the net radiation at the surface during
daylight when most of the evaporation occurs, a good
estimate of the net radiation of the surface is possible as
well. The heat budget relationship is

$$R_{net} - Evap - sensible - soil = 0 \qquad (4)$$

On a 24 h basis, the soil term is near zero. One needs the
ratio of sensible to latent heat for a solution.

A new approach suggested by Diak[21] makes use of a
direct measure of the sensible heat as observed by VAS.
Figure 18 shows the temperature change as a function of time
measured using VAS. One can consider the boundary layer as
a giant calorimeter and determine the heat added from the
temperature change. Unfortunately, because the
"calorimeter" is moving, advection must also be accounted
for. However, since one has the entire temperature and wind
field, this term can be assessed. Because evaporation is
the only remaining unknown, a solution is possible. Initial

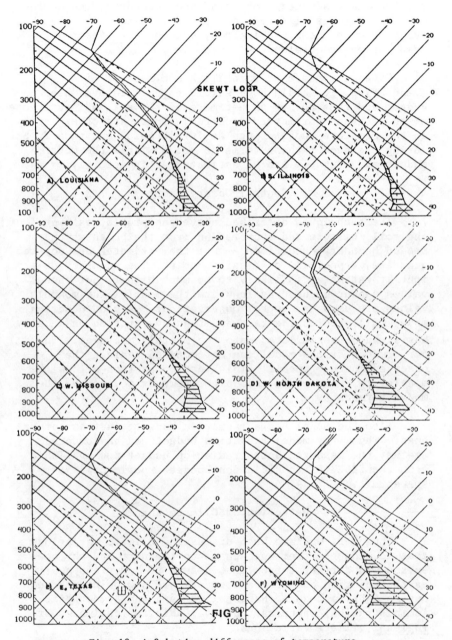

Fig. 18   A 9-h time difference of temperature.

studies show this approach to be quite promising. It has
the important advantage of being independent of the surface,
except for the easily obtained albedo. Details of the
evaporation process are ignored, but the net effect of
evaporation is obtained.

Given a measure of rainfall and a measure of
evaporation, it should be possible to calculate a water
budget and thus to get an estimate of the soil moisture, one
of the surface parameters required. There are other terms
in the moisture budget, such as infiltration and runoff, but
during the summer these terms do not dominate the water
budget and probably can be estimated satisfactorily.

Control Observations

The techniques described above can provide estimates of
the soil moisture and evaporation from the ocean as the
needed boundary conditions -- but the estimates are not too
accurate, especially on a daily basis. The accuracy of
monthly estimates is likely to be much higher, but these
values cannot be used as input to the model. The monthly
values are used as control observations. A good numerical
model will predict the rain and then evaporation on a daily
basis can be assimilated into the monthly averages. The
performance of the model can be compared against the
observed monthly totals. This intercomparison allows the
modeler to " fine-tune" his algorithms or to improve the
model physics.

Also,the model has a radiation budget, just as nature
does. Thus, the model radiation budget can be compared
against the measured earth radiation budget now available
from the ERBE (Earth Radiation Budget Experiment)
spacecraft.

Detection of Climate Change

Thus far, we have been discussing climate variations,
that is, changes from one season to the next and why one
season was different from that season the previous year.
Earth radiation budget measurements are now being carried
out on ERBE, and NOAA (National Oceanic and Atmospheric
Administration) spacecraft are valuable for estimates of
regional climate variations.

In principle, it should also be possible to determine
from radiation measurements whether or not the Earth is

warming or cooling. The accuracy required for this
observation is very high -- at least 1 part in 500.
Instruments now in orbit have this accuracy, but it is not
clear whether they have the stability for defining trends
over a long time period. One must be sure that the Earth is
changing -- not the instrument. Even if one had an
instrument possessing the needed stability, it is not likely
that Earth radiation budget measurements could be used to
detect slow climate change. The problem is sampling.
The diurnal variation of cloudiness is large and variable
and the geometry of the reflection from the cloud cover
highly angle-dependent. Thus, it is not likely that Earth
radiation budget measurements can serve to detect subtle
climatic change on a year-to-year basis before other
manifestations also make themselves evident.

Data Assimilation

    This proposed climate observing system will not provide
images synchronized in time, i.e., uniformly synoptic over
the Earth. A means must be developed to assimilate the data
into the model. Too often we ignore this important part of
the task and leave it entirely up to the modelers. How one
introduces data into the model can have a profound impact on
the subsequent behavior of the model and also a very
significant impact on the computer burden the assimilation
task requires. The problem is to produce the best analysis
possible. The analysis is the actual input for the model
and has a real or virtual value at every grid point and at
every level. Since the data are not simultaneous nor
uniform in coverage, it is necessary to use four-dimensional
assimilation schemes, three dimensions in space and one in
time. Several methods are possible:

    1) Forward assimilation. Using this scheme, one
updates the data set as the data arrives, as shown
schematically in Fig. 19. In this scheme one finds the best
solution provided by the latest data added.

    2) A more satisfactory method is a variational accumu-
lation scheme shown in Fig. 20. Here one finds the model
solution that best fits data over the entire assimilation
interval. It does this by finding initial conditions to the
model that will produce a forecast best fitting the data
over the total assimilation interval.

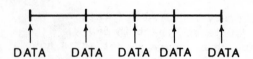

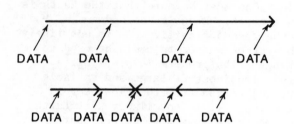

Fig. 19   Forward assimilation.

DATA   DATA   DATA   DATA   DATA

DATA   DATA   DATA   DATA

Fig. 20   Variational accumulation.

DATA   DATA   DATA   DATA   DATA

     The best fit is defined in terms of a positive scalar called the functional error

$$I = \tfrac{1}{2} \sum_{obs} w \, (\phi - \tilde{\phi})^2 \tag{5}$$

which represents the weighted difference between the observation and the forcast for that interval. One wishes to find the ϕ which will minimize I and satisfy a forecast model. This will produce a four-dimensional analysis consistent with the dynamics of the controlling forecast. The traditional meteorological methods for the solution of variational problems do not work well on this problem. A recent thesis by Derber[22] uses instead standard nonlinear minimization and optimum control techniques. It is not appropriate to discuss the procedure in great detail here, but a simple example shows its advantages. More important, it gives some insight in how to best provide observational data for the model.

     Assume a linear model with only two components in the initial condition vector. The functional values over all of the two initial conditions would look something like Fig. 21. Then the object is to get from the current state p to the optimal state p*. Note that the gradient of I, given by

$$Grad = \begin{bmatrix} \dfrac{\partial I}{\partial \phi_1} \\[2mm] \dfrac{\partial I}{\partial \phi_2} \end{bmatrix} \tag{6}$$

will be equal to zero at p*.

A three-step algorithm can be used to find p*. Step 1 is to define a search direction which is the estimate of the direction from p to p*. In step 2, one finds the step size (distance in the search direction) which minimizes I. Step 3 goes back to step 1 unless already converged. The determination of the search direction is different, dependent on the specific minimization algorithm; however, nearly all require the calculation of Grad I. This is done through the use of an adjoint model. This model is a mathematical trick which allows Grad I to be found. Grad I is found by inserting the weighted differences between the forecast and the observations in the backward integration over the assimilation period as shown in Fig. 22.

The great advantage of the scheme is that it does not matter how many observation times are used. This has practical advantages because remote sensing observations even from geosynchronous spacecraft do not occur at the same time. Also, data with horizontal and temporal resolution greater than that stated in the requirements allow one to find the solution much more accurately. Finally, the computational resources used to find Grad I are roughly equivalent to one integration of the forecast model. The basic characteristics have been estimated using a simple

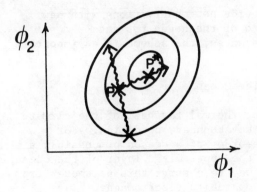

Fig. 21 Linear model.

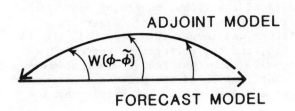

ADJOINT MODEL

$W(\phi - \tilde{\phi})$

FORECAST MODEL

Fig. 22 Integration of adjoint model.

five-level channel model that, while being simple, does
reveal the following advantages of the approach:

    1) Relative insensitivity to the spatial structure of
the errors.

    2) Rapid convergence, which becomes slower as the
assimilation interval increases.

    3) The optimal analysis is close to the average of the
analysis integrated to analysis time.

    4) The algorithm is independent of the number of
analysis times.

    5) The procedure cannot eliminate errors temporally
correlated to the model solution -- that virtual data error
again!

    What was briefly outlined above is a very simple
picture of the full four-dimensional assimilation problem.
One merely needs to look again at Figs. 9-14, which show
additional wind information from tracking water vapor
studies, to appreciate that it is necessary to include all
four dimensions since the data have different geographical
coverage at different altitudes.

    Those who wish to provide new observations with new
instruments should be aware of the needs for data
assimilation. In some instances, the scheme is as important
as the observations.

The Ocean

    The ocean is the giant thermal flywheel of the climate
system and its state is a key boundary condition. For
climate predictions of the order of a season or possibly a
year, the heat content of the upper mixed layer of the ocean
is required. There is no way to observe this parameter from
space, since the ocean is opaque to electromagnetic
radiation. We must use in situ observations. One of the
most successful elements of the global observing system used
during FGGE was the drifting buoy system.[23] Experience
showed that their lifetime was longer than expected, the
cost lower than expected, and the performance better than
first expected. An equally important factor was that many
nations could make a contribution to the program -- some
provided buoys and some deployed them. The latter was a
large expense item.

These buoys were equipped to measure pressure. The satellite data relay and platform location system (ARGOS) carried on the NOAA polar-orbiting satellites provided location as well as surface pressure, so it was possible to obtain surface currents as well, but the latter was possibly contaminated by the wind loading on the buoy. It seems straightforward to equip similar drifters with a thermistor chain suspended below the buoy to obtain the temperature structure of the upper mixed layer. Plans are underway to do this. The upper mixed layer is not uniform and contains internal waves that could cause serious aliasing errors at any one measurement time. The low-cost digital techniques now available make it possible to obtain a time average from each thermistor that will be more representative. We are interested in the total heat content of the upper mixed layer. This can be changed from heat gain or loss at the surface by advection in several layers and by vertical motions of the thermocline at the bottom. What we need is the mean temperature in the vertical as well. Also, it would be useful to add a long hairpin-like resistance thermometer that could detect very small changes in the heat content of that layer. Precautions must be taken against mechanical strains so that the long resistance thermometer does not become a strain gage instead. A parallel constantan wire hairpin must be part of the same line. This notion has been added to Fig. 4. The writer found this scheme to be very accurate for assessing soil heat content changes. The specific heat of water is much more uniform than that of soil, so it ought to work better.

New Ocean Measurements

Plans are underway for a Navy Remote Ocean Sensing System (NROSS) satellite to measure the wind at the surface using the scatterometer technique demonstrated on Seasat. Proposals also have been made to launch a precision radio altimeter on the the ocean Topography Experiment (TOPEX) early in the 1990s. With these observations, oceanographers should be able to make significant advances in plotting the world ocean circulation and, if atmosphere/ocean-coupled models are developed, to extend the climate forcast to seasons and possibly interannually as well. The writer suggests that a new instrument be added to TOPEX to make it even better. The measurement of atmospheric surface pressure from a LEO satellite has recently been demonstrated by aircraft trials.[24] Measurements of the strength of echoes from the ocean surface in the 60 GHz O_2 band can be used to estimate the mass of oxygen in the vertical column and hence the surface pressure. Both the aircraft trials

and numerical simulations show that rms accuracies of ±1
millibars (mb) can be achieved. Measurements at a number
of frequencies in the 26-75 GHz range allow the effects of
varying sea state, atmospheric temperature, water vapor, and
cloud to be compensated. In the simulations, total power
was limited to 12 W, so solid-state transmitters can be
used. Side viewing of 10-20 deg off the vertical is limited
by the specular reflection from the ocean surface.
Integrated column water (high quality) and sea state can
also be retrieved from the measurements.

There is considerable meteorological and oceanic
significance to these measurements. First, the surface
pressure is a key parameter for observation. These data can
also help constrain the temperature sounding consideration.
Further, the ocean acts as a water barometer and a
correction must be applied to the precision altimetry
measurement of the ocean topography due to atmospheric
pressure. One mb corresponds to about 1 cm of water and
this is definitely in the range of interest. Finally, there
may be an important third benefit of direct measurement of
the momentum transfer from the atmosphere to the ocean,
i.e., the all-important vector wind stress. Surface
pressure fields determine the gradient wind. Surface wind
cross-isobar flow is a direct result of friction with the
underlying surface. The momentum removed from the
atmosphere due to friction is added directly to the ocean.

Observations from NROSS will provide the surface wind
speed and direction and the surface pressure field
observations just suggested will provide the gradient wind
information. The vector difference between the two is
related to the vector wind stress at the surface.

Conclusions

What we have tried to outline in this paper is a
climate observing system for the immediate future. Plans
and proposals have been put forth outlining many new
instrument possibilities now that large spacecraft with
ample power are being proposed.

Many will be flown and tested on the future spacecraft
in several nations' space programs. What we have tried to
do here is to show that a viable operational World Climate
Research Programme observing system is feasible. This
system, while not meeting every modeler's dream in full,
does bring many of their data dreams much closer to reality.

References

[1]Lorenz, E., personal communication.

[2]Bengtsson, L., and Simmons, A.J., "Medium Range Weather Prediction Operational Experience at ECMWF," informal internal ECMWF paper, 1983, 23 pp.

[3]World Meteorological Organization, Committee on Atmospheric Sciences, "Report of the Study Conference on the Global Atmospheric Research Program (GARP), 1967, Appendix VII, Suomi, V.E., "Observing the Atmosphere, Some Possibilities."

[4]World Meteorological Organization, "Programme on Weather Prediction Research," No. 1, Proceedings of WMO-CAS/JSC Expert Study Meeting on Long-Range Forecasting, Princeton, 1-4 December 1982, 235 pp.

[5]Rodgers, C.D., "Retrieval of Atmospheric Temperature and Composition from Remote Measurements of Thermal Radiation," Review of Geophysics and Space Physics, Vol. 14, No. 4, November 1976, pp. 609-624.

[6]Smith, W.L., "An Improved Method for Calculating Tropospheric Temperature and Moisture from Satellite Radiometer Measurements," Monthly Weather Review, 96, 1968, pp. 387-396.

[7]Susskind, J., Rosenfield, J., Reuter, D., and Chahine, M.T., "The GLAS Physical Inversion Method for Analysis of HIRS-2/MSU Sounding Data," NASA Technical Memo 84936, 1982.

[8]Chedin, A., Scott, N.A., Wahiche, C., and Moulinier, P., "The Improved Initialization Inversion Method: A High Resolution Physical Method for Temperature Retrievals from Satellites of the TIROS-N Series," Journal of Climate and Applied Meteorology, Vol. 24, No. 2, February 1985, pp. 128-143.

[9]McLain, E.P., Pichel, W.G., Walton, C.C., Ahmad, Z., and Sutton, J, "Multi-Channel Improvements to Satellite-Derived Global Sea Surface Temperatures," Advanced Space Research, Vol. 2, No. 6, 1983, pp. 43-47.

[10]Rasmusson, E.M., "El Nino: The Ocean/Atmosphere Connection," Oceanus, Vol. 27, No. 2, Summer 1984, pp. 5-12.

[11]Johnson, L.R., Global Winds by Tracking Meteosat Water Vapor Patterns, M.S. Thesis, Department of Meteorology, University of Wisconsin-Madison, 1979, 28 pp.

[12]Stewart, T.R., Hayden, C.M., and Smith, W.L., "A Note on Water Vapor Wind Tracking Using VAS Data on McIDAS," Accepted by Journal of Climate and Applied Meteorology, 1985.

[13]Menzel, W.P., Smith, W.L., and Stewart, T.R., "Improved Cloud Motion Wind Vector and Altitude Assignment Using VAS," Journal of Climate and Applied Meteorology, Vol. 22, No. 3, March 1983, pp. 377-384.

[14]World Meteorological Organization, "Report of Workshop on Interim Ocean Surface Wind Data," 24-27 October 1983, Madison, Wisconsin.

[15]Sadler, J.C., and B.J. Kilonsky, "Trade Wind Monitoring Using Satellite Observations," Department of Meteorology Report UMET81-01, University of Hawaii, 1981, 72 pp.

[16]Wylie, D.P., and Hinton, B., "A Summary of the Wind Data Available from Satellites from the Past History to Future Sensors," Large-Scale Oceanographic Experiments and Satellites, D. Reidel Publishing Co., NATO ASI Series, Vol. 128., pp. 125-146.

[17]Esbensen, S.K., and Reynolds, R.W., "Estimating Monthly Averaged Air-Sea Transfers of Heat and Momentum Using the Bulk Aerodynamic Method," Journal of Physical Oceanography, Vol. 11, April 1981, pp. 457-465.

[18]Liu, W. T., and Niiler, P.P., "Determination of Monthly Mean Humidity in the Atmospheric Surface Layer over Oceans from Satellite Data," Journal of PHysical Oceanography, Vol. 14, No. 9, September 1984, pp. 1451-1457.

[19]Laughlin, C.R., "Estimation of Rainfall from Sample Observations," unpublished manuscript originally submitted to Monthly Weather Review, July 1980, 38 pp.

[20]Stout, J.E., D.W. Martin, and D.N. Sikdar, "Estimating GATE Rainfall with Geosynchonous Satellite Images," Monthly Weather Review, 107, 585-598.

[21]Diak, personal communication.

[22]Derber, J.C., "The Variational Four-Dimensional ASsimilation of Analyses Using Filtered Models as Constraints," Ph.D. Thesis, Department of Meteorology, University of Wisconsin-Madison, 1985, 142 pp.

[23]Fleming, R.J., Kaneshige, T.M., and W.E. McGovern, "The Global Weather Experiment. 1. The Observational Phase Through the First Special Observing Period," Bulletin of the American Meteorological Society, Vol. 60, No. 6, June 1979.

[24]Peckham, G.E., Gatley, C., Flower, D.A., "Optimizing a Remote Sensing Instrument to Measure Atmospheric Surface Pressure," International Journal of Remote Sensing, Vol. 4, No. 2, 1983, pp. 465-478.

Chapter III.   Remote Sensing of the Land Resources

Landsat-D and -D′—The Operational Phase of Land Remote Sensing from Space

Edward W. Mowle*

National Oceanic and Atmospheric Administration, Washington, D.C.

Abstract

The Landsat program began in the late 1960s as a key element in NASA's Earth Resources Survey Program. Three spacecraft, Landsats-A, -B, and -C, were constructed based upon the Nimbus meteorological research satellites. The initial spacecraft was launched in 1972 and became Landsat-1, observing the Earth with a three-camera return beam vidicon (RBV) and a multispectral scanner (MSS). Landsat-2, launched in 1975, and Landsat-3, launched in 1978, carried similar instrumentation. Landsat-D carried development of civil land remote sensing one step further with the initial launch in July 1982 of a new instrument, the thematic mapper (TM), a seven-band, mechanically scanned radiometer with 30 m ground resolution and using the NASA multimission modular spacecraft (MMS) in lieu of the Nimbus-derived spacecraft used for Landsats-1, -2, and -3. The data returned from the new sensor have been widely acclaimed; however, component failures in several supporting subsystems have marred the operational usefullness of Landsat-4. Design improvements in the affected subsystems were completed and the backup spacecraft, Landsat D', was launched in March, 1984. Both Landsat-4 and -5 are currently operated by the National Oceanic and Atmospheric Administration (NOAA) as a result of decisions made by President Carter in late 1979 defining national space policy for civil remote sensing from space. Each of the current satellites can provide complete coverage of the Earth's surface once every 16 days. However, Landsat-4 with its reduced

This paper is declared a work of the U.S. Government and therefore is in the public domain.

*Chief, Land Observation Systems Group, NESDIS.

capabilities provides direct MSS data to foreign ground stations, while Landsat-5 is the primary source for TM data worldwide.

Introduction

In the late 1960s NASA began a satellite program designed to routinely sense the surface of the Earth with high-resolution multispectral instruments tailored to detect and transmit the unique reflected and emitted signatures associated with many of our natural resources. Interpretation of the images produced on a repetitive basis promised to identify the existence and changes over time of many critical resources such as water, vegetation, and minerals. With sufficient resolution, man-made features and surface alterations could be identified, permitting generation of maps and land use inventories.

The challenges were formidible, both in sensor and spacecraft technology and in the ground data system required to process and archive the great quantities of information to be returned from space. NASA selected the generic Nimbus spacecraft with proved attitude control, power generation, and command and data handling capabilities. New sensors were developed along with the wideband data formating and communications subsystems required to store and transmit the 15 megabit/s image data to both NASA and selected foreign ground stations.

The initial spacecraft, Earth Resources Technology Satellite ERTS-1, was launched in July 1972 aboard a two-stage Delta 900 (DSV-3N-1) from the Vandenberg Air Force Base Missile Test Center and placed into a sun-synchronous orbit with an altitude of 916 km (495 n.mi.) at an inlcination of 99.14 deg with the equator.

The primary instrumentation carried by the first satellite, later renamed Landsat-1, consisted of a three-camera return beam vidicon (RBV) subsystem and a multispectral scanner (MSS) subsystem, both designed to capture images of the Earth in several different spectral bands ranging from the visible to near infrared.

The RBV subsystem contained three individual cameras operating in the blue-green (0.475-0.575 μm), yellow-red (0.580-0.680 μm), and red to near infrared (0.698-0.830 μm) portions of the spectrum. Each camera was aligned to cover the same 185 X 185 km (100 n.mi.) square frame on the ground with a resolution of 79 m. The cameras could operate every 25 s to provide images with about 10% overlap along the ground track.

The multispectral scanner (MSS) subsystem produced a continuous strip image of the Earth in four spectral bands as indicated in Table 1.

The first three bands are equivalent to the three RBV bands and use six photomultiplier tubes per band as detector elements. The fourth band extends the infrared coverage beyond that available from the RBV and uses six silicon photodiodes to detect the energy. An oscillating scan mirror directs energy from the scene onto the detector matrix and the resulting electrical signals are formated into a digital data stream at a rate of 15 megabit/s.

Technical difficulties in the spacecraft power switching subsystem resulted in a NASA decision to minimize the use of the RBV subsystem and concentrate on the MSS as the primary sensor.

Landsat-2 was launched in 1975 and carried similar instruments, a three-camera RBV and MSS sensor subsystem with two wideband video tape recorders for remote data acquisition when out of range of system ground stations. Each tape recorder was capable of storing 30 min of either 3.2 MHz analog video from the RBV or 15 megabit/s digital data from the MSS.

The MSS subsystem carried on Landsat-3, launched in 1978, was configured with a thermal infrared band to provide images in the 10.4-12.6 μm portion of the spectrum in addition to the visible and near-infrared bands used previously. The solid-state detectors used for the thermal band were radiatively cooled and lost sensitivity soon after launch, resulting in the loss of useful data from that band. The Landsat-3 RBV subsystem contained only two cameras, both operating with a panchromatic bandwidth of 0.505-0.750 μm and longer focal length lenses resulting in 24 m ground resolution, but with one-fourth of the image size of the three-camera subsystem. The two smaller frames were aligned to image side-by-side frames covering the same swath width, 185

Table 1 Landsat-1, -2, and -3 MSS spectral bands

Band designation	Spectral response, μm
4	0.5-0.6
5	0.6-0.7
6	0.7-0.8
7	0.8-1.1
8	10.4-12.6 (Landsat-3 only)

km, and were operated twice as often, every 12.5 s, as
the earlier three camera subsystems on Landsat-1 and -2.

A nonimaging payload subsystem called the data
collection system (DCS) was carried on each of the first
three Landsat spacecraft and provided an in-orbit capability to relay data collected at remote sites to
cooperating ground stations within mutual radio range of
the satellite. A small transmitter at each data collection site, located primarily in the United States and
Canada, was connected to environmental sensors selected
by the investigator or user agency to satisfy mission
needs. The DCS in the satellite acted as a simple radio
relay, transponding the received 400 MHz signal to an S-
band subcarrier in real time with no onboard storage.

The configuration of the Landsat-1, -2, and -3
series spacecraft is illustrated Fig. 1 and indicates
the strong Nimbus heritage in the bus and supporting
subsystems. The payload complement shown is that of
Landsat-3 with the two-camera RBV and the five-channel
MSS instruments as described above.

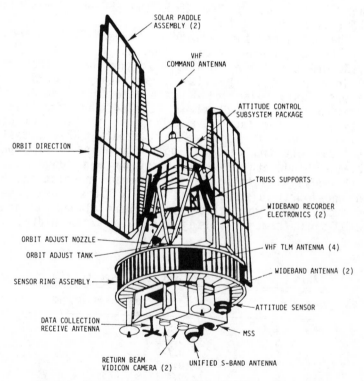

Fig. 1 Landsat-1, -2, -3 spacecraft configuration.

The data returned from the early Landsat program over a period of 10 years received widespread acclaim and generated considerable enthusiasm in the research community. NASA has invested heavily in technology transfer programs designed to identify specific applications and to educate potential users in mineral exploration, agriculture, land use, and other Earth resource disciplines. Foreign participation has grown through cooperative operation of foreign ground stations for direct image reception and through programs of the Agency for International Devleopment (AID) and other federal agencies that provided data and applications assistance to users in less developed countries around the world.

The Landsat-D Program

The Landsat-D program, begun during the operation of Landsat-2 and -3, represents the second generation of spacecraft and ground system technology applied to civil land remote sensing from space. The principal improvements in the system are:

1) The initial space flight of a new instrument called the thematic mapper (TM), a seven-band mechanically scanned radiometer with 30 m resolution capability.

2) The use of the multimission modular spacecracft (MMS) in lieu of the Nimbus-derived spacecraft previously flown.

3) Capability for real-time global data readout via the tracking and data relay satellite system (TDRSS).

4) A completely new dedicated ground data processing system with high throughput to shorten data turnaround time.

Two spacecraft, Landsat-D and a backup, Landsat-D′ were authorized for construction along with the ground system required for satellite control and image data processing. The choice of the thematic mapper as the principal sensor drove the baseline design toward a new class of spacecraft to support the required weight, power, and pointing accuracies. NASA selected the multimission modular spacecraft (MMS) for the Landsat-D mission. Pressure from the remote sensing user community resulted in a later decision to include the MSS in addition to the TM in order to protect the investment in systems and software in use for information extraction from MSS class data.

Decisions made by the administration under President Carter in late 1979 changed national policy for land remote sensing from space, emphasising the operational aspects of the civil program. Accordingly, the National Oceanic and Atmospheric Administration (NOAA) was selected to operate Landsat-D and -D' during the transition to a fully operational program. Program objectives were realigned to reflect this new emphasis. The major objectives of the Landsat-D program are:

1) To assess the capability of the TM to provide improved information for Earth resources management.

2) To provide for system-level feasibility demonstration in concert with user agencies to define the need for and characteristics of an operational system.

3) To encourage continued foreign participation in the Landsat program.

4) To continue the availability of MSS data for users whose needs are met by this class of data.

5) To provide a transition for both domestic and foreign users from the MSS to the higher resolution and data rate of the TM.

Landsat-D was launched in July 1982 on a Delta 3920 expendable launch vehicle and has provided an operational capability for U.S. and foreign users of MSS data despite technical problems that have greatly reduced the ability of the satellite to return data from the TM sensor.

The backup spacecraft, Landsat-D', was modified and successfully launched on March 1, 1984, restoring full system capability in the space segment. A system description of the Landsat-D space and ground segments follows. A brief discussion of the performance in-orbit and the modifications made to Landsat-D' to correct the problems discovered in Landsat-D will also be provided.

Landsat-D System

System Overview

The Landsat-D system consists of one or more Landsat-D series satellites in orbit together with a distributed data acquisition and processing system. The majority of the Landsat-dedicated equipment is located within a single facility at the NASA Goddard Space Flight Center (GSFC) in Greenbelt, MD. Figure 2 depicts the flow of image data, commands, and telemetry between

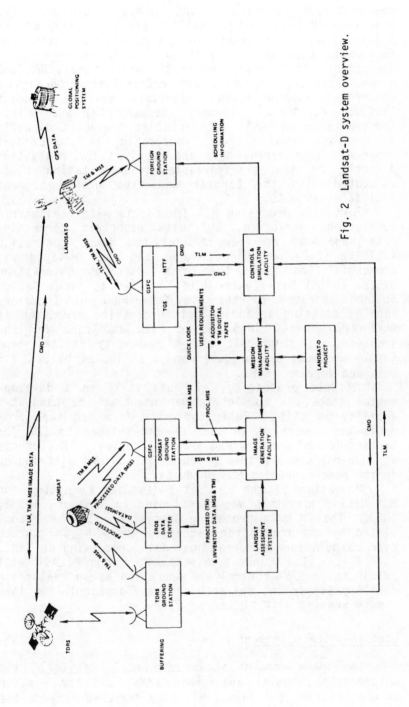

Fig. 2 Landsat-D system overview.

the pricinpal elements of the Landsat-D system. The
Tracking and Data Relay Satellite (TDRS) is used as the
primary link for commands in the forward direction and
for image data and satellite telemetry in the return
direction. After reception at the White Sands, NM, TDRS
ground station, the data are retransmitted through a
commercial communications satellite to the Landsat
facility at GSFC. Thematic mapper (TM) and multispectral scanner (MSS) data are also broadcast directly
to foreign ground stations cooperating in the Landsat
program. Engineering data are received for evaluation
directly by the transportable ground station (TGS)
colocated with the Landsat dedicated ground segment
facilities at GSFC.

Partially processed MSS image data with radiometric
corrections performed, but with geometric correction
data appended, are recorded at the iamge generation
facility (IGF) on product tapes and then relayed via
commercial Domsat to the Earth Resources Observation
System (EROS) Data Center (EDC) located at Sioux Falls,
SD, and operated by the U.S. Department of Interior.
Final processing including full geometric correction is
performed at EDC into master film and tape for the
archives. Photographic and high-density digital tape
(HDDT) products are produced and distributed by EDC for
U.S. and foreign users.

TM data processing, although still in a developmental stage, is completely performed at the Landsat-D
facility at GSFC. Fully corrected film and tape products are generated in the IGF and shipped to EDC for
preparation of masters and archival copies. TM products
for general use are then produced at EDC and distributed
in the same manner as MSS products.

Operation of the Landsat-D (Landsat-4) system for
MSS data acquisition was turned over to NOAA on Feb. 1,
1983. The TM data procesing subsystem (TIPS) was completed by the contractor, accepted by NASA, and turned
over to NOAA for TM operational data processing on Sept.
1, 1984. The Landsat Assessment System (LAS) will
remain under NASA control and operation as an evaluation
facility supporting research and development in the land
remote sensing disciplines.

Landsat-D Space Segment

The space segment shown in Fig. 3 consits of the
multimission modular spacecraft (MMS) and the mission
unique instrument module (IM). Key features include the

high-gain antenna for TDRS communications and the large oriented solar array.

Multimission Modular Spacecraft (MMS). Developed by NASA as a standard spacecraft compatible with both expendable launch vehicles and the Space Shuttle, the MMS provides basic spacecraft functions of power, attitude control, communications and data handling, and propulsion in unique modules that are mounted on a triangular structure. Primary functions of each module are described below.

Modular Power Supply. The power module controls and regulates power from the mission unique 13.6 m^2 (147 ft^2) solar array located on the instrument module and capable of generating over 2 kw at beginning of life providing primary system power. Three 50 A·h nickel-cadmium batteries are located in the MPS for eclipse power and to handle peak demands during sensor payload operation. Various power switching and protection circuits distribute the nominal 28 V primary power to spacecraft subsystems.

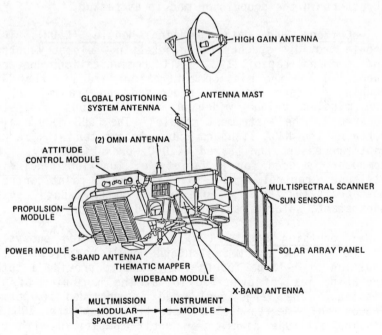

Fig. 3 Landsat-D space segment.

Modular Attitude Control Subsystem (MACS). The
attitude control subsystem is a high-precision zero-
momentum system with three-axis pointing accuracy of
0.01 deg and a stability of 10^{-6} deg/s. It achieves
this precision using an inertial reference unit with
attitude updates from two fixed head star trackers.
Since the specific pointing modes are mission unique,
all control algorithms are implemented in software
executed in the onboard computer located in the command
and data handling module. A two-axis Earth sensor is
mounted external to the MACS for the Landsat-D mission
and provides backup attitude reference for coarse attitude control modes. Safe-hold modes of operation are
automatically switched on in the event of failures
either in the onboard computer or in one of the primary
attitude sensors and can maintain control within 10
deg with rates of 0.1 deg/s. After ground analysis and
evaluation of the cause for safe-hold, the appropriate
redundant set of components can be selected and precision attitude control regained by ground command.

Actuators employed by the MACS include four
reaction wheels: three in pitch, roll, and yaw and one
skewed for redundancy. Magnetic torquers are the primary means of wheel momentum control with 12 0.2 lbf
thrusters in the propulsion module as backup.

Command and Data Handling Module (C&DH). This
module provides spacecraft housekeeping—telemetry output
and command capability. All communications between
Landsat-D and the mission controllers are via the C&DH
module. Sensor data are processed and transmitted by
the mission unique wideband communications subsystem
located in the instrument module. The C&DH module also
contains the NASA standard onboard computer with redundant processors and shared 64,000 words of memory. The
computer is used for a variety of functions including
attitude control, high-gain antenna point/control,
spacecraft/TDRS/solar ephemeris computation, power
management, solar array control, and telemetry monitor.

Propulsion Module (PM). The propulsion subsystem
is the PM 1-A, the MMS standard module modified by the
addition of a large fourth fuel tank to provide a total
hydrazine load of over 500 lb at the beginning of the
mission. The large fuel load is provided to permit
deboost of the Landsat-D satellite from the 700 km
mission altitude down to an orbit compatible with the
Space Shuttle for eventual retrieval. Four 5 lbf
thrusters are fired together for orbit adjust burns

while 12 0.2 lbf thrusters provide backup attitude control capability.

Instrument Module. The instrument module is custom designed for the Landsat-D mission and provides mounting for the primary sensors, MSS and TM, the wideband communications subsystem, the mission unique solar array, and the TDRS antenna.

Multispectral Scanner (MSS). The MSS on Landsat-D is very similar to those flown on Landsat-1 and -2, with the optics and scan mechanism modified for the lower altitude of the Landsat-D orbit. The instrument contains four spectral bands in the visible and near infrared spaced as shown in Table 2. Bands 1-3 employ six photomultiplier tubes per band to detect the visible portion of the spectrum while band 4 uses six silicon photodiode detectors to extend the sensitivity into the near infrared.

The motion of the scan mirror is controlled at a precise rate such that six lines, each 80 m wide, are imaged onto the detector array while the satellite moves 480 (6 x 80) m along the ground track between each scan period, active plus retrace, as shown in Fig. 4. The resolution (instantaneous field of view or IFOV) of each detector element is equivilant to an 80 m square projected on the ground resulting in an output data rate of 15 megabit/s containing data from a 185 km (100 n.mi.) wide swath plus calibration information inserted during the retrace portion of the scan mirror cycle. Time code information is included in the image data stream in order to correlate the image time with satellite ephemeris and attitude during geometric correction processing on the ground.

Thematic Mapper (TM). The TM is a new instrument flown for the first time on Landsat-D with improved

Table 2 Landsat-D and -D' MSS spectral bands

Spectral band	Micrometers	Radiometric sensitivity (NEΔP), %
1	0.5-0.6	0.57
2	0.6-0.7	0.57
3	0.7-0.8	0.65
4	0.8-1.1	0.70

resolution and seven spectral bands. Summary performance specifications, together with some anticipated
applications, are shown in Table 3. Bands 1-5 and 7
cover the visible and near infrared, while band 6 provides data in the thermal portion of the spectrum. As
in the MSS, the energy for each scan line is imaged onto
an array of detectors. Bands 1-4 employ 16 monolithic
silicon detectors per band and are located on the
uncooled prime focal plane to provide data in four
narrow visible spectral bands. The infrared energy is
refocused onto a cooled focal plane containing 16
indium-antimonide (InSb) detectors for each of the two
near-infrared bands (band 5 and 7) and four large
mercury-cadmium-teluride (HgCdTe) detectors for band 6
responding in the thermal infrared.

All bands with the exception of band 6 have detectors sized to provide an equivilant IFOV of 30 m
projected onto the ground, while the band 6 detectors
have an equivilant IFOV of 120 m. The output data rate
for the TM is 85 megabit/s, including image data and
time code for ground data procesing. Like the MSS, the
TM image data are returned from a swath 185 km (100
n.mi.) wide and arbitrarily divided into square "scenes"
during the ground processing to facilitate comparison
with other data sources. In addition to the increased
number of detector elements, the scan concept used in
the TM adds significantly to the complexity of the
instrument when compared with the MSS. In order to

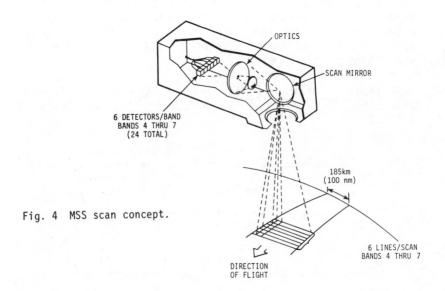

Fig. 4 MSS scan concept.

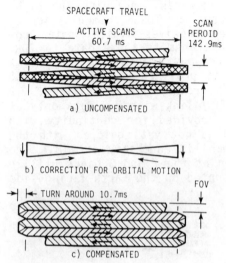

SCANNER GROUND PATTERNS

SPACECRAFT TRAVEL

a) UNCOMPENSATED

b) CORRECTION FOR ORBITAL MOTION

c) COMPENSATED

Fig. 5 Thematic mapper
scan line correction.

reduce the scan rate of the much larger mirror, energy
is reflected onto the detectors and their outputs are
processed into data signals during both the forward and
reverse scans of the mirror, which oscillates at a 7 Hz
rate. If not compensated, the forward motion of the
satellite would cause the imaged areas to form "zig-zag"
strips as shown in Fig. 5, with considerable areas of
underlap and overlap seriously reducing the effective
resolution.

A pair of scan line corrector mirrors inserted near
the prime focal plane and driven at the scan rate alter
the imaged areas into parallel strips uniformly imaging
the entire area within the desired swath.

A schematic representation of the TM scan concept
showing the scan line correction function and the locations of the prime and cooled focal planes is provided
in Fig. 6. A comparison of the physical characteristics
of the TM and the MSS is illustrated in Table 4 and
indicates the dramatic increase of 4:1 in weight and
power required to gain the increased resolution and
thermal infrared band.

Wideband Communications Subsystem. The basic concept of the multimission modular spacecraft program
assigns the mission-unique payload communications functions to the instrument module. In the Landsat-D
configuration, the wideband payload communications ele-

ments are packaged in a "minimodule" that contains the
RF components and several antennas, including the high-
gain boom-mounted antenna used for TDRSS communications.
    The wideband subsystem receives digital data from
the TM and MSS sensors and transmits these data to TDRS
at the Ku band.   Direct readout transmission at the X
band (8025-8400 MHz) is also provided for TM and/or MSS
data readout to selected foreign ground stations.   A
single S band (2206-2300 MHz) link with MSS data only at
the 15 megabit/s rate is provided for continuity with
those foreign ground stations not yet equipped with the
X band data reception capability necesary for TM.   The
direct readout transmission at the X and S bands utilize
Earth coverage antennas mounted on the Earth-facing side
of the spacecraft.

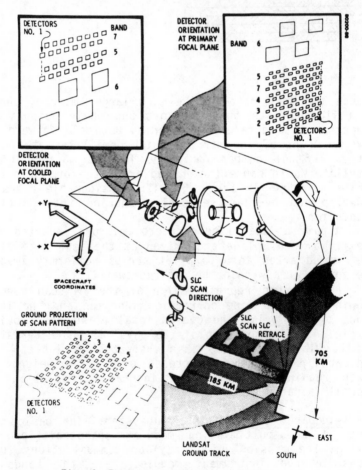

Fig. 6 Thematic mapper scan concept.

Table 3   Thematic mapper (TM) performance and applications

Band	Spectral range, µm	Radiometric resolution [a]	Principal applications
1	0.45-0.52	0.8% NEΔp	Coastal water mapping
			Soil vegetation differentiation
			Deciduous/coniferous differentiation
2	0.52-0.60	0.5% NEΔp	Green reflectance by healthy vegetation
3	0.63-0.69	0.5% NEΔp	Chlorophyl absorbtion for plant species differentiation
4	0.76-0.90	0.5% NEΔp	Biomass surveys Water body delineation
5	1.55-1.75	1.0% NEΔp	Vegetation moisture measurement
6	10.4-12.5	0.5K NEΔT	Plant heat stress measurement
			Other thermal mapping
7	2.08-2.35	2.4% NEΔp	Hydrothermal mapping

[a] NEΔp = noise equivilant reflectance, NEΔT = noise equivilant temperature difference.

Table 4   Physical characteristics of the TM and MSS

Parameter	TM	MSS
Number/Detectors	100	24
Power, W	300	75
Weight, kg (lb)	243 (535)	65 (143)
Length, cm (in.)	203 (80)	88 (35)
Width, cm (in.)	60 (24)	41 (16)
Height, cm (in.)	100 (40)	59 (23)
Scan mirror major diameter, cm (in.)	53 (21)	33 (13)

Wideband links between Landsat-D and the TDRS at Ku band use the pointable high-gain antenna mounted on the deployed boom attached to the instrument module. Program track with an accuracy of +0.25 deg and auto-track, which controls the antenna at +0.1 deg modes of operation, are available with acquisition angles and tracking rates computed onboard from uplinked data.

A system comparison of the Landsat-1, -2, and -3 space segment with the corresponding Landsat-4 and -5 is provided in Table 5 and illustrates the significant increases in weight, power, and attitude control required to support the TM and MSS instruments in orbit.

Landsat-D Ground Segment

The dedicated ground data processing system located at NASA GSFC is shown in the block diagram in Fig. 7. The processing system is sized to produce 50 TM scenes/day and 200 MSS scenes/day with a 48 h turnaround time, averaged over 10 days, with no backlog buildup. Budget constraints combined with user demand have set the current rate for MSS scenes at 136/day, while due to the developmental nature of the TM, only 12 scenes/day are processed with the remainder saved on magnetic tape. The TM portion of the processing facility became operational in Oct. 1984 and actual output in the future will also be a function of budget and user demand constraints.

The ground segment consists of the control and simulation facility (CSF), the mission management

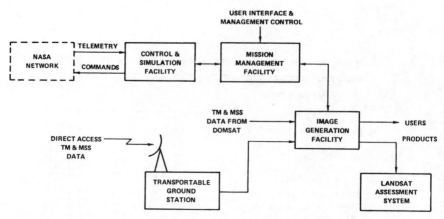

Fig. 7 Landsat-D ground data processing facility.

facility (MMF), the image generation facility (IGF), and the transportable ground station (TGS).

Control and Simulation Facility (CSF). The CSF operates as a Landsat-dedicated control center with the capability for controlling two Landsat-D series satellites. Principal functions of the CSF are:

1) To coordinate scheduling of ground resources for acquisition of image data, communication with the satellite, and computation of orbital ehemeris data.

2) To provide off-line mission planning and analysis.

3) To control, monitor, and analyze satellite performance.

4) To coordinate TM and MSS operations for acquisition of image data and routing of these data to the IGF.

The hardware in the CSF consists of three VAX 11/780 computers, necessary peripherals, voice communications intercoms, control and display consoles, and interface equipment for communication with the NASA networks. Major software packages provide for flight scheduling, flight operations, performance evaluation, and test and simulation of onboard computer operations.

Mission Management Facility (MMF). The MMF consists of the hardware, software, operations, and procedures necessary to process user data requests, control image production, and generate management reports on the ground system operations. Separate hardware and software are provided for TM and MSS operations with interfaces to allow for exchange of data when required.

Image Generation Facility (IGF). The IGF receives and processes the raw instrument data to produce film and digital products for both the TM and MSS sensors. A common data ingest subsystem is shared by separate TM and MSS processing systems, the MSS image processing subsystem (MIPS) and the TM image processing subsystem (TIPS). Redundancy and additional capacity for production peaks are assured by dividing the MIPS into three separate processing strings containing one VAX 11/780 and the required peripherals for stand-alone operation. Normally, two strings provide sufficient capability for currently scheduled image acquisition, including time for routine maintenance. Two TM processing strings are provided for the operational phase. Each employs a VAX

11/780 coupled with a higher-speed array processor than used in the MIPS to accommodate the higher data rate, increased number of detectors and channels, and the more complex algorithms required to process TM data. Sufficient high-speed tape drives, disks, and other peripherals are provided to permit stand-alone operation of either TIPS string, allowing for maintenance and modifications when required.

Table 5 System comparison -- Landsat-1, -2, -3 vs Landsat-4, -5

Parameter	Landsat-1, -2, -3	Landsat-4, -5
Bus configuration	Nimbus	MMS
Orbit		
Altitude, km (n.mi.)	917 (570)	700 (435)
Inclination, deg	99.1	98.2
Orbit repeat cycle, days	18	16
Equator crossing time	0930	0945
Launch vehicle	Delta 900	Delta 3920
Weight, kg (lb)	935 (2100)	2000 (4400)
Power		
Array area, m^2 (ft^2)	4.5 (48)	13.6 (147)
BOL power, W	560	2000
Attitude control		
Pointing accuracy, deg	0.7	0.01
Stability, deg/s	0.01	10^{-6}
Data handling system		
Data transmission	S band	S band, X band Ku band (TDRSS)
Data rates, megabit/s	15	85, 15
Data storage	Tape recorders	None (TDRSS)
Mission Payload		
Instruments	MSS, RBV	MSS, TM
Secondary	Data collection relay	Global positioning system

MSS Image Processing. Processing of the MSS image data is divided into two distinct phases, the initial preprocessing at the GSFC facility and the subsequent final processing at the Department of Interior's EROS Data Center. The preprocessing consists of archival generation, control point processing, film generation for local quality assessment, and statistical data for trend analysis. The link between the two processing centers is via a commercial Domsat as previously shown in Fig. 1. Upon receipt at EDC, each scene of MSS data is routed to the EROS digital image processing system (EDIPS), which corrects geometry and generates high-resolution black and white 241 mm latent film of each band. The EDIPS film is then processed photographically, chipped into working masters, and inspected for quality and cloud cover. High-density tapes and film chips are archived at EDC and used to generate film and computer-compatible tape products in response to user requests.

TM Image Processing. Image data acquired by the TM sensor are recorded on high-density tape after relay from the TDRS ground station at White Sands via another commercial Domsat link. Taped data are processed by the TIPS into fully geometrically corrected products, both digital and 241 mm film. As with the MSS data, performance evaluation products and statistical data are generated for local control and for management reports. TM data are shipped to EDC in both computer-compatible tape and film formats. The incoming film is verified and assessed for quality and cloud cover and then reproduced to generate a working master. The original film is archived and the working masters are chipped and used to generate user-requested film products. Original tapes are archived and reproduced as required to satisfy user requests.

Product Generation and Distribution. Standard photographic products are produced by a high-throughput production laboratory at EDC from the working masters. Fully corrected products are available on both film and paper, in positive and negative format, in black-and-white and color, and in sizes ranging from 70 mm to 40 in. Computer-compatible tapes (CCT) are reproduced from the tape library and may contain one or more scenes on each tape for the MSS data. Fractional scenes of TM data may be requested in order to reduce the volume of data inherent in a full scene (30 s x 85 megabit/s) to a more manageable data set.

System Performance

Landsat-D (Landsat-4) was launched on July 16, 1982, from the Western Test Range on a Delta 3920 launch vehicle.   Activation on-orbit proceeded smoothly, requiring approximately 30 days to check out the sub- systems and perform minor orbit adjust burns to bring the satellite onto the precision orbit necessary to register the image data to the World Reference System.

All system performance objectives were achieved or exceeded, including end-to-end system performance for the thematic mapper data acquisition and product genera- tion.   Absolute performance of the attitude control system continued to improve as operational procedures and in-orbit calibrations were fine tuned.   Several unexpected safe-hold conditions were encountered due to improper limits set in the onboard computer tables during orbit adjust burns and again due to several erroneous ephemeris data sets uplinked from the ground.

Serious failures have occurred in three subsystems. A component failure in the central unit of the command and data handling module has eliminated system redundancy in the critical command path, although system operation remains nominal using the redundant central unit.   The second function affected by component failure was the thematic mapper direct downlink at the X band. Similar failures in both the primary and redundant components in the frequency multiplication chain have eliminated the X band transmission capability.   The third major problem was the loss of over half of the available solar power due to progressive degradation and finally failure of the interconnecting cables on two of the four panels.

The principal system impact of these failures was a sharp reduction in TM data acquisition as only the TDRS link at the Ku band remains usable to transmit TM data. Availability of the TDRS system has also been limited as only one satellite of the planned three is in orbit. The second factor limiting TM data transmission is the reduction in solar power due to the cable failures and subsequent operational procedures that attempted to extend the remaining satellite lifetime by tilting the array away from the sunline and reducing thermal excur- sions.   Adequate power is available to support nominal MSS data acquisition and direct transmission at S band to the U.S. and foreign ground stations.

Analysis of In-orbit Failures

Central Units. After two months of operation, the primary central unit (CU) in the C&DH module failed, halting the onboard computer and placing the system in safe-hold. Switching to the redundant CU restored system operation. The CU is critical to satellite operation because it provides command decoding, telemetry formating, spacecraft clock, and multiplex bus control between the subsystems.

Analysis and test of spare CU components indicated that a failure had occurred in one of the power strobe circuits. The most likely component was found to be a tantalum capacitor. The suspect tantalum capacitors were replaced with more reliable ceramic units in all critical circuits in the CUs flown on Landast-D'.

X Band Transmitter. As power was applied to the wideband communications susbystem following the safehold event induced by the CU failure, the X band direct downlink used for the TM data failed to respond. Selective switching of redundant components restored operation of the X band transmitter. Analysis of the redundancy switching indicated that a failure had occurred in a frequency source amplifier that drives the X band chain.

In February 1983, the system again entered safehold, removing power to all noncritical components including the X band transmitter. Restoration of power failed to bring up the X band link. All possible combinations of redundant components were exercised and the conclusion was reached that the redundant frequency source amplifier had failed.

Investigation of the design and manufacturing processes led to the conclusion that an improper ceramic substrate had been installed in both frequency source amplifiers on Landsat-D. Insufficient mechanical clearances in the package after assembly led to an induced strain that most likely cracked the ceramic across a connecting trace after in-orbit thermal cycling. The correct substrates were installed on the amplifiers flown on Landsat-D'.

Solar Array Harness. After six months of operation, an intermittent condition developed in first one and then two of the four solar panels that comprise the Landsat-D solar array. The output from each affected panel was interrupted about 15-20 min after the satellite entered sunlight on each orbit. Following several months of intermittent operation, both panels failed completely, reducing the array output to less than half of the expected power.

Analysis and ground test of the interconnecting cables on the solar array indicated a failure mode in the soldered interface between the flat ribbon cable and the connector pins. Potting compound, intended to provide strain relief, was found to undergo glassification at the low temperatures experienced during each eclipse, which placed a strain on the ribbon cable conductors sufficient to induce buckling and eventual low-cycle fatigue fractures.

Cables for Landsat-D' were redesiged using discrete wires woven into a flat braided form and terminated in a standard crimp connector without the potting material. Extensive qualification testing demonstrated the ability of the improved design to survive the required temperature cycling.

Landsat-D' Performance

Landsat-D' (Landsat-5) was launched on March 1, 1984, into a nominal near-polar orbit by a Delta 3920 expendable launch vehicle from the Western Test Range. Activation of all primary functions was completed satisfactorily during the first 30 days. All of the modified subsystems have performed as expected, with no signs of the degradations experienced with Landsat-4. After several months in orbit, one of the four orbit adjust thrusters failed to operate when commanded; the failure was diagnosed to be in the electronic control circuitry. These thrusters are normally fired in pairs to reduce the torques generated during orbit adjust firings. Both thrusters in the redundant pair are operational and will be used for future planned orbit corrections.

The payload sensors, TM and MSS, have operated at a reduced schedule due to the system problems experienced by NASA with the TDRSS program. When a second TDRS is launched and made operational, Landsat imaging schedules will be brought up to the planned levels.

Practical Applications of Landsat Data

P.K. Conner* and D.W. Mooneyhan†
NASA National Space Technology Laboratories,
NSTL Station, Mississippi

Abstract

The application of Landsat data has evolved over the past decade from image intepretation through automatic image analysis and geobased information system modeling. This evolution is discussed and application examples are presented.

Many applications of the world's first synoptic view imagery have been developed by an expanding group of users. Early applications produced new and updated maps and users were able to identify large geologic formations and map snow and ice, forest cover, agricultural lands, and surface water resources.

As digital techniques for enhancement and processing evolved, applications were developed that took advantage of the full information content of the Landsat multispectral data. Computer algorithms were developed to identify specific surface phenomena, and automated techniques enabled users to discriminate and accurately measure major cover types for generalized surface cover inventories.

Repetitive Landsat data permitted the user to monitor changes in land cover/use such as urban encroachment of agricultural lands, surface mining, irrigation, shoreline erosion, and catastrophic events. The compatibility of Landsat digital data with geobased information system (GIS) technology increased the potential applications of Landsat-derived surface cover information for predictive flood, fire, and erosion modeling.

The advanced optical instrumentation of the Thematic Mapper on later Landsats is opening new areas of site-specific applications. The improved TM resolution, GIS

This paper is declared a work of the U.S. Government and therefore is in the public domain.

*Chief, Applications Research Group, Earth Resources Laboratory.
†Director, Earth Resources Laboratory.

technology, and affordable hardware are expected to result in entirely new applications by a much larger community of users.

Introduction

Satellite remote sensing for Earth resources esentially came of age in the 1970s following the launch of the first Earth Resources Technology Satellite (ERTS-1) on July 26, 1972, by the National Aeronautics and Space Administration. Although there had been many studies of the Earth's surface and its resources based on space-generated imagery, the data collection instrumentation was not primarily for resources studies. Thus, ERTS-1 (renamed Landsat-1) was the first satellite equipped with a sensor package designed specifically for Earth resources assessments (Fig. 1).

As initially defined in the late 1960s, the primary Landsat mission was to demonstrate the feasibility of multispectral remote sensing from space for practical Earth resources management applications. The overall system requirements included the acquisition of multispectral images produced as photographic and digital data in quantities and formats most helpful to potential users. In addition, it was required that the data be taken to provide repetitive coverage over the same location at the same local time on an approximate 18 day cycle.

Since the 1972 launch, a family‡ of Earth-orbiting Landsat satellites performed beyond expectations, transmitting back more than 1,000,000 scenes of the Earth. These scenes have formed the basis for worldwide Earth resources investigations through which experience has ably demonstrated a broad spectrum of both feasible and useful applications of the imagery to almost all areas of resource management and environmental monitoring.

Each Landsat platform has been equipped with a multispectral scanner (MSS), an optical mechanical instrument which senses simultaneously in four bands of the electromagnetic spectrum. Separate data are collected at wavelengths of 0.5-0.6 μm (green), 0.6-0.7 μm (red), 0.7-0.8 μm and 0.8-1.1 μm (both near infrared). In addition, Landsats -4 and -5 (Fig. 2) are also equipped with an experimental multispectral scanner, the thematic mapper (TM), which greatly improves on the accompanying MSS instrumentation. The TM is equipped with seven more narrowly defined bands

---

‡Landsat-1 launched on July 23, 1972; -2 launched on January 22, 1975; -3 launched on March 5, 1978; -4 launched on July 16, 1982; and -5 launched on March 1, 1984.

located in the blue, green, near infrared, middle infrared, and thermal regions of the spectrum. Table 1 describes band configurations of both the MSS and TM instruments and their areas of potential application. (Landsat-1, -2 and -3 were also equipped with three return beam vidicon (RBV) cameras.)

Landsat-acquired data have provided investigators with a wealth of spectral and spatial information about the surface of the Earth from its synoptic view, multispectral

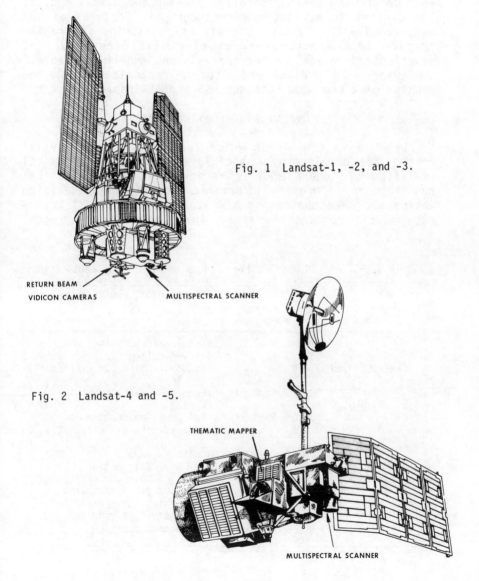

Fig. 1 Landsat-1, -2, and -3.

RETURN BEAM
VIDICON CAMERAS   MULTISPECTRAL SCANNER

Fig. 2 Landsat-4 and -5.

THEMATIC MAPPER

MULTISPECTRAL SCANNER

characteristics, and multitemporal capabilities. The synoptic view encompasses 185 x 185 km (115 x 115 statute
miles), which equates to approximately 3.5 x 10^6 hectares
or 8.6 x 10^6 acres captured in each scene of data. The
multispectral characteristics permit establishment of
unique signatures for some features, such as vegetation,
and allow image enhancement to distinguish and locate
others. The temporal capability provides the opportunity
to explore change over time and at intervals throughout the
year or growing season to follow plant phenological cycles.
The digital format and near orthographic features of the
data considerably expand the utility, allowing for registration to a map base and overlay with other types of
geographic data for further analysis and modeling. Table 2
summarizes the orbital and data characteristics for the
Landsat platforms and both the MSS and TM instruments.

Overview of Applications

We live in a world in which information plays a vital
role. The complexity of social, economic, and political
realities of modern society necessarily imposes critical
requirements to provide information to policy and decision
makers who make choices on almost a daily basis as to how
our natural resources will be used, developed, and con-

Table 1   MSS and TM band configurations and principal applications

MSS Band[a]	Spectral range, μm	TM Band	Spectral range, μm	Principal applications
		1	0.45-0.52	Coastal water mapping
				Soil/vegetation differentiation
4	0.50-0.60			Deciduous/coniferous differentia-tion
		2	0.52-0.60	Green reflectance by healthy vegetation
5	0.60-0.70			
		3	0.63-0.69	Chlorophyll absorption for plant species differentiation
6	0.70-0.80			
		4	0.76-0.90	Biomass surveys
7	0.80-1.10			Water body delineation
		5	1.55-1.75	Vegetation moisture measurement
				Snow/cloud differentiation
		6	10.40-12.50	Plant heat stress measurement
				Other thermal mapping
		7	2.08-2.35	Hydrothermal mapping

[a]Bands 1-3 on RBV.

served. The use of natural resources is influenced at the
global, national, state, regional, local, and individual
landowner levels. At all levels, improved information is
needed to meet the challenges created by changing relationships among population, food, and land and energy supplies.
     Given   the   breadth   of   information   requirements,
Landsat-acquired data have offered the opportunity for
resource managers and scientists alike to view the world
from a new perspective and to move inventory and assessment
to a regional, national, and even a global level. Landsat
data provide information with unique and valuable characteristics. They can be generated in unbiased form, acquired at a known point in time, displayed accurately,
geographically referenced, prepared in real time, prepared
in useful and storable formats, and produced in volumes
never attainable before. Together with other data collection methodologies, Landsat is a tool for deriving objective information on the type, amount, distribution, and
condition of resources on the Earth's surface.
     Resource managers and scientists the world over have
accepted the challenge and have been using Landsat technology for inventorying, monitoring, and assessing crop,
forest, range, water, and mineral resources in an effort to
support rational decision making. The results are presented in this section.

Renewable Resource Inventory and Monitoring

     Probably the most important application of Landsat
technology has been in inventory, monitoring, and providing

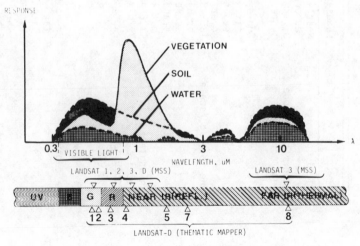

Fig. 3 Spectral response of land covers.

Table 2 Landsat orbital and data characteristics

	Landsat -1, -2, and -3	Landsat -4 and -5
Orbital coverage	Nearly all land surface and select-ed ocean areas	Same
Spacecraft altitude	917 km (570 n. mi.)	705 km (423 n. mi.)
Repeat coverage	14 rev./day, 18 day cycle	14.5 revolutions/day, 16 day cycle
Orbit	Sun-synchronous near-polar orbit fixed time (ea. 9:30 a.m. local sun time at equator) of pass over image scene	Same
Scene coverage/scale	185x185 km (115x115 statute miles) or 34,225 km² (13,225 mi²) ground scene in each image; orthographic; standard image scale in 9 in. format 1:1,000,000	Same
Scan angle	11.6 deg	14.9 deg
Effective ground resolution	79 m x 56 m; 0.45 hectares or 1.1 acre	MSS: Same TM: 30x30 m; 0.09 hectares or 0.22 acres for bands 1-5 and 7; 120x120 m, 1.44 hectares or 3.56 acres for band 6
Data capture	On-board digitization; recording on tape of data collected when satellite beyond line of sight of any Landsat ground receiving station	On-board digitization; transmission via tracking and data relay and domestic communications satellites eliminating need for data recording.
Digitization	6 bits (64 levels of gray reflectance values)	MSS: 6 bits (64 levels of reflectance values);TM: 8 bits (256 levels of reflect. values)

information for the management of renewable resources on a
county, state, and regional basis. Agriculture, forest,
rangeland, and wetlands represent land cover vegetation
types that are observable and measurable from a space
platform. Together they constitute a significant portion
of the Earth's land surface and are vulnerable if not
managed properly to meet growing demands for their products
or space.

Comprehensive large-area land cover inventories, where
the intent is to classify the landscape into categories
such as agriculture, forest, range, and wetlands, as well
as urban and water classes, have been produced by many resource management organizations at all levels of government. These inventories continue to be used to meet legis-
lative and internal planning requirements for quantitative
information on natural resources within their jurisdictional boundaries.

While an enormous amount of information resides in the
raw imagery, computer-assisted digital analysis techniques
provide the best method for mapping to the extent that the
detected reflectance of these features can be defined in
unique statistical terms. Distinctive reflectance properties of vegetative cover in the visible and near-infrared
bands of MSS data permit discrimination of general land
cover types with relative ease and operational reliability
(Fig. 3). Additionally, the digital format allows registration to a selected map coordinate system for locating
the positions and calculating the acreages of the individual land cover types.

Once an inventory baseline has been established, the
temporal characteristics play an important role in monitoring the changes over time in the way we use and develop
our resource base. Assessing the encroachment of urban
development on prime agricultural and forested lands, the
increase in irrigated lands, the environmental impact of
industrial development, and the increasing rates of deforestation are primary examples of large-area change detection applications (Fig. 4). As the historical MSS data
base continues to accumulate with time, the utility of the
data for long-range trend assessments and predictions will
take on even more importance.

The ability to stratify within these general class
categories is based on the spectral, spatial, and temporal
characteristics of the data vs the type, homogeneity, size,
and dynamics of the target features of interest. In agricultural regions, applications of Landsat MSS data have
been developed to address both single-crop targets and
multicrop inventories. Early in Landsat's history, re-

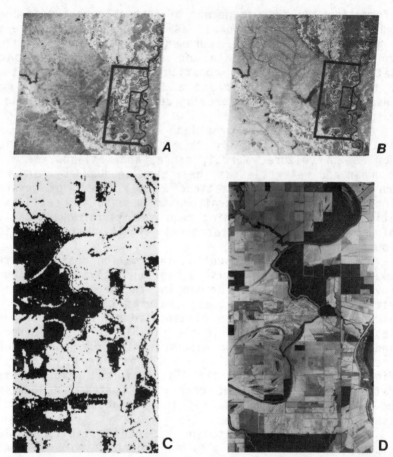

Landsat MSS scenes for 1973 (A) and 1977 (B) were used to map land conversion from forestland to cropland as plotted in (C). Areas in black (C) are those experiencing change between 1973 and 1977. Color IR aerial photography (D) taken in 1979 is used here as a reference. The study site is located in eastern Louisiana.

Fig. 4   Change detection using temporal Landsat MSS data sets acquired in 1973 and 1977.

source managers were anxious to evaluate the multispectral data for agriculture purposes.   Annual yield estimates of food production form one of the most critical information requirements for farmers and governmental agencies for determining markets and distribution to meet growing demands.

One of the first efforts tested single MSS data sets for identifying winter wheat. The results achieved in this and other studies led to the planning and implementation of major cooperative research programs such as the Large Area Crop Inventory Experiment (LACIE). LACIE, conducted jointly by the U.S. Department of Agriculture (USDA), NASA, and the National Oceanic and Atmospheric Administration (NOAA), developed multispectral scanner and meteorological satellite capabilities for forecasting wheat production that were successfully tested in the United States and the Soviet Union.

At the same time, agricultural industries interested in multicrop inventories for estimating fertilizer, farm implement, and transportation requirements have found that discrimination of crop types could be achieved using sequentially acquired MSS data sets. By correlating data collection windows with individual crop calendars, plant phenological cycles and, in some cases, management practices such as double cropping can be captured and extracted from the data.

The procedures for identifying crops and estimating yields utilizing remote sensing technology are frequently complex. Studies aimed at perfecting techniques for agricultural inventory and assessment have intensified with improvements and increased availability of Landsat imagery. Following the success of LACIE, a new interagency program, Agriculture and Resources Inventory Surveys through Aerospace Remote Sensing (AgRISTARS), was initiated in 1980 by NASA, USDA, U.S. Agency for International Development, and NOAA. Crop production forecasting research using multispectral Landsat data was extended to corn and soybeans in several countries, including Brazil and Argentina.

Accuracy with present Landsat data has been reported as high as a 90% confidence level in studies of areas where there are large, homogeneous rectilinear fields with few competing crops. However, in other areas where these variables break down, the spatial and spectral limits of the MSS imagery are reached. The application of TM data to these difficult agricultural inventory requirements has already begun and it is anticipated that the new TM band 1, for instance, will improve crop discrimination by adding the blue-green portion of the spectrum where further differences in chlorophyll absorption can be differentiated. Further, the middle infrared bands (5 and 6) are expected to be particularly useful for discriminating crop types as well as plant health and condition based on the leaf water content. With these new bands, higher spectral resolution and 30 m spatial resolution offered by TM data, improvements in mapping crop types and management practices, as well as condition, have already been documented. All of these variables are important parameters for calculating worldwide accurate yield predictions.

Inventories of forest and rangelands are also critical requirements in the management of these resources for multiple use and sustained yield. Timber harvest, grazing, wildlife habitat, and recreation constitute valuable uses and when properly combined can form complementary utilization. Generally, the approach used in the inventory of forest and rangelands involves multistage sampling; in this scenario, MSS data have been employed in conjunction with medium- and/or large-scale aerial photography and ground sampling to derive a multitude of information.

While the detailed cover variables required for determining standing volumes of timber, for instance, are beyond the capability of MSS data, many applications have been developed to address inventory requirements at the level II of the land classification system and, in some cases, at level III.§ Both photointerpretation and digital techniques using bands 5 and 7 have been employed to address forest inventory. However, multitemporal data sets have proven to be the most successful. Combining winter (dormant) ·and summer (full growth) data, using digital techniques, investigators have demonstrated the ability to separate deciduous and coniferous forest, some density classes, clearcuts, and regeneration. Others have been equally successful in further stratifying coniferous forests into stand associations by overlaying MSS classification results with topographic data.

Preliminary studies using TM bands 4 and 5 already indicate the potential for discriminating at the species level within certain pine forest and forested wetlands (see Plates 7 and 8 in color section of this volume). Other investigations have also demonstrated the resolving power of TM-type data for detecting some silvicultural practices as well as forest stress conditions.

Within naturally vegetated areas such as forest, rangelands, and wetlands, one of the important applications of MSS data has been in wildlife habitat assessment. Determining habitat quality over large areas and monitoring trends in habitat condition are essential activities in the

---

§Levels of a classification system refers to a stratification of land use and land cover into meaningful categories. At level I, these categories include urban, forest land, agriculture land, water, etc. Level II further stratifies within the level I categories and level III further stratifies within level II. For instance, level II categories within forest land would be deciduous, evergreen, and mixed forest. Each level II category would be further stratified into stand composition including species, age, and density classes.

development of strategies for the conservation and management of wildlife resources. Landsat data have played an important role in the assessment of various land covers needed for sustaining wildlife populations.

Large-area assessments have provided a means of systematic study of the intermixing of habitat types needed to fully evaluate carrying capacity for a particular species in a given location. A wide range of applications have been developed for wildlife management and the utility of MSS data has been clearly demonstrated for inventorying habitat and determining range quality and the impact of changing conditions on wildlife populations.

As the need for more near-real time information accelerates, governmental and industrial natural resource managers are increasingly recognizing the value of Landsat data for updating certain aspects of established detailed inventories and are maximizing the utility of the data through the analysis in a geographic information system (GIS) context. GIS technology permits the integration and analysis of data from a variety of sources in such a manner to derive additional information from any one or combination of geographically referenced data planes. The marriage of Landsat data with GIS technology offers resources managers the capability to assimilate and analyze enormous amounts of the data over a given study area as

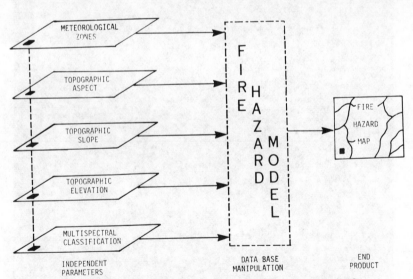

FIRE HAZARD AND BEHAVIOR PREDICTIVE MODELING

Fig. 5 Data base diagram for Plate 9.

never possible before. The forest fire hazard assessment, shown in Fig. 5 and Plate 9 (see color section of this volume), and soil erosion applications provide significant examples of practical applications and insight into the potential utility of these technologies.

The results of on-going TM investigations for renewable resource inventories will serve to improve the discrimination of land cover components by more detailed stratifications of vegetation. The higher spatial resolution will also contribute to these improvements by being able to address the heterogeneity of the natural landscape and small features previously unresolvable with the MSS 80 m pixel size.

Water Resources Inventory and Assessment

Water, a fundamental substance for sustaining life itself, is a key factor in maintaining agricultural production, energy production, and other activities at optimum

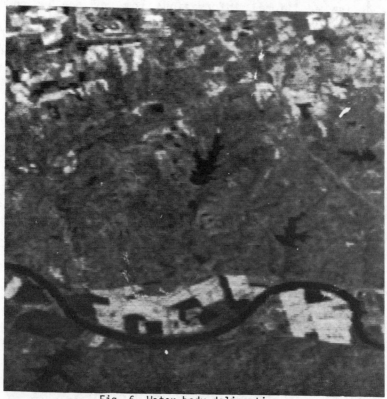

Fig. 6 Water body delineation.

levels. The assessment of the water resources of an area
and the change of these resources with time means, in its
simplest sense, the assessment of the individual components
of the hydrologic cycle.

Applications of Landsat MSS data have been particularly
useful for mapping several of these components and effectively employed in identifying and monitoring various hydrologic aspects of lakes, rivers, and wetlands, as well as
snow and ice. Because reflected infrared wavelengths are
absorbed in only a few centimeters of water, MSS data have
been readily applied to locating and delineating surface
water bodies. These features are easily distinguishable in
the imagery itself, as illustrated in Fig. 6, where a
simple MSS band 5/7 black-and-white composite print shows
black water bodies standing out in sharp contrast to
lighter-toned land features of the surrounding environment.
Digital image enhancement techniques have proved to be one

Fig. 7 Snow cover delineation.

of the most useful methods for interpretation of hydrologic features over large land areas; however, for quantitative inventories in which the location and acreages of surface water bodies are required, digital classification procedures are the only effective and efficient method.

Extending surface water inventories one step further, some investigations have also been successful in detecting and mapping subtle hydrologic variations. Changes of only a few meters in lake and reservoir levels can produce notable change in the total water surface area (i.e., new land area inundated or exposed shorelines). During a given year, when average rainfall, snow melt, and other conditions are notably different from previous years, investigators using the temporal features of MSS data and digital change detection techniques have been able to measure these differences. The implications of this application are important in monitoring certain episodic events such as flooding and evaluating available water supplies against demands.

Mapping and monitoring the Earth's snow and ice coverage represents another important area of application that can be effectively accomplished from the Landsat space platform. Again, because of the sharp contrast between snow-covered and no-snow areas in the red and near-infrared portions of the spectrum, photointerpretation of the imagery has found widespread application (Fig. 7). One limitation of the MSS data has been the inability to distinguish between clouds and snow cover. With the TM bands 5 and 6, snow now appears very dark in the data while clouds remain quite bright, providing even more accurate baseline information for snow melt estimates.

The near-infrared bands have also been found to be useful in tracking the source and occurrence of surface melting and have provided an effective means for obtaining critical values for snow cover input parameters used in snow melt models. Through the use of Landsat MSS-derived snow cover information and conventional temperature and precipitation data combined in a modeling context, snow runoff has been accurately measured in mountainous basins as large as 50 square miles.

Digital enhancement of Landsat imagery has also been successful, under favorable conditions, for delineating certain water quality variables in rivers, lakes, estuaries, and marine environments. Billions of dollars are spent annually in the United States alone to protect the quality of surface waters. Unless carefully managed, residual wastes from municipalities, industry, and agriculture can seriously interfere with many beneficial water uses.

Using Landsat MSS imagery, land/water interfaces in brackish lagoons and bays have been delineated in bands 6 and 7 and in false color composites, while particulate matter has been distinguishable in bands 4 and 6. However, chlorophyll-bearing algae and suspended inorganic matter produce a composite spectral signature that is difficult to separate with MSS data. Given the importance of discriminating chlorophyll levels as an indicator of the trophic status and possibly the presence of man-made pollutants in lakes, resource managers are anxious to test the improved radiometric, spectral, and spatial characteristics of TM data for monitoring these water quality characteristics.

Other water resource applications are addressed with the new blue-green band on the thematic mapper that will also allow further the penetration of relatively clear water. Bathymetric measurements, coastal water bottom topography mapping, reef mapping, and uncharted island and atoll surveying are some of the new applications offered by the thematic mapper.

Urban Land Use Analysis

Urban areas are a land use of critical interest simply because the greatest losses of prime agriculture, forest, and range resources and wildlife habitat occur at their boundaries. The U.S. Department of Agriculture reported that during the 1960s some 295,000 hectares (730,000 acres) of the U.S. land base were urbanized annually, recreational land uses increased annually by some 410,000 hectares (1 x 10^6 acres), and transportation-related land uses expanded at an annual rate of 55,000 hectares (136,000 acres). The ability to accurately detect changes in land use patterns is central to land resource planning and management. Rates of change in land use vary greatly by category and location and certain types of conversions and trends tend to create more problems than others. Urban development represents one of the most active and irreversible types of change and as such is the subject of intensive investigation.

Urban land use consists of industrial plants, transportation networks, businesses, parks, residences, and a variety of mixed uses. The term "land use" then refers to the cultural use of the land as opposed to the term "land cover," which describes the actual material present on the surface of the Earth. The diverse composition of the city surface has presented limitations in the use of these data for intensive urban analysis. Within a small area exists an extremely complex array of surface materials, which usually result in a high spatial frequency of change in land cover over short distances. Hence, reflectance from surface materials such as asphalt pavement, rooftops, grass yards, and concrete roadways become mixed within the 80 m pixel resolution. Further, procedures successfully applied over U.S. cities have not had the same results in other countries. Outside North America where building practices take on a vertical as opposed to horizontal nature, the contrast between materials is further reduced and finer spatial resolution is needed.

While the broad spectral bands and spatial resolution of the MSS instrument were not designed for urban application, Landsat data have been used to obtain a significant amount of urban information. The utility of MSS data for a variety of general urban applications has been relatively widespread, particularly at the regional level. Despite the apparent limitations, investigators have presented a fairly concise perspective of the general urban applicability of MSS band 5 for delineating boundaries between natural and cultural features and bands 6 and 7 (near infrared) for delineating vegetation, open water, and cultural features.

A diverse range of analysis techniques, from traditional photointerpretation to sophisticated digital processing algorithms, have been employed for classifying urban land use patterns with varying degrees of success. Urban areas have been photointerpreted and mapped from false color composites at level I with little difficulty. This also holds true for studies that have employed digital techniques for urban applications. However, the most successful procedure has employed digital image enhancement methodologies to improve the interpretability of the data.

The TM presents a new dimension for the discrimination of surface features, particularly within the complex urban environment. Because of the extreme heterogeneity of land covers and variance within each cover type that comprise the urban surface, the 30 m resolution, together with the new middle and thermal infrared bands, provides additional opportunities--if not challenges--to differentiate urban land use/cover with better results than those derived from an analysis of MSS data.

Although investigations employing TM data for urban applications have only recently begun, there are indications that these data will greatly improve the observation of urban environments. Digital enhancement techniques to generate photointerpretable TM images (Fig. 8) as well as classifications have produced promising results; however, the full potential of TM data for urban analysis has yet to be realized.

Again, the most important use of both MSS and TM data
for urban applications resides in the temporal characteristics for change detection to monitor urban growth and
associated encroachment on agriculture, forest, and rangelands.   Ultimately, data base modeling also offers the
capability to bring land cover derived from Landsat data to
bear for determining land use suitability, flood hazard,
and other critical parameters important to devising rational uses of the land resource base.

Geologic Applications

The field of geology encompasses a multitude of information concerning the structure of the Earth and manifestations of this structure on the surface. Geoscientists
are concerned with everything from crustal dynamics, geomorphology, mineral exploration, and glaciation to natural
hazards.

Fig. 8 Digitally enhanced urban scene of TM data.

In the first few years of Landsat data acquisition geoscientists ably demonstrated that the data would become a near-universal tool for geologic applications. The availability of MSS images over most land areas of the Earth has provided new opportunities for geologic studies, particularly in previously unmapped areas. The ability to "see" and integrate extremely large tracts of land in a single MSS image has had multiple uses in general geologic mapping and in the preparation of tectonic, metallogenic, and hydrogeologic maps.

Landsat images have been used for broad regional geomorphic studies, such as the classic study of sand seas of the world, a recent study of the deserts of China, and a continuing study of the Earth's glaciers. Much of the utility of the data is found not only in the synoptic view, but in the fact that the synoptic view is captured at a constant, low-azimuth sun angle which creates an apparent relief map. Such maps accentuate linear geomorphic features such as straight valleys, shorelines, and escarpments, most of which result from differential erosion along faults and other fracture systems.

For mineral exploration, which represents one of the major areas of geologic applications, some rock types, lineaments, and alteration zones have been distinguished using bands 4, 5, and 7. Early studies demonstrated that MSS spectral bands could be useful in displaying areas of hydrothermal alteration in which limonite occurs in association with and, in some cases, is the surface expression of mineralized ground. Lineament studies of a Landsat-derived mosaic of Mexico, for instance, showed a high degree of correlation between ore deposits and the intersections of major lineaments observable in the imagery. In a joint study by the U.S. Geological Survey and a Mexican geological team, Landsat data were used along with geochemical sampling and aeromagnetics to identify a major polymetallic copper-molybdenum ore deposit (which was subsequently verified through drilling). Petroleum exploration geologists have shown that a systematic study of Landsat images, especially those in remote and poorly mapped areas of the world, can help significantly in cutting costs of exploration.

While major contributions have been made to the field of geology over large arid and semiarid regions of the world, techniques have also been developed to address heavily vegetated areas. The surficial expressions of economic deposits of fuels or heavy metals are in some places distinctive enough to have detectable effects upon the vegetation measurable in the visible and near-infrared

spectra. Using inferential techniques, the identification
of vegetation anomalies such as marked plant community
transitions, changes in plant morphology or chlorophyll
content, and sparse or barren areas in an otherwise lush
vegetative environment provides a means for targeting
ground-based exploration.

Further, nearly all geologic hazards such as volcanic
eruptions, earthquakes, landslides, and floods are amenable
to study or monitoring from space because almost everything
that creates a hazardous situation to man or his works
leaves major surficial alterations. Volcanic eruptions,
for example, produce a variety of effects in the immediate
vicinity of the event, but can also affect areas thousands
of kilometers away. The major hazards to human life and
property include hot avalanches, hot particle and gas
clouds, mudflows, tephra falls, lava flows, volcanic gases,
and floods. Although real-time analysis of such events is
precluded from a remote platform due to atmospheric perturbations, Landsat data are invaluable for assessing and
documenting, in a quantitative form, the postevent impact.
Plates 10-12 (see color section of this volume) clearly illustrate the capability of the imagery to delineate the
overall impact and stratification of damage classes caused
by the 1980 eruption of Mount St. Helens.

Additionally, the temporal characteristics of the data
provide glacial geologists and geomorphologists opportunities to monitor other types of geologic dynamics. The
capability to delineate and measure snow and ice cover, as
previously discussed, provides glacial geologists with information for a variety of applications in engineering,
sedimentation, exploration, and even trafficability or
navigation. Further, coastal zones represent one of the
most difficult areas in which to conduct accurate geologic
and geomorphic mapping. The inhospitability of many of
these areas and the continually changing nature of coastlines discourage traditional survey methodologies and
geomorphologists are using Landsat imagery to fill the gap.

Most geologic applications to date have employed a
skilled image interpreter at some point in data analysis
processing. This is simply because the features of interest are almost always subtle occurrences obscured by
vegetation, soil, man-made artifacts, or irrelevant variations, such as those caused by topography. Since quantitative classifications of surface materials are not required, the geologic community has relied heavily on both
photo-optical and digital enhancements to produce images
with improved interpretability. However, many geologists
are now attempting to develop computer-assisted algorithms

Table 3   Summary of applications of Landsat MSS and TM data in the various Earth resources disciplines

Agriculture, forestry and range resources	Land use and mapping	Geology	Water resources	Coastal resources	Environment
Discrimination of vegetative types	Classification land uses	Mapping of major geologic units	Determination of water boundaries and surface water areas	Determination of turbidity patterns and circulation	Monitoring surface mining and reclamation
crop types	Cartographic mapping and map updating	Revising geologic maps	Mapping of floods and flood plains	Mapping shoreline changes	Mapping and monitoring of water pollution
timber types		Recognition of certain rock types		Mapping of shoals and shallow areas	
range vegetation	Categorization of land capability		Determination of areal extent of snow and ice	Mapping of ice for shipping	Determination of effects of natural disasters
Measurement of crop acreage	Monitoring urban growth	Delineation of unconsolidated rocks and soils	Measurement of glacial features	Tracing beach erosion	Monitoring environmental effects of man's activities
Estimating crop yields	Regional planning	Mapping igneous intrusions	Measurement of sediment and turbidity patterns	Tracing oil spills and pollutants	(lake eutrophication, defoliation, etc.)
Measurement of timber acreage	Mapping of transportation networks	Mapping recent volcanic surface deposits			
Forest harvest monitoring	Mapping of landwater boundaries	Mapping landforms	Delineation of irrigated fields		Assessing drought impact
Determination of range readiness and biomass	Flood plain management	Search for surface guides to mineralization	Inventory of lakes		Siting for solid waste disposal
Determination of vegetation vigor	Siting for transportation and transmission routes	Determination of regional structures	Estimating snow melt runoff		Siting for power plants and other industries
Determination of vegetation stress		Mapping linears			
Determination of soil conditions					
Determination of soil associations					
Assessment of grass and forest fire damage					
Wildlife habitat assessment					

to automatically find linear features, recognize and differentiate between types of alteration, and   remove the
effects of topography where topographic relief hinders
certain investigations.

The multispectral qualities of the TM will significantly improve geologic mapping previously achievable from
MSS images. The new infrared bands will permit geologists
to spectrally differentiate a wider variety of rock and
soil types. Experimental studies have already demonstrated
that the two middle infrared bands will be most useful for
detecting variations in the type and abundance of clay
minerals exposed at the Earth's surfaces, as illustrated in
Plate 13 (see color section of this volume). TM data will
also be able to distinguish hydrothermal clay minerals from
other species in semiarid regions and can potentially contribute to base metal exploration in certain geographies.
This same clay mineral/clay delineation capability may also
have utility for soil type mapping.

The emitted thermal energy band (10.4-12.5 μm) on the
TM is a measure of surface temperature. This capability
allows another fundamental dimension of multispectral data
to be added to that already present in thematic mapper
bands measuring reflected solar energy. Differences in the
heat capacity characteristics are useful for mineral and
petroleum exploration. Further, the 30 m resolution of the
TM enables photointerpreters to detect smaller land forms
and river channels and to recognize more isolated occurrences of specific rock types.

Summary

Although it is close to impossible within the framework
of this chapter to review all of Landsat applications that
have been developed since the first launch in 1972, the
examples and the capability discussed here clearly illustrate the overall success of the program. Landsat data
have resulted in totally new methodologies for resources
inventory and environmental assessment for a worldwide
community of users and as such have served an important
role in bringing resource managers into the computer age.

Today, there are nearly a dozen nations worldwide that
have their own capability to receive and process data
directly from the satellite. In addition, more than 100
countries make use of Landsat data for indigenous resource
development and management. Landsat images of the Earth
are internationally recognized for their value in oil and
mineral exploration, agriculture, land use planning, forestry, water management, mapping, and other endeavors. A
summary list of applications is provided in Table 3.

The versatility of the system speaks for itself, offering synoptic, multispectral, and repetitive coverage, all of which are important for monitoring what is happening on the surface of the Earth. The simultaneous development of data processing systems such as the GIS computer capability has further enhanced the utility of Landsat-derived information. Matching the sophistication of the user community, computer technology now takes on many new aspects, such as artificial intelligence and communications for data sharing between large data bases now in existence all over the world.

Confidence in the future of Earth-observing satellites is not only demonstrated by the advanced Landsat TM follow-on missions for the 1980s, but by the MSS operational status achieved in 1979. The Landsat satellite and MSS instrument moved from an experimental NASA program to NOAA as the operational agency, with plans for turning the total system over to industry during this decade. Further, plans by other countries such as France and Japan to launch similar space-borne instruments also attest to the success of the Landsat Program.

And what lies beyond this decade? Advancements in our knowledge of the world in which we live have also taken on new dimensions. There is now a growing interest in understanding this planet as a functioning ecosystem at a level that will allow us to accurately predict and influence the long-range interactions of mankind and the environment. Interdisciplinary studies, which bring together land, oceanic and atmospheric scientists, will address even more complex information requirements over the next several decades.

It is expected that this interdisciplinary approach to global processes will spawn further technological advancements needed in space-borne imaging systems, in digital analysis and information management systems, and in communications. Already Shuttle missions carry radar experiments and a new generation of multispectral systems using advanced electronic linear arrays is scheduled. NASA has also initiated plans for a low-Earth-orbital, man-tendable satellite system known as the Earth Observation System (EOS).

The EOS is to be a permanent, highly adaptable, civil space facility for the scientific study of the Earth and the development of advanced, user interactive, distributed data systems. The EOS is intended to address the scientific issues of the 1990s using a number of remote sensors. The on-board and ground data system components are to accommodate man-tending and robotics for controlling the mission and selected sensors and will use expert systems technology to aid in rapid assessment of satellite conditions and scientific information. Ultimately, EOS is being designed to support international interdisciplinary teams in their study of major environmental issues, thus providing enormous amounts of information on the Earth's atmosphere, climate, ocean dynamics, geology, natural resources, and land use.

Acknowledgment

Our thanks to investigators in the Earth Resources Laboratory for their contributions to this paper: Charles L. Hill, William G. Cibula, Dale A. Quattrochi, Douglas L. Rickman, Kenneth J. Langran, Eugene F. Zetka, and Gregory S. Burns.

Bibliography

Anderson, J. E. and Kalcic, M. T., "Analysis of Thematic Mapper Simulator Data Acquired During Winter Season Over Pearl River, Mississippi, Test Site," NASA, Earth Resources Laboratory, National Space Technology Laboratories, Rept. 202, 1982.

Anderson, J. R., Hardy, E. E., Roach, J. T., and Witmer, R., "A Land Use and Land Cover Classification System for Use with Remote Sensor Data," U.S. Geological Survey Professional Paper 964, 1976.

Barker, G. R., "Operational FRIS (Forest Resource Information System). Conference on Space Technology and Industrial Forest Management," St. Regis Paper Co., Jacksonville, Fla., 1981.

Baumann, P. R., "Evaluation of Three Techniques for Classifying Urban Land Cover Patterns Using Landsat MSS Data," NASA, Earth Resources Laboratory, National Space Technology Laboratories, Rept. 178, 1979.

Baumgardner, M. F., "Remote Sensing for Resource Management: Today and Tomorrow," Remote Sensing for Resource Management, Pt. 1, Soil Conservation Service, 1980, pp. 16-29.

Blanchard, B. J. "Investigation of Use of Space Data in Watershed Hydrology," USDA Southern Great Plains Research Watershed, Chickasha, Okla., Final Report NASA Contract S-70251-G, Task 5, 1975.

Bonner, W. J., Rohde, W. G., and Miller, W. A., "Mapping Wildland Resources with Digital Landsat and Terrain Data," Remote Sensing for Resource Management, Pt. 2, Soil Conservation Service, 1980, pp. 73-80.

Brannon, D. P., "Interim Report on the Crop Mensuration and Mapping Joint Research Project," NASA Earth Resources Laboratory, National Space Technology Laboratories, Rept. 226, 1983.

Brown, D. and Sizer, J. E., "ERTS-1 Role in Land Management and Planning in Minnesota," Third Earth Resources Technology Satellite-1 Symposium, NASA, 1973.

Bryant, N. A., "Integration of Socioeconomic Data and Remotely Sensed Imagery for Land Use Applications," Proceedings of Caltech/JPL Conference on Image Processing Technology, Data Sources and Software for Commercial and Scientific Applications, California Institute of Technology, Pasadena, 1976.

Cibula, W. G., "Computer Implemented Land Cover Classification Using Landsat MSS Digital Data: A Cooperative Research Project Between the National Park Service and NASA--II, Vegetation and Other Land Cover Analysis of the Olympic National Park," NASA Earth Resources Laboratory, National Space Technology Laboratories, Rept. 193, 1981.

Colvocoresses, A. P., "Proposed Parameters for an Operational Landsat," Photogrammetric Engineering and Remote Sensing, Vol. 43, 1977, pp. 1139-1145.

Dornback, J. E. and McKain, G. E., "The Utility of ERTS-1 Data for Applications in Land Use Classification," Third Earth Resources Technology Satellite-1 Symposium, NASA, 1973, pp. 439-455.

Estes, J. E., Stow, D., and Jensen, J. R., "Monitoring Land Use and Land Cover Changes," Remote Sensing for Resource Management, Pt. 2, Soil Conservation Service, 1980, pp. 100-110.

"The Landsat Tutorial Workbook," NASA RP 1078, 1982.

Hannah, J. W., Thomas, L., and Esparze, F., "Satellite Information on Orlando, Florida," Proceedings of the NASA Earth Resources Survey Symposium, NASA, 1975.

Heller, R. C. and Ulliman, J. J. (eds.), "Forest Resource Assessments," Manual of Remote Sensing, 2nd. ed., Vol II, American Society of Photogrammetry, 1983, Ch. 34, pp. 2229-2310.

Hill, C. L., "Analysis of Landsat-4 Thematic Mapper Data for Classification of Forests in Baldwin County, Alabama," Proceedings of the Eighth William T. Pecora Memorial Remote Sensing Symposium, Sioux Falls, S. Dak., 1983.

Joyce, A. T., "Final Report on the Natural Resources Inventory System ASVT Project," NASA TM-58211, 1979.

Joyce, A. T., Ivey, J. H., and Burns, G. S., "The Use of Landsat MSS Data for Detecting Land Use Changes," NASA, Earth Resources Laboratory, National Space Technology Laboratories, Rept. 184, 1980.

Kan, E. P. and Weber, F. P., "The Ten Ecosystem Study: Landsat ADP Mapping of Forest and Rangeland in the United States," Proceedings of the 12th International Symposium on Remote Sensing of Environment, Ann Arbor, Mich., 1978, pp. 1809-1825.

Krebs, P. V., "Multiresource Inventory and Mapping of Alaska Wildlands: A Cost-Effective Application of Remote Sensing," Remote Sensing for Resource Management, Pt. 2, Soil Conservation Service, 1980, pp. 81-90.

Lillesand, T. and Kiefer, R., Remote Sensing and Image Interpretation, John Wiley & Sons, New York, 1979, pp. 141-144.

McKee, E. D. and Breed, C. S., "Sand Seas of the World: in ERTS-1, A New Window on Our Planet," U.S. Geological Survey Professional Paper 929, 1976, pp. 81-88.

Mausel, P. W., Todd, W. J., and Baumgardner, M. F, "An Analysis of Metropolitan Land Use by Machine Processing of Earth Resources Technology Satellite Data," Proceedings of the Association of American Geographers, 1974.

Mooneyhan, D. W., "The Potential of Expert Systems for Remote Sensing," Paper presented at 17th International Symposium on Remote Sensing of the Environment, Ann Arbor, Mich., 1983.

Mooneyhan, D. W., "Mechanisms for Accessing Information Sources Globally," Paper presented at United Nations International Meeting of Experts on Remote Sensing Information Systems, Feldafing and Oberpfaffenhofen, Federal Republic of Germany, 1983.

Mooneyhan, D. W., "Organizing Information for Effective Resource Management," Remote Sensing for Resource Management, Pt. 1, Soil Conservation Service, 1980, pp. 30-40.

"Landsat D to Test Thematic Mapper, Inaugurate Operational System," NASA Press Release 82-100, 1982.

Quattrochi, D. A., "Analysis of Landsat-4 Thematic Mapper Data for the Discrimination of Urban Features," Decision Support Systems for Policy and Management, Urban and Regional Information Systems Association, Bethesda, Md., 1983, pp. 391-403.

Quattrochi, D. A., "Analysis of Landsat-4 Thematic Mapper Data for Classification of the Mobile, Alabama Metropolitan Area," Proceedings of Seventeenth International Symposium on Remote Sensing of Environment, Environmental Research Institute of Michigan, Ann Arbor, 1983.

Quattrochi, D. A., Brannon, D. P., Anderson, J. E., and Hill, C. L., "An Initial Analysis of Landsat 4 Thematic Mapper Data for the Classification of Agricultural, Forested Wetlands, and Urban Land Covers," NASA, Earth Resources Laboratory, National Space Technology Laboratories, Rept. 215, 1982.

Raines, G. L., Frisken, J. G., Kleinkopt, M. D., and de la Fuente-D., M., "Integration of Remote Sensing into the Exploration Process," Paper presented at Sixth Annual William T. Pecora Memorial Symposium, Sioux Falls, S. Dak., 1980.

Rango, A. and Peterson, R., (eds.) Operational Applications of Satellite Snowcover Observation, NASA CP 2116, 1980.

Rickman, D., "The Mt. Emmons, Colorado Geology Study Site: Acquisition and Computer Processing of Airborne Thematic Mapper Simulation Data for a Mountainous Partially Vegetated Area," NASA, Earth Resources Laboratory, National Space Technology Laboratories, Rept. 220, 1983.

Rudd, R. D., "Remote Sensing: A Better View," The Man-Environment Series, Duxberry Press, North Scituate, Mass., 1974.

Salomonson, V., "Water Resources Assessment," Manual of Remote Sensing, 2nd ed., Vol. II, American Society of Photogrammetry, 1983, Chap. 29, pp. 1516-1530.

Salas, G. P., "Relationship of Mineral Resources to Linear Features in Mexico as Determined from Landsat Data," Proceedings of First Annual William T. Pecora Memorial Symposium, U. S. Geological Survey Professional Paper 1015, 1975.

Strahler, A. H., Logan, T. L., and Bryant, N. A., "Improving Forest Cover Classification Accuracy from Landsat by Incorporating Topographic Information," Proceedings of the 12th International Symposium on Remote Sensing of Environment, Ann Arbor, Mich., 1978, pp. 927-942.

Stoner, E. R., "Agricultural Land Cover Mapping in the Context of a Geographically Referenced Digital Information System," NASA, Earth Resources Laboratory, National Space Technology Laboratories, Rept. 205, 1982.

Vincent, R. K., "Ratio Maps of Trou Ore Deposits, Atlantic City District, Wyoming," Proceedings of Symposium on Significant Results Obtained from the Earth Resources Technology Satellite-1, NASA SP-327, V. 1, Section A, 1973, pp. 379-386.

Walker, A. S., "Deserts of China," American Scientist, Vol. 70, No. 4, 1982, pp. 366-376.

Williams, D. L., "A Canopy-Related Stratification of a Southern Pine Forest Using Landsat Digital Data," Proceedings of the 1976 Fall Convention of the American Society of Photogrammetry, 1976, pp. 231-239.

Williams, D. L., Irons, J. R., Markham, B. L., Nelson, R. F., Toll, D. L., Latty, R. S. and Stauffer. M. L., "A Statistical Evaluation of Advantages of Landsat Thematic Mapper Data in Comparison to Multispectral Scanner Data," IEEE Transactions on Geoscience and Remote Sensing, 1984.

Williams, R. S. Jr., "Geological Applications," Manual of Remote Sensing, 2nd. ed., Vol. II. American Society of Photogrammetry, 1983, Chap. 31, pp. 1667-1916.

Williams, R. S. Jr. and Ferrigno, J. G., "Satellite Image Atlas of the Earth's Glaciers," Satellite Hydrology, 1981.

Chapter IV. Remote Sensing of the Ocean Resources

Seasat – A Retrospective

S.W. McCandless Jr.*
User Systems, Inc., Annandale, Virginia

Abstract

In recent years, the potential for remote sensing of
physical phenomena has been advanced by research and by
development in the fields of meteorology and Earth observations. With the exception of cloud-cover photographs and
infrared-derived temperature determinations, little use has
been made of such techniques for oceanological purposes.
Recognizing the dynamic nature of ocean phenomena and the
difficulty and expense of obtaining in situ measurements
(particularly the needed globally consistent and
geographically and temporally dense data), a need existed
to consider the potential for the application of remote
sensing techniques to the ocean. The Seasat-A program was
initiated as a "proof-of-concept" mission to evaluate the
effectiveness of remotely sensing the ocean from a
satellite-borne platform in space. Seasat also pioneered
the utilization of remote active and passive microwave
sensors capable of penetrating weather and cloud layers and
operating in all lighting conditions. Requirements for the
system were derived from the expressed needs of potential
users. In response to this need, Seasat was launched into
space on June 26, 1978, and began providing heretofore
unavailable coverage of the world's oceans. Seasat
uniquely mapped the global oceans every 36 h until the
power failed 106 days into the mission. What survived was
a large collection of radar images of surface conditions; a
continuous synoptic view of global surface wind and
temperature measurements; important topographic data
ranging from the essentially stable geoid to the varying
behavior of currents, tides, and daily sea state of surface

*President.

roughness conditions; and, more importantly, the unquenched interest of thousands of users that had been preparing for over 5 years for Seasat. The early data that poured forth from Seasat fanned the already eager interest of domestic and international scientists and industrial users. What remains is a rare and valuable data set that proves that such a system will work, balanced with an unfulfilled need to apply these technologies for the public good in future programs. This paper provides an overview of the Seasat experience and comments on future progams influenced by the Seasat results. Special attention is given to the program objectives and accomplishments, including the approach used to verify the measurements being taken, the applications experiments designed to confirm the benefits and effectiveness of the system in meeting the needs of the ocean data user community, and finally the ongoing efforts to distill further information from the data set in special scientific and applications areas.

Seasat Flight History

Seasat was launched from Vandenberg Air Force Base, Calif., into a near-polar (108 deg inclination) circular orbit 800 km above the Earth on Monday, June 26, 1978. In this orbit, Seasat circled the Earth 14 times daily, covering 95% of the global ocean area every 36 h. On Monday, Oct. 9, 1978, a catastrophic failure occurred in the satellite power subsystem, causing a loss of radio signals soon after it passed over an Australian tracking station shortly before midnight. On Tuesday, Nov. 21, Seasat was officially declared lost. The satellite operated from June 26 to Oct. 9, a period of 106 days. The sensors were turned on for data collection on the 19th day after launch. The synthetic aperture radar (SAR), radar scatterometer (SCATT), and scanning multichannel microwave radiometer (SMMR) operated as planned thereafter, while the radar altimeter (ALT) was shut off for two 9 day periods because of satellite thermal control and power problems. The visible and infrared radiometer (VIRR) had failed some 62 days following launch. All of these instruments, however, returned large quantities of global data of excellent quality. During the 106 days between launch and failure, Seasat relayed a massive amount of information on surface winds, currents, temperatures, wave heights, ice conditions, ocean topography, and coastal storm activities. A significant amount of full-sensor complement data was obtained during the major surface truth activities, as well as at several times the satellite overflew storms. Using three U.S.-based ground stations at Fairbanks, Alaska; Goldstone, Calif.; and Cape Kennedy, Fla., virtually complete SAR coverage was obtained for the North American continent, Alaska, and adjacent waters. Coverage for the Shoe Cove (near St. Johns, Newfoundland) and Oakhanger (near London) stations were less complete, but critical experiment areas in the North Atlantic did receive coverage.

In the interval between launch and Julian day 230 (mid-August), no orbit adjustments were made. The decision to leave the initial orbit unadjusted resulted in large measure from the "Cambridge-like" character of the launch orbit. The Cambridge orbit, favored by many of the Seasat Experiment Team members, has the property of generating an approximate 1 deg subsatellite track spacing every 3 weeks, providing rapid global sampling at a grid size intermediate between the 3 day separation (approximately 900 km) and the final, 152 day geodetic grid, a dense network with 18-20 km spacing at the equator. The launch orbit had a 17 day closure at 1.67 deg subsatellite track spacing and two geodetic cycles were completed in the first 6 weeks of the mission. The Bermuda orbit, entered on Julian day 253, provided an exact 3 day repeat with the satellite passing directly over the island of Bermuda. This characteristic permitted near-zenith ranging from the laser site on Bermuda for the purpose of calibrating the radar altimeter. A tide gage, accurately surveyed relative to the tracking station, provided a precise tie to the sea surface in the vicinity of the island.

Users and the Seasat System

The nations users were the architects of the Seasat program. Beginning as early as 1969, during a conference at Williams College in Williamstown, Mass., the needs and requirements for a global "proof of concept" ocean remote sensing system were established by the users.

Not since 1872 when scientists set out on a 4 year voyage to explore the world's oceans on the HMS Challenger had scientists banded together to sponsor an oceanographic mission with such single-minded purpose. Challenger was, in a way, a voyage to prove that scientists could study the ocean from ships; Seasat was also a "proof-of-concept mission" -- to see if microwave sensors in space could provide clear, accurate, understandable information of direct use to a variety of oceanographic and meteorologic diciplines and to government and industrial users of the oceans as well.

Six years elapsed before the Seasat program was approved in 1975 and 30 months later the system was ready to begin its mission. Condensed in this statement were years of hard work and painstaking committment by a large group of scientific and marine industry users with wide and diverse interests and needs. Meeting several times a year, first as a nonaffiliated user working group, later as a NASA-sponsored advisory group, and finally on their own again during the last year after the advisory group was disbanded by NASA, the users created, defined, and protected the program. Many times a meeting would draw more than a hundred participants representing government, institutional, and industrial interests. When the program encountered difficulty during House appropriations subcommittee hearings in 1975, these users addressed the issue with direct appeals to the U.S. Congress and the program was re-established by the Senate and emerged victorious from a House/Senate conference. Why were so many users with different affiliations and seemingly diverse interests so devoted to the concept of. Seasat?

In the decade preceding Seasat, satellite remote sensing of physical phenomena had been advanced by research and development programs in the fields of meteorology and land observations, with emphasis on visible and infrared remote sensing technologies. With the exception of surface and cloud-cover images and infrared derived surface temperatures, little use had been made of remote sensing techniques to obtain oceans data. Suddenly, modest aircraft and Skylab experiments with active microwave sensors (radars) and passive microwave sensors (radiometers) and the highly successful GEOS-3 application of a radar altimeter presented a technology that would be capable of collecting synoptic surface observations in spite of cloud cover and lighting conditions. In addition to focusing on a technology that opened new frontiers for many users of ocean data, the objectives of the Seasat program indicated an awareness of the needs of more than a narrow corridor of potential users. The users established the program objective and engineering guidelines.

The Seasat-A program objectives were:

1) To demonstrate the capability for
        a)   Global monitoring of wave height and directional spectra, surface winds, ocean temperature, and current patterns.

   b)   Measuring precise sea surface topography.

   c)   Detecting currents, tides, and storm surges.

   d)   Charting ice fields and navigable leads through
ice.

   e)   Mapping the global ocean GEOID.

   2)   To provide for user applications such data as

      a)   Predictions of wave height, directional wave
spectra, and wind fields for ship routing, ship design,
storm-damage avoidance, coastal disaster warning, coastal
protection and development, and deep water port development.

      b)   Maps of current patterns and temperatures for
ship routing, fishing, pollution dispersion and iceberg
hazard avoidance.

      c)   Charts of ice fields and leads for navigation
and weather prediction.

      d)   Charts of the ocean GEOID fine structure.

   3)   To determine the key features desired in future
operational systems for global sampling, near-real-time
data processing and dissemination, and user feedback for
operational programming.

   4)   To demonstrate the economic and social benefits of
user agency products.

Users from government agencies such as the U.S. Departments of Commerce, Defense, Interior, and Transportation
were joined by users from the National Science Foundation,
National Academy of Science and universities and scientific
institutions such as Scripps Institute and Woods Hole.
From the private sector, users representing shipping, oil,
gas, fishing, mining, and other areas of marine commerce
were involved. Users began to plan and develop programs to
transfer and assimilate Seasat data to match their special
interests and in most cases they were willing to devote not
just time but investment to the cause. The system fueled
by this interest began to take shape.

The System

Seasat was conceived and developed by the National
Aeronautics and Space Administration. Many domestic and

foreign government and private groups also contributed
materially to the program. The Jet Propulsion Laboratory
performed ably as the project center for Seasat, contributing in creative scientific, engineering and management ways
too numerous to mention. The Seasat spacecraft, built by
the Lockheed Missiles and Space Company in Sunnyvale,
Calif., consisted of a modified version of the Agena launch
vehicle system to which had been added a sensor module containing the five Seasat mission-unique sensors. Lockheed
was instrumental in defining and integrating new "one-of-a-
kind" sensors within challenging budget and time constraints and made many important contributions to program
success. The spacecraft was approximately 13 m long and
weighed 2274 kg in orbit. Figure 1 provides a view of the
Seasat satellite showing both launch and on-orbit configurations. As shown in Fig. 1, sensors were nested in
separate modular sections of the sensor module. The sensor
module was mated to the Lockheed Agena, which in addition
to providing power, attitude stability, orbit control and
adjustment, data processing, storage, and transfer to
ground stations, helped propel the satellite to its
operating orbit in space. The Agena was the second stage
of the Atlas F/Agena launch vehicle. The sensor module was
tailored specifically for the Seasat-A payload of four
microwave instruments and their antennas and had a maximum
diameter of 1.5 m without the appendages deployed. Atop
the Atlas booster rocket, the entire satellite was enclosed
within a 3 m diameter nose fairing, which matched the
diameter of the Atlas.

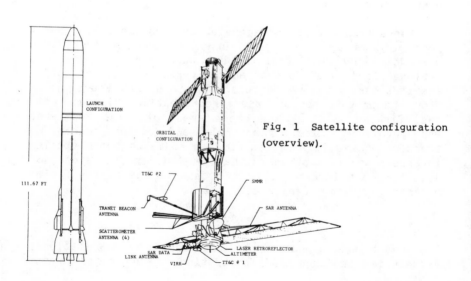

LAUNCH
CONFIGURATION

ORBITAL
CONFIGURATION

Fig. 1 Satellite configuration
(overview).

111.67 FT

TT&C #2

SMMR

TRANET BEACON
ANTENNA

SAR ANTENNA

SCATTEROMETER
ANTENNA (4)

SAR DATA
LINK ANTENNA

LASER RETROREFLECTOR
ALTIMETER

VIRR

TT&C # 1

Following the launch phase, the appendages (which were latched securely within the nose fairing) were deployed to their orbital configuration. The Agena ordnance subsystem actuated pin pullers to release nearly a dozen deployable spacecraft elements, including solar panels, antennas, and support booms.

In orbit, the satellite was oriented in a "stand-on-end" configuration, with the sensor and communications antennas pointing toward Earth and the Agena rocket nozzle and solar panels opposite toward space. A dominant feature of the Seasat is the SAR antenna, a 2.1 x 10.7 m planar array deployed perpendicular to the satellite body. The long dimension of the antenna was aligned with the direction of flight. This radar turned out to be capable of producing 25 x 6 m images of surface conditions with picture-like clarity, no matter what the weather or lighting conditions. As pioneering efforts go, it worked better than anyone expected, producing nearly 15,000 frames of 100 x 100 km data of ocean, coastal, Arctic, and geological data during Seasat's lifetime. Figure 2 emphasizes some of the challenging electrical and mechanical features of the SAR antenna, which was designed and manufactured by Ball Aerospace.

Seasat-A was continually stabilized on three axes by a momentum wheel/horizon sensing system to accurately point the sensors at the Earth's surface.

Two 11-panel solar arrays were the primary source of electrical power. Two nickel-cadmium storage batteries

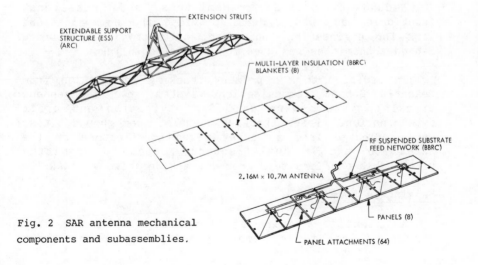

Fig. 2 SAR antenna mechanical components and subassemblies.

were used prior to solar panel deployment and to store
energy for peak power requirements and during solar eclipse
period operations.

Data storage capacity on the satellite was about 350 x
10^6 bits of information -- the equivalent of more than two
full orbits of measurements from all sensors with the
exception of the SAR.

Sensor pointing requirements included control to an
accuracy of 0.5 deg in roll, pitch, and yaw and telemetered
data on satellite orientation to an accuracy of 0.2 deg on
all axes. Scan wheels provided pitch and roll references
viewing the Earth's horizon and pitch and roll fine
control. Yaw attitude was maintained by gyro compassing.
Sun sensor data was used to determine accurate yaw
orientation, but was not used for control. Excess momentum
accumulated in the wheels was removed by providing
adjustable torque on the satellite using electromagnets
that interacted with the Earth's magnetic field.

The sensor module provided a platform for the operation
of the five sensors to achieve the mission objectives
within the required resolution and accuracy. The sensors
were located in positions relative to one another and to
the beacon, laser retroreflector, and communications
antennas so that each had an unobstructed field of view and
each achieved the required pointing and scan angles.
Mounting positions were also selected to prevent
electromagnetic interference between multiple radiating
sources.

Redundant S-band transmitters and receivers,
functioning as transponders, provided the communications
link for engineering and sensor telemetry. A separate
S-band transmitter was used for the SAR downlink.

In addition to the primary tracking information from
Seasat's S-band communications system, two independent
tracking systems were used for navigation and orbit
determination. Laser tracking signals, from ground sites,
were reflected from an array of retroreflectors on the
satellite and a dual-frequency beacon transmitted
ultrastable carriers to a ground tracking network, TRANET.

Sensing Instruments

As specific requirements evolved within the user
community, candidate remote sensing instruments were

evaluated jointly by the users and NASA for Seasat-A applications. A set of three active microwave sensors were selected. These radars included a pulse-compressed radar altimeter, a microwave radar scatterometer, and the synthetic aperture imaging radar. Passive sensors consisted of a scanning multi-frequency microwave radiometer and a visible/infrared scanning radiometer.

Altimeter. The Seasat radar altimeter served two functions: it monitored average wave height to within 0.5-1 m along its narrow (2-12 km) swath by measuring the broadening of its returned echo caused by increased surface wave actions and it measured to a sensor precision of 10 cm the changes in the ocean geoid due to gravity variations and ocean tides, surges, and currents. Wave height measurements from the Seasat altimeter have particularly important application in both commercial and military activities. General correlations with wave heights computed by the U.S. Navy's spectral ocean wave model (SOWM) have been excellent and the altimeter provides an unusual degree of detail concerning wave patterns. This detail is important to optimum track ship routing and is of sufficient accuracy to be used in the correction of wave propagation errors. Until Seasat, ship logs had been used to compile wave histories, but since ships follow shipping routes and avoid severe storms, the sea-state climatologies are deficient in many ocean areas.

Many think that the radar altimeter was the most sophisticated instrument on Seasat. Its 3 ns pulse width was its most publicized feature, because its 10 cm altimetric accuracy was expected to usher in a new era in geodetic and precise topographic measurements. However, another aspect of performance -- tracking response and stability -- was a major contributer to the improved systems applications. This sensor captured the intense interest of geodesist and physical oceanographer alike and elaborately constructed conversion algorithms were developed and are even now processing data so that scientists can refine and further study the shape of the Earth or watch the synoptic state of the ocean as it was monitored orbit by orbit.

The Seasat altimeter clearly fanned an interest that has evolved into new programs featuring altimeters such as Geosat (U.S. Navy) and Topex (NASA).

Scatterometer. As surface winds increase, so does fine-scale surface roughness. The radar scatterometer measured the signal strength of its returned echoes. Signal strength increases with the increase in wind-driven waves, which can be converted directly into wind speed. The radar and wind vector orientation is also important to signal strength and multiaspect (two in Seasat's case) views permitted wind speed and direction derivation. The scatterometer measured wind speeds of 3-28 m/s with an accuracy of 2 m/s and direction within 20 deg over two 500 km swaths beginning 200 Km from the nadir on either side of the spacecraft ground track. The sensor was capable of measuring higher-speed winds at up to 750 km on either side of the ground track. Analysis of scatterometer sensor data coverage reveals that ship report coverage of surface winds can be increased from a single satellite by a factor of 5 in the Northern Hemisphere and by a factor of 60 in the Southern Hemisphere. Improvements in the accuracy of surface wind field analysis over the oceans may be on the order of 10-20%; this means that national weather centers can significantly improve specification of near-surface mass/motion parameters used to initialize numerical atmospheric forecast models. Forecasts of 36 h that incorporate scatterometer wind observations may exhibit no more errors than 24 h forecasts made without the benefit of these satellite observations.

The scatterometer experiment on Seasat spawned new sensors on the upcoming U.S. Navy N-Ross and European Space Agency ERS-1 programs.

Scanning Multichannel Microwave Radiometer. The five-frequency microwave radiometer served several functions: it measured surface temperature by measuring the microwave brightness of the surface to within $1^{\circ}C$. Also measured was foam brightness which can in turn be converted into a high (up to 50 m/s) wind speed, commonly associated with major storms or hurricanes. The sensor mapped ice and provided atmospheric correction data to the active radars by measuring liquid and gaseous water content in the upper atmosphere. The surface swath of the microwave radiometer was 600 km.

Visible and Infrared Radiometer. This Seasat instrument provided clear weather surface temperature data, cloud coverage patterns, and corroborative images of ocean and coastal features with a resolution of 5 km over a swath of 1500 km.

These four sensors, known as the global sensors, collected data 100% of the time while monitoring the oceans and adjacent coastal waters and were left on over ground areas to provide data of selective interest. Their data were recorded on satellite magnetic tape recorders and played back while the spacecraft was over one of the ground stations supporting Seasat.

Virtually complete global coverage was achieved by the scatterometer, microwave radiometer, and visible and infrared radiometer every 36 h.

Synthetic Aperture Radar. This unique imaging sensor provided extraordinary information of surface conditions with its 25 m (cross track) by 6 m (along track) resolution. Open-ocean, coastal, and ice-covered regions were imaged in a detailed way using this sensor. Inland geology, agriculture, hydrology, and demographic areas were also imaged with great clarity. Images could be made in cloud-covered areas and were formed independent of lighting conditions. New insights and applications are still emerging from the wealth of collected data and many phenomena observed by the SAR are not yet clearly understood. Experimental investigation is continuing using the Seasat SAR spare hardware on Space Shuttle flights (Shuttle imaging radar: SIR-A, November 1981; SIR-B, October 1984). Early analysis of SAR images has shown that its application has very high potential, particularly in ice operations. Commercial users have stated that regular SAR coverage would significantly improve the ice reconnaissance that is currently done in spot areas by aircraft. This includes ice surveillance for offshore oil and gas exploration and production operations and shipping concerned with Arctic resupply operations. Cost savings could also be realized by the U.S. Coast Guard International Ice Patrol. The potential value for obtaining information on wave, swell, and current characteristics is also assessed as being high.

The SAR was a pioneering experience leading to the U.S. Shuttle imaging radars SIR-A and B with SIR-C, European Space Agency ERS-1, Japanese JERS-1, and Canadian Radarsat sensors planned for operation near the end of the decade.

The Ground System

The data products of the Seasat sensors served a variety of users. For example, weather data are highly perishable. To be of value, it must be processed quickly and immediately applied to be of any practical value. Professional meteorologists state that data older than 8 h

is of no value whatsoever. At the opposite end of the
spectrum is the geodesist whose data are not truly time
variant. The geodesist's approach to analysis is to fit
and refit data by a bootstrap approach, finally achieving a
best fit model of the ocean geoid. Some of the users had
sizeable ground data systems available to assist them in
processing and analysis; others had limited inexpensive
terminal equipment. Some users care only for specific
outputs such as wind and wave data for use in ship routing;
others, such as university researchers, want as much of the
data as is available for application to the development of
advanced prediction models. Thus, Seasat's "end-to-end"
data system had to be flexible enough to meet the demands
of this broad spectrum of user applications.

Although the space system was largely the result of
NASA-managed efforts, the ground system was conceived and
participated in by many users. Seasat became an international program with large installations and investments
in Canada and Europe. Around the world interest in the
promise of previously unavailable data products increased.

This international data system consisted of:

1) A global ground tracking system that included
military and civil radio tracking systems as well as laser
tracking. Data acquisition included NASA and foreign
participant stations.

2) A mission operations and control function performed
by the NASA Goddard Space Flight Center (GSFC). This
included collecting global sensor data from the ground
stations, monitoring satellite and sensor health, reducing
tracking data to provide satellite ephemeris, merging
satellite attitude data with ephemerides to provide sensor
footprints and delivery of sensor, and tracking data to the
Seasat project office at JPL.

3) The project data processing subsystem located at JPL
had the primary objective of providing data processing
support to the "proof-of-concept" mission. It supported
Seasat users of the global data (the experiment teams) by
providing engineering and geophysical data records on a
production basis to the user-prescribed format.

4) Wideband SAR data was recorded digitally at five
specially equipped stations, three in the United States
(Alaska, California, and Florida) and one each in Canada

(Newfoundland) and Europe (London). The tapes were delivered to several SAR data processing systems, where selected data were processed into images that were in turn provided, along with ephemeris, attitude, and status data, to the SAR experiment team. SAR data processed by JPL was made generally available to any user through NOAA. Nearly all of the data was optically processed by JPL and selected images were digitally processed.

5) The Navy Fleet Numerical Oceanographic Center (FNOC) at Monterey, Calif., served the real-time users. Global sensor and status data received at NASA stations were retransmitted in near-real time via communications satellites to Monterey, where they were processed and redistributed to the operational ocean-using community (civilian and military) as weather maps and advisories with less than 8 h turnaround time.

A special NASA/Navy data system was created to interface with real-time users. This system was called the satellite data distribution system (SDDS). This system is still in use today, using other satellite data to serve users. The system has been renamed the Navy/NOAA oceanographic data distribution system (NODDS).

NODDS currently functions in series with the U.S. Navy FNOC system to produce user products. Conventional meterological and oceanographic observations provided to FNOC serve as the input set to the numerical analysis and forecast models. The analysis models produce a smoothed initial or "first- guess" field that serves as an input to the forecast model and a useful output product as well. Through the use of large mainframe computers (CDC 6500, Cyber 175, and Cyber 203), analysis and forecast products are developed on a routine, operational basis (at 6 and 12 h synoptic times). Selected sets of these products are collected by the NODDS and reformated and tailored to the specific needs and geographical regions of interest of commercial and other civil sector users.

The original concept of the Seasat demonstration program was based upon the use of the SDDS to serve as a pilot demonstration of the distribution, on a near-real-time basis, of Seasat data and the analysis and forecast products using these data. To facilitate this aspect of the demonstration program, the SDDS near-real-time data distribution network was implemented by NASA and the Jet Propulsion Laboratory in cooperation with the U.S. Navy.

When Seasat failed prematurely, the commercial user demonstration program was revised at the request of the commercial users. The revised program consisted of two major components. The first component was the evaluation of the commercial utility of selected parts of the data that had been collected during the Seasat mission. Since the satellite was no longer functioning, the second component became the evaluation of the SDDS. Other marine weather information was specialized for commercial users. Arrangements were made to receive and process data from other ocean-observing satellites (military and civil weather satellites and NASA's Nimbus-7 spacecraft), thus providing the capability to assess the utility of satellite-derived ocean observations in an operational setting.

Data Validation

Following the launch of Seasat, an extensive formalized evaluation process to validate the on-orbit performance of the Seasat sensors was set in motion. The evaluation process involved engineers, instrument scientists, and geophysicists from NASA, NOAA, DOD, academic institutions, and private concerns in the United States in concert with similar groups in Canada and Europe. The evaluation proceeded through an engineering assessment and sensor evaluation and finally to an evaluation of the performance of the sensor in terms of its geophysical measurement parameters. A summary of the results of this analysis is shown in Table 1. These results met or exceeded project goals in nearly every instance.

Table 1 provides a somewhat clinical summary about the value of the Seasat experience. Seasat can be viewed in more vital ways by considering its impact in operational terms.

Faced with the challenge of doing business in a constantly changing and dangerous environment, it is easy to see why the promise of satellite remote sensing is so appealing to ocean-dependent businesses. Remote sensing from space offers the only method to synoptically monitor the global oceans. Today, on the basis of pioneering efforts by the United States with the Nimbus and Seasat satellites, a technology that matches the peculiar and challenging nature of the oceans is available to users.

The Seasat economic benefit assessment, completed in 1975, identified substantial potential benefits from the

Table 1   Seasat sensor mission performance summary

Sensor	Objective	Status
Altimeter (ALT)	1) Range (height) precision $\pm$ 10 cm (1σ, 1 s average)	1) Objective met up to $H_{1/3} \leq$ 10 m
	2) Ocean topography solutions on submeter level	2) Submeter topographic features have been corroborated with surface truth (Gulf Stream and Kuroshio Current)
	3) $H_{1/3}$ (significant wave height of 1-20 m, $\pm$ 10% or 0.5 m, whichever is greater	3) Objective met within specification up to $H_{1/3} \leq$ 8 m (maximum $H_{1/3}$ during Goasex)
	4) σ_0 (backscatter coefficient $\pm$ 1 dB	4) σ_0 comparison with SASS nadir cells within specification for $2 < \sigma_0 < 16$dB Practical range for wind measurements from 2 to 30 m/s
	5) Precision orbit determination to submeter level globally, 10 cm in calibration zone	5) 0.5-1 m globally, 10 cm in calibration zone
Synthetic aperture radar (SAR)	1) 6 x 25 spatial resolution over 100-km swath	1) Objective met
	2) Demonstrate capability to measure wave length and direction	2) Objective met for range traveling waves. Minimum wave length detected was 100 m in Goasex data, 70 m in Gulf Stream squall. Azimuthal traveling waves can be observed using Doppler offset focusing. Internal waves measured in range 75-2000 m

(Table continued on next page)

Table 1 (cont.) Seasat sensor mission performance summary

Sensor	Objective	Status
Synthetic aperture radar (SAR)	3) Provide data for study of coastal processes	3) Data acquired, but sparse surface truth limits interpretability
	4) Ice field/lead charting	4) Objective met
	5) Iceberg detection	5) Objective not met because of absence of surface truth and season of operation
	6) Fishing vessel surveillance, ship and ship wake analyses	6) Objective met Extensive wake analysis to determine imaging mechanism still in progress
	7) Land imaging for geological, hydrological, and glaciological experiments	7) Data acquired, but surface truth limited
Microwave scatterometer (SASS)	1) Wind speed of 4-26 m $\pm$ 2 m/s or 10%, whichever is greater	1) Objective met
	2) Wind direction $\pm$20 deg	2) Objective met for vertical polarization for winds 2-20 m/s using external means of ambiguity removal
	3) 50 km resolution with 100 km grid spacing, 500 km swath each side of satellite	3) Objective met

(Table continued on next page)

Table 1 (cont.) Seasat sensor mission performance summary

Sensor	Objective	Status
Microwave scatterometer (SASS)	4) Global, all-weather capability	4) Limited evidence indicates that for large-scale weather features, SMMR attenuation corrections bring SASS measurements within specification
Scanning multichannel radiometer (SMMR)	1) All weather global measurement of sea surface temperature ± 2 K absolute, +0.5 K relative	1) Data internally consistent to ~ 2 K, but contains biases of several degrees. Demonstration of performance better than 1.5-2 deg requires use of T_B and SST algorithms
	2) Wind speed from 7-50 m/s, +2 m/s or 10%, whichever is greater	2) Objective partially met for winds $\leq$ 30 m/s. High-speed winds measured
	3) Measurement of integrated atmospheric water vapor and liquid water	3) Objective demonstrated for water vapor to $\pm 20\%$ level with 10 radiosonde observations. Wet tropo correction for ALT accurate to ± 2 cm
	4) Measurement of rainfall rate	4) Rain has been detected in data, but quantitative comparisons have not been made because of limitations in surface truth data set

use of operational Seasat data in areas that are extensions
of current operations, such as marine transportation and
offshore oil and natural gas exploration and development.

In 1977, NASA entered into a unique cooperative
arrangement as a part of the Seasat program with several
industries and organizations that conduct or support
commercial operations in the ocean environment. The
primary objectives of this cooperative arrangement were to
help to identify those features of an ocean satellite
system of importance to the ocean commercial community and
to aid in the transfer of the use of satellite weather and
ocean data products to these commercial users. A secondary
objective included obtaining estimates of the importance
and value of these data to commercial users. The work
performed under this cooperative arrangement by industry
and government was known as the Seasat Commercial
Demonstration Program. One part of this program was the
evaluation of the Seasat data by the commercial
participants in the program. This work took the form of
retrospective case studies in which the commercial
participants worked with the Seasat data provided by NASA
to evaluate its usefulness to their operations. This
involved case studies by companies that conduct commercial
activities and by government organizations that foster
these commercial activities in areas of commerce such as
offshore oil and gas exploration and development, deep
ocean mining, ocean fishing, and marine transportation.
The results of these case studies provide dramatic evidence
of the importance of improved weather and ocean condition
forecasts to these operations and the opportunities for
cost savings through the use of these data.

It was concluded that very large potential benefits
from the use of Seasat data could be possible in an area of
operations that is now in the planning or conceptual stage,
namely, the transportation of oil, natural gas, and other
resources by surface ship in Arctic regions. A further
area of large potential benefits that was identified stems
from the use of Seasat data in support of ocean fishing
operations.

The Future

At the present time, the balance of investment in ocean
and polar region remote sensing is not in the United
States. The current world status of programs is:

1) ERS-1. The operational successor to the Seasat
mission is being sponsored by the European Space Agency.
Although the specific sensor design is different, the basic
instrument complement is nearly identical to the Seasat
design. This mission is in a hardware development phase
and will begin to return data from space in 1989.

2) Radarsat. This mission will use a SAR and other
sensors to monitor the Arctic several times a day.
Near-real-time distribution of data to commercial users is
a program objective. The mission was conceived in Canada
and is being supported by the U.K. System development is
in progress with a launch planned in the late 1980s.

3) MOS-1. The first Japanese entry into space-based
ocean sensing is a modest mission using optical and passive
microwave sensors. However, it represents the first of a
series of similar missions that will be progressively more
valuable. The first MOS mission is scheduled for 1986,
with a second launch in 1990. The second mission will
include active radar sensors.

4) N-ROSS-1. The U.S. Navy will launch a Seasat
derivative operational ocean sensing system in the 1989/90
time period. The first system provides improved
altimeter, scatterometer, and microwave radiometer data,
but does not have a SAR. This mission is important to both
Navy and ocean commercial user interests.

5) Topex. NASA is considering an advanced altimeter
ocean topography and circulation mission near the end of
the 1980s.

It is clear that the value of the pioneering ocean
remote sensing work performed by the United States has been
widely recognized. Major investments by our foreign
neighbors attest to this fact. A continued activity by the
United States is essential to American business interests
and to the critical retention and further development of
powerful new technologies.

"An embarrassment of riches" was the way Sea Technology
magazine described the mass of data spewed out by the
Seasat satellite during its short 3 month life in 1978.
The products of Seasat's sensors have been put to use in a
variety of ways that benefit industry through sea floor
mapping and environmental monitoring. The space age has
penetrated oceanography, with Seasat leading the way. Six

years after Seasat's demise, scientists are still analyzing
the mass of data that poured forth from the satellite.

However, there remains much to be done in using space
age tools in ocean observations. Planning for future
satellite systems, a preciously rare commodity in the
government these days, needs to be pursued. The field is
wide open. The time of discovery is still with us.

Seasat Data Applications in Ocean Industries

D.R. Montgomery*

*Jet Propulsion Laboratory, California Institute of Technology,
Pasadena, California*

Abstract

The Seasat Program was initiated as a proof-of-
concept mission to evaluate the ability to remotely sense
oceanographic phenomena from a satellite platform. The
program was user oriented, with significant participation
from a wide spectrum of users, including government,
academia, and the private sector. While an early failure
of the satellite deprived these users of a real-time,
multiseasonal data set, the program did yield a rare and
valuable archive of data that has been analyzed and
validated by the user community, including commercial
users. Thus, with Seasat began the new and exciting
technology of satellite oceanography. In 1977 the
National Aeronautics and Space Administration entered into
a unique cooperative arrangement with several industries
that conduct or support commercial operations in the ocean
environment. The objective of this cooperative arrangement
was to identify those features of an oceanic
satellite system of importance to ocean industries and to
assess the utility of the remotely sensed data to
commercial users. The work performed under this
cooperative arrangement by industry and government was
known as the Seasat Commercial Demonstration Program.
This paper highlights the results of this program and
describes the studies and evaluation efforts conducted by
the private sector in such areas as offshore oil and gas
exploration and development, deep-ocean mining, commercial
fishing, marine transportation, and private weather
forecasting. The results of this assessment have provided
dramatic evidence of the importance of improved weather
and ocean condition forecasts to ocean industries and the
opportunities for cost savings and increased safety through
the near-real-time application of satellite oceanography.

This paper is declared a work of the U.S. Government and therefore
is in the public domain.
*Director, Office of Ocean Services, National Ocean Service,
National Oceanic and Atmospheric Administration.

419

Introduction

For centuries, ocean shipping has been the primary
medium for international commerce. In recent years, the
world population expansion and resulting shortages of
food, minerals, and fuel have focused additional attention
on the world's oceans. All components of the ocean
commercial industry have increased their activities in
this area because of these shortages. As the world
population continues to grow, the economic benefits of
improved short-range weather prediction as well as
monitoring/prediction of long-range climatic anomalies
become more important. Specification of oceanic heat
shortage, transport of heat by ocean current, and air/sea
exchange processes for heat, moisture, and momentum is
essential to improvement of both short- and long-range
forecasts. It appears, however, that the greatest dollar
benefits to commercial operations from remote ocean
sensing derive from better assessments of present
environmental conditions and more accurate predictions out
to two days.

Since the launch of TIROS I in 1960, satellites have
revolutionized the collection of weather data.
Observations of cloud cover are so extensive that it is
virtually impossible for a major storm system to go
undetected. At the same time, satellite sensors are
routinely measuring atmospheric profiles of temperature and
moisture. In spite of these technological advances,
significant gains in the accuracy of meteorological and
oceanographic forecasts have been hampered by the scarcity
of good surface observations over ocean areas. Even
though there are over 50,000 ships at sea with gross
tonnage exceeding 500 tons, our national forecast centers
receive fewer than 2500 weather reports from these ships
each day in near-real time. National and international
buoy systems augment the total coverage to a minor degree,
but it is generally agreed that the commercial ocean
industry and our naval forces now suffer from inadequate
data and forecast products related to the oceans.

More accurate environmental prediction requires
bigger and faster scientific computers, better models,
improved observations over the oceans, and faster data
collection and transmission to our national weather and
oceanographic centers. The Seasat Program and the planned
Navy-Remote Oceanographic Satellite System (N-ROSS)
represent major contributions to improved observational

coverage and the processing needed to achieve better forecasts.

The Seasat Program was initiated as a proof-of-concept mission to evaluate the effectiveness of remotely sensed oceanographic phenomenon from a satellite platform. The program was unique because it focused on measurements at the air/sea/ice interface and emphasized user requirements. NASA's efforts to plan for ocean commercial users were particularly noteworthy because they stressed worldwide observational coverage instead of coverage around the continental United States, applied an engineering approach to an integrated spacecraft/ground processing/user support system, and developed plans based upon direct contact with oceanographic user groups in the context of their daily commercial operations. This emphasis on preparing tailored products has resulted in data and services that are of real use to the "oceanographic community."

The Seasat Program provided a base for the use of space platforms for global and local explorations into the dynamics and resources of the ocean, the effect of the ocean on weather and climate, and the role the ocean plays in ice and coastal processes. It has now been conclusively demonstrated that wave heights, sea-surface directional wind velocities, sea-surface temperature, and ocean topography can be measured from space. This information can be used in such economic and social applications as improving the efficiencies of weather or sea-state-related operations in the marine industries; providing better warning of severe wind and wave conditions; providing a means of improving and managing the resource yield in many marine industries; providing improved navigation through ice and currents; and creating a better understanding of the ocean and its dynamics.

Although the Seasat mission ended prematurely in October 1978, nearly 100 days of data were collected upon which to base an analysis of the benefits of this first oceanographic satellite program. These data were valuable because they demonstrated sensor performance, supported user experiments, emphasized deficiencies in conventional observation coverage, served as input data in model accuracy studies, and led to formation of a growing Satellite Data Distribution System (SDDS).

Commercial Users Program

From its inception the Seasat Program has been user oriented. These users, having served as the architects of the program, comprised three major segments of the ocean community, namely, academic users, users within various government agencies, and commercial users. This user constituency provided an advisory function through the auspices of the Ocean Dynamics Advisory Subcommittee.

Commercial users within this advisory body represented a broad spectrum of commercial industries, including:off-shore oil and gas operators, marine transportation, marine fisheries, deep ocean mining, marine safety, and marine weather forecasting. These commercial users, drawing upon the assessment and projections of a cost/benefit analysis conducted in support of the Seasat Program development, proposed to NASA to carry out a pilot demonstration to assess the utility of Seasat data in the private sector. The concept accepted and implemented by NASA was a cost-sharing arrangement with the commercial users, involving no transfer of funds from NASA to the users. Each participating user contributed resources in order to utilize the satellite data in an operational setting. These resources contributions collectively totaled in excess of $12 million.

Commercial users, in contrast to users in the academic and government agency communities, in general, require that ocean condition data be made available on a near-real-time basis. Ocean observational and forecast data are highly perishable and, to be useful in terms of tactical operations, must be provided in sufficient time to permit analysis and action on the part of the user/recipient.

The Commercial Demonstration Program, as initially proposed, envisioned the processing and distribution of Seasat data (along with forecast products prepared with the use of these data and with conventional observations) in near-real time. The functional arrangement to implement this near-real-time concept is shown in Fig. 1. The demonstration program was structured to assess the impact of the remotely sensed ocean surface characteristics of winds, waves, and sea-surface temperatures upon the operational activities of the users. The possible impact areas, as viewed by the various user groups, are outlined in Table 1.

Table 1   Possible oceanographic satellite applications

Activity	Application

Off-shore oil and gas	Increased ocean condition forecast accuracy
	    Exploration operations
	        Seismic surveys
	        Drill ships
	        Towout operations
	    Production operations
	        Crew scheduling
	        Platform and crew safety
	Ice observations
	    Ice dynamics for platform design criteria
	    Ice movement--platform and crew safety
	Environmental data
	    Replace platform instrumentation
	Subsurface and seabed dynamics
	    Gas pipeline applications

Environmental forecasting	Increased observations (particularly in Southern Hemisphere)
	Consistent observations
	    Wave height measurements
	    Wind averages

Marine transportation	Increased ocean forecast accuracy
	    Optimum routing
	    Port scheduling
	Ice observations
	    Arctic resupply
	    Vessel/personnel safety

Deep-ocean mining	Increased ocean condition forecast accuracy
	    Mining operations
	Improved tropical storm, storm-track prediction
	    Mining operations and safety
	Historical data base
	    Unbiased climatology
	        Mining equipment design
	        Operational criteria

Marine fisheries	Increased ocean condition forecast accuracy
	    Efficient search efforts
	    Efficient gear operations
	    Reduced gear losses
	    Crew and vessel safety
	Ice observations/forecasts
	    Gear losses
	    Crew and vessel safety

The program objectives were to:

1. Determine the utility of satellite-derived ocean
condition data and corresponding processing and
distribution methods in the commercial ocean community.

2. Attempt to validate earlier cost-benefit
estimates for operational oceanographic satellite systems.

3. Begin to transfer the technology involving the
operational use of real-time ocean condition data to the
private sector.

Case Studies

The premature end of the Seasat mission deprived the
commercial users involved in the Seasat Program from
evaluating the impact on their various ocean activities of
satellite-derived ocean observations and forecasts
delivered in near real time. In contrast and in lieu of
real-time processing and distribution of Seasat data, some
16 American and Canadian commercial users conducted a
series of case studies that utilize Seasat data in various
sets of analysis efforts designed to assess the usefulness
of these data in marine operations -- assuming these data
had been delivered to each participating user in near-real
time. The commercial users that conducted these case
study activities are shown in Table 2.

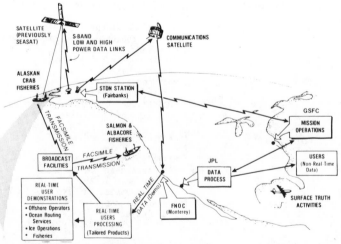

Fig. 1 Commercial demonstration program: real-time system
configuration.

Table 2   Participating commercial users case studies

Demonstration title	Participating organizations	Nature of demonstration
1) Beaufort Sea oil, gas, and arctic operations[a]	Canadian Marine Drilling, Ltd.; Esso Resources, Ltd.; Gulf Oil of Canada	Comparison of Seasat and other radar data against surface truth. Evaluate ability of satellite data to benefit oil and gas operations in Beaufort Sea
2) Labrador Sea oil, gas, and sea ice[a,b]	Esso Resources, Ltd.; Total Eastcan Exploration, Ltd.	Comparison of Seasat wind, wave, and ice data against surface truth data. Evaluate utility of data for aiding off-shore facilities design and production operations in Labrador Sea
3) Gulf of Mexico pipelines[a,b]	American Gas Association	Evaluate ability of Seasat data to improve storm prediction capability for determining ocean bottom conditions as they affect subsurface pipelines
4) U.S. east coast off-shore oil and gas[a,b]	Continental Oil Co.	Comparison of Seasat data against surface truth data from instrumented platforms. Develop data base for improved structural design and production operations
5) Worldwide off-shore drilling and production operations[a]	Getty Oil Co.	Develop data base to aid in operations planning. Comparison of Seasat data against surface truth data to determine benefits to off-shore drilling and production operations
6) East Pacific ocean mining[a,b]	Deepsea Ventures, Inc.; Kennecott Exploration, Inc.; Lockheed Ocean Laboratories	Evaluate ability of Seasat data to improve prediction accuracy of severe storms in tropical Pacific to aid deep-sea mining operations
7) Bering Sea ice project[b]	Alaska Oil and Gas Assn., Arctic Research Subcommittee	Assess ability of SAR data to identify ice characteristics in Bering Sea to aid in determining ice loads on off-shore drilling and production structure

(Table 2 continued on next page.)

Table 2 (cont.) Participating commercial users case studies

Demonstration title	Participating organizations	Nature of demonstration
8) North Sea oil and gas	Union Oil Co.; Continental Oil Co.	Use of Seasat data to develop improved design load data for off-shore drilling and production structures
9) Marine environmental forecasting in Gulf of Alaska[a]	Oceanroutes, Inc.	Use of Seasat data in generating improved ocean condition forecasts in North Sea to aid off-shore oil and gas drilling and production operations
10) Ocean thermal energy conversion[a]	Ocean Data Systems, Inc.	Use of Seasat to aid in evaluation and selection of plant sites for ocean thermal energy conversion facilities
11) International ice patrol Northern Survey	U.S. Coast Guard	Demonstrate feasibility and benefits of conducting pre-season survey of icebergs and sea ice in Labrador and Baffin Island coasts using Seasat SAR data in place of aircraft reconnaissance
Drift analysis	U.S. Coast Guard	Use of SAR data to observe repetitive iceberg drifts for use in ice drift model. Improve reliability of ice limits in north Atlantic shipping lanes
Environmental data[a]	U.S. Coast Guard	Evaluate use of Seasat wind and SST data in drift model to improve knowledge of iceberg position and deterioration
12) Optimum ship routing[a]	Oceanroutes, Inc.	Use of Seasat data to improve forecasts used in developing optimum ship routing information for various marine transportation operators

(Table 2 continued on next page.)

Table 2 (cont.) Participating commercial users case studies

Demonstration title	Participating organizations	Nature of demonstration
13) Tropical and temperate tuna fisheries[a]	National Marine Fisheries Service, Southwest Fisheries Laboratory	Use of ocean condition data from Seasat to aid in possible improvement of planning and fishing operations of salmon vessels operating along U.S. Pacific coast
14) Pacific salmon fishery[a]	Oregon State University/ Marine Advisory Program and Humboldt State University/Marine Advisory Service (participating vessel)	Use of ocean condition forecasts incorporating Seasat data to improve planning and fishing operations of salmon vessels operating along U.S. Pacific coast
15) Improved real-time weather forecasting[a]	Atmospheric Environmental Service (Canada)	Use of Seasat data as synoptic observations in preparation of ocean and weather analyses and forecasts. Determine what improvements in forecasts may result

[a] Real-time data product users.
[b] Non-real-time data product users.

Real-Time System Operations

Because of a need to more fully understand and refine the commercial user requirements for a real-time oceanographic processing and distribution system, it was decided, following the failure of the satellite, to complete and operate a data system capable of processing satellite-derived ocean observations, generating ocean analysis and forecast products, and distributing these products to a limited set of commercial users. This system, now known as the Satellite Data Distribution System (SDDS), is based upon the system and products of the U.S. Navy Fleet Numerical Oceanography Center (FNOC) and serves as a pilot demonstration from which the general processing and distribution system requirements may be developed for future operational, ocean-oriented satellite programs.

The SDDS is designed to provide several levels of
data products to the commercial users. The SDDS
operationally distributes data products that represent the
state-of-the-art in global oceanic weather products and
are of substantial interest and use to commercial ocean
operations. Products currently include near-real-time
satellite observations of sea ice, derived from the
scanning multichannel microwave radiometer (SMMR) on the
NASA Nimbus-7 satellite.

The SDDS, shown in Fig. 2, functions in series with
the FNOC system to produce user products. Conventional
meteorological and oceanographic observations provided to
FNOC serve as the input set to the numerical analysis and
forecast models. Through the use of large mainframe
computers (CDC 6500, Cyber 175, and Cyber 203), analysis
and forecast products are developed on a routine,
operational basis (at 6 and 12 h synoptic times).
Selected sets of these products are collected by the SDDS
and are reformated or tailored to the specific needs and
geographical regions of interest to the commercial users.
The products that are available to the commercial users
include: sea-level and upper atmospheric pressure,
sea-surface temperature, marine winds, significant wave
heights, primary wave direction and period, spectral wave
data, and sea ice distribution. These products are

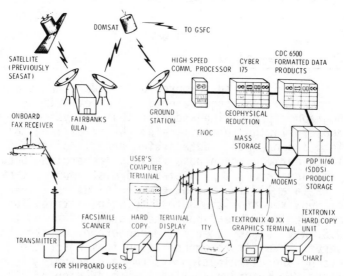

Fig. 2 Commercial demonstration program: satellite data distribution
system configuration.

transferred to a NASA-owned PDP 11/60 computer, colocated in the FNOC facility, for storage and distribution to the commercial users.

Commercial users can access the analysis and forecast products in one or more ways. A commercial dial-up packet-switching network provides access to the SDDS. Alpha-numeric products may be obtained on standard teletype terminals at data rates as low as 300 baud. Graphics, as well as alpha-numeric products, are received at a transmission rate of 1200 baud on CRT terminal displays (such as the Tektronix Terminal model 4006-1) and companion hard-copy units. Alternatively, a direct computer-computer connection can be established using conventional long-distance telephone circuits with a transmission rate of 4800 baud.

A number of participating commercial fishing vessels along with several deep ocean mining vessels require ocean forecast products while operating at sea. To provide an onboard capability, daily high-frequency radio-facsimile broadcasts have been made from radio station WWD (cooperatively operated by Scripps Institution of Oceanography and the NOAA National Marine Fisheries Service) in La Jolla, Calif. Product sets are derived from the SDDS by means of a CRT display terminal and hard-copy unit -- the resulting hard-copy charts being used in a facsimile scanner for subsequent radio broadcast.

Impact of Seasat Data on Industry Sectors

Sensor Impact

Synthetic Aperture Radar (SAR). Analysis of SAR images (an example of which is shown in Fig. 3) has shown that its application has very high potential, particularly in ice operations. The potential value for obtaining information on wave, swell, and current characteristics is assessed as being high.

Seasat studies, along with the experimental results from the Canadian Sursat Program have shown conclusively that synthetic aperture radar observations from a satellite platform can monitor Arctic ice conditions under all-weather conditions with sufficient precision to meet a majority of the off-shore oil and gas industries requirements in terms of ice edge position, ice concentration, freeze-up and breakup patterns, and ice

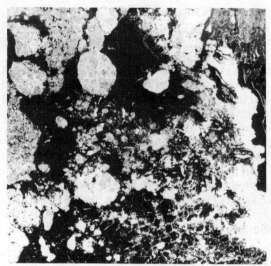

Fig. 3 Synthetic aperture radar image.

movement. Canada has estimated the benefits of a SAR
satellite to be on the order of $200 million/year and the
costs to be an order of magnitude less than for equivalent
aircraft reconnaissance. One U.S. commercial user has
estimated that up to 80% of all aircraft ice
reconnaissance could be replaced by a satellite-borne SAR.

    Non-real-time or historical information is required
for the statistical model verification and hindcast
studies needed to define operational and design criteria.
Real-time information is required for environmental
monitoring and forecasting on a long-range basis in
support of off-shore operations.

    Ice characteristics important to Arctic oil and gas
operations include a determination of the extent and type
of ice coverage, the movement of ice, ice growth, ice
pressure (rafting, ridging, and hummocking), amount of
snow cover, extent of puddling within floes, and the
locations and dimensions of open-water leads in
ice-infested waters.

    Marine transportation in Arctic regions is severely
hampered by ice conditions, including icebergs. Resupply
of off-shore installations is highly seasonal and
conducted at exceptional expense. Future liquid natural
gas ice breaking tankers, each costing $100 million each,

must operate with highly accurate ice forecasts in order
to be profitable. SAR observations of ice to determine
the location and dimensions of leads and potential routes
in Arctic transportation areas can yield significant
economic benefits to the shipping industry.

In the area of marine safety, SAR observations can
aid in the location of ice jams on navigable rivers, in
the detection and tracking of large icebergs, and in the
monitoring of rivers during breakup for purposes of flood
control. SAR observations have potential in the detection
and location of incidents requiring search and rescue
operations.

Altimeter (ALT). Wave height measurements from the
Seasat altimeter show particularly high application in
both commercial and military activities. General
correlations with wave heights computed by the U.S. Navy's
spectral ocean wave model (SOWM) have been excellent, but
the altimeter provides an unusual degree of detail
concerning wave patterns. This detail is important to
optimum track ship routing and is of sufficient accuracy
to be used in the correction of wave propagation errors.
Since ships follow shipping routes and avoid severe
storms, the sea-state climatologies are deficient in many
ocean areas.

Scatterometer (SASS). Analysis of scatterometer
sensor data coverage reveals that ship report coverage of
surface winds can be increased by a factor of 5 in the
Northern Hemisphere and by a factor of 690 in the Southern
Hemisphere from a single satellite. Improvements in the
accuracy of surface wind field analysis over the oceans
may be on the order of 10 - 20 %; this means that national
weather centers can significantly improve specification of
near-surface mass/motion parameters used to initialize
numerical atmospheric forecast models. Forecasts of 36 h
incorporating scatterometer wind observations may exhibit
no more errors than 24 h forecasts made without the
benefit of these satellite observations. All components
of the oceanographic community would benefit from improved
short-range weather prediction and it is reasonably safe
to assume that such improvements will be realized when
oceanographic satellite coverage becomes routine.

Scanning Multichannel Microwave Radiometer (SMMR).
Analysis of SMMR data has shown the sensor to be an
important observational tool for sea ice observations,

providing measurements on distribution and ice type. The
sensor further provides observations of higher-level wind
speed, which is a useful input to operational numerical
wind prediction models. Observations of sea surface
temperature (SST) are made by this sensor; however, the
sensor footprint is sufficiently large that the utility of
the SST in commercial fishing applications is quite
limited. The sensor is also important in terms of its
ability to measure water vapor/rain measurements needed to
correct the attenuation effects on other microwave
sensors.

Impact on Selected Industries

Within the context of various industrial segments, it
has been possible, again through the case study analysis,
to extract certain assessments of the impact of Seasat
data upon certain commercial ocean operations.

Weather influences all aspects of fishing operations.
Wind and wave conditions affect such factors as vessel
safety, the ability to deploy and secure gear, travel time
from the fishing grounds to processing plants, the ability
to avoid hull and gear damage, etc. Vessels operating in
the Alaskan crab fishery can experience losses of income
as high as $60,000/day if operations are suspended due to
adverse weather. All fall and winter fishing operations
in the Bering Sea and Gulf of Alaska regions experience
vessel and crew losses due to vessel icing conditions
(Fig. 4). Based upon Seasat data analysis, improved
forecasts of these conditions are anticipated through
satellite observations of wind and surface temperature
phenomena. Some fish species exhibit strong preference
for certain temperature ranges; tuna are a notable
example. The majority of west coast albacore is caught at
temperatures between 17-19°C and the tuna fleets need to
be directed to these areas. Gear losses due to
unanticipated ice pack movements in the Bering Sea area
aggregate hundreds of thousands of dollars.

Ocean satellite data, if made available on a near-
real-time basis through tailored products, would greatly
benefit the commercial fisherman. Such information would
improve overall efficiency and safety. Fuel costs could
be reduced, gear losses could be minimized, catch
statistics could be improved, and insurance could be
lowered.

Fig. 4 Vessel and crew loss due to severe icing.

Fig. 5 Deep-ocean mining operations.

Deep-ocean mining (Fig. 5) is an industry still in its infancy but one which is expected one day to grow rapidly. The major ocean mining companies participated in the Commercial Demonstration Program. Resource surveys conducted to date indicate that many of the areas with the richest potential now have the poorest conventional observation coverage. Due to unreliable climatological information in some of these areas, mining companies are experiencing difficulty in the formulation of operations plans/schedules. Interpretations to on-site operations

disrupt schedules throughout the total operation (e.g.,
transport and processing). If sufficient advance warning
of coming adverse weather and sea conditions were secured
and if the forecasts were accurate, operators could elect
to lift the miner off the bottom, maneuver so as to
minimize ship motion, and ride out the storm on-station.
This tactic reduces loss of operating time significantly
below that required to flee the area completely because of
lack of information.

Recent increases in the costs of natural gas and oil,
coupled with growing scarcity in the more accessible
regions of the world, have given the off-shore oil and gas
industry incentives to explore the more remote and, hence,
severe environments of the world. It has proved difficult
and expensive to acquire weather, oceanographic, and ice
data in these areas. Exploration and production in
off-shore fields involve important economic and safety
considerations -- vessel selection and routing, selection
of operational "windows" with acceptable weather conditions
for critical operations, platform tow-out and construction
activities, and day-to-day operations.

The economics of off-shore oil and gas operations are
probably greater than for any other ocean industry.
Somenew mobile rigs cost $50-100 million and have daily
lease costs in the range of $50,000-$100,000. In
addition, the off-shore oil and gas industry has need for
continuous, high-quality observations to monitor the
local environment and provide the historical data necessary
to improve design. Deep-ocean drilling rig designers have
overdesigned rigs by $4-8 million a piece because of
inadequate wind/wave climatologies for many ocean areas.
In the Baltimore Canyon area, compliance with the U.S.
Department of Interior Notice 775 concerning platform
instrumentation costs at least $100,000/instrumented
platform.

Environmental data are also important to design and
installation of pipelines on the sea bed. Swell from
distant storms and local water surges due to local wind
systems cause currents that act on these pipelines. The
safety of these installations is becoming an increasingly
important consideration as more large-diameter pipelines
are being planned for off-shore areas all around the
world. Seasat has shown that an operational oceanographic
satellite system could impact the economics of the entire
off-shore oil and gas industry through better observation
of wind, wave, temperature, current, and ice conditions.

It is now estimated that about 25% of all ships over 5000 tons utilize shore-based ship routing and/or enroute surveillance of some sort. The most important parameter to automated ship routing is sea state; however, winds, currents, and hazards to navigation such as fog, rain, snow, and ice are also significant. Good sea-state analysis and prediction can reduce transit time up to 10% with a resulting savings in operating costs of $15,000-$40,000 for a typical Pacific voyage. Optimum selection of shipping routes needs better medium-range forecasts as well as improved ocean climatologies. Evaluation of Seasat wave observations reveals that they are of very high quality. They agree well with the few direct observations available from instrumented buoys [e.g., the NOAA Data Buoy Office wave measurements systems as well as with theoretical computations from the FNOC spectral ocean wave model (SOWM)]. The Seasat observations show detail that can be used to tune models such as the SOWM and it appears they could be used directly to make phase adjustments in long-distance propagation of swell trains. The observations of wave height obtained from the Seasat altimeter are unique and appear to have major marine transportation applications.

Ice surveillance in Arctic (and Antarctic) regions provides information on ice coverage, extent, and movement, along with definitions of openings and leads. Such observations greatly aid the navigation of marine shipping operating in these regions and also benefit fishing operations along the edge of the ice sheets. The off-shore oil and gas operations in the Arctic regions (Figs. 6 and 7) are highly sensitive to the environmental factors of ice, weather, and waves, since they govern both facility design and the long-range, strategic, and tactical planning necessary for safe and efficient operations.

Applications in Commercial Fishing

The private sector studies of Seasat data have illustrated the utility of satellite-derived observations of the ocean surface in commercial applications. To further test these conclusions, a fisheries-oriented demonstration is being conducted on the U.S. west coast using the coastal zone color scanner (CZCS) on the Nimbus-7 satellite. Ocean color boundaries derived from the Nimbus-7 CZCS along with SMMR sea-surface temperature measurements, also from Nimbus-7, are being merged with

Fig. 6 Drill ship in Arctic operations.

Fig. 7 Drilling operations from artificial island during winter.

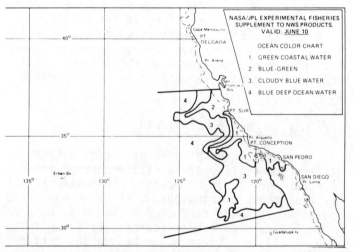

Fig. 8 Special satellite-derived ocean color chart tailored for commercial fishing applications.

conventional and other satellite observations to form
charts depicting key environmental properties that may
contribute to more efficient and safe commercial fishing
operations. These charts are made available to commercial
fishing vessels through daily radio-facsimile broadcasts.
Overall, the investigation proceeds in an experimental
fashion but within the context of an operational setting,
thus providing a valid basis for evaluating the commercial
utility of the satellite observations.

Fig. 8 shows a chart that depicts key color
boundaries as derived from CZCS observations of the ocean
surface in cloud-free areas (Fig. 9). Color boundaries
may identify nutrient-rich regions in which fish may
congregate. Fig. 10 is a chart depicting a number of
ocean surface properties, including key isotherms that
define the boundaries of surface temperatures preferred by
albacore, coastal surface temperature of importance to
trawl fisheries, wind and wave parameters, and areas of
wind convergences indicative of both squall activity
and possible concentrations of nutrients.

This investigation, proceeding over a 3 year period,
involves a continuing evaluation by participating
commercial fishermen. The results of the investigation
will affect whether the use of satellite observations and

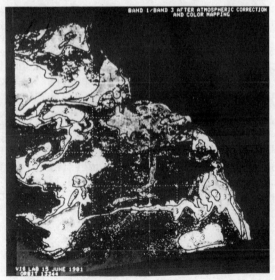

Fig. 9 CZCS image showing ocean surface in cloud-free area.

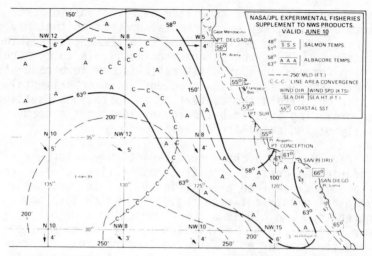

Fig. 10 Special fisheries-aid chart depicting several satellite-derived ocean properties of potential use in commercial fishing applications.

derived products will be continued fully funded by the participating fishermen or discontinued because of lack of experimental success and interest.

In the Future

In the next decade, ocean commercial users will require an operational oceanographic satellite system or systems capable of maximizing real-time data coverage over all ocean areas. Seasat studies to date indicate that three spacecraft are required to achieve the desired data coverage. The sensor suite should measure surface winds, wave heights (and spectral energy distribution), ice characteristics, sea-surface temperature, ocean colorimetry, height of the geoid, salinity, and aid in the determination of the subsurface thermal structure. From the commercial operations viewpoint, it is essential that oceanographic data and derived products be distributed to user entities within 2 h of observation time and that a responsive oceanographic satellite data archive becomes a reality.

Acknowledgments

The author wishes to thank the commercial firms participating in the Commercial Demonstration Program and their technical staff members who were involved in the detailed analysis of Seasat data. Special thanks are extended to W. E. Hubert and P. M. Wolff of Ocean Data Systems, Incorporated, for their assessment efforts. Acknowledgments are also gratefully extended to M. Humfreville for his efficient composition and administrative support.

Bibliography

Born, G. H., Dunne, J.A., and Lame, D. B., "Seasat Mission Overview," Science, Vol. 204, 1979, pp. 1405-1406.

Ferrari, A. J. and Renfrow, J. T., "An Analysis of the Seasat Satellite Data Distribution System," Proceedings of the International Ocean Engineering Conference, 1980, published by Institute of Electrical and Electronic Engineers.

McCandless, S. W., "Radar Remote Sensing and Offshore Technology," Proceedings of the Offshore Technology Conference, Offshore Technology Conference 3718, 1980.

Montgomery, D. R., "The Impact of Seasat Data on Commercial Marine Operations - A Preliminary Assessment," Jet Propulsion Laboratory, Pasadena, Calif., Informal report, 1979.

Montgomery, D. R. and McCandless, S. W., "Seasat-A, A User Oriented Ocean Monitoring Satellite Program," Proceedings of WESCON 77, 1977, pp. 1-11, published by Western Electronic Show and Convention.

Montgomery, D. R. and Wolff, P. M., "Seasat-A and the Commercial Ocean Community," Proceedings of AIAA Conference on Satellite Technology Applications to Marine Technology, 1977, pp. 276-283.

"Final Reports, Forecast Impact Study, Tasks 1, 2 and 5, "Ocean Data Systems, Inc., Monterey, Calif., December 1, 1980.

Renfrow, T., Fujimoto, B., and Malewicz, K., "Seasat Satellite Data Distribution System - Interim Evaluation Report," Jet Propulsion Laboratory, Pasadena, Calif., Internal Doc. 622-219, Rev. A, April 15, 1980.

Wright, B. and Hnatirek, J., "Satellite Applications to the Oil and Gas Industry in the Canadian Arctic," Internal Pub., Gulf Canada Ltd., Calgary, Alb., Canada, 1976.

The Navy Geosat Mission Radar Altimeter Satellite Program

W.E. Frain,* S.C. Jones,† C.C. Kilgus,‡ and J.L. MacArthur§

The Johns Hopkins University Applied Physics Laboratory,
Laurel, Maryland

ABSTRACT

The satellite radar altimeter has proven to be a versatile and powerful tool for remote sensing of the oceans. Data from the GEOS-C and Seasat-A altimeters supported research in geodesy, bathemetry, mesoscale oceanography, tides, ice topography, winds, and waves. The Navy Geosat mission is designed to extend this data set by placing a radar altimeter spacecraft in approximately the Seasat-1 orbit in early 1985.

Abbreviations

A/D	= analog-to-digital
AGC	= automatic gain control
BCR	= battery charge regulator
bps	= bits per second
CCM	= command, control, and monitor
CCT	= computer-compatible tape
CMOS	= complementary metal oxide semiconductor
CRT	= cathode ray tube
DCG	= digital chirp generator
DMA	= Defense Mapping Agency
DoD	= Department of Defense
FET	= field effect transistor
GaAs	= gallium arsenide

*Spacecraft Manager.
†Ground System Engineer.
‡Program Manager.
§Program Scientist.

GEOS-C	=	Geodynamics Experimental Ocean Satellite
GMT	=	Greenwich Mean Time
GOAP	=	Geosat-A Ocean Applications Program
HDR	=	housekeeping data record
JHU/APL	=	The Johns Hopkins University Applied Physics Laboratory
LSB	=	least significant bit
NASA	=	National Aeronautics and Space Administration
NAVSPASUR	=	Navy Space Surveillance (System)
NDR	=	NORDA data record
NORDA	=	Naval Ocean Research and Development Activity
NRL	=	Naval Research Laboratory
NROSS	=	Navy Remote Ocean Sensing System
NSWC	=	Navy Surface Weapons Center
OIS	=	orbit insertion stage
SAW	=	surface acoustic wave
SDR	=	sensor data record
SSB	=	single sideband
STF	=	satellite tracking facility
TOPEX	=	ocean topography satellite
TTL	=	transistor-transistor logic
TWT	=	traveling wave tube
TWTA	=	traveling wave tube amplifier
VCS	=	velocity control system
WDR	=	waveform data record

Introduction

Background

Conceptually, the radar altimeter is a simple instrument. Essentially a short pulse radar, it measures the distance between the satellite orbit and the subsatellite point on the ocean surface with a precision of a few centimeters. Since the shape of the orbit can be independently measured, this provides a precise measurement of the shape of the ocean's surface along a line under the satellite. Satellite altimetry data have been used to support research in geodesy, bathemetry, mesoscale oceanography, tides, ice topography, winds, and waves.[1,2]

In the absence of disturbing forces, the ocean flows under the influence of gravity until its surface conforms to the shape of the geopotential field of the Earth. The altimeter can then directly measure the marine geoid. This process is disturbed by both time-dependent oceanographic features (e.g., rings and eddies) and time-independent components of ocean circulation (e.g., the Gulf Stream). A long-term average of altimeter data reduces the impact of the "noise" introduced by oceanographic features and produces a "mean surface" that is a good approximation to the marine geoid in many areas (Fig. 1). The direction of the normal to this mean surface, the "local vertical," is an important term in navigation models. Interest by the U.S. Department of Defense in precise navigation has made geodesy the most important application of radar altimeter data.

Time-dependent oceanography, essentially "noise" on the geodesy data, can be recovered from the altimeter data by subtracting the long-term mean surface (Fig. 2). Recent research has indicated that the time-dependent mesoscale (50 to 300 km) features (e.g., rings and eddies) that can be sensed by the altimeter have a strong impact on underwater acoustic propagation. The generation of tactical products for submarine and antisubmarine users will be an important application of altimeter data from future missions.

Finally, the significant wave height and reflection coefficient of the ocean surface can be determined by measuring the leading-edge slope

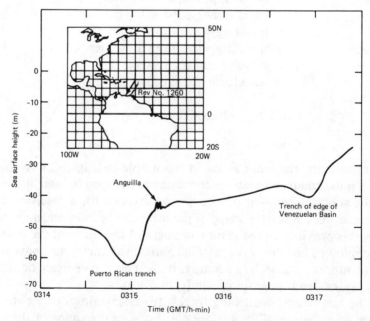

Fig. 1   Ocean topographic features as measured by satellite radar altimetry (Ref. 3).

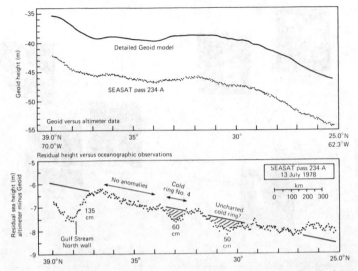

Fig. 2   Seasat altimetry data with corresponding geoid profile (Ref. 1).

and amplitude of the reflected radar pulse. Ground processing allows the surface wind speed to be derived from the reflection coefficient. Since the altimeter measures only a narrow swath along the subtrack, this is a sparse data set used primarily for research applications.

Missions

The in-orbit measurement precision of the altimeter has improved from the 1 m precision accomplished by the Skylab mission to the 10 cm precision realized by Seasat-A (Fig. 3). Unfortunately, Seasat-A data return was limited to 90 days because of a power system failure in the spacecraft.

The Geosat altimeter incorporates a number of design changes that will result in improved measurement precision. Ground testing of the Geosat-A altimeter indicates a precision approaching 5 cm for moderate wave heights.

The Navy Remote Ocean Sensing System (NROSS), the next generation Navy mission, will implement a completely redundant altimeter with approximately the Geosat-A measurement precision. Advances in microminiaturization will allow an instrument of about the same weight and size as the nonredundant Geosat-A instrument.

The Topography Experiment (TOPEX) Satellite, a future NASA mission, will measure altitude using both C- and Ku-band frequencies. The measurements will be combined to achieve 3 cm ranging independent

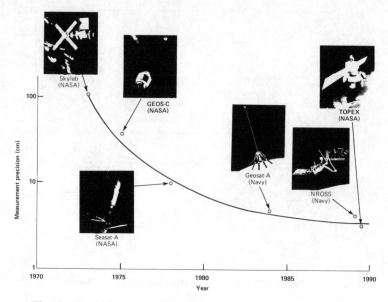

Fig. 3   Evolution of satellite altimetry measurement precision.

of the long-wavelength ionospheric propagation errors that have contaminated basin-wide ocean circulation measurement data taken with
previous altimeters.

The Navy Geosat Mission

The primary mission of Geosat-A is to provide the dense global grid
of altimeter data required for improvements in the Earth's gravitational
models. The secondary mission is the timely detection of mesoscale
oceanographic features.[4]

The mission will employ a single instrument, the radar altimeter, with
3.5 cm precision at 2 m significant wave height. An 800 km altitude,
108 deg inclination orbit will provide 3 day, near-repeat ground tracks.
Dual-frequency Doppler tracking will allow precise orbit determination. Data will be stored on board the spacecraft for approximately
12 hours and then transmitted to the Satellite Tracking Facility at The
Johns Hopkins University Applied Physics Laboratory. The Geosat-A
ground station will preprocess the data for distribution to a variety of
users.

The following sections describe the Geosat-A altimeter, the spacecraft, and the ground system.

Geosat-A Radar Altimeter

The Geosat-A radar altimeter is identical to the Seasat-A altimeter in terms of the mechanical, thermal, and electrical interfaces.[5] Several changes were made, primarily to support an 18 month mission goal. These include use of a 20 W long-life traveling wave tube (TWT) amplifier and, for improved radiation tolerance, an 8085 microprocessor. Other changes include substitutions for parts no longer available and revised firmware tracking algorithms for reduced height noise.

Ocean Return Signal Characteristics

Before describing the altimeter, it is of interest to consider the characteristics of a signal reflected from the ocean surface. These signals strongly influence the altimeter design and impose limits on the precision attainable, given even a perfect instrument. A pulse-limited mode of operation is used, in which the intersection of a spherical shell (representing the locus of points equidistant from the radar) with the ocean's surface defines regions whose lateral extent is small compared

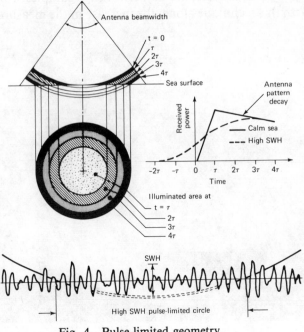

Fig. 4   Pulse-limited geometry.

to that defined by the antenna beamwidth (see Fig. 4). The earliest returns come from wave crests. Reflecting facets deeper into the waves then gradually contribute, accompanied by an increase in the illuminated area, until a point is reached at which the surface of constant range reaches the wave troughs. Beyond this point, the illuminated area remains essentially constant. The signal amplitude would also remain constant, if not for the antenna pattern attenuation that imparts an exponential decay in amplitude. The result is a waveform whose average shape is given by the double convolution of the system point target response, the ocean surface height distribution, and the two-way antenna pattern. The angles involved are much steeper than Fig. 4 suggest (< 1 deg); thus, the effect of Earth curvature and changing geometry have been ignored.

The sharp-rising leading edge of the waveform is the basis for the precise height estimation. The half-power point conforms closely to mean sea level. The instrument tracks the location of this point with respect to the transmitted pulse and this height measurement is telemetered to the ground. The slope of the leading edge directly affects the measurement precision and degrades performance with increasing wave height. Two factors allow this effect to be counteracted. First, if the rise time set by the wave height is greater than the basic pulse resolution of the system, combining adjacent range samples will reduce the noise. With this technique alone, the increase in the measurement noise

Fig. 5   Geosat-A radar altimeter.

is proportional to the square root of the wave height. Second, the geometry is such that the diameter of the illuminated area in the vicinity of the leading edge increases as the square root of the wave height increases. The composite return in each range cell is the result of a vector summation of the reflections from a large number of surface facets. As the spacecraft moves, the phase relationships between the various reflectors change. The larger the diameter of the illuminated area, the less motion required to decorrelate the return, which in turn allows a higher pulse rate for the altimeter.[3] The measurement precision for a given averaging time will improve inversely as the square root of the number of available independent samples. The 1020 Hz pulse rate for Seasat-A (and Geosat-A) was selected as a compromise. A higher rate would reduce height noise slightly, but at the expense of an increase in instrument power requirement.

As part of the overall height and wave height estimation process, the amplitude of the ocean return signal is normalized via an automatic gain control (AGC) loop. Properly calibrated, the AGC setting is a measure of the backscatter coefficient at the surface, which in turn is dependent on wind speed.

In summary, the altimeter provides three basic measurements with precisions specified as

    (1) Altitude: 3.5 cm for 2 m significant wave height.

    (2) Significant wave height: 10% of significant wave height or 0.5 m.

    (3) Wind speed: 1.8 m/s over the range 1 to 18 m/s.

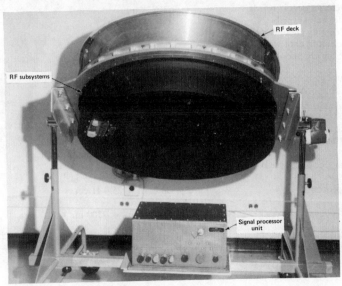

Fig. 6   Geosat-A RF deck.

Table 1   Geosat-A radar altimeter characteristics

Waveform		Antenna	
Type	Linear FM	Type	1 m parabolic dish
Center frequency	13.5 GHz	Gain	> 37.6 dB
Pulse width	102.4 μs	Beam width	2.0 deg
Band width	320 MHz		
Interpulse period	980 μs	Receiver	
		Type	Dual conversion
Transmitter			500 MHz
Type	TWT		(1st i.f.)
Peak power	20 W (min)		0 Hz (2nd
Power consumption			i.f.)
(28 V bus)	70 W		
		AGC	0 to 63 dB in 1 dB steps
Signal Processor			
A/D converters (2)	4 bits plus sign		
Filters (range gates)	63	Inputs	
Equivalent height,		Bus (24 to 33 VDC)	
LSB	0.7325 cm	5 MHz reference	
Adaptive tracker	8085 microprocessor	Commands	
		8 pulse 10 bit data	

		kg	lb
Operation Modes	Weight		
Standby I and II	Signal processor	21.3	(47)
Track (4 modes)	RF section	65.3	(144)
Calibrate	Total	86.6	(191)
Test (7 modes)			

TM outputs: 85 words (10 bit each)
  at 850 bits/s
  16 science words
  63 waveform sample words
  4 mode/status words
  1 engineering channel word
  1 engineering data word (32 engineering channels)

Power, W
  Standby   103
  Track   160

Envelope
  RF section (less antenna)   104.8 dia × 29.2 H cm = 0.251 m³
                              (41.25 × 11.5 in. = 15,369 in.³)
  Antenna (including feed)   104.8 dia × 48.6 H cm = 0.419 m³
                              (41.25 × 19.125 in. = 25,559 in.³)
  Signal processor   50.8 L × 34.3 W × 25.4 H cm =
                                0.044 m³
                              (20 × 13.5 × 10 in. = 2700 in.³)

Altimeter Implementation

The altimeter functions as a 13.5 GHz nadir-looking pulse compression radar. The major characteristics are listed in Table 1. The altimeter is comprised of two major subsystems: an RF section and a signal processor (Fig. 5). The RF section consists of a 2 in. thick honeycomb deck with the various subsystems attached to one surface and a parabolic dish antenna attached to the opposite surface (Fig. 6).

A simplified block diagram of the altimeter is shown in Fig. 7. The system generates a linear FM (chirp) waveform for transmissions by a traveling wave tube amplifier (TWTA). The 2 kW TWTA used on Seasat-A and GEOS-3 gave evidence of not being able to support more than a few thousand hours of operation. Therefore, an existing 20 W TWTA, space qualified and in production for the Landsat program, was selected for use on Geosat-A. Two design changes were made to compensate for the reduction in transmit power from 2 kW to 20 W: (1) the pulse width was increased from 3.2 to 102.4 μs and (2) a lower-noise GaAs field effect transistor (FET) preamplifier was added to improve the noise figure from 9 dB to 5 dB.

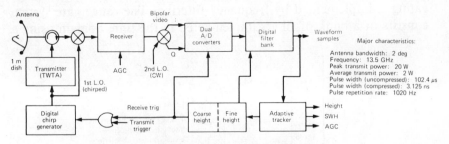

Fig. 7   Geosat-A radar block diagram.

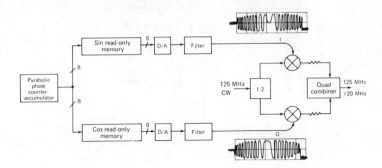

Fig. 8   Digital chirp generator block diagram.

In the Seasat-A altimeter, the basic linear FM waveform was generated in a surface acoustic wave (SAW) filter. The transmitted waveform had a time-bandwidth product of 1024 (3.2 μs × 320 MHz), including a up-converter frequency multiplier of 4. The SAW device parameters were close to the state of the art. To accomodate an increase in pulse width to 102.4 μs (time-bandwidth product of 32,768), a digital chirp generator (DCG) developed previously with NASA support was incorporated. A block diagram of the DCG is shown in Fig. 8. A linear ramp is accumulated to provide a number representative of the signal phase that varies parabolically with time. The sine and cosine of this number are extracted from the contents of a read-only memory and converted to a pair of analog signals that are then applied to a single sideband (SSB) modulator to impart a parabolic phase (linear frequency) modulation on a carrier signal. A subsequent multiply by 8 then results in the desired 320 MHz bandwidth pulse.

The receiver employs dual conversion, with the final conversion to base band for digital processing. Dual analog-to-digital (A/D) converters digitize the in-phase (I) and quadrature (Q) bipolar video outputs from the second mixer.

As a result of the full-deramping process in the first mixer, range gating is implemented by frequency filtering. The range gate system consists of a bank of filters implemented in the time domain using a

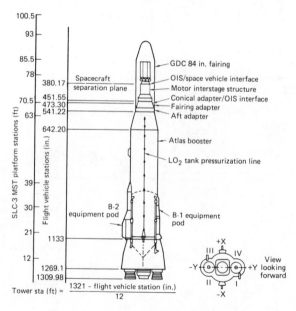

Fig. 9 Launch vehicle configuration.

discrete Fourier transform process. The outputs of 60 contiguous wave-form samples are applied to the adaptive tracker, using a microcomputer processor based on an 8085 microprocessor. The adaptive tracker also controls the altimeter through the various calibrate, track, standby, and test modes in response to commands received via the uplink and formats the altitude and wave height data for telemetry to the ground.

In addition to the changes from the Seasat-A altimeter design already noted, an increase in antenna beamwidth from 1.6 to 2.0 deg is needed to accomodate the 1 deg attitude stabilization provided by the Geosat-A type of gravity gradient system. The change is implemented by increasing the dimensions of the antenna feed, causing a corresponding increase in the amplitude taper across the 1 m dish. The result is an increase in beamwidth and a decrease in the antenna gain from 40 dB to 37.6 dB. This reduces the system margin, but has no effect on measurement precision.

The effect of attitude variations on height, AGC, and (to a lesser extent) wave height measurements has been studied extensively since, in the case of Geosat-A, no on-board sensor is available to provide an attitude readout. Instead, advantage is taken of the effect of attitude variations on waveform sample amplitudes in the trailing-edge region to provide corrections. This is accomplished as part of the sensor data record (SDR) processing during postpass operations on the ground station SEL 32/77 computer. In addition, ground testing procedures now

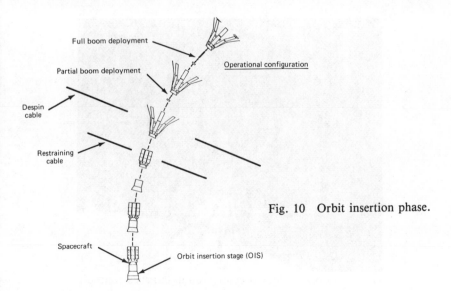

Fig. 10   Orbit insertion phase.

incorporate waveform simulations with attitude errors included, which was not previously done.

Geosat-A Spacecraft

Introduction

GEOSAT-A will be launched in early 1985 by a General Dynamics Corp., Convair Division, Atlas-E launch vehicle and a Fairchild Space Co. mission-unique orbital insertion stage with a Star 27 motor. The launch site is Space Launch Complex 3 at Vandenberg Air Force Base. Figure 9 shows the assembled launch vehicle.

The 1400 lb spacecraft will be placed in a 800 km circular orbit with an inclination of 108 deg. This orbit, having a period of 6045 s, will provide equatorial crossings separated by 18 km after 6 months of data collection.

The on-board spacecraft velocity control system is capable of correcting launch vehicle dispersions within ± 37 km (semimajor axis) and an eccentricity of 0.006. These dispersions are 3σ statistical estimates.

The mission allows for a daily launch opportunity throughout the year. A launch window of 1 h duration has been established to provide a maximum sunlit orbit during the early phases of on-orbit activities.

The spacecraft, spinning at 90 rpm, will be injected into orbit approximately 21 min after liftoff. Spacecraft timers, initialized by separation from the orbit insertion stage (OIS), will activate the yo-yo despin

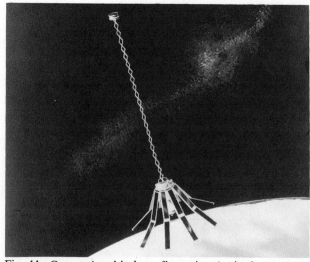

Fig. 11 Geosat-A orbital configuration (artists's concept).

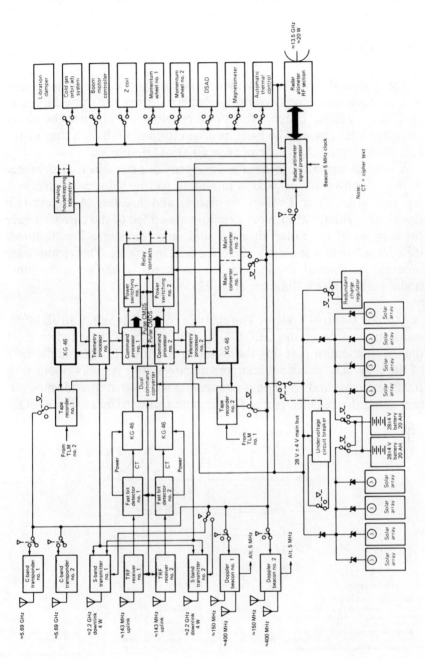

Fig. 12   Geosat-A system block diagram.

system and deploy the solar arrays. Figure 10 shows the spacecraft deployment.

Spacecraft Systems

The spacecraft (Fig. 11) provides the necessary structure, power, thermal, attitude and velocity control, telemetry, command, tape data storage, and tracking beacon functions required to support the radar altimeter instrument. The basic configuration is similar to that of the core structure of the flight-proven GEOS-C design.

A conical structure below the core provides structural attachment of the launch vehicle as well as mounting for the velocity control system fuel tanks, shutoff valves, regulators, and thrusters. A honeycomb shield and cylindrical support structure are added to the core structure for support of the radar altimeter and tape recorders. The altimeter includes redundant telemetry and command interfaces. This redundancy is continued through the spacecraft subsystems, as shown in the functional system block diagram (Fig. 12).

Attitude Control System. The attitude control system, a straightforward application of the GEOS-C system, has been designed to meet the requirement of pointing the altimeter to within 1 deg of nadir 98% of the time. The principal components are a 20 ft scissors boom with 100 lb end mass and redundant momentum wheels that provide momentum along the velocity vector for pitch and yaw stiffness. The GEOS-

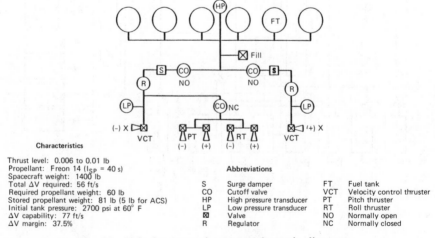

Characteristics
Thrust level: 0.006 to 0.01 lb
Propellant: Freon 14 (I_{SP} = 40 s)
Spacecraft weight: 1400 lb
Total ΔV required: 56 ft/s
Required propellant weight: 60 lb
Stored propellant weight: 81 lb (5 lb for ACS)
Initial tank pressure: 2700 psi at 60° F
ΔV capability: 77 ft/s
ΔV margin: 37.5%

Abbreviations

S	Surge damper	FT	Fuel tank
CO	Cutoff valve	VCT	Velocity control thruster
HP	High pressure transducer	PT	Pitch thruster
LP	Low pressure transducer	RT	Roll thruster
⊠	Valve	NO	Normally open
R	Regulator	NC	Normally closed

Fig. 13 Velocity control system schematic diagram.

C boom design was enhanced by the addition of a gimballed base for correcting unanticipated biases due to mass offsets. Attitude sensing is through the use of solar aspect detectors and a three-axis vector magnetometer.

Velocity Control System. The velocity control system (VCS) is used to correct the orbital insertion errors stated earlier, as well as to reposition the spacecraft for different operational scenarios. Since there were no stringent weight constraints, 84 lb of Freon 14 (the propellant) are stored in six spherical tanks. Each tank is initially pressurized to 2700 psi, which is reduced by pressure regulators to 15 psia at the 0.01 lb thrusters. Two thrusters are located fore and aft along the velocity vector and four additional thrusters are provided to generate pitch and roll torques. These units are operated initially to reduce libration oscillations that result during early gravity-gradient capture and, if necessary, can also be used to dampen oscillations generated by the velocity control thrusters. The system (Fig. 13) can provide a velocity change of 77 ft/s.

Command System. Spacecraft commanding is via a VHF uplink from the JHU/APL ground station. The command system receives, authenticates, and executes commands for spacecraft configuration control on a real-time or delayed basis. The command system is redundant and consists of two linearly polarized antennas mounted on the solar arrays, tuned radio receivers, bit detectors, decryptors, command processors, and one set of power-switching relays using redundant coils and contacts. Command capabilities consist of relay contact closure for power switching (relay commands), pulses to drive relays contained within user packages (pulse commands), and generation of parallel and serial data words to control subsystem internal configurations (data commands). The system supplies 68 relay commands, 28 pulse commands, and 21 data commands.

Telemetry System. The Geosat-A telemetry system consists of a redundant telemetry processor, two S-band transmitters, two tape recorders, and two encryption units. The subsystem receives the digital science data stream from the radar altimeter at 8.5 kilobits/s and combines it with the housekeeping data (1.5 kilobits/s) that are collected from the spacecraft subsystems. The data are formated into a single-time annotated frame and transmitted to the ground station via the S-band link (2207.5 MHz) either in real time or as the dump of 12 hours of stored encrypted data from the Odetics (5×10^8) dual-track tape recorder. The telemetry processor consists of two electrically identical redundant halves sharing a nonredundant housekeeping commutator. the digital circuitry employs complementary metal oxide semiconductor (CMOS) chips with some transistor-transistor logic (TTL), where required by higher speeds or interface requirements.

Doppler System. Spacecraft ephemerides will be derived by tracking the dual-frequency (150/400 MHz) Doppler system transmissions. The Doppler system consists of two spaceborne transmitters and a ground network of tracking stations. The two ultrastable and coherent frequencies are broadcast by the satellite continuously. These signals are received at ground stations that are a part of the Defense Mapping Agency (DMA) complex. The received Doppler signals, along with time data from a precise ground clock, are recorded on magnetic tape and routinely forwarded to DMA for ex post facto spacecraft position determination.

Power System. Spacecraft power is generated by an array of 16 (18 × 60 in.) solar cell panels. Two panels are joined end-to-end on each of the eight faces of the spacecraft body, resulting in an array that is approximately conical. The panels contain 12,032 solar cells wired into 32 individually controlled circuits. In full sunlight and at normal inci-

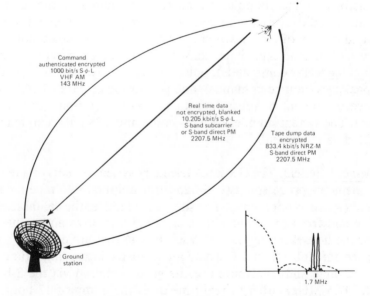

Fig. 14   Geosat-A telecommunication characteristics.

dence, each circuit produces 1.4 A at 35 V. Solar array output varies considerably with the angle of the orbit relative to the sunline and the position of the spacecraft within the orbit. The angle from the orbit normal to the sunline progresses from near 0 to 90 deg and back over a period of 140 days. This progression results in two distinct "seasons" for power generation. Typical spacecraft loading is 7.5 A at 30 V. The orbit average power generation is 230 W.

Energy storage is accomplished by two sealed, 20 A-h nickel-cadmium batteries. Each battery has 22 cells in series for a nominal battery voltage of 28 Vdc.

Redundant battery charge regulators (BCR) sense battery voltage, current, and temperature and regulate the solar array output to limit battery overcharge. The BCRs are microprocessor-based units that can operate in several different modes, depending upon the orbital situation and thermal limitations placed on battery charging. Solar array control is implemented by shorting the surplus solar array current directly to ground by very compact hybrid FET circuits. Heat generation is thus virtually eliminated.

Geosat charge control methods include selectable temperature-dependent voltage limits, current limits, and a coulombmeter that measures battery discharges and activates a selectable trickle charge when an adequate recharge has occurred. Upon an indication that the array

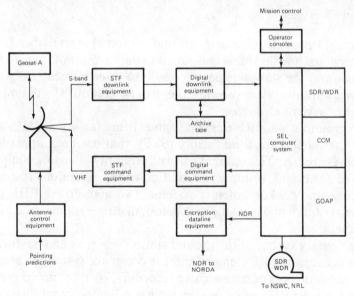

Fig. 15   Ground station overview.

current should be reduced, a solar array circuit is shorted by a FET contained within the BCR. Circuits are shorted sequentially at one circuit per second until the desired battery condition is achieved. As a result of this "digital" approach to charge control, a given voltage or current limit is maintained by using two or more step changes in the battery current. This approach is quite unique in that an average battery voltage or current is maintained rather than, as is typically used, some slow changing dc value.

Geosat-A Ground Station

Geosat-A altimetry data will be acquired by a single JHU/APL ground station that will also archive, process, and distribute the data. The ground station, at a location midway between Washington and Baltimore, will also command and control the spacecraft and monitor its health and status. Because altimetry data transmitted during any pass over the ground station will be unique in terms of ocean surface coverage, there is a program requirement for a 24 hour/day operational station with a high degree of reliability and maintainability. The spacecraft command and health monitoring functions will be free from single-point failures and automation is used to reduce operator error. Store-and-forward techniques are employed extensively to minimize altimetry data loss and facilitate recovery from failures.

Station Overview

Figure 14 provides Geosat-A ground station characteristics for uplink command and downlink real-time and dump transmissions. In terms of hardware, the station is partitioned into three elements. Figure 15 is a hardware overview showing the ground station RF, digital, and computer system elements.

The ground station RF element is an existing facility at JHU/APL, called the satellite tracking facility (STF), that has been upgraded to support Geosat-A. This element consists primarily of analog equipment required for uplink transmission and downlink reception. It includes the prime and backup antenna systems, two high-power VHF transmitters, redundant receiving and demodulating systems, and timing equipment.

The digital element of the ground station serves as an interface and buffer between the RF element and the computer system. It also performs the functions of data archive recording, encryption/decryption, and time-tagging. The digital element has a limited capability to perform command and real-time telemetry monitoring functions in the event of a computer system failure. The digital element includes fully redundant bit synchronizers, decommutators, analog tape recorders, time-management devices, and crypto equipment. Microcomputer controllers play a key role in the digital element as functional devices and for automation purposes.

The ground station computer element supports a number of functions, including spacecraft command, control, and monitoring; data acquisition and processing; and the formating and transmission of data products. The data processor must accommodate numerous I/O demands resulting from real-time processing during satellite passes as well as from postpass processing of the voluminous data set (approximately 450 megabits) presented during the satellite dumps. The computer system also supports peripheral functions such as prepass readiness tests, pass logging, and dump telemetry analysis. The ground station computer has a 32 bit word architecture with real-time capability and high throughput. It consists of an SEL 32/77 minicomputer with associated peripherals, including 300 megabyte disk drives, digital tape units, cathode ray tube (CRT) display consoles, line printers, and high-speed input interfaces.

There are three distinct software packages associated with the ground station computer. Taken together, software operations using these packages will consume most of the 24 hour day.

The command, control, and monitor (CCM) software package consists primarily of real-time satellite support functions performed during passes. The CCM software also supports prepass readiness test functions and postpass data logging and data test operations.

The sensor data record/waveform data record (SDR/WDR) software package is used on a postpass basis to perform altimetry data processing and to produce output data products in the form of computer-compatible tapes (CCT). The SDR (the prime data product) is generated using algorithms derived from the Seasat-A mission and from several recently developed radar altimetry techniques. Major SDR/WDR processing objectives are to remove Geosat-A instrument and spacecraft-related errors from the altimetry data and to time-tag the data accurately. After further processing at the Naval Surface Weapons Center (NSWC), the SDR data are used to provide improvements in the Earth's gravitational models used by submarine launched ballistic missile (SLBM) systems.

The Geosat-A Oceans Application Program (GOAP) software package performs similar functions and produces a data product similar to that of the SDR/WDR software. The difference is that the GOAP data product, called the NORDA data record (NDR), must be quickly generated and transmitted to the Naval Ocean Research and Development Activity (NORDA) over a 9.6 kilobit/s data line. After further processing at NORDA, the NDR data are used to provide timely and accurate environmental information for prediction of oceanographic parameters.

Station Operations

The Geosat-A orbit is such that two to three satellite passes (denoted as a cluster) will occur in view of the ground station approximately 100 min apart. Cluster spacing is approximately 12 hours. The timing of the clusters precesses so that they occur at various hours of the day over the 18 month Geosat-A mission span. There are four to six daily contacts with the satellite. These passes represent the only opportunities to acquire altimetry data, to transmit commands, and to monitor real-time telemetry.

During a dump-supported pass, Geosat-A is commanded to play back data from its on-board tape recorder using the 2207.5 MHz S-band downlink. The recorder typically will contain 450 megabits of encrypted data accumulated during the elapsed 12 hour period since the last cluster dump. Data playback at the 833.4 kilobit/s downlink dump rate requires about 10 min. The 10.205 kilobit/s real-time bit stream generated during the pass is also transmitted on the S-band downlink on a modulated 1.7 MHz subcarrier.

Figure 16 is a detailed system drawing of the Geosat-A ground station. A 60 ft dish is used as the primary downlink (and uplink) antenna system and also receives the composite S-band downlink from Geosat-A. Antenna-pointing control is based on Navy Space Surveillance (NAVSPASUR) orbital predictions provided daily by the NSWC.

The phase-modulated downlink is received and demodulated. The encrypted dump data and the unencrypted real-time data streams are separated by appropriate filters, bit-synchronized, and recorded on separate tracks of an analog tape. Timing information and voice annotation are also recorded on this tape, which becomes a Geosat-A archive tape. The archive tapes, containing the altimetry data in encrypted form, will be stored at APL for an extended time following the mission operational phase.

The 10.205 kilobit/s real-time bit stream is decommutated and the spacecraft clock count extracted and entered into a time-management unit along with the station time. The time-management unit output consists of a series of time-tag messages, each message having a unique

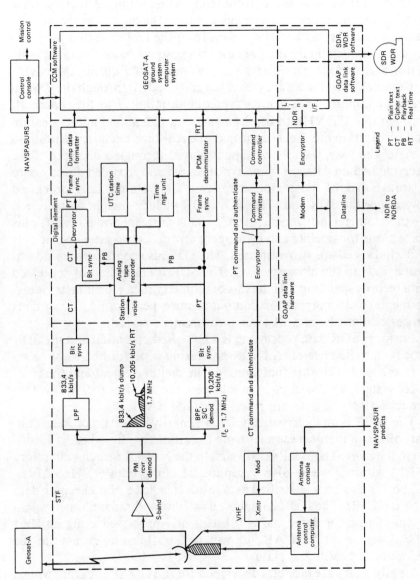

Fig. 16 Geosat-A ground station system diagram.

spacecraft clock count and a concomitant station GMT time. These messages are entered into the ground station computer and used to generate a corrected time-tag for each processed altimetry data frame.

Spacecraft status is also derived from the real-time telemetry stream for display, monitoring, and logging during the pass. The ground system can also display and check data from the real-time dump telemetry data recorded on the archive tape on a postpass basis. Ground station status and control parameters are also monitored during the pass.

Command sequences are generated and checked through the ground station computer and then encrypted and uplinked to the spacecraft through the STF VHF transmitting system. Command authentication and verification are checked through the real-time telemetry downlink.

After the pass, the archive tape is played through a decryptor. The decrypted dump data are frame-synchronized and recorded directly onto a storage disk of the computer system. The data are later processed to produce the SDR and WDR. The SDR includes height as measured by the altimeter instrument, AGC, and significant wave height, plus corrections for satellite and instrument errors. Backscatter coefficients and wind speed are also estimated. The SDR also combines ground station data with the altimetry data. The SDR is comprised of processed data records spanning 1 s intervals of altimetry data (10 altimeter measurements) with corrections computed once per second. It contains processed data from a 24 hour measurement period.

Postpass SDR data processing is a classified operation and the SDR tape is classified Secret. All SDR processing is performed within a secure shielded enclosure that contains the digital element and the computer system. The SDR tapes are delivered to the user (NSWC) within 2 weeks after the data are received at JHU/APL.

The WDR is an unclassified CCT. Primarily, this data product consists of raw waveform samples from the altimeter plus a header identical to the SDR. The WDR is delivered to the Naval Research Laboratory (NRL) within 2 weeks after reception of dump data at JHU/APL.

There is also an unclassified data product called a housekeeping data record (HDR). The HDR contains all satellite and radar altimetry data (excluding height data) and is subsequently processed using an IBM 3033 computer at JHU/APL to provide a postpass assessment of the spacecraft's health and status.

Finally, software modules developed for the GOAP program will be used to process the altimeter data to form the NDR. The NDR results from a processing operation similar to that for the SDR, but optimized for execution time. This data product is also classified Secret and is used for the prediction of oceanographic parameters. As it is being processed, the NDR is transmitted through an encryptor into a 9.6 kilobit/s communications line to the NORDA facility in Bay St. Louis, Miss. The NDR is processed and delivered as soon as possible after the dump data reception. Ordinarily, NDR processing operations precede SDR/WDR processing.

Abnormal spacecraft dumping scenarios may occur, e.g., when data from a missed pass are dumped at a later time. When this happens, additional processing time is required to achieve proper data merging. This can lead to bottlenecks in ground station operations that delay the delivery of the SDR/WDR products by up to 4 weeks. The occurrence of abnormal data dump operations is projected to occur less than 5% of the time.

Acknowledgments

The Navy Geosat-A Mission is sponsored by the Office of Naval Research, R. Gracen Joiner, Program Manager. The secondary oceanographic mission is sponsored by Cmdr. D. McConathy of the Naval Electronic Systems Command (PDE-106).

References

[1] "SEASAT Special Issue I, Geophysical Evaluation," American Geophysical Union, Washington, D.C. (reprinted from *Journal of Geophysical Research,* Vol. 87, No. C5, Apr. 30, 1982).

[2] "SEASAT Special Issue II, Scientific Results," American Geophysical Union, Washington, D.C. (reprinted from *Journal of Geophysical Research,* Vol. 88, No. C3, Feb. 28, 1983).

[3] Townsend, W. F., "An Initial Assessment of the Performance Achieved by the SEASAT-1 Radar Altimeter," NASA Tech. Memo. 73279, Feb. 1980 .

[4] Mitchell, J. L. and Hallock, Z. R., "Plans for Oceanography from the U.S. Navy GEOSAT," Paper presented at Pacific Congress Marine Technology (PACON '84), University of Hawaii, Honolulu, Apr. 1984 .

[5] MacArthur, J. L., "SEASAT-A Radar Altimeter Design Description," The Johns Hopkins University, Applied Physics Laboratory, SDO 5232, Nov. 1978 .

TOPEX—A Spaceborne Ocean Observing System

George H. Born*
The University of Texas at Austin, Austin, Texas
Robert H. Stewart†
Scripps Institution of Oceanography, La Jolla, California
and
*Jet Propulsion Laboratory, California Institute of Technology,
Pasadena, California*
and
Charles A. Yamarone‡
*Jet Propulsion Laboratory, California Institute of Technology,
Pasadena, California*

Abstract

The vastness and inaccessibility of the oceans make difficult the collection of the measurements necessary to develop detailed models of the oceans. Satellite altimetric measurements of surface currents and scatterometer measurements of winds, technologies developed and demonstrated by the National Aeronautics and Space Administration, together with enhanced in situ measurements, can provide a major improvement in our ability to observe the oceans globally and synoptically. Pending government approval, NASA plans to launch the ocean Topography Experiment (Topex) satellite in 1990 to collect a highly accurate 3-5 year set of global altimeter data. In addition to a dual-frequency altimeter, the satellite payload includes a three-frequency radiometer, a laser retroreflector array, a Tranet beacon, and an experimental high-precision radiometric tracking device. In the U.S./French option, currently named Topex/Poseidon, two additional French experimental sensors shall be carried: a solid state altimeter sharing the U.S. altimeter's antenna and Doris, a precision tracking system. Data from the instruments on the satellite will be used to study ocean

*Senior Research Engineer, Center for Space Research.
†Adjunct Professor and Topex Development Flight Project Scientist.
‡Topex Development Flight Project Manager.

currents and will lead to substantial improvement in our understanding of ocean circulation and its fluctuations. In turn, this will lead to significant progress in understanding of global-scale oceanic processes. The Topex data set will be a keystone in the World Climate Research Program, an international program to better understand the interaction between the oceans and atmosphere and the modeling and prediction of their weather and climate.

Introduction

Earth is the blue planet. The oceans ameliorate the climate of our planet, support large fisheries, carry the bulk of our commerce, serve as a playground for shoreside cultures, and influence our lives in many direct and indirect ways. The key to the ocean's influence on life is its general circulation. Currents carry heat from the tropics toward the poles; upwelling currents carry nutrients from depths to the surface layer where they sustain the plankton and the food chain that culminates in the world's great fisheries; strong currents influence shipping; and weaker deep currents disperse wastes dumped into the sea.

Significant progress toward understanding the ocean's circulation has occured over the past few decades. In the years since World War II, oceanographers have developed a good understanding of the fundamentals of the geophysical fluid dynamics that governs the oceanic circulation. At the same time, the development of large fast computers has allowed the theory of fluid flow to be incorporated into numerical models able to describe the dynamics of entire ocean basins. This provides a framework into which can be placed oceanic data.

The development of means to observe the oceans has progressed in parallel with the development of the theoretical framework. The development includes satellite-borne altimeters and scatterometers able to measure surface currents and winds from space; moored arrays of instruments able to measure subsurface currents and temperature for several years; satellite-tracked drifting buoys able to follow parcels of water; acoustic tomography for measuring velocity, currents, and temperature at various depths over oceanic areas a thousand or more kilometers on a side; and sensitive techniques for measuring trace elements carried along by the deep circulation of the oceans. The combination of satellite and in situ observations will soon make possible a network to monitor the three-dimensional circulation of the ocean over a period of years.

Taking advantage of the advances in theory, computers, and instrumentation, the oceanographic community has begun plannning a program to understand the general circulation of the oceans and its interactions with the atmosphere. Knowledge of the permanent and time-variable component of the ocean circulation gained from this program would help provide answers to a number of questions being asked by society, including:

1) What is the role of the ocean in determining our present global climate and its fluctuations? The rate at which the oceans will absorb the increasing amount of CO_2 being emitted into the atmosphere and an understanding of the atmosphere/ocean interaction during the El Nino/southern oscillation phenomena are topics of particular interest.

2) What is the trajectory and ultimate fate over long times of wastes in the ocean, especially radioactive wastes?

3) What factors control and modulate the oceanic upwelling[1] that supports the world's fisheries?

Satellite Altimetry

By measuring the height of the sea surface and its variations in time and space, satellite altimeters are able to map geostrophic currents at the sea surface from space every few days. An altimeter measures the range from the satellite to the sea surface by determining the time for a radio pulse to travel from the altimeter to the sea surface and back. Such measurements, when combined with the orbit height obtained by tracking the satellite, make possible the determination of the topography or shape of the ocean surface. The shape of the ocean surface, which deviates at some points by as much as 100 m from the best-fitting reference ellipsoid, closely approximates an equipotential surface referred to as the marine geoid.

The small deviations (<1 m) of the ocean surface from the marine geoid are caused primarily by geostrophic currents and tides. Generally speaking, water movements having spatial scales greater than about 30 km (the Rossby radius of deformation) and time scales longer than about a day are in quasigeostrophic balance to a good first approximation. This means that, to lowest order, the velocity field is such that the Coriolis force is balanced by the pressure field. Water movement tends to be along, rather then down, the pressure contours, just as winds in the atmosphere circulate around highs and lows. The pressure field in the ocean manifests itself as a slope of the constant-density surfaces in the sea relative to level (equipotential) surfaces apart from the tides. The slope of the sea surface is a direct result of that part of the surface flowfield which is geostrophic. As an example, the slope of the ocean surface relative to the geoid can be as large as 10^{-5} across the Gulf Stream and as small as 10^{-7} across ocean basins. Measurement of these slopes would thus provide direct observation of the major component of large-scale oceanic flow.[2]

Altimeter range measurements can also be made over land and ice, providing topographic profiles and the location of ice edges. In addition, the altimeter measures wave height and surface wind speed from the shape and amplitude of the reflected pulse with an accuracy comparable with that obtained from in situ instruments.

Satellite altimeters have improved during their brief ten-year history from the 1 m precision of Skylab to 30 cm for GEOS-3 and a subsequent 5 cm precision for Seasat. The GEOS-3 and Seasat missions demonstrated the potential of satellite altimetry for geodetic studies and data from the satellites have substantially improved our knowledge of the marine geoid. Seasat, with its much improved altimeter and more accurate orbit, demonstrated the ability of altimetric satellites to study mesoscale variability of surface geostrophic currents (Fig. 1) and has provided impressive evidence of the potential ability of satellite altimeters to improve our understanding of the permanent ocean circulation (Fig. 2).

The usefulness of satellite altimetry has been noted by many countries. The European Space Agency, Japan, France, and the United States all have plans to launch Seasat-class altimeters. The similarity between the U.S. and the French programs and goals for satellite altimetry has lead the respective agencies (the National Aeronautics and Space Administration and the Centre Nationale d'Etudes Spatiales) to study the possibility of combining NASA'S Ocean Topography Experiment Topex with CNES's Poseidon Project.

The Topex/Poseidon Mission

The goals of the combined Topex/Poseidon mission are to increase our understanding of ocean dynamics by making precise and accurate observations of the oceanic topography for a period of 3 years and to lay the foundation for a continuing program to provide long-term observations of oceanic circulation and its variability.

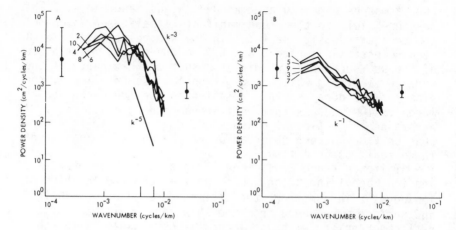

Fig. 1 Spectra of the sea surface height variability obtained
from Seasat altimeter height data in a) high-energy areas (near
major currents) and b) low-energy areas. The 10 labeled curves
are from different areas in the world's oceans, the error bars
are 95% confidence limits (left error bar in each figure is for
wavelengths greater than 250 km). The two large tick marks on
the wave number axis indicate the wavelengths of 150 and 250 km,
respectively. These spectra show that altimeter data provides
information on the statistics of mesoscale variability that can
be used by models of ocean circulation (from Ref. 4).

To provide these observations, the Topex/Poseidon
satellite will carry a dual-frequency altimeter to measure
the height of the satellite with a precision of $\pm$ 2.0 cm
(Tables 1 and 2). The height measured at frequencies of
13.6 GHz (the primary measurement) and 5.3 GHz provide a
first-order correction for the pulse delay in the
ionosphere. A three-frequency radiometer observing at 18,
21, and 37 GHz will provide a correction for the pulse
delay due to water vapor in the troposphere.

The satellite will also carry a solid-state French
altimeter that will share the antenna with the
dual-frequency altimeter. To avoid interference, the
French altimeter will be operated 5% of the time, for 1 day
out of 20, while the other altimeter is turned off.

The satellite will carry a primary and two secondary
tracking systems so that the geocentric height of the
satellite can be calculated at any point in the orbit with
an accuracy of 14 cm. The primary system uses an
ultrastable quartz oscillator to control a Doppler beacon
on the satellite. The signal from the beacon will be
tracked by the Defense Mapping Agency's Tranet system; and
data from the system will be analyzed by groups at the NASA

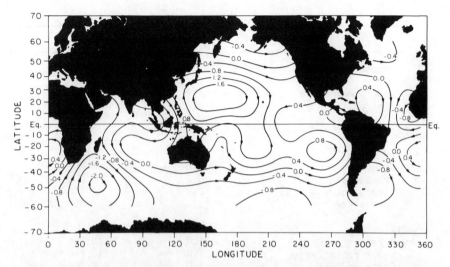

Fig. 2a Dynamic topography of the oceans determined   by a
spherical harmonic expansion complete to degree and order   six of
the difference between Seasat altimeter height measurements and
the best available long wavelength geoid from the Goddard Space
Flight Center.

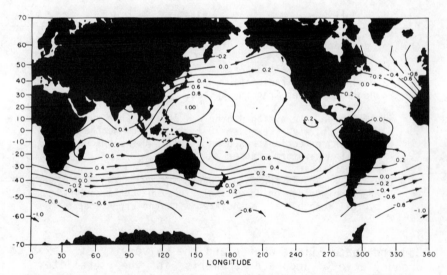

Fig. 2b Equivalent expansion of dynamic topography based on
hydrographic data and published by S. Levitus.   while there are
obvious differences in Figs. 2a and 2b (for which there are
plausible   explanations),   their   striking   similarity   is
tantalizing evidence of the potential of a mission such as Topex.
(Both Figs. 2a and 2b are from Ref. 5.)

Table 1   Topex height measurement error budget

Error source[a]	Uncertainty, cm (1σ)	Decorrelation distance,[b] km
Altimeter		
Instrument noise	2.0	20
Bias drift	2.0	(Many days)
Media		
EM Bias	2.0	200-1000
Skewness	1.0	200-1000
Troposphere, dry	0.7	1000
Troposphere, wet	1.2	100
Ionosphere	1.3	50
Orbit		
Atmospheric drag	1.0	>10,000
Solar radiation	1.0	10,000
Earth radiation	<1.0	10,000
GM	2.0	10,000
Gravity	10.0	10,000
Earth and ocean tides	1.0	10,000
Station and spacecraft clock	1.0	10,000
Troposhere	1.0	10,000
Station Location	5.0	10,000
Higher-order ionosphere	5.0	10,000
RSS absolute error	13.3	

Major assumptions

1) Dual-frequency altimeter
2) Dual-frequency radiometer
3) Upgraded Tranet Tracking System, 40 stations
4) Altimeter data averaged over 3 s
5) $H_{1/3}$ = 2m, wave skewness = 0.1
6) Tabular corrections based on limited waveform-tracker comparisons
7) ~1300 km altitude
8) No anomalous data, no rain
9) Improved gravity model
10) $\pm$ 3 mbar surface pressure from weather charts
11) 100 μs spacecraft clock

[a] Dominant errors in the determination of the ocean height above a reference surface using a single Topex height measurement.
[b] A typical length scale associated with the error source.

Goddard Space Flight Center and the University of Texas to produce a very accurate ephemeris for the satellite. A secondary system consists of a French Doris receiver on the satellite receiving signals from 30-40 fixed beacons on the ground. Another secondary system will probably use a receiver to extract pseudoranges from the transmissions of the global positioning system (GPS) Satellites. Pseudorange from four or more GPS spacecraft can be

Table 2 Topex/Poseidon instruments

Altimeters

System	Frequency, GHz	Radiated power, W	PRF	Pulse compression ratio	Accuracy, cm (integration time, s)
Topex	13.6	20	4000	33,000	2.4a (3)
	5.3	20	1000	33,000	3.1 (3)
Poseidon	13.65	2	1700	33,000	10b (1)

Microwave radiometer

Frequency, GHz	Field of view, km (half-power beamwidth, deg)	Noise equivalent T, K	Averaging time, s
18.0	50.86 (1.81)	0.11	1
21.0	39.76 (1.49)	0.11	1
37.0	27.37 (0.92)	0.15	1

Tracking systems

System	Frequency, MHz	Ground stations	Ephemeris accuracy, cm
Tranet II	150 400	30 - 40	13
Dorisc	401.2 2036	30 - 40	10 - 20
GPSc	1227.6 1575.4	6 - 8	3 - 6
Laser	Light	2	Not applicabled

[a] After correction for ionospheric delay, $H_{1/3}$ = 2 m, wave skewness = 0.1.
[b] Without correction for ionospheric delay.
[c] Experimental systems not yet tested or flown in space.
[d] Laser data will be used for orbit determination on an as-available basis.

combined to determine the position and clock bias of a receiver on the Topex/Poseidon satellite. If pseudoranges to a ground receiver and a receiver onboard the satellite are measured simultaneously from two GPS spacecraft, these range measurements can be doubly differenced, thereby eliminating all clock errors. By using double differenced range measurements from the anticipated 18 satellite operational GPS constellation and 7 or 8 ground stations, it should be possible to determine global orbits for Topex to subdecimeter accuracy.

Because the ionosphere influences all of the tracking signals, each tracking system will use two radio frequencies to provide a first-order correction for this error.

An array of laser retroreflectors will be carried on the satellite, probably circling the altimeter antenna, to allow the height of the satellite to be measured independently by lasers at two calibration sites. One site is to be operated by NASA at Bermuda and the other to be operated by CNES at Dakar. The laser measurements will be used to verify and calibrate the altimeter height measurement. The laser site will be tied by survey to local mean sea level; tide gages around the site will measure local variations in sea level at the time of satellite overflight. The satellite will directly overfly the laser, thereby allowing an independent measurement of the satellite height. In addition, one or two buoys will be located offshore along the satellite ground track in order to verify the altimeter's measurement of wave height and wind speed.

The accuracy of the satellite's ephemeris will be determined locally at the laser sites as well as globally. The laser systems will operate as part of a global geodetic network and their positions will be accurately known in geocentric coordinates. Hence, the laser measurements of range to the satellite also give the geocentric height of the satellite above the laser. The global tests of orbital accuracy will use the altimeter measurements of the height of the sea level calculated at crossovers of the subsatellite track. If the time between crossovers is less than, say, 3 days, then the ocean is fixed and any variation in height between crossovers must be due to orbital errors. In a similar way, differences in orbital heights along overlapping areas used to calculate the ephemeris also yield estimates of orbital errors. Both techniques will provide continuous bounds on the accuracy of the satellite's measurements of oceanic topography over the duration of the mission.

Satellite

In order to minimize costs, NASA through its lead center for Topex, the Jet Propulsion Laboratory has investigated the feasibility of using existing satellite buses for the Topex/Poseidon mission. Work during several years of phase A and prephase B studies indicated that existing designs could be used; and in March 1984 satellite definition studies contracts were won by Rockwell International, Fairchild Space Company, and RCA Astro-Electronics. One of the three candidate satellites will be used for Topex/Poseidon.

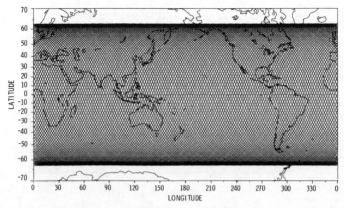

Fig. 3 Ground track traced out by Topex during one 10 day repeat cycle.

The Orbit

Current plans are to place the Topex satellite in a circular orbit inclined at 63.4 deg to the equator at an altitude of 1334 km. This nominal orbit was chosen because: 1) it avoids aliasing tidal signals into annual and semiannual frequencies; 2) the inclination is such that the orbit covers the southern limit of the Drake Passage and still provides reasonable crossing angles between ascending and descending orbital arcs for the recovery of both zonal and meridional components of topography; and 3) the altitude is high enough to mitigate the effects of atmospheric drag and gravitational perturbations on the orbit, thereby allowing a more accurate determination of the orbital height. The orbit will be controlled so that its ground track exactly repeats (to within $\pm$ 1 km) every 127 revolutions or about 10 days resulting in spacing between equatorial tracks of 315 km (Fig. 3). The repeat period was chosen as a compromise between the desire to obtain both high temporal and high spatial resolution.

One of the major challenges facing the Topex Mission will be the determination of the ephemeris of the satellite. As seen from Table 1, uncertainty in knowledge of the height of the orbit is the major contributor to the error budget. During the Seasat program, impressive progress was made in the ability to reconstruct the satellite trajectory using laser and radiometric tracking data (Fig. 4). However, considerable improvement in knowledge of the longer wavelength (>1000 km) components of the Earth's gravity field is necessary in order to reconstruct the Topex radial ephemeris to the required

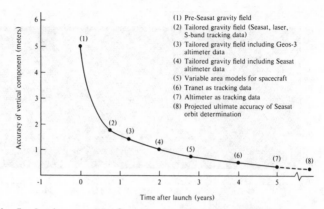

Fig. 4 Evolution of Seasat orbit determination accuracy. Following the launch of Seasat, significant increases in orbit determination accuracy resulted from the development of and subsequent improvements to a gravity model tailored for the Seasat orbit. Current orbit determination accuracy for Seasat (40 cm) is not far from that required for Topex and the timely development of the necessary models and methodology to achieve the Topex objectives appears feasible (from Ref. 6).

accuracy. A four-year program was started in 1984 by both NASA and European investigators to improve our knowledge of the gravity field at spacecraft altitude by at least a factor of two over the current best unclassified models. This field will be derived by using much more of the available satellite tracking data than have previously been used for gravity recovery.

The improved gravity field, together with global tracking by the Tranet system, will allow the satellite's orbit to be determined with decimeter accuracy. If still better gravity fields become available later, the tracking data can be reanalyzed to produce even better orbits.

Data

The Topex/Poseidon mission will produce both environmental and research data. Environmental data from the NASA altimeter will be supplied to Navy's Fleet Numerical Oceanographic Center within 4 h of receipt and will include wind magnitude and measurements of wave height. The primary data for research will be height data corrected for instrument, atmosphere, and surface effects, as well as measurements of wave height and wind magnitude. Additional information to be supplied on the science data record includes the precise position of the spacecraft and the geoidal and tidal height at the satellite nadir point based on the best available models, plus all corrections applied to the satellite data.

The first six months after launch will be used to assess the performance of the satellite and ground processing systems and to verify the accuracy of the satellite measurements. To ensure that data will be available to scientists and to the Navy soon after launch, the Topex/Poseidon data system will include a dedicated central processing system that will be in place and operational six months before launch.

Routine production of science data will begin about six months after launch. Data from the NASA instruments will be processed and distributed by NASA and data from the French instruments will be processed and distributed by CNES. Data from each country will be placed in national archives and will be exchanged between the countries. The U.S. archive will be either the ocean data system at the Jet Propulsion Laboratory or the National Environmental Satellite Data Information Service of the National Oceanic and Atmospheric Administration. The French archive is still being discussed and may be either at the Toulouse Space Laboratory of CNES or at the Centre Oceanologique de Bretagne at Brest.

The primary data for scientific studies will be altimeter data over nearly all the world's oceanic areas for a period of 3 years. However, the spacecraft will carry sufficient expendables to allow an additional 2 years of operation. The Topex data set will be augmented with the necessary ancillary and corrective data to allow scientists to compute global sea surface topography maps accurate to about 14 cm at intervals of the satellite ground track repeat period (nominally 10 days). Differences of these maps will reveal the time-varying component of ocean circulation. The 3-5 year data set will provide 100-200 of these maps, which can then be averaged to provide a multiyear mean sea surface accurate to a few centimeters. Differences of this mean surface from the marine geoid will yield a global map of mean geostrophic flow. While the production of maps of global mean geostrphic flow requires a geoid with greater accuracy than is currently available except at wavelengths greater than about 10,000 km, maps of the time-varying circulation are independent of the geoid and could be produced immediately from Topex/Poseidon data. Because the ocean varies on all length and time scales, the quantification of its variability in a statistical sense is important to the development of ocean circulation models.

At first, mean circulation will be studied at long wavelengths and on a regional basis in areas where high-precision geoids exist. Shipboard gravity surveys can be carried out before, during and after the Topex mission to increase the number of local geoids suitable for mean circulation studies. However, solution of the general problem of global mean circulation requires a global geoid with an accuracy of 2-5 cm on length scales of a few hundred kilometers to the size of the ocean basins. The short and intermediate wavelength portion of such a geoid could be measured by the geopotential research mission that NASA hopes to begin in the early 1990s.[3] Satellite tracking data and surface gravity data currently available have the potential to improve the long-wavelength components of the geoid to useful accuracy for studies of the mean (permanent) circulation.

Ancillary Program

Satellite measurements of surface topography are not adequate for determining the deeper circulation. Hence, Topex/Poseidon measurements must be supplemented by subsurface measurements, the most important being measurements of subsurface density from shipboard hydrographic measurements, midlevel and deep curents measured by drifting buoys, and the deep circulation inferred from shipboard measurements of the distribution of trace elements in the deep ocean. These larger-scale measurements can be supplemented in a few areas of special

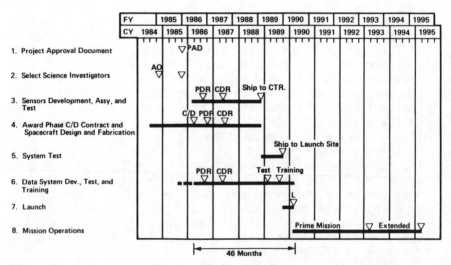

Fig. 5 Topex project schedule.

interest by in situ measurements from moored current meters, pressure and tide gages, and other specialized instruments. These regional areas could be such places as the Straits of Florida or the Drake Passage where local information would make a direct and immediate contribution to a knowledge of larger circulation scales.

Clearly, an in situ program on a scale needed to supplement the satellite measurements will require international cooperation and participation. The worldwide meteorological and oceanographic community, under the auspices of the International Council of Scientific Unions, the United Nations Educational, Scientific and Cultural Organization, and the World Meteorological Organization has begun a World Climate Research Program (WCRP). The major oceanographic elements of WCRP include the world ocean circulation experiment (WOCE), the tropical oceans/global atmospheres experiment (TOGA), and a global ocean monitoring program for repeated measurements of the internal structure of the ocean in critical regions. Overall, WCRP is equivalent in scope to the Global Weather Experiment of 1979-80. The Topex Program will be closely coordinated with WOCE and TOGA and will provide a critical source of data for WOCE. Topex in turn will benefit from the extensive in situ observations planned for these experiments.

The general circulation of the ocean is known to be forced by winds and by air-sea transfer of heat and fresh water. In order to understand the details of this forcing as well as to test our ability to compute circulation from the forcing by winds, synoptic global windfields will be required. The only feasible way to obtain these is with a satellite-borne windfield scatterometer. This instrument, which was proved on Seasat, will be carried by the U. S. Navy's N-ROSS satellite planned for launch in 1989. The combination of 2 cm precision altimetry from Topex and global synoptic wind measurements provide by N-ROSS will allow oceanographers to test hypotheses of the linkage between ocean circulation and winds.

Present Status

Topex is managed by the Jet Propulsion Laboratory for NASA and Poseidon is managed by the Toulouse Space Center for CNES. Pending governmental approval, which is expected in 1985, the satellite should be ready for launch in October 1990.

Figure 5 presents a top-level program schedule indicating major project events.

A number of organizations within the U.S. will make substantial contributions to the program. The Goddard Space Flight Center has a substantial role in Topex and is responsible for supplying the two-frequency altimeter and precise orbits for distribution with the altimeter data. The altimeter will be built by the Applied Physics Laboratory at The Johns Hopkins University. The Center for Space Research at the University of Texas at Austin will participate in and will be responsible for certain activities associated with verifying the accuracy of geophysical data products and precise orbits. Present plans call for the Defense Mapping Agency to provide globally distributed Tranet tracking data, the Fleet Numerical Oceanographic Center to provide atmospheric pressure, temperature, and water vapor fields, and for the National Oceanic and Atmospheric Administration to provide the necessary in-water observation data to verify the altimeter geophysical data products--height, wave height, and wind speed.

Within France, the Group de Recherches en Geodesie Spatiale will contribute to the analysis of Doris data and the computation of accurate orbits, the Office de la Recherche Scientific et Technique d'Outre-Mer and the Centre National pour L'Exploitation des Oceans will provide surface observations and information useful for calibrating the satellite observations and the interpretation of the data.

An announcement of opportunity soliciting proposals for scientific research based on Topex/Poseidon data will be issued jointly by NASA and CNES in 1985.

Conclusion

The Topex satellite proposed for launch in 1990 will provide global over-ocean altimeter data with the potential to determine ocean topography accurate to a few centimeters. Topex data will be used in concert with meteorological data from other satellites and in situ data gathered as part of the World Climate Research Program.

This international program has as its goal better understanding of the interaction between the oceans and atmosphere and the modeling and prediction of their weather and climate. The Topex data set will be a keystone in this effort to more completely understand critical elements of man's environment.

Acknowledgment

The research described in this paper was carried out by the Jet Propulsion Laboratory, California Institute of

Technology, under a contract with the National Aeronautics and Space Administration.

References

[1]"Global Observations and Understanding of the General Circulation of the Oceans", National Academy of Sciences and National Research Council Board of Ocean Science and Policy, 1984.

[2]"Satellite Altimetric Measurements of the Ocean", Report of the Topex Science Working Group, Jet Propulsion Laboratory, Pasadena Calif. Pub. 81-4, pp. 78, March 1981.

[3]Taylor, P. T., Keating, T., Kahn, W. D., Langel, R. A., Smith, D. E., and Schnetzler, C. C., "GRM: Observing the Terrestrial Gravity and Magnetic Fields in the 1990's," EOS, Transactions of the American Geophysical Union, Vol. 64, No. 43, October 25, 1983.

[4]Fu, L. L., "On the Wave Number Spectrum of Mesoscale Variability Observed by the Seasat Altimeter," Journal of Geophysical Research, Vol. 88, No. C7, 1983, pp. 4331-4342.

[5]Tai, C. K. and Wunsch, C., "An Estimate of Global Absolute Dynamic Topography," Journal of Physical Oceanography, Vol. 14, 1984, pp. 457-463.

[6]"Ocean Topography Experiment (Topex) - Mission Description," Jet Propulsion Laboratory, Pasadena, Calif., Internal Doc. D-601-A, July 1983.

Several survey articles have recently appeared that have extensive bibliographies and describe progress made in the application of altimetry to geodetic and oceanographic problems:

1) Marsh, J. G., "Satellite Altimetry," Reviews of Geophysics and Space Physics, Vol. 21, No. 3, April 1983, pp. 1216-1230.

2) Brown, O. and Cheney, R. E., "Advances in Satellite Oceanography," Reviews of Geophysics and Space Physics, Vol. 21, No. 3, April 1983, pp. 1216-1230.

3) Fu, L. L., "Recent Progress in the Application of Satellite Altimetry to Observing the Mesoscale Variability and General Circulation of the Oceans," Reviews of Geophysics and Space Physics, Vol. 22, Nov. 1983, pp. 1657-1660.

In addition, a special issue of Marine Geodesy has been dedicated to satellite altimetry (Vol. 8, No. 1-4, April 1984).

Chapter V. International Remote Sensing Space Programs

The Operational Meteosat Program

Claude Honvault*

European Space Agency, Paris, France

Abstract

Meteosat is the longest running project of the European Space Agency's Earth Observation Programs. In 1972, eight member states of the European Space Research Organization decided to embark upon a program for the development of preoperational meteorological satellites (Meteosat) and entrusted its execution to the organization that later became the European Space Agency (ESA). Subsequently, ESA was charged with the in-orbit operation of the spacecraft, of which two models (F1 and F2) were successfully launched in 1977 and 1981. Nevertheless, the intention remained to establish a community that would be responsible for setting up a system of operational meteorological spacecraft derived from the original Meteosat. The aim was achieved, with the signature in Geneva on May 24, 1983, of a convention creating an international organization known as EUMETSAT, whose main purpose is to establish, maintain, and operate systems of operational meteorological satellites, the initial one being the continuation of the Meteosat preoperational program. The convention was signed by 12 countries on that date; two others signed later and signatures by additional countries is expected. EUMETSAT will rely on ESA to carry out the program. The Meteosat Operational Program foresees the launch of three satellites in August 1987, mid-1988, and 1990 and their subsequent exploitation until 1995. It fulfils the five missions described in this paper.

*Head of Meteosat Operational Program.

The Meteosat System

Two segments make up the Meteosat system, as outlined below.

Space Segment

The satellites are put into geostationary transfer orbit (200–36 000 km) by the Ariane launcher (except for the first model F1 launched by Thor Delta) from the Guiana Space Center in Kourou. The MAGE-type solid-propellant apogee boost motor (ABM), built by Société Européenne de Propulsion (SEP), then injects the satellite into geosynchronous orbit. The position of Meteosat in this orbit is 0° longitude, with a maximum inclination of 0.8 deg. The satellite is shown in Fig. 1.

F1 operated successfully from November 1977 to November 1979, at which point a failure in the power subsystem shut down the radiometer. Only the operations of the data collection mission have continued since that time.

F2 reached its 3 yr nominal lifetime in June 1984 and continues to operate satisfactorily, except for the data collection mission that failed just after launch.

The construction of the Meteosat satellites has been entrusted to a European industrial consortium under the prime contractorship of Aérospatiale, most of whose members

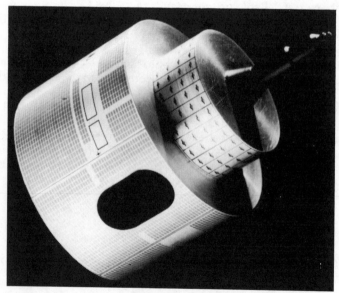

Fig. 1 Meteosat satellite.

have already taken part in the development of the two pre-operational satellites currently in orbit. The co-contractors are ANT (FRG) for the telecommunications transponder, MBB (FRG) for the structure and the electrical ground support equipment, ETCA (Belgium) for the power supply subsystem, MATRA (France) for the radiometer, SELENIA (Italy) for the synchronization and image channel electronic equipment, the Housekeeping (HK) components, and the antennas, IGG (United Kingdom) as the procurement agent for the components, and MSDS (United Kingdom) for the **altitude** measurement and the attitude and orbit control subsystems.

Ground Segment

The ground segment of Meteosat is composed of a data acquisition, tracking, and telecommand station (DATTS) located in Michelstadt, FRG. This station was integrated by MBB and is to be refurbished prior to the launch of the first operational satellite in 1987. The station is 40 km away from its associated equipment for the control of the satellite and the processing of the radiometer data, using Siemens computers (see Fig. 2).

The Earth Imaging Mission

The radiance of the Earth's surface and of its cloud cover are detected simultaneously in three spectral bands:
1)The visible (VIS) image in the 0.5-0.9 μm region of the spectrum is made up of 5000 lines, each containing 5000

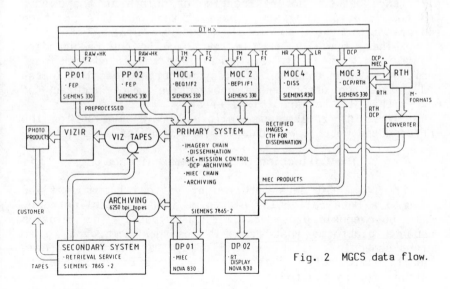

Fig. 2 MGCS data flow.

picture elements. The resolution at the subsatellite point is 2.5 km. The signal-to-noise ratio will be greater than 200 for 80% albedo.

2)The thermal infrared (i.r.) image covers the 10.5-12.5 μm region of the spectrum. It comprises 2500 lines, each containing 2500 picture elements. The resolution at the subsatellite point is 5 km. The performance, given as NEΔT, will be better than 0.65 K for a blackbody at 290 K.

3)The water vapor (WV) absorption band image is in the 5.7-7.1 μm region of the spectrum. It consists of 2500 lines, each containing 2500 picture elements. The resolution at the subsatellite point is 5 km. The performance given as NEΔT will be better than 1 K for a blackbody at 260 K.

For each spectral channel, the radiometric information is encoded into 256 grey levels.

The Dissemination Mission

Preprocessed images and other meteorological data are relayed to user stations. The transmissions are made in both digital and analog formats (WEFAX pictures).

The processing of images is performed in two stages, preprocessing and image processing proper. Preprocessing consists of demultiplexing the data stream and compensation for the radiometer and imaging chain imperfections, including amplitude equalization of both visible channels. The processing of images provides:

1)The computation of a deformation model to specify the difference between actual location of points in the images and the location they would have if the satellite position and orientation were absolutely fixed and ideal.

2)The conversion of the raw image to one of standard aspect, i.e., as if it were taken from the fixed and ideal position with an absolute accuracy of better than two infra-red pixels rms error and a consecutive image accuracy of better than 0.5 infrared pixel error.

3)Absolute radiometric calibration information for the infrared and water vapor channels provided for every image.

The Collection of Environmental Data

Environmental data gathered by various types of fixed and mobile data collection platforms (DCP) are collected by up to 66 channels provided for this purpose. This mission supports platforms that transmit messages according to an agreed schedule (self-timed platforms), as well as platforms that transmit only in response to specific environmental criteria (alert platforms).

The Extraction of Meteorological Products

The actual extraction of products is performed automatically for the region within at least a 50 deg great circle arc (up to 55 deg) from the subsatellite point. Before the data are distributed, they are "quality controlled" by experienced meteorologists. Products have a 32 x 32 i.r. pixel resolution, except for the cloud top height charts, which have a 4 x 4 i.r. pixel resolution. The products include:

1)Cloud motion vectors (CMV): extracted twice per day at 0000 and 1200 UT and distributed by 0230 and 1430 UT. Around 600 vectors per run are produced with a target accuracy ranging from 5 m/s rms for low level to 10 m/s for high level CMVs.

2)Sea surface temperatures (SST): extracted daily at 1200 UT and based on a 3 h composite, distributed by 1430 UT. Eight hundred pieces of data are processed per day with a target accuracy of $\Delta T < 1.5°C$ rms.

3)Cloud analysis (CA): provides cloud cover in up to three layers together with cloud top temperature. Extraction occurs at 0000 and 1200 UT and is distributed by 0230 and 1430 UT, respectively.

4)Upper tropospheric humidity (UTH): provides average relative humidity between 700 and 300 mb in line with the WV channel contribution function. Extraction occurs at 1000 and 1200 UT and is distributed by 0230 and 1430 UT. The target accuracy is $\Delta R < 20\%$ rms relative humidity.

5)Cloud top height (CTH): provides in image form a WEFAX map of cloud tops in 1500 m intervals between 4.5 and 12 km. Extraction is done at 0300, 0900, 1500, 1200 UT and disseminated within 1 h via Meteosat.

CMV, SST, CA, and UTH are encoded into WMO SATOB Bulletins and injected into the Global Telecommunications System (GTS) via the Offenbach Regional Telecommunications Hub (DWD). The CTH maps are broadcast as WEFAX pictures via the satellite.

The Archiving of Digital Data and Image Negatives

All available images are regularly archived in digital form with the extracted meteorological products (except the CTH maps). Two slots of images per day are archived on photographic film. A comprehensive catalog will be maintained to cover all archived data.

The Meteosat Satellite

The basic design of the operational satellite will be that of the Meteosat F2 with two major improvements to the mission capability:

1)The mission performance transponder provides eight additional channels (2400 bits/s) for meteorological data dissemination.

2)The water vapor absorption channel (5.7-7.1 μm) is available in parallel with visible and infrared channels.

A number of minor modifications based on the F1 and F2 experience and on technology improvement are incorporated, leading, inter alia, to an increased reliability.

Meteosat is composed of two cylindrical bodies concentrically stacked. The initial weight of the satellite is 320 kg, including 39 kg of propellant (hydrazine). The overall height is 3.20 m and the diameter 2.1 m.

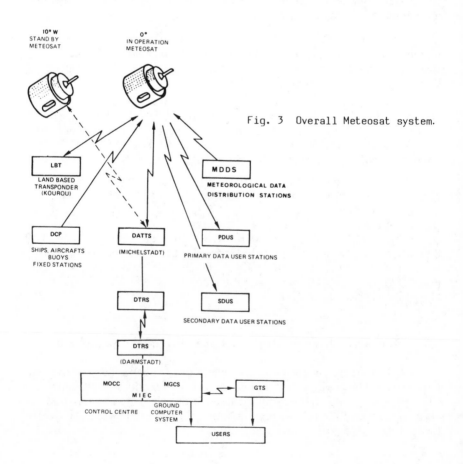

Fig. 3   Overall Meteosat system.

The main body is covered with 2 x 2 cm N/P silicon solar cells for supplying the required electrical energy for the satellite functioning: 210 W after 3 yr in orbit EOL. The solar array is complemented by two batteries of 16 Ni-Cd elements with a capacity of 7 A.h each. Most of Meteosat subsystems, including the radiometer, are located in this cylinder.

The second cylinder carries: 1) an array of radiating dipoles electronically fed in such a way that they simulate an S-band antenna that is artificially and permanently oriented toward the Earth (electronically despun antenna, EDA); 2) most of the telecommunications equipment; and 3) additional antennas.

The two cylinders mounted on top of the drum are toroidal pattern antennas (S and UHF frequency bands).

The payload consists of a high-resolution radiometer and a data transmission system. The radiometer is an electro-optical instrument that includes a large telescope with a focal length of 3650 mm; a set of detectors (Si photodiodes of 250 x 250 µm in the visible spectral band, Hg-Cd-Te 70 x 70 µm detectors for visible and infrared) located in the focal plane of the telescope measure the radiance of the Earth and its cloud cover in the visible, thermal-infrared and water vapor absorption spectral bands. By virtue of the spin motion of the satellite at 100 rpm, the radiometer scans the Earth along the east-west axis; the scan along the north-south axis is achieved by tilting the optical telescope axis slightly at the end of each east-west scan. A set of three images, one in each of the spectral bands, is produced once every 30 min.

The communication package consists of a transponder and an associated antenna system. The transponder operates in the S (1675-2105 MHz) and UHF (402 MHz) bands and insures the dissemination of satellite images (WEFAX and high resolution) and data collection platform messages toward user stations on 2 channels, the collection of data transmitted from platforms on up to 66 channels, and the exchange of meteorological data between users on 8 channels.

The attitude measurement subsystem (including two accelerometers, two pairs of sun sensors, and two Earth infrared sensors) permits an attitude reconstitution on the ground to within 0.1 deg after 3 h. The attitude and orbit control subsystem (AOCS) includes three hydrazine tanks, six thrusters (two each axial of 10N, radial of 10N, vernier of 2N) and two passive dampers. It permits the execution of the following main tasks: orbital correction maneuvers, spin axis control and correction maneuvers, nominal spin rate acquisition and control, and passive mutation damping.

Table 1   Performance of attitude and orbit control system
===

Spin rate	100 rpm ± 1%
Spin rate control	Possibility of adjustment
	better than ± 0.1 rpm
Spin axis control	Within 0.4° west of the
	Earth's spin axis
Nutation	<5 arc s after damping
Longitude station keeping	± 1°
(east-west)	
Inclination (north-south)	< 0.8°
Eccentricity of the orbit	< 0.002
Maximum amount of hydrazine BOL	29 deg

===

The performance of the AOCS is shown in Table 1.

The Meteosat Ground Segment

The ground segment (Fig. 3) is split into two parts: the ground facilities needed to carry out the Meteosat missions and the user stations.

Ground Facilities

The ground facilities consist of four elements:

1)The Meteosat Operations Control Center, which is entrusted with the operational management of the satellite and the tracking facilities. It controls the performance and operation of the satellite and ensures that the missions are carried out correctly.

2)The Data Referencing and Conditioning Center, which is mainly responsible for processing the image data and for the formatting needed for their subsequent exploitation.

3)The Meteorological Information Extraction Center, which extracts specifically meteorolgical information (such as wind fields, sea surface temperature charts, cloud system analyses, and radiation balances) from the processed images.

(The three elements are located in ESOC, Darmstadt, FRG.)

4)The Data Acquisition Telecommand and Tracking Station, located at Michelstadt, near ESOC, is responsible for the acquisition of the satellite's radiometric and housekeeping data and of messages from the data collection platforms. It transmits to the satellite telecommands and meteorological data or images for dissemination to user stations. Finally, in association with a land-based transponder at Kourou, French Guiana, it carries out the ranging measurements needed to locate the satellite precisely.

User Stations

The different user stations are:

1)The primary data user stations, which receive the rectified Earth images disseminated in digital form through the satellite.

2)The secondary data user stations, which are conceptually simpler and thus cheaper and which receive the image data in a standardized (WEFAX) format and messages from the data collection platforms, all of which are disseminated through the satellite.

3)The data collection platforms, which take measurements of the local environment and transmit them to the satellite.   They can be installed in extremely varied locations: on the ground, buoys, ships, and aircraft.

4)The meteorological data distribution stations, which include receiving and transmission facilities and which can disseminate meteorological information to and from national meteorological services.

There exist more than 500 secondary data user stations as well as about 10 primary data user stations dispersed in the telecommunication field of view of Meteosat, which are used operationally every day for weather forecasting as aid to airlines.

In addition, cloud motion vectors are used by the European Center for Medium Range Weather Forecasts (ECMWF) in the atmospheric model and contribute to the improvement of the forecasts between 48 h and 5 days.

In spite of the low space resolution of the images, Meteosat is used experimentally as a remote sensing tool inter alia in the following application areas:

1)Agrometeorology: An experiment took place over a test period of 18 days at the beginning of the 1979 growing season in the Sahel of Africa to map and monitor key agrometeorological parameters such as rainfall, surface radiation, evaporation, and thermal inertia, with the objective of defining a germination-mapping approach.   It was concluded that Meteosat had the ability to provide unique and consistent climatological surface data over large areas.

The FAO conducted a pilot project on the application of remote sensing techniques, including data from Landsat, NOAA series, and Meteosat satellites for improving desert locust survey and control.

2)Aid to fisheries: The Meteosat data are used to increase the efficiency of fishing ships (Gulf of Guinea, East Coast of Africa) by providing the fleet with accurate sea surface temperature relative values.

Conclusion

Since 1977 the preoperational Meteosat system has been participating in the GARP and has given satisfaction to the user community during its operating periods. When defining the operational program, the European Space Agency took into consideration the results of the analyses performed in order to improve the performance of the system and to satisfy the growing demand of the users who are now in a position to judge the merits of Meteosat after 6 yr of experience. At the end of the operational program (1995), the Meteosat satellite concept will be more than 20 yr old. This is the reason why the Agency is starting to prepare the next generation of geostationary satellites in cooperation with the European meteorological community for establishing the mission objectives and with the other satellite operators in the framework of the Coordination Group for Geostationary Meteorological Satellites for improving the compatibility between the different systems.

Summary

The paper describes the Meteosat system of the European Space Agency, the operational satellites with their differences compared to the initial preoperational satellites, the ground segment central facilities, and the products derived from the system and distributed to the users. It gives some applications in the field of remote sensing.

The SPOT Satellite System

Michel Courtois*
Centre National d'Etudes Spatiales, Toulouse, France
and
Gilbert Weill†
SPOT IMAGE Corporation, Washington, D.C.

Abstract

Digital imagery from the SPOT series of satellites will become available in early 1986, providing a novel source of worldwide information on a commercial basis. The program is expected to last 10-12 years. The data will be distributed by SPOT IMAGE (a dedicated entity) and its affiliate corporations and agents, some of which are equipped with their own receiving capabilities. This paper reviews the mission objectives and its most crucial parameters. It describes the satellite, the payload instruments, and the supporting ground system that provides the satellite programming, spacecraft control, image acquisition, and preprocessing. Finally, some image quality concepts and distribution arrangements are outlined.

Introduction

Remote sensing from space began in 1972. The success of the program has been proved with the Landsat satellites. The French government decided in February 1978 to undertake, with Belgium and Sweden, the development of the "Systeme Probatoire d'Observation de la Terre", or SPOT. The SPOT system[1] comprises:

1) The SPOT satellite which has two parts: the platform--one model of a multimission bus

---

*SPOT Project Manager, Centre National d'Etudes Spatiales.
†President, SPOT IMAGE Corporation.

developed with the SPOT project--and the mission specific payload.

2) The ground segment itself, divided into ground control and ground image reception segments.

The first SPOT spacecraft is presently under development. The production and launch of a second satellite, SPOT 2, has been approved. This second satellite will be launched when SPOT 1 fails or ages or alternatively, to increase by appropriate phasing of the orbit, the repetitivity of passes by the whole system.

This paper provides an updated description of the SPOT program, covering aspects of both data acquisition and data distribution.

The SPOT Mission

Objectives

The objectives of the SPOT mission are to:

1) Contribute to establishing remote sensing from space as a viable, major worldwide source of operational terrain-related information.

2) Research and develop applications requiring data with one or more of several attributes: high (10-20 m) resolution, rapid visit or revisit time, frequent access, and stereo terrain perception.

3) Build up and progressively market a data base of planimetric and stereo data over important areas of the world.

4) Qualify a multimission platform and linear array sensors for extended free-flying missions.

Choice of Spectral Bands

Desires for high radiometric performance (8 bit coding or equivalent), for a sizable swath width (60 km/instrument), and for practical data transmission and processing rates (taking into

consideration the limits of the spectral sensitivity of the detectors on hand during the design
phase) have governed the choice of the number of
spectral bands. Each instrument produces one
"color" data stream of three spectral bands of
20 m (nadir) resolution on the ground and one
"black and white" data stream of one panchromatic
band having 10 m (nadir) resolution.

The location and widths of the bands[2] were
optimized for thematic discrimination, taking
into account the spectral signature of ground
targets, while staying away from difficult-to-
correct signal degradations introduced by the
variable atmosphere. The band limits at half
maximum response are 0.50-0.59 μm for XS1, 0.61-
0.68 μm for XS2, 0.79-0.89 μm for XS3, and 0.51-
0.73 μm for Pa.

Choice of Orbit

A circular, sun-synchronous orbit was the
obvious choice to achieve constant resolution and
global coverage at reasonable sun angles
throughout the year. A midmorning (10:30 a.m.)
descending node was chosen; this choice limits
the risk of specular reflection over water
surfaces at low latitudes when the sun is high.
A phased orbit was retained so that systematic,
fixed-angle acquisition of all land areas be
secured in a repetitive manner. Assuming such
systematic acquisition is made with both
instruments operating as a pair (overall swath
width of 117 km), the orbital cycle, as defined by
the time between two successive overflights of a
particular ground track, could be no less than 25
days. Those criteria could be met by many
different orbits. The orbit finally selected was
a compromise between the need to spread evenly
over the orbital cycle the many opportunities to
observe a particular target area (reduce access
time to designated sites), and the need to
provide the capability to acquire stereo coverage
of a designated site with a good base-to-height
ratio within a short period of time.

The orbital characteristics, summarized in
Table 1, provide the system with important

```
        Table 1   Orbital parameters of SPOT 1
===========================================================

Revolutions/day                      14 + 5/26
Nodal period                         101.46 min
Mean altitude (45  deg N)            832 km
Inclination (mean)                   98.37 deg
Orbital (repeat) cycle               26 days
Number of tracks/orbital cycle       369
Intertrack distance (equatorial)     108.4 km
Accessibility pattern at
  45  deg latitude            1,4,1,4,1,4,1,4,1,4,1 days
Mean local solar time at
  descending node                    10:30 a.m.
===========================================================
```

operational properties:

1) Seventy-one nodal revolutions (5 days, 4 min) after a particular track is overflown, the next track immediately to the west is overflown. This is generally the first and best opportunity to retry an acquisition prevented by cloud cover. For many practical purposes, this 5 day subcycle will be more important than the 26 day cycle.

2) Fourteen nodal revolutions (19.5 min short of 24 h) after a particular track is overflown, the fifth track to the east of it will be overflown. Two vantage points some 500 km apart (at the equator) provide a good base-to-height ratio for completing a stereo pair before terrain radiometry or solar illumination changes impair human perception or automatic determination of terrain relief.

Operational Plans

The first satellite (SPOT 1) is due to be launched in the fall of 1985 from Kourou, French Guyana. The same Ariane launch will also place in orbit a Swedish scientific mission, the Viking satellite. The launch will be followed by two months of in-flight acceptance testing. SPOT 2, a nearly identical satellite, is currently under construction. It is due to be launched by the end of 1987, but could be launched, if necessary, as early as 12 months after SPOT 1. Items having long lead times are currently being procured for a backup of SPOT 2 (SPOT 2').

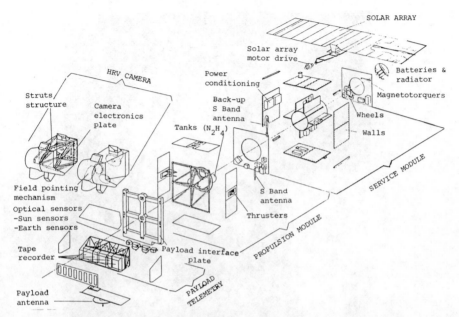

Fig. 1 Exploded view of the SPOT spacecraft.

Beyond this initial series, a follow-on series called SPOT 3 and 4 is under study. The tentative launch date of SPOT 3 is 1990. These follow-on satellites may include significant capability upgrades, enhanced application capabilities (spectral bands), and increased cost effectiveness (operational lifetime). They are currently under a "phase A" study due to be completed in May 1985.

The SPOT Satellite

An important objective of the SPOT program has been that the research and development investment ultimately serve to reduce procurement costs and lead times for future Earth observation missions. This fundamental aim is achieved by adopting a structure composed of two main parts, platform and payload. The spacecraft is shown in Fig. 1.

A view of the electrical model of the spacecraft during ElectroMagnetic Compatibility (EMC) tests is presented on Fig. 2.

Fig. 2 Electrical model of the SPOT satellite.

The SPOT Platform

The platform carries mission-independent subsystems: attitude and orbit control, power supplies, an onboard computer, telemetry and command equipment, etc. In a different configuration the platform will be used for the Earth Resources Satellite (ERS1) being developed by the European Space Agency (ESA). Major characteristics of the multimission platform are summarized below:

1) Use in sun-synchronous circular orbits between 600 and 1200 km with local solar time at ascending or descending node between 8:00 and 16:00.

2) Maximum payload weight: 1100 kg.

3) Solar array power: up to 2.2 kW (beginning of   life).

4) Design lifetime: 3 years.

5) Pointing accuracy: 0.05 deg (rms).

6) Drift rate: 6.10^{-4} deg/s (max).

The SPOT 1 Payload

The SPOT 1 payload includes two identical high-resolution visible-range instruments (HRV). The instruments are pointable in the across track direction in order to allow rapid access to any point on the globe and the acquisition of stereoscopic image pairs from different satellite passes. Data generated by the instruments are to be transmitted to the ground over the payload-specific X-band telemetry link or stored by means of two onboard recorders for later recovery by the Toulouse and Kiruna receiving stations.

The HRV Instruments. To satisfy SPOT mission performance requirements, the HRV will meet the following specifications:

1) High radiometric resolution to discriminate very low variations of radiation in each of the four spectral bands.

2) High spatial resolution.

3) High structural stability to minimize effects that would result in both image distortion and viewing axis deviation.

4) The off-nadir viewing mechanism will have an absolute pointing accuracy (without ground calibration) of 4×10^{-4} rad for any position   0.023° within a range of ± 27 deg.

5) Capability for simultaneous operation in the panchromatic and multispectral modes for periods on the order of 12 min (mean value for 14 consecutive orbits including peak demand periods of up to 30 min).

The HRV system performance specifications are summarized and presented in Tables 2 and 3.

Table 2   Radiometric performance

Parameters	Channels			
	Pa	XS1	XS2	XS3
Spectral Band, um	0.51-0.73	0.5-0.59	0.61-0.68	0.79-0.89
Detector IFOV, rad	1.2×10^{-5}	2.4×10^{-5}	2.4×10^{-5}	2.4×10^{-5}
Detect.numbers/line	6000	3000	3000	3000
Modulation transfer function:				
To CCD line	0.26	0.62	0.55	0.52
Along CCD line	0.27	0.43	0.38	0.26
S/N at radiance, max	>233	>212	>230	>274
On-orbit calibration, %				
Relative	1	1	1	1
Absolute	10	10	10	10
Number of gains	8	8	8	8
Signal encoding, bit	6 or DPCM 8/5/5/8	8	8	8

Table 3   Geometric characteristics

Ground swath width	60 km/HRV
	117 km SPOT payload
Off-nadir viewing capability	±27 deg or 460 km
(field center)	on ground
Ground resolution	
Spectral Band XS	20 m
Panchro Band Pa	10 m
Band-to-band registration	
Spectral Band	6 m
Pa/XS	10 m (level 2 image)
Image distortion	
Anisomorphism	10^{-3}

The HRV instrument includes a number of innovations. It uses the "push-broom" technique for image generation, thus eliminating the need for mechanical scanning. A wide-angle optical assembly images the totality of the line (perpendicular to the satellite ground track) over a linear array of solid-state detectors that are sampled at the appropriate frequency as the satellite moves along its orbit. The industrial availability of charge-coupled devices (CCDs) permitted this imaging technique to be implemented. Also, commercial CCDs can be readily submitted to stringent selection and space environment qualification procedures that offer the potential for obtaining excellent radiometric and geometric performance.

1) Optics and Detection System. The HRV optical system (Fig. 3) is a folded catadioptric telescope with a focal length of 1082 mm and a numerical aperture of f/3.5. The aberrations of the spherical collector mirror are corrected by a lens doublet mounted just behind the entrance pupil. The field curvature inherent in such an optical combination is compensated by a second lens doublet mounted close to the focal plane. Displacement of this doublet permits the correction, when required, of the focal length of the HRV. The optical quality of this assembly corresponds to a concentration of 80% of the available energy in an elementary field of less than 1.2×10^{-5} rad.

Spectral separation of the four channels is performed in the focal plane by a beam-splitter assembly. In the multispectral mode, two elementary CCD devices are used to produce each image element (or pixel). This means that , in the focal plane, the spacing between pixels is 26 μm (or double the interdevice pitch of 13 μm). In the panchromatic mode, there is one-to-one correspondence between the sensing elements and the pixels.

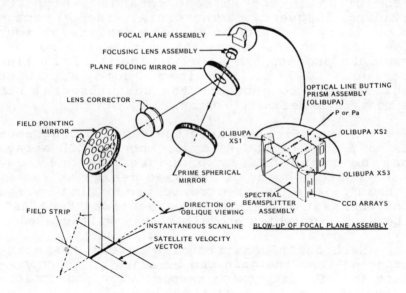

Fig. 3 HRV optical system.

For each spectral band, the detection
assembly contains 4 optically butted detector
arrays accurately positioned in a staggered configuration on "Divolis". These optical devices
(which use semitransparent mirrors) recombine the
four basic arrays to produce a continuous line
covering the entire 60 km field.

The optical path is deflected at the
telescope entrance by a plane elliptical mirror.
It is this mirror, mounted on bearings and driven
by a stepper motor, that permits each HRV to
record off-nadir imagery over an angular range of
+ 27 deg. The off-nadir viewing capability
offers the following major advantages:
systematic coverage of the entire globe;
increased capability to revisit sites; and the
possibility of recording stereopairs of a given
scene from neighboring orbits.

2) Electronics. The signals generated by
the CCD arrays are handled by two separate image
processing electronic systems. The multispectral
system (XS) processes the 12 arrays (4 x 3)
corresponding to the XS channel. The
panchromatic (Pa) system processes the four
arrays of the Pa band. The 10 m ground
resolution in the Pa mode demands a high CCD
reading frequency. Therefore, the Pa image
processing electronic system consists of four
identical "chains" operating in parallel so that
each can process one array during the full line
period. All of the image data are then
multiplexed to generate the output serial bit
stream in a definite format.

In the XS mode, where the reading frequency
is half that of the Pa mode, the two CCD arrays
can be sequentially processed by only one
electronic "chain" of the same design as the Pa
"chain". The XS electronic processing system
thus consists of six (2 x 3) identical "chains",
the data from which are ultimately multiplexed.

Each chain consists of a purely resistive
stage so that the gain can be adjusted to compensate for CCD dispersion responsivity and optical
transmission; a programmable gain amplifier

stage; a sample-and-hold circuit that extracts
the useful information from the raw analog
signals; and an analog-to-digital converter that
encodes the sampled image signals, leaving the
sample-and-hold circuit as 8 bit words. Each of
the Pa and XS image processing electronic system
is associated with its own sequencer to
synchronize all of the operations from CCD
clocking through final message organization.

The rate at which bits are output by the
panchromatic processing system is one third
higher than that for the multispectral system.
To overcome this potential problem, the
panchromatic signal processing system includes a
data compression function which ensures that the
system output bit rate is identical to that of
the multispectral system. The data compression
function is capable of operating in two modes
that can be selected by ground command: a linear
mode in which only the six most significant bits
out of each eight are transmitted and an 8-5-5-8
differential pulse code modulation (DPCM) mode
permiting the reconstruction on the ground of the
original message with a minimum of information
loss.

3) Off-Nadir Viewing Mechanism. The
mechanism that drives the steerable mirror was
identified at the beginning of the program as one
of the most critical items of the whole design.
The performance of this mechanism determines how
accurately the instrument viewing axis is known,
which, as was emphasized earlier, is an important
parameter in image utilization.

The design concept adopted is simple: the
complete steerable mirror assembly is mounted on
two bearings, each of which consists of a pair of
prestressed ball bearings. A 1200 step revolution stepper motor drives the mirror assembly
directly, each motor step corresponding to a
mirror step of 0.3 deg. The mirror position is
measured by a shaft angle encoder with its output
connected to the on board computer (OBC).

During launch and ascent, the mirror is
locked in position. Once the satellite is in

orbit, the locking mechanism is released by a pyrotechnic device.

The main performance requirements of the off-nadir viewing mechanism are a linear displacement law as a function of motor stepping (30 arc-s each step) and reproducible step positioning to within better than 30 arc-s.

4) Calibration. In order to maintain the radiometric accuracy of the instrument during its lifetime in orbit and to correct for any changes in response that may occur (aging of optical coatings, contamination of optical surfaces, degradation of CCD detectors, etc.), the HRV is equipped with a calibration system placed under ground control. Whenever necessary, this device provides a means of illuminating the CCD arrays through the entire optical train, using a lamp of known radiance (relative calibration) or, when the satellite is leaving the Earth's shadow, of directing a known quantity of solar flux onto a number of elementary CCD detectors. This second possibility results in a high-precision absolute calibration of the entire optical and image processing electronics system. In either case, the steerable mirror is first placed in the "calibration" position. In this position, the instrument entrance baffle is largely blocked off and the risk of stray light entering during calibration is eliminated. The calibration unit consists of a five-element objective that forms an image of the exits of the optical fibers coming from the solar collector in the telescope focal plane or, for relative calibration, uniformly illuminates all four CCD array lines with light from one of two redundant lamps. The image of the lamp filament is conjugate to the entrance pupil of the objective by a Petzval condenser. Separation between the lamp and solar flux channels is achieved using a Lummer's cube. The solar flux is collected outside the HRV instrument from three different directions corresponding to three different sun/satellite attitudes and is transmitted to the focal point of the calibration unit by 48 optical fibers arranged in two layers corresponding to the instrument's panchromatic and multispectral channels.

A light energy propagation mode mixer on the flux transmission path insures uniform illumination at the fiber bundle exit over the useful field. Two mechanisms are associated with the calibration device: one is used for lamp changeover (lamp backup), and the other to move the cover that normally protects the solar collector.

5) Calibration operation. The standard calibration source used is a tungsten filament lamp. The flux uniformity required across instrument field is better than 5% with no local defect higher than 1%. These performance specifications which are to be maintained after environmental testing and launch ascent, result in critical design constraints on the mechanical stability of the lamp mounting pad. The spectral stability of the lamp requires a highly stable dc-dc converter. This calibration system will provide for the determination of two coefficients for each of 15,000 CCD elements; the first coefficient corrects for individual element dark current and electronic offset, the second for individual gain variations.

The Payload Telemetry Subsystem. Each of the two HRV instruments can operate in the multispectral mode (XS) and/or the panchromatic mode (Pa). Each HRV delivers two bit streams corresponding to the Pa and XS instrument modes. Only two among the four bit streams available are transmitted to the ground or recorded onboard. Since the bit rate transmitted by the payload telemetry system is limited to 50 megabit/s (i.e., 2 x 25 megabit/s), only two of the four possible modes can be used at one time. In accordance with the applicable regulations, the transmission frequency is in the X band (8.025-8.400 GHz). The two preselected 25 megabit/s data rates are merged (time multiplexed) and fed to the transmitter and/or onboard recorders for later transmission.

The payload telemetry system consists of an 8 GHz quadriphase modulator (QPSK), a traveling wave tube (TWT) with a nominal power of 20 W, a set of filters to limit the spectral bandwidth, and a fixed antenna covering the entire cone of

visibility of the Earth. It is compatible with
acquisition by ground stations at a 5 deg
elevation angle (Fig 4).

In addition to image data, data concerning
both the payload (calibration and synchronization) and the platform (attitude parameters) are
multiplexed and transmitted by the payload telemetry system. This ensures that the data
required for preprocessing the images are
available at the image receiving station.

Physical Outline

Dimensions. The dimensions of the satellite
body are 2, 2, and 4.7 m along the roll, yaw and
pitch axes, respectively. The solar panel is
located 2.3 m away from the satellite body, its
extended dimension is 8.12 m long and its area
is 12 m^2.

Mass Breakdown. The mass breakdown of the
satellite at launch is listed in Table 4.

Table 4   SPOT 1 mass breakdown, kg

Platform	
Structure	370
Computer system	35
Solar generator and controls	128
Power pack (incl. batteries)	158
Orbit and attitude control	106
Propulsion system	194 BOL[a]
	(44 EOL[b])
Wiring	43
Thermal control	18
Telemetry, localization	10
Miscellaneous	16
Total Platform	1078 BOL
Payload	
HRV1	241.5
HRV2	241.5
Recorder & Telemetry	248
Miscellaneous	3
Total payload	734
Total satellite	1806 (BOL)

[a] Beginning of life.
[b] End of life.

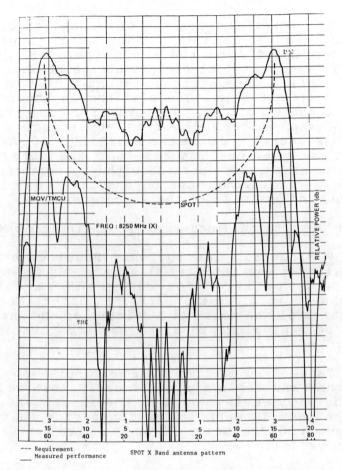

--- Requirement
___ Measured performance   SPOT X Band antenna pattern

Fig. 4 Transmission characteristics of the onboard X band antenna.

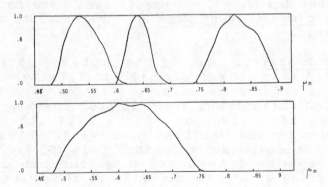

Fig. 5 Spectral bands of SPOT 1 as measured on the engineering model.

The Power Budget. The power budget can be summarized as follows. The solar generator produces 1230 W on the sunlit portion of the orbit in equinoxal conditions at the beginning of life (BOL). A 15% decrease is expected over the satellite lifetime. The platform in the normal mode consumes 323 W. The payload consumption is 148 W when idle and varies according to the various active modes between 390 and 520 W. The power system thus insures that the satellite instruments can be operated without limitation in the direct reading mode on the day side of the Earth, and over all of the land masses.

First Results obtained with the Engineering Model

Radiometric Resolution. Requirements on signal-to-noise ratio (S/N) at the output of the HRV are specified for different levels of luminance (L1, L2, L3, L3/8), in order that the variance of the noise at the input of the instrument be equivalent to a reflectance fluctuation of 0.5×10^{-2}.

Table 5 summarizes signal-to-noise specifications, and Table 6 reports early test results on the engineering model of the instrument. All of the results support the confidence that all system requirements will be met with the proto-flight model.

Spectral Bands. Measurements of spectral bands on different pixels have been made. Figure 5 gives the measured spectral responses in the different bands. These measurements are made by sampling every 10 nm with a 4 nm bandwidth monochromator.

Uniformity. All of the problems have not yet been solved regarding the uniformity of the response and the use of a calibration lamp to do relative calibration. The main problems come from the use of a fraction of the full telescope aperture by the calibration device. Figure 6 gives the response at nominal gain (G3) for the third spectral band XS3 with the use of an integrating sphere at the entry of the telescope and shows good uniformity. This response is not

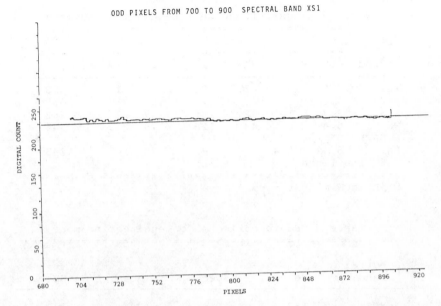

ODD PIXELS FROM 700 TO 900   SPECTRAL BAND XS1

Fig. 6 Constant level relative calibration with integrating sphere (Gain 3).

as smooth with the use of the lamp. This led the project team to develop and test in flight another relative calibration procedure, based on the use of specific Earth surface areas imaged by the two HRVs.

Dark current measurements at gain G8 (high gain) are shown in Table 7. The instrument stability was kept under 1.5 mV within the calibration sequence.

Modulation Transfer Function (MTF). The MTF specifications at half the sampling frequency are given (without integration time effect) in Table 8. Measurements made on the engineering model of an HRV are in agreement with these figures. Taking into account the integration time, the "column" figures must be multiplied by 0.63, giving: 0.39 for XS1, 0.34 for XS2, 0.39 for XS3, and 0.16 for Pa.

To compensate for the effects of this relatively low MTF (essentially for the Pa band), a

Table 5   Signal-to-noise specification summary

Spectral Band	L1 L^a	L1 S/N	L3/8 L	L3/8 S/N	L2 L	L2 S/N	L3
XS1	8.56	10	43.8	124	181	212	350
XS2	4.00	5	44.4	126	184	230	355
XS3	2.36	5	32.8	156	129	274	262
Pa, DPCM	5.4	6	43.1	128	178	233	345
Pa, 6 bits linear	5.4	2.4	-	-	178	147	345

[a] L in $W.m^{-2}.St^{-1}.\mu m^{-1}$.

Table 6   Radiometric S/N on engineering model

Spectral band	L3/8 Meas.	L3/8 Spec.	L2 Meas.	L2 Spec.
XS1	159	124	296	212
XS2	141	126	253	230
XS3	206	156	315	274
Pa	101-144[a]	128	228-265	233

[a] Depending on CCD channel.

Table 7   Dark current measurements [a]

Spectral band	Dark current, LSB [b]
Pa, even pixels	0.52
Pa, odd pixels	1.68
XS1	2.9
XS2	4.2
XS3	1.67

[a] All measurements with gain 8.
[b] LSB: least significant bit.

deconvolution process may be executed to produce
enhanced forms of imagery on the ground.

Geometric Image Quality. Main results are
relative to the alignments, angular drifts, and
multispectral band-to-band registration. Alignment performances are quite satisfactory on the
engineering model and, together with the pointing

accuracy, they insure localization of the images within 1.5 km rms in nadir viewing.

Registration measurements performed on the spectral dichroic beamsplitter show less than 0.3 pixel dispersion. The agreement between attitude simulation results and specifications regarding angular drift rate is presented in Table 9.

The Supporting Ground System

The ground system for SPOT performs three distinct functions: payload programming, spacecraft control, and image acquisition and processing (see Fig. 7).

Payload Programming

The mission center is responsible for mission management and, in particular, for scheduling image acquisition and processing in accordance with user requirements, which are handled by SPOT IMAGE. Also, the mission center is the point of contact for direct receiving station operators for spacecraft scheduling. The

Table 8 Modulation transfer function at Nyquist frequency

	XS1	XS2	XS3	Pa
Column (along track)	0.62	0.55	0.52	0.26
Line (cross track)	0.43	0.38	0.26	0.27

Table 9 Angular drift rates [a]

Axes	0-0.05		Band, Hz 0.05-2		$2-\infty$	
Roll	0.12	(0.4)	0.08	(0.25)	b	(0.2)
Yaw	0.1	(0.4)	0.17	(0.3)	b	(0.2)
Pitch	0.1	(0.4)	0.28	(0.6)	b	(0.4)

[a] All values in 10^{-3} deg/s at three standard deviations. The figures in parentheses are the specified values.

[b] Insignificant.

mission center receives pass reservations and
special acquisition requests from station
operators; it also sends the data necessary for
acquisition and processing of data, especially
the ephemeris data.

Several parameters can be programmed:
viewing angle of the instruments, choice of
channels, sensor gain for each of the spectral
bands, type of coding for the panchromatic band
(linear or differential coding).

Spacecraft Control

The control center performs all satellite
management functions, monitors satellite operation, generates commands, and establishes the
orbital parameters. It communicates with the
SPOT platform in S-band (2 GHz). During the
operational phase, all ground command operations
are executed through the Toulouse station.
During the launch and development phases, additional stations are used.

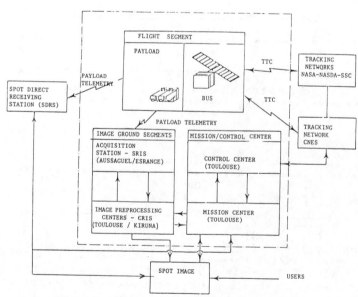

Fig. 7 SPOT system architecture.

Image Reception and Processing

Two stations, Toulouse and Kiruna, have been developed in order to insure a large playback transmission capacity. Night passes and some day passes over Kiruna and Toulouse are used for transmitting data recorded on board. The two stations are managed by the mission center in Toulouse. Apart from these two stations, direct read out X-band stations can be implemented to receive image telemetry.

The station image products output from the Toulouse processing center are listed in Table 10. In addition, an equivalent production capability has been developed in Kiruna for product levels 1A and 1B. Other precision products will be produced and distributed by SPOT IMAGE, its affiliate organizations and the various members of the reception and distribution networks.

Image Quality Assessment, Monitoring, and Adjustment

Image quality[3] is a compound function of the detector and the optical instruments' characteristics in orbit, as well as precise knowledge of the viewing geometry as a function of time. While many of the necessary determinations are made or simulated on the ground prior to flight, conditions may be slightly altered by the launch environment, and to a lesser extent, by inflight aging processes. Prime remedies for maintaining and controlling image quality are an adjustment of ground preprocessing parameters and, eventually, inflight refocalization of the telescopes.

Immediately after launch, the system will undergo a two month inflight qualification period. This period will include an image quality assessment program[4] to ascertain that image quality specifications are met, and at the same time to establish appropriate initial preprocessing parameters. The procedures will be repeated periodically to insure stability of image quality throughout the satellite lifetime.

Table 10 Initial types of SPOT data products

Product characteristics	Product throughput and Turnaround time
Deliverable products	
Archiving outputs	Archiving outputs
Updating SPOT IMAGE catalog computer file	Media: CCT[a] 1600 bpi[b] and film quick-look, dry silver 70 mm (these products are systematic)
Quick look:	Turnaround time: 24 h max
Film 70 mm, 1 image per scene	Production: 800 scenes
Pa: sampled 1 pixel out of 6	
1 line out of 6	
Xs: sampled 1 band out of 3	
1 pixel out of 3	
1 line out of 3	
(with crude geometric and radiometric corrections)	
Level 1A	Level 1A
Radiometric corrections: detector gain and offset correction	Media: CCT 6250 bpi + checking quick-look
Localization accuracy: 1500 m rms (nadir viewing)	

a CCT: computer compatible tape
b bpi: bits per inch

(Table 10 continued on next page.)

Table 10 (cont.) Initial types of SPOT data products

===

Level 1B

System correction, systematic geometry
Localization accuracy: 1500 m rms
(nadir viewing)

Level 2

Mapping to different projection
Lambert conformal
Universal transverse Mercator
Universal polar stereographic
Equatorial Mercator

Same radiometric corrections
as level 1B
Localization accuracy: 50 m rms
(nadir viewing)

Level S

Registration with level 1B or 2 scene
Same radiometric and geometric corrections as
for level 1B or 2

Registration accuracy: 0.5 pixel
Pa: 5 m; Xs: 10 m (same viewing angle)
Xs/Pa: 10 m

Level 1B

Media: CCT 6250 bpi + checking
        quick-look
   or: CCT 6250 bpi + 241 mm
        precision film
   or: only 241 mm precision film
        (these products are preprocessed
        on order).

Turnaround time: 24 h max
Production: for level 1 (A or B)
            80 scenes max

Level 2 and S

Media: CCT 6250 bpi + checking
        quick-look
   or: CCT 6250 bpi + 241 mm
        precision film
   or: only 241 mm precision film
        (these products are preprocessed on
        order)

Turnaround time: 8 days (if maps are
            present in the map library)
Production: 1 scene every 35 min

===

Image Geometry

Reference Systems. There are four important geometric reference systems.

1) The local orbital reference system is geometrically defined for any satellite location. One of the axes looks away from the geocentric direction, the other two are forward in the orbital plane and across the speed vector.

2) The attitude measurement reference system is linked to the satellite platform. It is the function of the attitude control system to maintain any axis of the attitude measurement reference system within .15 deg of the local orbital reference system, and to maintain the angular drift rates within the specified limits (see Table 9).

3) One reference system for each HRV instrument. Each instrument is tilted by $\pm$ 0 .163 deg in order to insure a nominal sidelap of 3 kms on the ground when the instruments are operated in the twin HRV vertical mode ($\pm$ 6 steps from the quasi-vertical position). Since the geometry of the HRVs is known, (having been both specified and precisely measured on the ground prior to launch), the direction corresponding to any particular detector and any particular step of the pointing mirror is also known in that reference system.

Satellite Location. The satellite location is provided by CNES to the preprocessing centers for each satellite pass at one minute intervals. The predicted location, for antenna pointing purposes, is within 1 km along the trajectory and within 0.5 km across the trajectory. For data preprocessing, the computed (a posteriori) ephemeris is normally used, with a satellite location accuracy of 0.3 km in every direction. The computed ephemeris data are communicated each day at 1:00 a.m. and 1:00 p.m. GMT for the group of orbits preceding that time by more than two hours. To the first order of accuracy, a satellite location error is equivalent to a pointing or attitude error: a mislocation along the trajectory and a pitch error both result in a forward displacement of a point on the ground, while an error on the lateral positioning of the satellite and on the roll angle both produce a lateral displacement. An error on satellite altitude or the instrument's focal length results in a difference of scale along the scanline.

Determination. Determination of geometric image quality is an important part of the inflight acceptance testing program to be conducted during the first 60 days after satellite launch. The tests are based on the use of ground control points (GCPs) on the real imagery. The geographic coordinates of the GCPs are read from the best available topographic maps and compared to the coordinates derived from the nominal satellite system geometry. For each HRV, the test uses about 15 panchromatic images obtained vertically and 10 oblique images, using 15 different satellite revolutions in the vicinity of the Toulouse receiving station. Imagery obtained in the southern hemisphere will be used in addition to the northern hemisphere test. 3 to 6 GCPs are extracted from each image. The analysis of all GCP localization errors provides an offset matrix (3 independent parameters), thereby positioning the "actual" HRV reference system vis-a-vis the preflight instrument reference system and thus, the attitude control reference system. This procedure corrects for any mechanical adjustments incurred at launch. The offset matrix system is then fed back to the preprocessing chains so that the overall system, including the space and ground segments, will deliver 1A or 1B products to the specifications quoted above (1.5 kms rms, nadir). The same approach is used to control tolerances in scale and an isomorphism; however, a greater number of GCPs (30) is used on a smaller number of images (9).

Image Coregistration. Image coregistration is checked on the ground for the three "color" channels of each instrument; it is also checked in flight during acceptance testing in order to eliminate the possibility of distortion at launch. This is done by automatic correlation of filtered imagery from the color channels. As

specified, the channels should be coregistered
to within a 6 m radius circle on the ground. A
similar approach is used to check the registration specifications for two images obtained from
the same vantage point 26 days apart (level S
products).

Image Radiometry

Signal/Noise. A maximum signal-to-noise
ratio is defined for each particular detector
along a column of raw pixels. It should be less
than .5% equivalent to noise reflectance and
"normal" conditions of observation with a
standard atmosphere. This includes the quantization errors both on board the spacecraft and at
the time of level 1A preprocessing when the
detectors are equalized. The onboard calibration lamps are stable enough to provide a check
of this particular specification.

Relative, Absolute and Interband Calibration
The relative calibration of the 3000 or 6000
individual detectors in a spectral band array is
performed periodically using one or both of two
redundant methods: a constant light level on all
detectors is provided either by the lamp calibration system or by a homogenous extended ground
target such as snow surfaces at high latitudes.
The dark current is measured when the satellite
is on the night side of the Earth, with the
pointing mirror in a shutter position. Test
results on the ground indicate that the local
precision of this procedure (on a few pixels) is
of the order of 0.2% whereas the overall residual
error over an array is of the order of 1%. Sixty
thousand coefficients (gains and offsets) are
generated by a full calibration sequence of both
instruments and are subsequently used at the
relevant preprocessing stations. Calibration
sequences are to be performed as needed within
the visibility of participating ground receiving
stations.

Interband (3%) and absolute (10%) calibrations are also done using either or both of two
redundant methods. The first method uses fiber
optic bundles that illuminate a small number of

detectors in each array at the time the satellite crosses the terminator (horizontal sun). The other method uses a reference test site at White Sands, N. Mex. where supporting ground measurements are carried out by the Optical Sciences Center at the University of Arizona in Tucson.

Modulation Transfer Function. The modulation transfer functions (MTF) have been measured on the ground; once in flight they will be visually estimated by comparing the space imagery to artificial photographic data sets. The data sets have been established for 20 urban test sites in southern France, by degrading to preset MTF high-altitude, high-resolution aerial photographs.

Refocalization

If necessary, an adjustment of the focal lens[5] can be made for any of the HRVs by using the imagery from the other instruments as a reference. This would normally be done by stepping up the focal length during one pass over the Toulouse station and stepping it down during the next pass. Successive pairs of frames (HRV1 vs HRV2) are then compared by calculating the ratio of their Fourier transforms; and the step corresponding to the sharpest focus is selected.

Data Distribution

As developer and principal owner of the SPOT system, the French government (CNES) operates the system and owns the data and related copyright. It is committed to making the data commercially available worldwide on a nondiscriminatory basis and in accordance with applicable international law. The most visible outcome of this commitment was the incorporation of the SPOT IMAGE (a French Societe Anonyme) in July 1982 and that of its U.S. subsidiary, SPOT IMAGE Corporation.

Mission of SPOT IMAGE

The SPOT IMAGE organization was created for the purpose of developing a worldwide market for SPOT data and for serving that market. SPOT IMAGE

has received from the Centre National d'Etudes
Spatiales (CNES) an exclusive license to organize
the promotion, distribution, and sale of SPOT data
and a mandate to negotiate and sign on behalf of
CNES for the direct reception of data by licensed
organizations. Such agreements include a distribution sublicense covering the national territory
of the receiving stations. SPOT IMAGE can also
choose from a range of options: sell directly;
appoint national or private entities as distribu-
tors (sublicensees); create, either alone or
together with local partners, an affiliate
entity. This option was exercised in December
1982 with the creation of SPOT IMAGE Corporation.
With headquarters in Washington, D.C., it has an
exclusive sublicense to serve the U.S. market.

It is SPOT IMAGE's special responsibility to
see that such entities, which represent the
diversity of the world, operate as a network in
which information and data circulate efficiently.

Acquisition and Archiving of Data

The two master stations (Aussaguel-Issus in
France and Kiruna in Sweden) are set up to
receive within the SPOT system both local (real
time transmission) imagery and imagery from all
over the world played back by the onboard
recorders. SPOT IMAGE acts as the focal point
for the whole network and compiles and provides
the SPOT Mission and Control Center with data
acquisition and preprocessing orders to be
executed by the satellite and by the two ground
stations. The satellite is operated in the
direct transmit mode within the visibility of
subscribing ground stations, providing them with
such satellite services as may be needed for
their market and as contractually agreed with
SPOT IMAGE.

Archiving

The raw data received by the ground stations
will generally be preserved in the form of high-
density digital tapes. The major part of international exchanges is expected to be on computer
compatible tapes and in photographic form.

SPOT IMAGE is establishing a worldwide computer catalog of SPOT data. The catalog lists the holdings of the two central stations and, as they are received from subscribing stations, the raw data holdings around the world. This multiple-entry catalog will allow users to find out what data are available for a given geographic location with what given observation parameters. The system also provides related services such as quality assessment and ordering information. Quick-look imagery is created at the receiving sites for browse purposes; SPOT IMAGE will thus compile a browse file on video tape.

Value Added Products and Services

The distribution of SPOT data is regulated by copyright law and the relevant sublicense agreements. Sales to end users are made on the condition that the data not be further disseminated by the purchaser. The distribution agreements recognize the existence of a demand for value-added products and product-related services. They make allowance for the development and sale of such products and services on a royalty basis. It is expected that the network will make available, early in the system life, market-specific data products using the SPOT capability or combining it with other sources.

Image Compatibility

For the benefit of users the world over, a minimum level of compatibility will be achieved. It is desirable that the telemetry be framed using a standardized SPOT world reference system, so that a common language is established for locating and identifying SPOT scenes.

A minimum quality standard for image products will also be required to facilitate the users' utilization of data. The level 1 products (1A--radiometric calibration only, 1B--radiometric calibration plus "bulk" geometric corrections) are precisely defined so that their quality can be consistent among preprocessing centers.

The CCT format is compatible with other
satellite data, particularly Landsat, thereby
facilitating data readout and exploitation for
data users.

Future Developments

Follow-on satellites to the SPOT 1 series
are currently being defined to extend the mission
into the 1990s. SPOT 3 and 4 will represent a
significant upgrade of several respects[6].

Mission Continuity and Augmentation

A high level of compatibility for data
acquisition, data processing and data utilization
is desired in order to assure program continuity
for the receiving stations, distribution network,
and end users. Within those constraints, the
mission characteristics will be enhanced through:
provision of precise coregistration of the systematic on higher and lower resolution data, extension of the spectral range to an additional
shortwave infrared band, and possible inclusion
of an auxiliary mission related instrument.

Data Continuity and Cost Effectiveness

The cost of maintaining the space segment
with additional satellites is a major part of the
system's costs. The two major improvements under
consideration in this area are extending operational lifetime of the satellite, and increasing
data rate at prime receiving sites. In addition,
the space and ground segments will be upgraded
and new preprocessing facilities will be designed
to turn out the main flow of high quality data
products in relation with the mission extensions.

Conclusion

In the flegling field of remote sensing from
space, the SPOT program can be seen as a model of
continuity and determination. The program will
have taken almost 10 years from conception to
launch and it is committed to no less than 10
years of operation. The prelaunch investigations and simulation exercises conducted with a

worldwide community of experts indicate that the mission objectives of high resolution, stereo, and access capability are currently right on target. Very early in the program, the decision to market the data was made, which significantly influenced the conception of the ground segment facilities and the current establishment of a distribution network. This network is nudging the system into an early operational mode, another innovation in the field. With SPOT 3 and 4, the system will be upgraded to take into account market demands and encourage further market development. We fully expect that SPOT will establish itself as a major source of geographic information in the years to come and will stand as a pillar of the fast developing information age.

References

[1] Chevel, M., Courtois, M., and Weill, G., "The SPOT Satellite Remote Sensing Mission" Photogrammetric Engineering and Remote Sensing, Vol. 47, Aug. 1981, pp. 1163-1171.

[2] Begni, G., "Selection of the Optimum Spectral Bands for the SPOT Satellite", Photogrammetric Engineering and Remote Sensing, Vol. 48, Oct. 1992, pp. 1613-1620.

[3] Begni, G., and Rayssiguier, M., "Specifications et Bilans de Qualite Image du System SPOT", Acta Astronautica, Vol. 10, 1983, pp. 37-42.

[4] Begni, G., Boissin, B., and Perbos, J., "Image Quality Assessment Methods", Advances in Space Research, Pergamon Press, New York, 1985, in print.

[5] Begni, G., Leger, D., and Dinguirard, M., "An In-Flight Refocusing Method for the SPOT HRV Cameras", Photogrammetric and Engineering and Remote Sensing, Vol. L, No. 12, pp. 1697-1705.

[6] Dulherm, L., Mizzi, A., "The SPOT 3 Program", Proceedings of the IAF, 1984, in print.

MOMS-01: Missions and Results

J. Bodechtel,* R. Haydn,† and J. Zilger‡
University of Munich, Munich, Federal Republic of Germany
D. Meissner§
Messerschmitt-Bölkow-Blohm, Ottobrunn, Federal Republic of Germany
P. Seige¶
*Deutsche Forschungs- und Versuchsanstalt für Luft- und Raumfahrt,
Oberpfaffenhofen, Federal Republic of Germany*
H. Winkenbach§
*Deutsche Forschungs- und Versuchsanstalt für Luft- und Raumfahrt,
Bereich Projektträgerschaften, Porz, Federal Republic of Germany*

Abstract

The modular optoelectronic multispectral scanner, MOMS, is designed for regional and global optical remote sensing applications. In two space missions it was mounted on the Shuttle Pallet Satellite SPAS aboard shuttle flights STS-7 June 83 and STS-11 February 84. The missions served the technological space verification of the sensor and the demonstration of geoscientific and application-oriented experiments in worldwide distribution areas.
Future development aims at the realization of a complex remote sensing device adaptable for different mission types and platforms, e.g., short-term missions aboard the Shuttle, free-flying missions with various space buses (EURECA, the European Retrievable Carrier of ESA, RADARSAT of Canada) or for the man-tended polar platform of the Space Station.

*Professor, MOMS Principle Investigator, Head of the Working Group for Remote Sensing, Institute for General and Applied Geology.
†Representative, MOMS Coinvestigator, Geologist.
‡Coordinator of MOMS Data Evaluation, Geologist.
§MOMS Project Manager, Physicist.
¶MOMS Project Engineer/Coinvestigator, Physicist.

Introduction

The modular optoelectronic multispectral scanner (MOMS) is
a new scanning system for airborne and predominantly spaceborne geoscientific remote sensing, developed by order of
the German Minister for Research and Technology under contract from the German Aerospace Research Establishment by
Messerschmitt-Bölkow-Blohm (MBB). Scientific guidance for
the experiment has been provided by the University of Mu-
nich/FRG.

The most important characteristic of MOMS is the modular arrangement of the sensors, electronics, optical lens system
and filters that allow the instrument to be adapted for completely different geoscientific tasks or missions ("dedicated instruments"), as well as the refurbishment between missions.

Operating either in a multispectral or stereoscopic data
collecting mode, dedicated instruments of the MOMS family
can fulfill specific tasks in geoscientific remote sensing
for: general geologic mapping, mineral resources exploration, hydrology; mapping and monitoring of renewable resources (agriculture, forestry, urban and regional planning); coastal zone monitoring; topographic mapping with
conventional methods; or evaluation of a digital terrain
model.

The first missions of a space qualified two-channel scanner, MOMS-01, took place an the MBB built satellite bus
Shuttle Pallet Satellite SPAS-01 flown on STS-7 in June
1983, and STS-11/41-B in February 1984. Both flights yielded

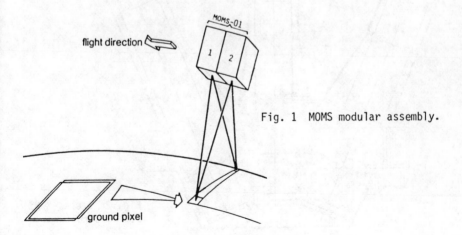

Fig. 1 MOMS modular assembly.

high-resolution images with 20 x 20 m^2 ground pixel size
from a 300 km orbital altitude. The missions incorporate
a few "firsts" in the scenario of optical spaceborne remote
sensing.

MOMS-01 is the first spaceborne scanner on the basis of
charged couple device (CCD) technology, the first space-
tested modular system, the highest resolving multispectral
system flown in orbit, the first Earth-oriented remote sensing satellite refurbished and reflown within a short period of time, and the first German remote sensing system in
space.

MOMS-01 Concept and Technical Specification

Modular Assembly

Each module representing one spectral band consists of filters, dual lens optics, 4 CCD sensors, and preamplifier
electronics (Fig. 1).The modular arrangement of the spectral
bands (MOMS-01 had 2 channels) allow for high flexibility
in meeting the requirements of different applications.

The grouping of different spectral modules is feasible, for
instance, high-spatial-resolution with medium-spatial/high-
spectral resolution modules, or a combination of tilted modules for stereoscopic imaging. (See Fig. 2.)

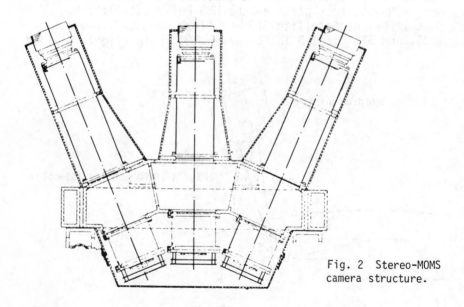

Fig. 2 Stereo-MOMS
camera structure.

Optoelectronic Concept

The optoelectronic concept makes use of CCD technology for scanning. The MOMS-01 sensors are Reticon CCPD-1728 type with 1728 photosensitive elements each (Fig. 3).

Scan line extension beyond one CCD array is achieved with the dual-lens principle (Fig. 4). In the case of MOMS-01, four arrays giving a total number of 6.912 pixels/scan line are linked.

For further MOMS development lines of up to 6 arrays/focal plane are feasible. The line frequency can be adapted to the relative flight velocity up to 500 lines/s. The refractive lens systems provide total fields of view (FOV) of up to $\pm$ 35 deg with undistorted focal planes.

Multispectral Configuration

MOMS-01 is designed as a multispectral sensor. The two bands used are optimized for geological applications and vegetation discrimination (Fig. 5).

Scan Principle

Digital data collected with a fully electronic push-broom scanner can be processed directly by means of computers without any intermediate steps.

The MOMS-01 system consists of five major parts (Fig. 6):

1) The optical module (scanner head) with four objectives, eight sensor arrays, and associated mechanisms (shutters) and electronics (controls and readout). The modular optical group, which contains all optical and allied components consists of a rigid plate with the objectives (manufactured by Optische Werke Rodenstock) and tubes mounted to it. The plate is statically determined mounted to the housing to prevent mechanical and thermal bending.

2) The power box for the overall power conditioning and thermal and shutter circuitry.

3) The logic box for the major tasks of controlling sensor functions, real-time correction, and formating of the digital data stream from the optical module, which controls the operational sequences.

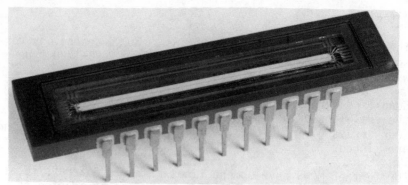

Fig. 3 MOMS optoelectronic concept, Reticon CCPD 1728.

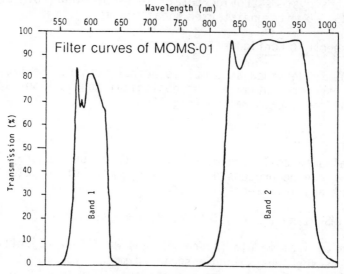

Fig. 4 MOMS dual-lens principle.

4) The high-density digital tape (HDDT) recording system, which is essentially a Bell & Howell MARS-1428 LT-3B for reformating and storage of the digital image data.

5) The container to guarantee a pressurized environment (about 3 psi) for the recording system.

The MOMS-01 was mounted to the modular carbon-fiber structure of the SPAS-01 carrier, which was the first reusable space platform to be deployed and retrieved by the orbiter's remote manipulator arm (see Plate 14 in the color section of this volume).

The MOMS-01 system parameters are summarized in Table 1.

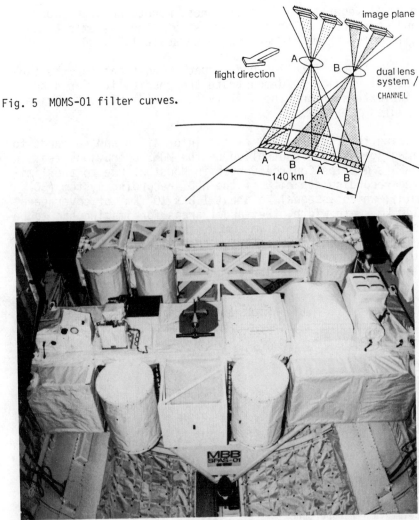

Fig. 5 MOMS-01 filter curves.

Fig. 6 SPAS-01 with MOMS-01 during integration in Shuttle cargo bay (STS-7).

MOMS-01 Missions on STS-7 and STS-11/41-B

The attached-mode experiment of the missions operation of MOMS fulfilled both the geoscientific and technical objectives of the missions, as follows:

1) Imaging of different ground targets with low-to-high contrast and albedo in the visible and near-infrared part of the spectrum over arid areas, areas with dense-to-sparse

natural vegetation, coastal zones, mountaineous regions, and open-ocean islands to demonstrate the system's capability for thematic mapping up to scale 1:50,000.

2) System verification under space conditions for the two-channel version to demonstrate the possibility for scan line extension and the ability to combine pixel-coincident modules.

During the flights, all status information and commands for imaging could be controlled by the MOMS operations team in NASA's Mission Control Center in Houston. Due to the limited recording capacity of the HDDT recording system (30 min), which is equal to about 1.8×10^6 km^2 of coverage at 140 km swath width, the target areas for imaging had to be selected carefully to maximize the geoscientific portion of the missions. The selected test sites were preferrably to be cloud-free with respect to MOMS' spectral bands in the visible and near-infrared range. An information net-

Table 1   MOMS-01 system parameters

Optical Module	
Sensor	Reticon CCPD 1728
No. of CCDs per line	4
Pixel size	16 x 16 μm
Channel 1	575-625 nm
Channel 2	825-975 nm
Ground pixels/line	6912
Ground pixel size	20 m (300 km orbit)
Swath width	138 km (300 km orbit)
Line frequency	50 Hz + 10%
Radiometric Resolution	128 (7 bit)
Gain factor	1 or 2
Focal length	237.2 mm
Relative lens aperture	1:3.5
Instantaneous field of view	67.5 urad
Total field of view	26.2 deg
Distortion	± 8 um (TFOV)
Recording System	
Units	Bell & Howell high-density-system MARS-1428/EDEM
Input data channels	14 parallel, plus clock
Total input data rate	40 megabit/s
Tape speed	60 in./s
Tape capacity	72 gigabit
Bit error rate	10^{-5} reproduced on M14L

work was set up to meet these requirements. On the basis of NASA's calculated orbit data geoscientific important areas were selected.

Real-time weather information over the test areas was obtained via the geostationary weather spacecrafts ESA-Meteosat-2, GOES-East, INSAT-2, and Japan's GMS-2 and evaluated by a team of geoscientists and meteorologists with special experience in synoptic and dynamic weather forecasts. The situation was telephoned to the imaging team at Houston Mission Control Center, where the final decision for imaging

Table 2 MOMS-01 STS-7 and STS-11 mission summary

	STS-7	STS-11
Launch date	June 18, 1983	February 3, 1984
Launch time, UTC	11:33	13:00
Mission duration, days	6	8
Inclination, deg	28.5	28.5
Orbit altitude, n.m.	158	152, 172
MOMS operation	24 h	4 days
No. of data takes	4	33
Shuttle landing	Edwards AFB	Kennedy Space Center

Table 3 Summary of MOMS-01 data sequences

Region	Sequences	Duration	Duration	Area covered
STS-7				
Africa/Arabia	1	1260	21.0	1 346 300
East Asia	1	90	1.5	89 900
India	1	90	1.5	89 900
South Africa	1	120	2.0	117 900
Total	4	1560	26.0	1 644 000
STS-11 (41-B)				
Africa/Arabia	9	1176	19.6	1 234 800
Australia	4	204	3.4	214 200
India	2	48	0.8	50 400
South America	5	259	4.3	271 950
Southeast Asia	1	72	1.2	75 600
USA	1	24	0.4	25 200
Total	22	1783	29.7	1 872 150

was met 1-1.5 h before the actual data sequence (Fig. 7).
Using this network, MOMS acquired 26 image sequences or
nearly 300 image frames with more than 90 % of them under
cloud-free or near cloud-free conditions and a sun elevation
of higher than 25 deg.

Four sequences were collected during the STS-7 mission,
where the decision for imaging was limited due to thermal
problems with the data handling system of the SPAS carrier,
and 22 sequences on STS-11. See Tables 2 and 3.

In spite of the limited recording capabilities and very
short mission duration (when compared to other optical remote sensing systems), an optimum set of data was obtained.
Plate 15 (see color section of this volume) is representative of the products from this mission.

With regard to future "dedicated missions" for specific geoscientific tasks, the efficiency of the missions can significantly be improved by avoiding unnecessary data.

MOMS Program Outline

The MOMS hardware development started in 1976 at MBB with
the realization of an electro-optical scanner (EOS) to demonstrate the concept feasibility with one array in the focal plane of a single lens. Several flight test programs
delivered the first push-broom scanner image data.

Breadboarding for a thermal infrared scanner was performed
in 1979-1980 together with the beginning of the MOMS-EM 1/2
development, which is the functional engineering model of
MOMS-01 d igned for aircraft application only. It incorpo-

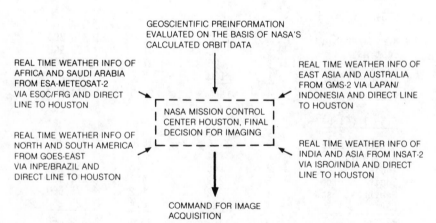

Fig. 7 Diagram of information network for the MOMS-01 image acquisition.

rated the technical concept of MOMS-01, featuring the same
two spectral bands, four objectives and eight detector arrays as well as data storage via the recording on high-density digital tape. Several airborne missions have been completed successfully, resulting in a series of high-resolution images. MOMS-EM 1/2 is scheduled for further airborne
missions, e.g., to map and monitor the effects of acid rain
on vegetation.

MOMS-01, the first space-qualified representative flown
aboard the Shuttle, returned the highest resolution remotely sensed data from space to date (excluding military reconnaissance sensors).

The future development of the MOMS instrument family aims
at the realization of a highly advanced remote sensing system, featuring in-track stereoscopic and three- or four-
band multispectral capabilities. These instruments have
been studied and an initial design has been completed. Some
preparatory hardware has been developed. The German Minister for Research and Technology (BMFT) has already funded
the development of a Stereo-MOMS operating in a panchromatic mode (Table 4), which is scheduled for space flight in
1987 or 1988.

Parallel to these activities, a phase-B study on a short-
wave-infrared MOMS module (SWIR-MOMS), financed by the BMFT
and supported by the European Space Agency (ESA) and the
German Aerospace Research Establishment (DFVLR) is under

Table 4 Specification of Stereo-MOMS (preliminary)

Bands	0.4-0.9 μm panchromatic
Ground pixel size	10 m
Height resolution	less than 15 m
Radiometric resolution	7 bit (8 bit possible)
Swath width	90 km

Table 5 Specification of a multispectral MOMS with SWIR module
(preliminary)

Band 1	0.6 ± 0.025 μm
Band 2	0.9 ± 0.075 μm
Band 3	1.6 ± 0.1 μm
Band 4	2.2 ± 0.1 μm
No.of pixels per line	Up to 10.000
Ground pixel size	20 x 20 m^2 visible and SWIR

way. Implementation began in 1984 with the development of applicable for aircraft missions in advance of a spaceborne version planned for space flight in 1988-1989 (Table 5).

Within the framework of these research and development programs, available array technology will be evaluated for both MOMS options.

The MOMS program is focussed on Shuttle-related activities without being dependent on the Space Transportation System. Complementary to Landsat and SPOT, MOMS can be operated in specific configurations during or between several Shuttle flights. For the latter type of mission, a Shuttle-retrievable platform such as a SPAS free-flyer or EURECA (an ESA development) has to be considered. Within this context, the idea of dedicated MOMS missions has been introduced. A dedicated mission may be purely scientific, application oriented, or both. In upcoming experimental or operational Radar missions (SIR, Radarsat) or aboard the man-tended polar platform of the Space Station a refurbished 3- or 4-channel MOMS instrument could provide the indispensable high-resolution spectral information.

Conclusion

The MOMS instrument development has proved its space qualification with the experimental missions aboard two Shuttle missions. As a result of its successful performance, a cooperative effort has begun between NASA and the German Minister for Research and Technology to exchange Landsat-Thematic Mapper and MOMS-01 data for comparative analysis. Although the MOMS-01 system offers limited spectral information because it has only two spectral bands, its modularity and high-resolution are significant steps toward the applicability of remote sensing for the benefit of Earth resources management.

Bibliography

Bodechtel, J.,"MOMS Program Outline and Future Aspects", Paper presented at IGARSS Symposium, Strasbourg, France, 1984.

Bodechtel, J., Haydn, R., Meissner, D., Seige, P.,and Winkenbach, H., "MOMS-01 on STS-7 and STS-11 Mission and Results," Paper presented at IGARSS Symposium, Strasbourg, France, 1984.

Bodechtel, J. et al., "The Information Network for a Real-Time Controlled Data Acquisition of MOMS," Paper presented at IGARSS Symposium, Strasbourg, France, 1984.

Bodechtel, J., Haydn, R., Laucht, H., and Meissner, D., "Modular Optoelectronical Multsispectral Scanner (MOMS) for Earth Observation, First Results of STS-7 Mission," Paper presented at IGARSS Symposium, San Francisco, 1983.

Bodechtel, J..et al., "MOMS, ein Modularer Optoelektronischer Multispektral Scanner, Spezifikation und Ergebnisse der Mission auf STS-7," Jahrbuch DGLR, 1983.

Bodechtel, J., Enderlein, G., Hauck, M., Hiller, K., Neukum, G., and Seige, P., "MOMS-01 and Landsat-MSS-Aufnahmen aus dem Altiplano, Bolivien," Geogr.Rundschau, Braunschweig, FRG, 1984.

Bodechtel, J., Meissner, D., and Zilger, J., "The MOMS-01 Experiments on STS-7 and STS-11/41-B, First Results and Further Development of the Modular Optoelectronic Multispectral Scanner," Paper presented at ISPRS Congress, Rio de Janeiro, 1984.

Kaufmann, H., Bodechtel, J., and Haydn, R., "Spectral Significance of MOMS Versus LANDSAT-Data and Future Aspects: Preliminary Results," Paper presented at IGARSS Symposium, Strasbourg, France, 1984.

Meissner, D., "Modular Optoelectronic Multispectral Scanner (MOMS) Development," Paper presented at 20th Goddard Memorial Symposium and 4th Joint AAS/DGLR Symposium, Goddard Space Flight Center, Goddard, Md., March 1982.

ERS-1: Mission Objectives and System Description

G. Duchossois*

European Space Agency, Paris, France

Abstract

The development and manufacture phase of the First ESA Remote Sensing satellite (known as ERS-1) started in January 1985 and is conducted by an industrial consortium of European and Canadian companies. The objective is to launch ERS-1 in mid-1989. This paper briefly describes the overall ERS-1 system and the various potential applications which may benefit from ERS-1 data.

Introduction

One of the major outcomes of the space programs has been the ability of remote sensing satellites to provide repetitive and continuous coverage of the Earth's surface on a very large scale, up to and including global scale. They can also provide access to remote and normally inaccessible areas where information is either sparse or nonexistent, such as the oceans.

ERS-1 and similar satellites will provide wide coverage that can be allied to conventional, more limited, but precise recording systems to yield more information than the sum of the individual parts. ERS-1 is expected to be the forerunner of a series of European remote sensing satellites to become operational in the 1990s. The ERS-1 mission objectives are of both and economic and scientific nature, such as :

1) To establish, develop, and exploit the coastal, ocean and ice applications of remote sensing data. These applications, related mainly to a better knowledge of ocean parameters and sea-state conditions, are important in view of the increasing development of coastal and offshore activities and the adoption by countries of the 200 n.mi. economic zone. Furthermore, all-weather, high-resolution

*Program Manager, ERS Program.

imaging capability over the Earth's surface with the synthetic aperture radar (SAR) will also provide useful data
as a complement to optical data received from other satellites such as Landsat or SPOT.
2) To increase the scientific understanding that of
Coastal zone and global ocean processes that, together
with the monitoring of polar regions, will provide a
major contribution to the World Climate Research program
(WCRP).
The overall concept selected for the ERS-1 space and
ground segments is characterized by a number of unique
and very challenging features or objectives :
1) ERS-1 is designed as an end-to-end data system covering all functions and tasks from the sensors onboard the
spacecraft to the acquisition, processing, and delivery
of data and/or products to end users on the ground,
irrespective of what entity, European Space Agency (ESA)
or national, is in charge of the various tasks or parts
of the complete ERS-1 system.
2) ERS-1 aims to be a global mission (except for the
Synthetic Aperture Radar sensor) capable of providing
worthwhile geographical coverage compatible, of course,
with the duty cycles of the instruments.
3) Particular emphasis has been put on microwave instrumentation with an all-weather capability.
4) It is planned to deliver a number of so-called standard products to end users within 3 h of observation.
This is particularly important for a number of applications (commercial or otherwise) aimed at the monitoring
of highly dynamic phenomena such as waves and winds.
5) Performances of both the space and ground segments are
very ambitious, but are mandatory to pave the way to
future operational systems.
6) ERS-1 aims to be both an experimental and pre-operational system : experimental to validate complete space
and ground segment concept, to tune algorithms, and to
prepare user communities, and preoperational to demonstrate on a limited scale the operational capability of
the system.
7) ERS-1, the first remote sensing satellite developed by
ESA, is the first element of an overall Earth observation
satellite program and is considered a test for Europe of
its capability to develop and implement such a complex
system. ERS-1 should be a "market opener" for Europe.

ERS-1 Payload

Priority in the payload has been given to a comprehensive
set of radar instruments designed to observe the surface

wind and wave structure over the oceans. These instruments consist of a C-band wind scatterometer designed to
measure wind speed and direction; a Ku-band radar altimeter to measure significant wave height and wind speed
at nadir and provide measurements over ice and major
ocean currents; and a C-band synthetic aperture radar
(SAR) to take all-weather high resolution images over
polar caps, coastal zones, and land areas. The latter
will also be operated in a sampled mode over oceans as a
wave scatterometer with the aim of measuring the wave
spectrum.

In addition to these priority instruments, the following
elements are included : laser retroreflectors for accurate tracking of the satellite and radar altimeter calibration; an along-track scanning radiometer completed with
a two-frequency microwave nadir sounder (ATSR-M) to
measure sea surface temperature and to provide information for the "wet-atmosphere" correction for the radar
altimeter; and a precise-range and range rate experiment
(PRARE) to provide high-accuracy tracking information in
support of the radar altimetry for ocean circulation
studies. The last two items on this list have been included as the result of an announcement of opportunity
issued by ESA to the participating states.

In order to reduce the required mass, volume and cost,
the wind scatterometer and SAR have been combined into
one hardware package known as the C-band active microwave
instrument (AMI). Mass and power budgets for the main
elements of the spacecraft are given in Table 1.

Table 2 lists the various geophysical parameters to be
measured by the onboard instruments. Paramater values for
each of the instruments are given in the Appendix.

                        Spacecraft and Orbit

The ERS-1 spacecraft will use the multimission platform
(PFM) developed under the French SPOT program. Characteristics and performances of the platform are given in
Table 3. The platform is configured to operate in a sun-
synchronous orbit. The spacecraft configuration is shown
in Fig. 1.

ERS-1 will be launched from Kourou, French Guiana, by the
Ariane launcher into a sun-synchronous (i.e., quasi
polar), circular orbit with a mean local time (descending
node) of 10:30. The baseline repeat cycle will be 3 days,
but there will be sufficient fuel to enable the repeat
cycle to be changed several times within the 3 year
mission by means of a small change of the orbit alti-

Table 1 Mass and power budgets of ERS-1 main elements

Spacecraft overall mass	2250 kg (including 300 kg hydrazine)	
Spacecraft overall power	2.5 kW at B.O.L. (2 kW after 2 years in orbit)	
Spacecraft overall size	Solar panel length = 11.30 m SAR antenna = 10 m Spacecraft body = 2m x 2m x 5.7 m Overall height = 12 m (deployed)	

	MASS (kg)	POWER (W)
Platform	1300 (inc. 300 kg hydrazine	280
Payload		
. AMI wind/wave mode	)	540
. AMI SAR mode	) 350	1270
. Radar altimeter	100	175
. ATSR	55	90
. PRARE	15	50
. Laser retroreflectors	2.5	
. Payload data handling and transmission	80	195
. Payload support structure	235	–

tude. In all cases, the stability of ground track repeat cycles will be maintained within ±1 km. The nominal orbit altitude of 777 km has been selected as a compromise between the higher air drag of a lower orbit and the need for greater power for the radar instruments at a higher orbit.

Downlink and Ground Segment

Three digital data streams are generated from the satellite payload and transmitted to ground on two frequencies at X-band, as follows :

Table 2   Geophysical measurements and ERS-1 performance parameters

Main Geophysical Parameter	Range	Accuracy	Main Instrument
Wind Field			
– Velocity	4-24 m/s	± 2 m/s or 10 % whichever is greater	Wind Scatterometer & Altimeter
– Direction	0-360 deg	± 20 deg	Wind Scatterometer
Wave Field			
– Significant Wave Height	1-20 m	± 0,5 m or 10 % whichever is greater	Altimeter
– Wave Direction	0-360 deg	± 15 deg	SAR Wave Mode
– Wavelength	50-1000 m	· 20 %	SAR Wave Mode
Earth Surface Imaging			
– Land/Ice/Coastal Zones etc.	80 km (minimum swathwidth)	Geometric/Radiometric Resolutions: a) 30 m/2,5 dB b) 100 m/1 dB	SAR imaging Mode
Altitude			
– Over ocean	745-825 km	2 m absolute ± 10 cm relative	Altimeter
Satellite Range		± 10 cm	PRARE
Sea Surface Temperature	500 km swath	± 0,5 K	ATSR (IR)
Water Vapour	in 25 km spot	10 %	μW Sounder

Table 3   Platform characteristics

PLATFORM BUS

IN-FLIGHT CONFIGURATION
OF THE
PLATFORM MULTIMISSION

– **PAYLOAD CAPABILITY : ≠ 950 kg**

– **POWER : SOLAR ARRAY ≠ 2 kw BOL**

– **ENERGY STORAGE : 4 × 23 A H BATTERIES**

– **ATTITUDE/ORBIT CONTROL :**

   – **POINTING : .15° ON ANGLES**
      $10^{-3°}$/Sec ON RATES
   – **POSSIBLE UTILISATION OF FAMS (30" ARC)**
   – **ORBIT CONTROL UP TO 580 000 N. sec**
     300 kg HYDRAZINE

– **COMMUNICATIONS**

   – **S BAND COMPATIBLE ESA/NASA**
   – **2 kbps TELEMETRY/TELECOMMAND**

– **DATA HANDLING**

   – **PAYLOAD MONITORING AND CONTROL**
    VIA PLATFORM ON-BOARD COMPUTER

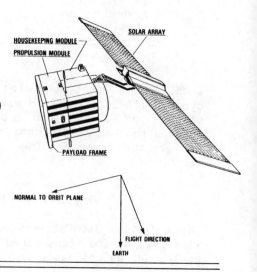

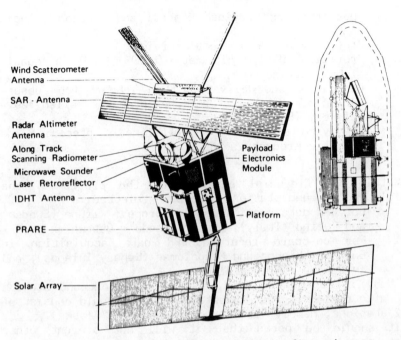

Wind Scatterometer Antenna

SAR - Antenna

Radar Altimeter Antenna

Along Track Scanning Radiometer

Microwave Sounder

Laser Retroreflector

IDHT Antenna

PRARE

Payload Electronics Module

Platform

Solar Array

Fig. 1 Satellite in flight and launch configuration.

- Link 1 : 8140 MHz
  Direct read-out of the raw SAR data (imag-
  ing mode of the AMI).
  Data rate: 105 Mbps

- Link 2 : Centre frequency for data transmission =
  8040 MHz

  . Channel A : Direct read-out of the low data rate
  instruments (i.e. all instruments
  except the SAR in full imaging mode).
  Data rate: 1 Mbps

  . Channel B : Playback of the recorded data, consisting of the output of the low data
  rate instruments. (Recorder capacity : 6.5 Gbits, corresponding to
  storage during one orbit period,
  i.e. 100 mins).
  Data rate: 15 Mbps

The ground segment concept which has been selected will
provide the following functions :

- Spacecraft and payload control and mission management
- Provision of SAR regional service
- Provision of low bit rate (LBR) global or quasi-global service
- Generation and delivery within 3 hours from observation of a number of selected products called fast-delivery (FD) products.
- Archiving and generation off-line of precision and thematic products.

Within the financial envelope of the programme, the following ground stations have been selected :
- For SAR data acquisition in Europe : Kiruna (Sweden) and Fucino (Italy), and in Canada : Ottawa
- For on-board recorded LBR data acquisition in Europe : Kiruna and Maspalomas (Canary Islands), and in Canada : Prince Albert

(N.B. : For the LBR data, an alternative ground station configuration is also investigated which would consist of 2 stations, namely Kiruna and Fairbanks in Alaska).
It should be noted that it will not prevent other stations (e.g. in Australia, Brazil, India, etc.) requesting access to ERS-1 data, both SAR and LBR, subject to an agreement with the Agency. This access will be limited only to the real-time data (no access to the LBR recorded on-board the spacecraft).
It is intended to achieve the generation of FD products and their dissemination to the users within 3 hours from observation (likely via satellite links). The following products are considered :
- SAR "Fast Delivery" images
- wind speed and direction over a 500 km swath
- wind speed at nadir
- wave height at nadir
- wave image spectra.

Functions such as :
- archiving facility(ies);
- generation of "precision products", i.e. products which will not be generated in near real-time, either because of the processing load involved, or because of the need for a posteriori data (e.g. refined orbit data for some altimeter products)
- SAR precision product
- Wave spectra
- From the radar altimeter data :
  . Geophysical products for land ice (land ice profile, roughness)

. Special ocean geophysical products (refined
   significant wave height, ocean skewness)
. High precision geophysical products (sea
   surface topography)
- Sea surface temperature field
- Cloud top temperature
- Water vapour distribution

Utilization and Potential Applications of ERS-1 Data

Two quite different commmunities will be served by ERS-1:
(a) The **applications community** using ERS-1 data on a continuous and operational basis for various projects such
as offshore petroleum activities, ship routing, fishing,
sea-ice monitoring, etc.   They require data/product
delivery within a few (1-3) hours of observation.   (b)
The **scientific community,** more concerned with the development of remote sensing techniques, sensors, basic
physics understanding, usually prefers to handle annotated raw data as input to models and algorithms and has
no requirement for short delivery times (computer-compatible tapes would meet their needs).

ERS-1 Missions

ERS-1 will fulfil a number of missions which can be divided, for convenience sake, into three main categories :

A.   Meteorological mission

This mission concerns mainly short and medium-term
weather and sea-state forecasts for which near-real-time
data acquisition and processing are mandatory. Forecast
activity includes a number of steps following the acquisition of satellite data and the transformation of these
data into physical quantities. These are:
1) Merging of satellite data with data from other
sources (i.e. buoys, radio sondes, research vessels,
other satellite data, etc.).
2) Implementation of a numerical model.
3) Interpretation of model predictions in terms of the
special operational conditions of the industrial activity.
4) Communication of refined information to field operators.
5) Monitoring of the accuracy and usefulness of forecasts
and feedback into operational systems.

The major limitation of current ocean and atmospheric forecasts is the lack of data over the open ocean. This is particularly severe in the vast oceanic areas of the Southern Hemisphere, but is also apparent in the Northern Hemisphere due to the reduction of the number of weather ships in the Atlantic. Numerical experiments in the United States and Canada using Seasat data and in Europe (by the European Centre for Medium Range Weather Forecasts) have shown that the inclusion of such data in the models provides more accurate forecasts, valid for longer periods of time.

Weather Forecast. The basic information required to initiate meteorological models is wind field, temperature, and humidity in three-dimensions and with boundary conditions. This information is used on three different levels: as initial conditions to numerical models; to validate and tune models; and to monitor climate parameters. Improvements are expected for local forecasts up to 36-48 h requiring fine-mesh models (100 km). Meteorological services in Europe utilize different models but, typically, they cover one-third of the hemisphere; data are fed every 6 h with a cutoff time of 2-3 h after the synoptic time.
Better medium and long range forecasts (up to 10 days) are also expected. These use a coarse mesh (300 km) and require hemispherical or even global data. Cutoff time after the synoptic time can be as long as 4-5 h.

Sea-state forecast. Most wave models use a wind field derived from the atmospheric forecast model. ERS-1's capability to generate wind information directly will result in improved forecasts. Various models exist in the United States and Europe for local and regional forecast up to 36-48 hours, leading to requirements similar to those above. An important additional benefit from ERS-1 will be the capability to check and tune the models with direct measurement of wave height (altimeter), wave spectrum (wave scatterometer) and wind field (wind scatterometer).

B.   Climatological mission

This is the long-term aspect of the previous mission where the continuous monitoring of various ocean parameters will allow the establishment of a data base providing statistical information for a number of scientific and application purposes. This mission does not need real-time data processing and distribution.

C. Imaging mission

The imaging capability provided by the SAR will be performed over the polar caps to monitor land ice and sea ice features, coastal zones to monitor costal processes, and land as a complement to optical data.
Depending on the applications, data may or may not have to be processed and distributed in near real-time. As an example, most of ice applications will require a very fast processing and distribution time (less than 3 h) as do similarly, land applications such as disaster monitoring (e.g., floods). On the contrary, coastal applications such as bathymetry are not real-time activities.
It should be recalled that the SAR will also operate in a sampled mode (called the wave scatterometer mode) over the oceans to provide small images (5 x 5 km) from which the wave spectrum will be derived. If requested, this mode could also be operated over land or ice areas to collect small size images.

ERS-1 Data Categorization and Utilization

Data generated by the ERS-1 instruments can be categorized as functions of their "maturity" for various applications and their ability to fulfill present and future user requirements. This does not necessarily lead to establishing priorities but only to indicating to satellite designers and operators the conflicting requirements in terms of platform resources (e.g. power allocation, storage capacity, etc.). Furthermore, this "categorization" may evolve with time, taking into account the rapid progress made in some application sectors linked to the development of new industrial activities. For instance, oil offshore activities in northern Canada (Beaufort Sea, Melville Straits) may trigger and increase the development of microwave remote sensing techniques for ice monitoring, an application currently considered to be in an early stage.

i)   Category A: Operational (or quasi-operational) data : These are typically data coming from the wind scatterometer, radar altimeter, and the along track scanning radiometer (ATSR). Wind field, wave height, and sea surface temperature (SST) data are used today by weather and sea-state forecast centres on an operational basis.Some of these data (e.g. SST) are measured by satellite and some are derived from non-satellite measurements (weather ships,

radio sondes, etc.). A major problem identified
here is the need for the development of models
accepting asynoptic data as generated by near-polar
satellites; work is already in progress on this
subject, both in Europe and the United States.

The industrial activities that will most benefit
from the forecast improvement and accurate
measurement of sea surface temperatures include:

1) Offshore activities by providing synoptic data
   for short-term forecasting for planning of
   operations during the construction of oil
   platforms and the exploitation phase of the oil
   field; and a continuous monitoring of ocean
   parameters for the establishment of statistics
   on the wave and wind fields for the engineering
   design of oil platforms. (Note: There is no
   real-time requirement for this activity.)

2) Ship routing by reducing the time on trade
   routes and, consequently, reducing total fuel
   consumption, and improving the safety by
   reduction in hull damage, cargo damage, marine
   insurance costs, catastrophic ship losses, etc.

3) Fisheries by accurate measurement of
   sea-surface temperatures that will allow the
   determination of temperature fronts. This
   information, combined with meteorological and
   oceanic data (e.g. wind field, wave field),
   will allow the evolution of the thermal fronts
   to be monitored, which is of prime importance
   to locate pelagic fish species living in the
   vicinity of the sea surface, e.g. tuna. This
   will lead mainly to a more efficient mangement
   of the fish resources and to an improvement in
   the efficiency of fishing fleets (navigation
   and routing aspects).

ii) Category B : Preoperational data, SAR imagery over
    ice : Experiments conducted, mostly in Canada, with
    airborne SAR and Seasat SAR data have demonstrated
    the capability of SAR to identify some ice features
    (extent, type, roughness, movement) that are of
    importance for operations and activities in the high
    latitude areas infested by ice. Today airborne SAR
    systems are operationally used over the Beaufort Sea

in support of oil and gas exploration activities.
It is expected that the C-band SAR on ERS-1 will
satisfy requirements from "ice users": this implies
a very fast process time and delivery (about 3 h
from acquisition). Daily (or even more frequent)
coverage of the area to be monitored would be required for an operational system.

iii) Category C : Experimental data, SAR imagery over
oceans and land : Sea surface and wave imaging
mechanisms are still in a relatively early stage of
understanding, although considerable progress has
been made since Seasat imagery over oceans has been
available. There is still some controversy on the
basic physics of the phenomena and also on the
interpretation of data, partly due to lack of simultaneous in situ measurements. This is particularly
true for the derivation of the wave spectrum information from wave images. Such potential applications of SAR imagery over oceans as surface pollution detection would require fast processing and
delivery of data (about 3 h) and this is again very
challenging, in particular for pollution where
complete scenes have to be processed. Conversely,
for wave (image) spectrum, only small 5 x 5 km
scenes will have to be processed.
ERS-1's capability to generate all-weather high
resolution images over land with the SAR will be
used to complement optical data provided by other
satellites (Landsat-4 and 5, SPOT ...) for a number
of land applications, e.g., geology, land-use, crop
monitoring, etc.
It should be noted that some data classed in category A will be of use for applications using data
put in category B or C. For example, ice drift
forecast, pollution trajectory prediction, etc.,
will make use of category A data (wind field, wave
height, etc.) as inputs in models.

iv) Category D : Scientific data. Although the above
list primarily addresses the economic/commercial
application aspects of ERS-1, it is clear that ERS-1
will also benefit the scientific understanding of
coastal zones and global ocean processes which,
together with the monitoring of polar regions, will
provide a major contribution to the World Climate
Research Program. ERS-1 data used alone or, more
commonly, in conjunction with complementary data
from buoys, radio-sondes, research vessels, other

near-surface platforms, and other satellites in pre-arranged or regional experiments, will enable significant advances to be made in several areas :

1)   Physical oceanography and glaciology : The measurements of wind field, wave spectra and wave height that are used in near-real time for forecasting ocean conditions will also be used to improve the understanding of wave generation and propagation and to produce more refined models of these dynamic processes. The little-understood mesoscale eddies are detectable by altimetry and a precise knowledge (decimeter level) of the satellite orbit would allow sea surface topography analysis.
A combination of altimetry measurements and microwave imagery can be used for the study of ice-sheet profiles and the behaviour of sea-ice in the polar regions.

2)   Climatology : A priority research topic envisaged with the World Climate Research Program is the "controlling effect of the physics and dynamics of the oceans on the global cycles of heat, water and chemicals (especially carbon) in the climate system."

The wind stress on the sea surface is one of the primary variables in climate research. Wind stress exerted upon the surface of the ocean is the major driving force that maintains the ocean currents and generates the surface waves responsible for downward mixing of heat, thereby increasing the thickness of the heat storage layer. It affects the amount of thermal energy in the ocean and is fundamental to modelling air-sea interactions.
Monitoring of the sea ice in the polar oceans is also important because of the strong thermal effects resulting from changing ice cover.
Satellite data will be used in conjunction with a wide variety of other data in international experiments that are already being planned, such as the World Ocean Circulation Experiment (WOCE), and the Tropical Ocean/Global Atmosphere (TOGA) experiment.
Table 4 illustrates the relevance of the various instruments to mission capabilities.

                    Demonstration Missions

It is essential when designing the ERS-1 mission to involve the user community in the development of the

Table 4   Relevance of instruments to mission objectives

	ALTIMETER + PRARE	ATSR IR	C-BAND ACTIVE MICROWAVE INSTRUMENTATION		
			IMAGING MODE	WAVE MODE	WIND MODE
Weather forecast		X			X
Sea-state forecast	X			X	X
Offshore activity	X	X		X	X
Ship routing	X	X		X	X
Fisheries (fish location)	X	X			X
Sea & iceberg monitoring	(X)	(X)	X		
Oil & pollution detection		X	X		
Coastal processes		X	X		
Land applications	(X)		X		
Ocean circulation	X^1	X	(X)		X
Ocean tides	X^2				
Wind fields^3	X		(X)	X	X
Wave fields^3	X		(X)	X	X
Sea surface temperature		X			
Polar oceans	X	X	X	X	X
Land ice	X		(X)		
Marine biology		(X)			

X : indicates a principal contribution to the objectives.
1 : for large-scale circulation, an accurate orbit determination over short arcs is required.
2 : for solar tides, measurements from other satellites in complementary orbits is required.
3 : the altimeter and the C-band active microwave instrumentation are mutually supportive in deriving the wind and wave fields.

requirements, the system and the evaluation of the performance of the system. ESA has made a special effort to involve these communities in the definition of the mission requirements and intends to pursue this effort through the development and exploitation phases of ERS-1, considered as both an experimental and preoperational system.
It will be experimental since, as the first ESA mission, it will have to demonstrate that the concept and technology for both the space and ground segments are correct

for the applications envisaged and that the users are
ready and able to use the data generated. This will
require a number of activities before and after launch
that are very important for the success of the mission,
such as : simulation and optimisation of sensor performances (airborne testing), development and testing of
algorithms and models, setting up and testing of data
products, definition of distribution networks to meet
user requirements, development of pilot projects (small
scale) and demonstration missions (large scale), and continuation of research and development to optimize the use
and value of the data provided by the satellite system.
On the other hand, ERS-1 will have to demonstrate an operational capability for some appropriate applications and
on a limited scale, an operational capability. This
will, of course, require that data or products be delivered in quasi real-time to corresponding existing operational services or end users. To this effect, the Agency
has set up teams of experts, called Instrument and Data
teams, to advise ESA on all user-related/scientific/
technical aspects of each instrument and, for the overall
system, on the operational aspects, data handling/ dissemination, and promotion aspects of the program. Scientific and application-oriented experts from the participating states are contributing to these teams throughout
the development and exploitation phases of the ERS-1
program.
To further promote the utilization of ERS-1 data, ESA
will issue an Announcement of Opportunity/Call for
scientific and application experiment proposals in
November/December 1985 with the aim of selecting
Principal Investigators by July 1986.

Preparation of Follow-on Operational Missions

With ERS-1, it is expected that a gradual transfer of
applications from experimental to operational users will
take place, preparing future users for later operational
satellite systems. Although not yet approved, as a first
step it is planned to propose to the participating states
in ERS-1 to consider the launch of a second flight unit,
nearly identical to ERS-1, 2-3 years after the launch of
ERS-1, i.e. in the 1992-1993 timeframe, thereby providing
the user community with 5-6 years of continuous data.
Lastly, the ultimate goal would be to set up or to contribute to an operational multi-satellite system for
global rather than regional monitoring.

Conclusion

Within Europe, there is particular interest in a satellite monitoring program over such important economic areas as the oceans, the coastal zones and ice caps. Equally, there exists an active European scientific community which recognizes the potential value of modern spaceborne sensors to longer-term studies of ocean processes and their relevance to climatological problems.

In conclusion, it is clear that if Europe wants to be present on the world scene with operational remote sensing satellite systems in the 1990s, it is necessary to develop now an experimental/preoperational satellite program with a first launch around 1989. All necessary capabilities, whether industrial, scientific or economic, exist in Europe and the positive decision taken in July 1984 by ESA Member States, plus Austria, Canada and Norway, to develop the ERS-1 program should allow Europe not only to guarantee its presence in the world competition but also to provide a contribution to future worldwide systems aiming at global monitoring of coastal zones and oceans.

Appendix: Instrument Characteristics

ERS-1 AMI SAR Mode Characteristics

Spatial Resolution	30 x 30 m
Swath width	80 km(1)
Radiometric Resolution	2.5 dB
at min σ_0 of	- 18 dB
Orbital height (nominal)	777 km
Incidence angle (nominal)	23°
RF frequency	5.3 GHz
RF peak power	4.8 kW
RF mean power	300 W(2)
Pulse length	37 μs
Compressed pulse length	64 ns
Bandwidth	19 MHz
PRF (nominal)	1700 Hz
Antenna length	10.0 m
Antenna height	1.0 m
Raw data quantisation	5I + 5Q

(1) The goal is to increase this to 100 km
(2) At output of power amplifier

ERS-1 Altimeter Parameters

Frequency	13.5 GHz
Bandwidth	400 MHz
Pulse length	20 µs
Peak RF power	50 W
PRF	1.0 kHz (approx)
Antenna diameter	1.2 m
Significant wave height	
measurement range	1 m to 20 m
measurement accuracy	0.5 m or 10%
Attitude measurement accuracy	10 cm (1σ, 1s)
Backscatter coefficient	
accuracy	± 1 dB (1σ)
Tracking window (ocean mode)	64 gates x 3 ns each
Tracking window (ice mode)	64 gates x 12 ns each

PRARE Characteristics

Up-link	10 MHz in the band 7.19-7.235 GHz
Down-link	10 MHz in the band 8.45-8.50 GHz
S-band downlink	1 MHz in the band 2.20-2.29 GHz
Power Consumption	50 W
Predicted Ranging Accuracy	5-10 cm

ERS-1 AMI Wind Mode Characteristics

Spatial resolution	50 km
Sample spacing (pixel size)	25 km
Swath (one sided)	400 km (500 km)(a)
Wind speed	
Range	4 ms^{-1} – 24 ms^{-1}
Accuracy	2 ms^{-1} or 10%
Wind direction	
Range	0-360°
Accuracy	20°
Frequency	5.3 GHz
Polarization	VV
Peak power (RF)	4.8 kW
Mean power (RF)	540 W
Min. signal-to-noise ratio per cell	0 dB (for each pulse)
No. of beams	3

(continued)

Orientation of beams(b)	0°	±45°
Pulse length	70 μs	130 μs
No. of pulses per 50 km per beam	256	256
Pulse repetition interval	4.347 ms	4.878 ms
Antenna size	2.5 m	3.6 m

(a) Data conforms to full specification only over 400 km swath
(b) 0° = perpendicular to the satellite ground track

ATSR-M Characteristics

Radiometer

Spectral channels	3.7, 11 and 12 μm
Spatial resolution	1 x 1 km
Radiometric resolution	0.1°K
Absolute accuracy predicted	0.5°K over 50 x 50 km in 80% cloud cover conditions
Swath width	500 km
Power consumption	60 W
Data rate	205 kilobit/s
Mass	33 kg

Microwave Sounder

2 channels	23.8 and 36.5 GHz
Instantaneous field-of-view	22 km
Power consumption	30 W
Mass	21.5 kg
Predicted accuracy	2 cm

Radarsat Enters Phase B

Edward J. Langham*

Radarsat Project Office, Ottawa, Ontario, Canada

Abstract

Radarsat is a Canadian program to launch and operate a remote sensing satellite whose primary sensor is a synthetic aperture radar. It will also carry a scatterometer and optical imaging sensor. The principal objectives are: 1) to provide daily sea ice and iceberg distribution maps for the arctic and eastern Canadian territorial waters; 2) to provide information for crop forecasting; and 3) to provide a global stereo data set for geological and resource management.

The program is shared with the United States and the United Kingdom, which together bear about 40% of the cost. (A third partner is expected to join the program shortly.)

The program is presently in Phase B -- the detailed design -- and funded until the end of fiscal year 1986-87 at which point Phase C/D will start. Phase C/D includes the construction of prototype components, testing, and construction of the engineering and flight models of the satellite.

The launch, which is scheduled for 1990, will be by the Space Shuttle. The satellite will be reserviceable in orbit which will permit the design life to be extended from the nominal five years to ten-year operations.

Introduction

The origins of Radarsat go back to the mid-1970s. At that time, there was a growing interest in oil and gas exploration in and around the Arctic Islands. The proposed shipping corridor for the transportation of both liquified natural gas and oil runs through the Parry Channel and then down through Baffin Bay and the Labrador Sea to eastern sea ports. In the vicinity of the Sverdrup gas basin at the westerly end of the channel and in the vicinity of Viscount Melville Sound, which controls access to the Beaufort Sea

---

This paper is declared a work of the Canadian Government and therefore is in the public domain.

*Project Development Manager.

oil deposits, multiyear ice may reach a thickness of around
10 ft. In addition, there are ridges of ice of
considerably greater depth. In the Davis Strait and along
the Labrador coast, there are great iceberg populations fed
by glaciers in Greenland. At any time of year, this is one
of the most difficult passages for navigation in the world.
Drill ships need the best ice information available for
planning their operations. Later, when the oil discoveries
are put into production, the efficient and safe operation
of these facilities as well as the transportation of the
oil will both depend on the availability of daily synoptic
ice information.

Also in the mid-1970s, Canada, like many other
countries, had extended the limits of its territorial
waters to 200 miles from the coast. Because of the great
length of the Canadian shoreline, this increased the area
of Canadian jurisdictional responsibility by a factor of
100 or more. Surveillance of such a vast amount of ocean
presented severe problems for the existing patrol system.

Faced with these requirements for extensive and
frequent surveillance information, in 1976 the Canadian
government established a task force to determine the extent
to which satellites could be used to meet the environmental
requirements for sea ice and oceans. In its report, the
task force laid special emphasis on the
value of synthetic aperture radar (SAR) and recommended
that Canada take part in the American Seasat Program (at
that time was a year or so away from launch). It also
recommended that an experimental program be set up to
verify those applications the task force had identified as
feasible and that the government begin a program of
technical developments in order to improve Canadian
industrial capability in the area of SAR technology.

All of these recommendations were accepted and to
implement them the Sursat Program was started in 1977.
The experimental campaign was conducted using the airborne
SAR leased (and later purchased) from the Environmental
Research Institute of Michigan and installed on the Canada
Centre for Remote Sensing Convair-580 aircraft. The
experiments conducted during the active life of Seasat
were arranged to coincide with Seasat overpasses, so that
wherever possible dual airborne and satellite SAR data
sets could be obtained. Other notable events of this
period include the early mission concept studies and the
development of the first digital SAR processor.

The conclusions of this study, reported in March 1980, were still very positive about the applications potential of spaceborne SAR and recommended that the Canadian government initiate a program that would lead to the launch of a Canadian satellite carrying a SAR. Again, the recommendations were accepted and a new program, Radarsat, began in the fall of 1980. Among its terms of reference was the requirement to seek international partners, primarily in order to share the cost of this venture (which for Canada would be very expensive). With this object, discussions were held with representatives of NASA during the summer of 1980, as a result of which it was agreed to conduct joint mission requirement studies 1 to determine the extent to which such a mission could serve the needs of both countries.

In 1979 the European Space Agency (ESA) started phase A studies for a European remote sensing satellite. Canada had earlier joined the Agency and took part in these studies. Shortly after the beginning of the Radarsat Program, the European Program entered phase B and, since the multinational partnership offered considerable benefit/cost leverage and the mission objectives complemented those of Radarsat, approval was given for Canada to subscribe first to phase B and, more recently, to phase C/D. The latter has now begun and will carry the program through to launch.

The Baseline Mission

The mission requirements studies, which were carried out during the first year of the Radarsat Program, were concerned primarily with the availability of data (orbit selection and data processing) and the quality of that data (radar design and data processing).

Orbit

Availability means the frequency of coverage at a given ground location and the delay between the time of data acquisition and the delivery of a user product. In both of these aspects, the requirements varied widely according to application, but it was found that the most demanding requirements determined the performance of the mission and that the less demanding requirements could then be accommodated without difficulty. Thus, for example, the requirement for frequent sea ice information in the Northwest Passage had a decisive influence on the selection of the orbit. The greatest coverage of this

shipping route is achieved if it also represents the most
northerly latitude reached by the SAR swath.   Fortunately,
not only does this produce the most dense coverage of SAR
imagery in terms of frequency of coverage, but it also
does this along an east-west direction that is
approximately the direction of the Northwest Passage.
This is achieved with a ground track that lies to the
north of the Passage and a radar that looks to the left,
which is to say always to the south of the ground track.
This gives poor coverage of the area to the north of the
shipping corridor, but is compensated for to some extent
by the data available from ERS-1 whose radar looks to the
right and approaches the North Pole more closely.   By the
same token, the southerly direction of the Radarsat SAR
swath makes the coverage of Antarctic very dense, almost
up to the South Pole.

A 1 day coverage map for Canada, plotted with a 140
km swath width, is shown in Fig. 1.   It can be seen that
there are still areas at the high latitudes that are not
covered every day.   The problem becomes worse through
Baffin Bay to the Labrador Sea.   To overcome this
difficulty, the baseline radar design has the capability
of steering the radar beam across a much wider ground
range than the swath width.   This procedure allows the
swath to be placed at one of several positions within a
500 km range of access.   Fig. 2 illustrates this feature
and shows how the position of the radar beam might be
stepped across the access swath several times during two
of the passes and in so doing cover the entire shipping
corridor.

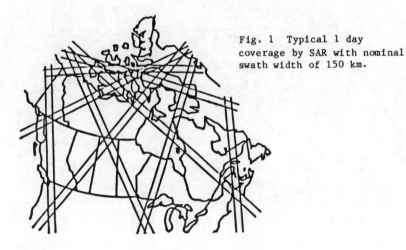

Fig. 1 Typical 1 day
coverage by SAR with nominal
swath width of 150 km.

Although this capability was introduced primarily to
meet shipping requirements, in fact it proves to be a
powerful tool for many other purposes. For example, at
lower latitudes over land, although during a particular
day the amount of surface coverage available is no
different from that shown in Fig. 1, the fact that the
swath can be moved around within the access swath enables
any part of Canada to be accessed during a 3 day
period. The limited access is not the drawback that it
might at first seem because applications dealing with very
large tracts of land (such as agriculture) can frequently
be handled very effectively by a sampling technique,
providing that the selected areas can be reached at
regular intervals for making measurements. Furthermore,
areas that have to be accessed on short notice because of
some kind of environmental emergency, for example, can
also be reached within this 3 day period.

As the position of the swath within the accessibility
range is moved about, the incidence angle also changes.
Again, this has benefits that can be exploited for various
applications. For example, it introduces the possibility
of acquiring stereo radar data and of exploiting the
variation of the radar cross section with the incidence
angle, which can assist in the identification of certain
surface materials or crops.

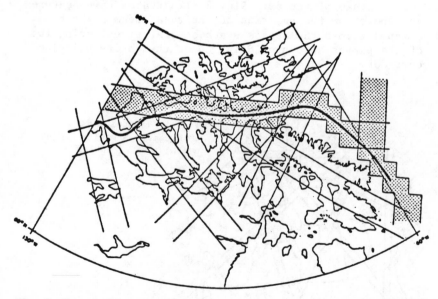

Fig. 2 Use of SAR swath displacement to optimize coverage of shipping
routes.

The orbit selected is in fact a 16 day exact repeat
with a 3 day subcycle. It is the 3 day subcycle that
gives the repeat coverage characteristics described above,
whereas the 16 day repeat allows the orbit to drift
through the subcycles and thus move the accessibility
swath so as to cover the entire circumference of the
equator twice during the repeat cycle. This orbit will
have a descending daylight pass that crosses the equator
at 09.44 hours.

This choice was made for a number of minor reasons
that together combined to make this the preferred orbit.
For example, the eclipse period is a little less than that
of the ascending daylight orbit, which has an impact on
the power management and the size of the solar panels. On
the applications side, this orbit allows both the optical
sensor and the radar to look toward the sun. This gives
more favorable illumination conditions at high latitudes
for the optical sensor and permits overlapping images to

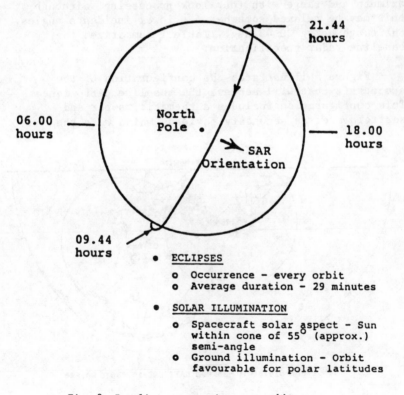

Fig. 3   Baseline sun-synchronous orbit.

be obtained. Because of the requirement to carry an
optical sensor, the baseline orbit is sun synchronous. It
has an altitude of 1001 km, and an inclination of 99.5
deg. See Fig. 3.

The receiving station in the baseline mission concept
will be at Ottawa, with a second station at Fairbanks,
Alaska, providing direct readout for the western Arctic.
The respective station masks are shown in Fig. 4.

Radar

After careful examination of existing data, the
Mission Requirements Study Teams agreed on the choice of
C band over L band as the optimal frequency for most
applications. Although X band was also examined, it was
felt that, for the marginal improvement in performance
for some applications, the technical risk was
unacceptable. The radar frequency will be 5.3 GHz and it
will normally operate in vertical transmit/vertical
receive mode. The impulse response width is 25 m in both
azimuth and range with four-look processing, although
this may be relaxed somewhat for lower incidence angles,
the range being 20–45 deg. Table 1 summarizes the
baseline radar specification.

Figure 5 illustrates the configuration of the
spacecraft that will achieve the baseline performance.
This configuration includes a thematic mapper and
scatterometer as secondary payload, which were the

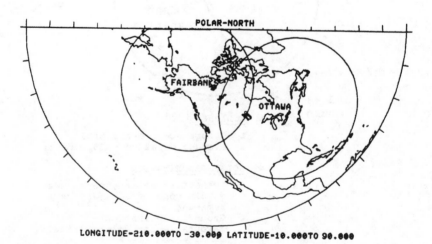

Fig. 4 Ground station coverage at 3 deg elevation angle.

nominal secondary sensor options for the phase A study. The scatterometer will be supplied by our American partner. At the time of writing, the supplier of the optical sensor has not yet been decided. The L-SAT bus in this illustration is the baseline for the mission. It was originally designed for geostationary orbit, but the manufacturer (British Aerospace) plans to modify it for low Earth orbit. The mass of the spacecraft at the final altitude will be approximately 4000 kg and the average power at the beginning of the mission will be about 7 kW.

The telemetry and ground segment components of the system concept are illustrated in Fig. 6. The satellite will downlink data either directly or from onboard recorders to the primary ground receiving station. These data will then be relayed at a lower rate through a communication satellite to the mission control center (which will be in Ottawa). Processing of SAR data and data from other sensors will take place there and the products distributed to user image analysis centers and to archiving facilities.

The most important of the image analysis centers is the Ice Information Center. There SAR data will be collated with data from other satellites, data from surveillance aircraft, and data from shipping vessels and other surface stations. Synoptic maps of ice conditions and also short-term ice forecasts will be prepared and relayed directly to users via a communication satellite. These and related products will be displayed on user systems for decisions on ship routing and drilling

Table 1   Nominal Radarsat baseline SAR

Frequency	5.3 GHz (C band)
Polarization	VV
Altitude	1000 km
Inclination	99.5 deg
Accessability swath	$\leq$ 500 km
Incidence angles	20–45 deg
Subswaths	4 (equal size)
Overlaps	10% minimum
Azimuth resolution	28 m
Looks	4 (independent)
Range resolution	25 m
(at reference position TBD within each subswath)	
Dynamic range	$\geq$ 30 dB
Output power	500 W mean
Weight	350 kg

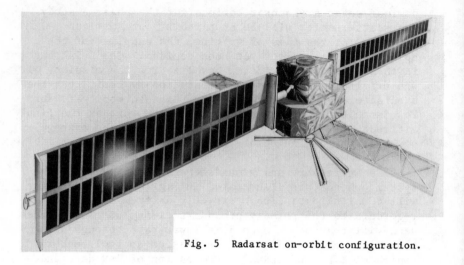

Fig. 5   Radarsat on-orbit configuration.

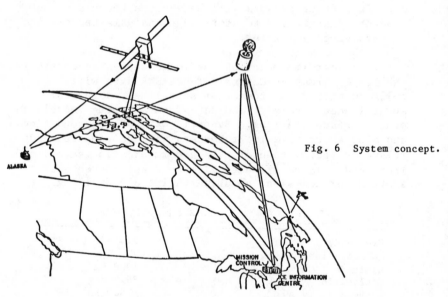

Fig. 6   System concept.

operations. It is expected that similar centers will
serve the oceanic community with forecasts of the sea
state and yet others will serve the land users with
information on agriculture, forestry, and hydrology.

International Partnerships
Since its inception, the Radarsat Program has
pursued its mandate to seek international partners.

Besides the agreement with NASA to conduct joint mission
requirements studies, a further agreement was signed in
September 1982 in which NASA expressed an interest in
providing a Space Shuttle launch and possibly one or two
other sensors for the payload. Also in September 1982,
an agreement was signed with Great Britain that expressed
an interest in providing the spacecraft (the modified
L-SAT bus) and possibly also a smaller sensor.

Besides these agreements (which refer to specific
contributions to the mission), there is the possibility
of other partners also joining the program to provide,
for example, parts of the synthetic aperture radar
subsystem. Although some discussions on such
possibilities have taken place, no agreements have yet
been signed.

SAR Research and Development

The Radarsat terms of reference also provided for a
research and development program to improve the
industrial and technical capabilities in the area of
synthetic aperture radar. This work has supported the
selection of C band for the mission by the design,
construction, and installation of a C-band scatterometer
on the Convair-580. This will be followed in 1985 by the
installation of a new C-band airborne SAR, called IRIS,
which will replace the old ERIM system developed
cooperatively by the Canada Center for Remote Sensing
(CCRS) and the Environmental Research Institute of
Michigan (ERIM). These facilities will be used in
support of the applications development program and to
assist in special problems relating to image quality and
radar cross section. Design studies for a ground-based
high-speed digital SAR processor have been conducted and
for the space segment studies of the high-power amplifer,
antenna, and space radar subsystems are in progress.

Applications Development

After the Radarsat mission requirements document had
been written, the experimental program, begun in order to
assist this work, continued in order to resolve
outstanding problems and also to continue research on
applications. The latter is an activity of growing
importance in the overall program because, for the full
benefit of the availability of radar data to be achieved,

before satellite launch there must be a complete suite of
algorithms and procedures to generate the products needed
by the users. Already, considerable progress has been
made in this direction. Table 2 illustrates the subjects
of interest and indicates some of the techniques being
developed. There is not space here to review this
work in detail, but some of the more interesting and
challenging topics are selected for comment.

Ice

The fact that the satellite will give twice daily
coverage over the entire Arctic shipping corridor gives a
temporal continuity to the available data. This is
important for two reasons: 1) it provides information
on ice dynamics that can be used in ice forecasting
models and 2) such frequent coverage will enable changes
in the mechanical and structural characteristics of the
ice masses to be monitored from day to day. Thus, for
example, the appearance of new ridges in the area being
tracked shows both the increasing difficulty of passage
and the presence of pressure in the ice field. In
support of this use of the data, experimental work in the
Arctic is conducted to collect information under
different ice conditions. Also, image analysis
algorithms are being developed that will emphasize
structural features and other patterns to enable the
various ice types to be differentiated.

Work on the recognition of icebergs is particularly
important because of their variable size and the
variation of radar return with the geometry of the
iceberg and the radar illumination. Of particular
concern is the lower limit at which icebergs can be
detected. For a given noise level in the scene, this
means the lower limit of the signal-to-noise level that
can be tolerated. This has been investigated by taking
an airborne SAR image, which has a much smaller
resolution element, and smoothing the radar speckle by
averaging the data to a resolution element representative
of the satellite data set. Assuming this to be an ideal
image, noise representing the radar speckle is then added
in increasing amounts and new images generated at each
stage. The first work of this kind was done with an
iceberg in a field of sea ice, but it can be readily
appreciated that, besides the effect of differing sea ice
conditions which might alter the conclusions of this
work, the variations of iceberg detectability in
different sea states in open water could be even greater.

Table 2   Applications of Radarsat

Ice

Sea ice
Seasonal variation of signature
Structural characteristics for SAR interpretation
C-band scatterometry (airborne and surface)
Ship tracks
Icebergs
Detectability (as function of size, shape, sea state,
incidence angle)
Discrimination (from ships)
Grounding

Oceans

Surface waves
Predominant wavelength and direction
Sea state
Internal waves
Distribution and directions of propagation
Ocean dynamics: currents, eddies, vortices, rings
Bathymetry: coastal and pingoes
Hurricanes, storms, squalls, windrows, oil slicks, fresh
water slicks, thermal slicks, shipping signatures
Vessel image (function of structure, orientation,
incidence angle)
Wakes (vessel type, speed, direction relative to SAR,
sea state)
Vessel and wake as function of sea state

Renewable Resources

Crop classification and condition
Digital analysis of multiple data sets
Digital analysis of multi-temporal data
C-band scatterometry (airborne and surface)
Forestry
Resource mapping
Cut areas, roads
Regrowth
Hydrology
Soil moisture
Flood mapping

Geology

SAR/VIR visual interpretation
Digital interpretation of multiple data sets: SAR, VIR,
geomagnetics, gamma, etc.
Stereo presentation: photo comparator, holograms, and
digitally generated products

For these reasons, the work on icebergs will also
continue, both in data acquisition and the development of
image analysis techniques during the coming years.

Oceans

Most of the oceanographic applications of interest
to Canada are concerned with sea conditions off the east
coast, because of the extreme sea conditions in the area
where offshore drilling is taking place. For this
reason, work on surface wave spectra is receiving
particular attention at this time. The current
experimental program includes flying patterns over areas
of ocean where there are directional wave buoys in order
to determine the limits of interpretability of the wave
spectrum as a function of the direction of travel of the
waves. This again has to be done in various sea states,
because the problem is a function of wave height.
Besides determining the limits of the data that can be
extracted from the SAR as such, the aircraft used for
these experiments will also collect C-band scatterometer
data for studying the relationship between the two. In
particular, the data on wavelength and direction as a
function of wind velocity will assist in the development
of models for sea generation that can be used in
forecasting.

Because the areas where drilling takes place are
frequently relatively shallow and have a bottom
topography that is conducive to the formation of internal
waves, this phenomenon is also of great interest.
Large-amplitude solitons can cause considerable
difficulty to drill ships; thus, forecasting their time
of arrival and magnitude will become increasing important
as offshore resource development increases. The ability
of SAR to map the dimensions of these features under
different conditions of wind and tide is being used to
obtain a better understanding of their behavior.

Renewable Land Resources

In applications relating to renewable resources on
land, there are two major areas of interest at this time.
The first concerns the use of multitemporal data sets for
following the progress of crops. The first experiment to
be conducted in Canada took place the summer of 1984 in
the prairies where the test site was visited by the
Convair-580 five times during the growing season. At
this time, the data are being processed and results will

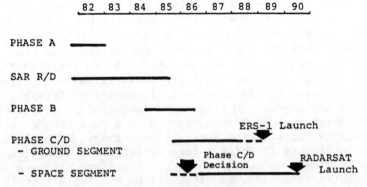

Fig. 7   Radarsat schedule.

be published in the scientific literature in the near future.

The use of the C-band scatterometer is also of considerable importance because the C-band radar cross section as a function of crop type, crop condition, soil moisture, and other parameters is not very well documented at this time. These are essential data for the analysis of the crop information that may be gathered at varying incidence angles by the satellite. They are also necessary for radar image simulations that will be used both for interpreting real radar images and for teaching purposes.

<u>Geology</u>

One of the more interesting applications activities in geology concerns the use of multiple data sets. Current work is being conducted using Seasat SAR, Landsat, geomagnetic, and gamma radiation data together. After analyzing these data jointly for geological information content, the results are compared with geological maps of the test area in order to evaluate the improvements to be achieved using this approach. The early results using a site in Nova Scotia led to many corrections to the existing map. A follow-up multiple site experiment is being conducted as part of the SIR-B Program.

Another area of endeavor, relating to geology in particular, in which we have been very active is concerned with stereo presentation of radar data. There are various approaches to this technique, depending on the end use made of the information. The efforts to date have been concerned with making geometric corrections for the distortions in the radar images. In the case of airborne data, this concerns, among other things, variable incidence angles across the scene. The same kind of approach that allows the incidence angle to be corrected to one standard figure also allows this figure to be changed by the same small increment uniformly across the scene. In this way a number of images of the same scene can be created, each with a small change of incidence angle. From a set of such images, a hologram can be created in which a three-dimensional radar image can be viewed using white light. The first of these scenes generated from airborne data will be available shortly.

Benefit Studies

During the early stages of the Radarsat Program a number of economic studies were conducted covering the areas of applications that offered the most significant benefits. Besides providing some justification for the Radarsat Program, these studies also assisted the mission requirements activities. One of the problems experienced during this work, for example, was to know exactly how much importance to attach to applications with dissimilar requirements. These benefit studies allowed a degree of weighting to be used in the selection of preferred requirements.

More recently, however, it became apparent that these specialized investigations were insufficient and that an economic overview was required. For this reason, a contract was given to a major economic consulting company with the object of integrating the previous work and including also some other benefits that had not previously been examined. Although the evaluation of potential benefits was very conservative in comparison with previous work, the conclusion was that a "worse scenario" would still give a undiscounted benefit/cost ratio of 3:1. One of the major tasks of the remainder of the program is to prepare the way for these potential benefits to be realized.

Program Status

At this time the phase B studies have just started and we are midway through the SAR Research and Development Program. These and the follow-up activities to launch are shown in the Radarsat schedule (Fig. 7). It can be seen that the ground segment leads the space

segment by 2 years approximately. This is so that we
will be in a state of readiness to receive and process
data from ERS-1 at the time of its launch. This is
partly to permit continued participation in the ESA ERS-1
Program, but also to benefit from the opportunity it
gives us both to make data from ERS-1 available to the
Canadian user community and to carry out practical tests
on data distribution and analysis facilities prior to the
launch of Radarsat.

Reference

[1]"Mission Requirements Documents (Phase A)," Radarsat Tech.
Rept. 82-7, 1982.

Geostationary Meteorological Satellite System in Japan

Masanori Homma* and Moriyoshi Minowa†

National Space Development Agency of Japan, Tokyo, Japan

and

Mitsuo Kobayashi‡ and Minoru Harada§

NEC Corporation, Tokyo, Japan

Abstract

GMS-3 of the Japan Meteorological Agency (JMA) and the National Space Development Agency of Japan (NASDA) was successfully launched on August 3, 1984, by the N-II rocket of NASDA, from Tanegashima Space Center. At the transfer orbit acquisition, GMS-3 was named "HIMAWARI-3", which means "The Sunflower" in English, and on August 16, it was placed in a geosynchronous orbit at 36,000 km above the equator and 140°E longitude. On August 28, the first cloud image of the Earth was successfully obtained from HIMAWARI-3. HIMAWARI-3 started its routine operations on September 27 succeeding HIMAWARI-2, which has been contributing to the weather watch for three years over Japan and the west Pacific Ocean countries

Introduction

Japan maintains a geostationary meteorological satellite system (GMSS) consisting of a geostationary satellite positioned approximately 36,000 km above the equator at 140°E longitude and associated with worldwide ground facilities. The first such satellite, known as GMS, was developed in response to the needs of the Global Atmospheric Research Program (GARP) and the World Weather Watch (WWW)

---

*Assistant Engineer, Second Satellite Design Group.

†Senior Engineer, Second Satellite Design Group.

‡Engineering Manager, Satellite Development Department, Space Development Division.

§GMS Program Manager, Space Development Division.

and launched in 1977. GMS-3, the successor of GMS/GMS-2, was launched in August 1984 by a Japanese N-II rocket.

The mission objectives of GMS-3 are:

1) Weather watch: to obtain and transmit pictures of the Earth and its cloud cover using a visible and infrared spin-scan radiometer (VISSR).

2) Collection of weather data: to collect weather data from data collection platforms (DCP) installed on ships, buoys, aircraft, and miscellaneous weather stations.

3) Distribution of weather data: to retransmit processed image data (facsimile) to data user stations in the western Pacific area.

4) Monitoring of solar particles: to monitor solar particles (protons, alpha particles, and electrons) influencing the Earth's atmosphere.

GMS-3 is a spin-stabilized satellite weighing approximately 680 kg.

The ground stations processing data received from the GMS-3 were built by the Japan Meteorological Agency (JMA) and the National Space Development Agency of Japan (NASDA). NASDA is responsible for the launch, initial on-orbit check, and stationkeeping during mission life, while JMA performs the on-orbit operation of GMS-3 and the processing of Earth images received from the spacecraft.

Outline of GMSS

The GMSS consists of a geostationary satellite positioned at 140°E longitude and associated worldwide ground facilities that include aircraft and ships. The satellite not only provides continuous Earth images and solar particle information, but also serves as a geostationary repeater for the collection and distribution of weather data. The general scheme of the GMSS is shown in Fig. 1.

Data Flow in the Geostationary Meteorological Satellite System

VISSR Data Transmission. VISSR data originating at the satellite are transmitted at S band to the command and data acquisition station (CDAS). The data are relayed to DPC and processed.

Collection of Weather Data. DCP interrogation signals are transmitted at S band by CDAS to the satellite, where they are frequency converted to UHF and transmitted to the DCP. DCP reports originate at UHF and are converted to the

S band by the satellite and repeated to the CDAS. Up to
133 channels can be transmitted simultaneously.

DCP reports can also be sent without interrogation at
a specific time.

Distribution of Weather Data. High- and low-resolution
facsimile data processed at DPC are transmitted at S band
to the satellite by CDAS. They are relayed at S band via
the satellite to medium- and small-scale data ulilization
stations (MDUS and SDUS). As of December 1982, 2 domestic
and 10 overseas MDUS are in operation, as well as 15
domestic and 15 overseas SDUS.

Trilateration. To provide accurate orbit determination, a trilateration ranging system is employed. The
master ranging station (MRS) within CDAS transmits special
S-band ranging signals to the satellite, where they are
retransmitted to the MRS and two remote turnaround ranging stations (TARS). Each TARS provides a different
frequency conversion and returns the signals at the S band
to the satellite, which in turn retransmits them to the
CDAS. Thus, two receptions and two transmissions of the
initial MRS signals are required with the two TARSs. The
three returned signals go from CDAS to DPC, where they are
used to determine the satellite orbit parameters.

Telemetry and Command. Satellite telemetry data and
data from the space environmental monitor (SEM) are transmitted at the S band to CDAS and the tracking and control
station (TACS). Command of the satellite is achieved at
the S band from either CDAS (mission operation) or TACS
(stationkeeping and housekeeping). Further, USB is provid-

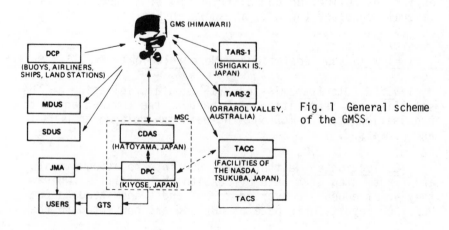

Fig. 1 General scheme
of the GMSS.

ed in the system as the primary link during orbit transfer and it is maintained as a backup during synchronous orbit.

Roles of the Ground Stations

TACC plays an important role in satellite station- and housekeeping. With a large capacity computer, it analizes telemetry data, deciding and predicting the satellite orbit and attitude. Command signals for station- and housekeeping are generated here. See Fig. 2.

TACSs receive telemetry signals from the satellite and transfer them to TACC. They also transmit command signals generated at TACC to the satellite. See Fig. 3.

CDAS receives VISSR and telemetry information from the satellite with an 18 m parabolic antenna and transfers it

Fig. 2 Tracking and control center (TACC).

Fig. 3 Tracking and control station (TACS).

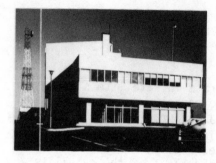

Fig. 4 Command and data acquisition station (CDAS).

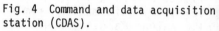

to the DPC. It also transmits facsimile and command signals generated at DPC to the satellite. The MRS for trilateration is installed here. See Fig. 4.

DPC, equipped with a large-capacity computer, serves as the brain of the GMS-3 system. Data from CDAS are processed here for meteorological analysis and various other calculations. Command signals for mission operations are also generated here. The center also produces facsimile signals for distribution of weather data. See Fig. 5.

Facsimile signals are received by the MDUSs and SDUSs. Several stations are in operation or being planned for the west Pacific and Asian countries. See Fig. 6.

DCP stations, installed on aircraft, ships, buoys, and remote islands, collect weather data in areas where such data are not readily available. See Fig. 7.

Role of the MSC in the GMSS

All the GMS data to be processed by the DPC are received at the CDAS and transmitted to the DPC by a microwave link. These data are then processed by a large-scale computer system that produces a variety of pictures for weather facsimile (WEFAX) dissemination and for extraction of meteorological parameters.

The Meteorological Satellite Center (MSC) system consists of the CDAS and the DPC. The DPC consists of the telecommunication, computer, satellite control, photographic processing, and cloud analysis systems.

These processed data are used for forecasting and warning of meteorological phenomena issued by the JMA and other domestic and foreign organizations.

Fig. 5 Data processing center (DPC).

Fig. 6 Medium- and small-scale data utilization stations (MDUS/SDUS).

Fig. 7 Data collection platform (DCP).

GMS-3 M/C #21 PRI/SENSOR A FULL FRAME VISSR IMAGE GAIN 0 DB   84:243:03:17 13 04

Fig. 8 Processed image data for distribution (HR-FAX).

The primary roles of the MSC in the GMS program are:
1) Carrying out the VISSR observations.
(Note the VISSR observations are carried out every 3 h and twice a day, at 00Z and 12Z, three additional wind extraction observations are performed.)
2) Producing full-disk pictures, enlarged partial-disk pictures, sectorized pictures, and polar stereographic and Mercator projected pictures form the VISSR images, and disseminating of these pictures to users by FAX transmission. See Fig. 8. (Note that the calibration of the radiance and brightness of the VISSR raw data and registration and transformation processing for each picture element are carried out for each image.)
3) Extraction of meteorological parameters, such as cloud motion vectors, sea surface temperatures, cloud amount data, etc., and transmission of these data to users via the automatic data editing and swiching system (ADESS) of the JMA and the global telecommunication system (GTS).
4) Construction of a nephanalysis map and a brightness temperature contour map and transmission of these data to users via the coded digital FAX (CDF) and JMA broadcast.
5) Collection and editing of the solar proton, alpha particle, and electron data in the SEM transmissions.

6) Determination and prediction of the GMS orbit and attitude. This is achieved by the collection and processing of trilateration range and range rate (TRRR) data from the two TARS. (TARS-1 is located or Ishigaki Island in Japan and TARS-2 is located at Orroral Valley in Australia.)

7) Transmission of command signals to operate the satellite subsystems and analysis of housekeeping data to monitor the status of satellite subsystems using telemetry data from the GMS.

8) Collection and editing of reports from buoys, airliners, and other DCPs and transmission of these data to users via ADESS/GTS.

9) Archiving of all data from the GMS and products of the MSC.

Spacecraft Configuration and Salient Characteristics

GMS-3 is a spin-stabilized geostationary meteorological satellite with mechanical despun antennas.

Table 1 Satellite characteristics

Dimensions	
Diameter	: 214.6 cm
Height	: 444.1 cm(with AKM)
	: 345.1 cm(without AKM)
Mass	
Separated weight	: 680.9 kg
On-station BOL	: 303.23 kg (include weight margin)
EOL	: 286.73 kg (include weight margin)
Life	
Mission life	: 4 - 5years
Design life	: 5 years
Reliability	
5 years	: 0.656
Orbit	
Geosynchronous,140°E longitude	
Stationkeeping	: 0.5°(E-W)
	: 1°(N-S)
Launch	
Vehicle	: N-II
Site	: Tenegashima Space Center

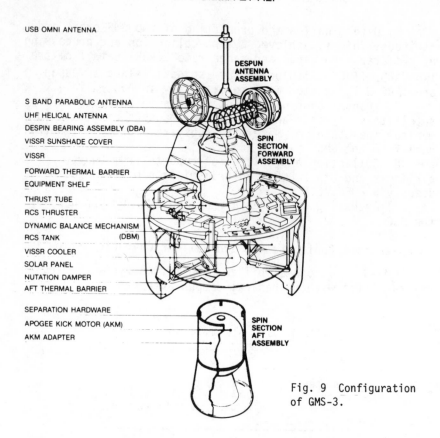

USB OMNI ANTENNA

DESPUN
ANTENNA
ASSEMBLY

S BAND PARABOLIC ANTENNA
UHF HELICAL ANTENNA
DESPIN BEARING ASSEMBLY (DBA)
VISSR SUNSHADE COVER
VISSR
FORWARD THERMAL BARRIER
EQUIPMENT SHELF
THRUST TUBE
RCS THRUSTER
DYNAMIC BALANCE MECHANISM
RCS TANK   (DBM)
VISSR COOLER
SOLAR PANEL
NUTATION DAMPER
AFT THERMAL BARRIER

SPIN
SECTION
FORWARD
ASSEMBLY

SEPARATION HARDWARE
APOGEE KICK MOTOR (AKM)
AKM ADAPTER

SPIN
SECTION
AFT
ASSEMBLY

Fig. 9 Configuration
of GMS-3.

The configuration of GMS-3 is shown in Fig. 9 and the characteristics are tabulated in Tables 1 and 2.

Overall size, weight, and shape of the spacecraft are designed to be compatible with the N-Ⅱ launch vehicles. The spacecraft length is 444 cm at launch and 345 cm on-station and the diameter is 215 cm. The weight when the GMS-3 is separated from the N-Ⅱ third stage is approximately 681 kg and the spacecraft dry weight on-station is approximately 287 kg.

The spacecraft consists of a despun Earth-oriented antenna assembly and a spinning section rotating at 100 rpm. Despun S-band and UHF antennas provide high gain for on-orbit communications with ground stations. Spinning sun and Earth sensors supply reference signals in daylight and eclipse periods to control the despun assembly. A noncontacting RF rotary joint, mounted coaxially within a despin bearing assembly (DBA), feeds RF signals between the despun antennas and a spinning equipment shelf.

Table 2 Satellite subsystem characteristics

VISSR & VDM

	Visible	Infrared
Spectral band	0.50 - 0.75μ	10.5 - 12.5μ
Resolution	1.25 km	5 km

SEM

Measurement range	:0.8 - 100 MeV(protons)
	:8 - 370 MeV
	(alpha particles)
	:≥ 2 MeV(electrons)

Communications

	S band	UHF	USB
Uplink	2026 - 2035 MHz	402 MHz	2100 MHz
Downlink	1682 - 1695 MHz	468 MHz	2280 MHz
Antenna	Parabola	Helical	Bicone
Coverage	Global	Global	Omni
G/T	- 22 dB/°K	- 23 dB/°K	- 40 dB/°K
EIRP	40±1.5dBm*[1] 34±1.5dBm*[2] 5/±1.5dBm*[3]	$46^{+2}_{-1.5}$dBm	27.5±1.5dBm

Telemetry and command

	Telemetry	Command
Capacity	256×2 channels	254 (pulse) +1(serial)
Modulation	PCM/PSK/PM*[4] FM/PM,FSK/PK*[4] PCM/PSK,*[1] FM/PM,FSK/PK*[1]	PCM/FSK-AM/PM
Bit rate	250 b/sec	128 b/sec

Controls

Spin-stabilized (spin rate 100 ± 1 rpm)
Antenna pointing : ± 0.5° (N-S)
                  : ± 0.39° (E-W, sun reference)

Electrical Power

Solar array power : 263 W (EOL S/S)
Batteries   : 5.5 A-hr × 2 set

RCS

Propellant   : Hydrazine
3 tanks, 2 axial and 4 radial thrusters

AKM

Thiokol TE-M-616

Thermal Control

Passive

*[1] S-band telemetry. *[2] DCPR. *[3] VISSR data. *[4] USB telemetry.

The spinning section includes VISSR and supporting subsystems. The forward assembly consists of VISSR, magnesium thrust tube, honeycomb equipment shelf, electronics, batteries, main wire harness, reaction control subsystem (RCS) tanks and thrusters, solar panel, and thermal barriers. The aft assembly includes an apogee kick motor (AKM), wire harness, AKM adapter, and separation hardware. The aft assembly is jettisoned after motor burnout. A block diagram of GMS-3 is shown in Fig. 10.

The satellite mission life is 4-5 years due to the limited amount of on-board hydrazine fuel; however, the design life is 5 years. Redundancy of mission-critical functions is provided to insure electronics lifetimes significantly in excess of 5 years. The solar panel power of 263 W includes an approximately 16 W margin at the end of 5 years (summer solstics).

VISSR and VDM

VISSR

The visible and infrared spin-scan radiometer (VISSR) is used to obtain visible and infrared spectrum mappings

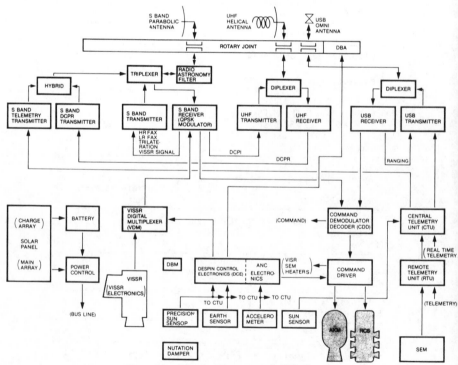

Fig. 10 Block diagram of GMS-3.

Table 3   VISSR characteristics

Functions	Provides visible and infrared spectrum mapping of Earth and its cloud cover.	
Design	Spin scan radiometer includes northsouth scan mirror, 40.64 cm diameter 291.3 cm focal length Ritchey-Chretien optical system, PMT and HgCdTe detectors,-95°K radiation cooler with servo temperature control, and beryllium housing.	
	Visible channels	Infrared channels
Number	4 (+4 redundant)	1 (+1 redundant)
Instantaneous geometrical field of view (IGFOV)	35×31μrad	140×140μrad
Band	0.50 to 0.75μ	10.5 to 12.5μ
Resolution	1.25km	5.0km
Scanning lines/frame	2500×4	2500
Scan step repeatability,(1σ)	±1.8μrad	±1.8μrad
Noise performance	S/N $\geq$ 45(albedo=100%) S/N $\geq$ 6.5(albedo=2.5%)	NEΔT $\leq$ 0.5°K(300°K) NEΔT $\leq$ 1.5°K(220°K)

of the Earth and its cloud cover with a specially designed optical telescope and detector system.

A complete 20 × 20 deg scan of the full-Earth disk can be accomplished every 30 min by utilizing the spacecraft's 100 rpm spin motion for west-east scans and 2500 steps (140 μrad each) of motoractuated VISSR mirror scans in the north-south direction. Primary scanning requires 25 min, mirror retrace 2.5 min, and spacecraft stabilization another 2.5 min.

Using its scan, primary, and secondary mirrors, the optical telescope collects visible and infrared energy from images of the Earth's surface and brings these images into focus at the focal plane. Visible fiber optics and infrared relay optics relay images from the telescope focal plane to redundant visible and infrared detectors. Photomultiplier tube (PMT) detectors convert visible light into visible analog signals and HgCdTe detectors, cooled by a radiation cooler, convert the Earth's radiation into infrared analog signals. The VISSR outputs are fed to a VISSR digital multiplexer (VDM) unit, which is internally redundant, for processing.

The VISSR characteristics are listed in Table 3.

Table 4 VDM characteristics

	Visible channels	Infrared channels
Number	4	1
Quantization	64(square root)	256(linear)
Sample rate	437.5K samples/sec	109.4K samples/sec
Bandwidth	150KHz	37.5KHz
Output format	Differentially encoded into two 2-bit bites	

VDM

The VISSR digital multiplexer (VDM) is a high-speed /, pulse code modulation (PCM) encoder. It converts four-channel visible and one-channel infrared VISSR signals into digital form, multiplexes them with image and message synchronization data, and differentially encodes them.

Hybrid indegrated circuits are extensively used in VDM to minimize size and weight. To conserve power, the visible portions of VDM are strobed on and off during satellite spin.

The VDM characteristics are shown in Fig. 11 and Table 4.

Space Environment Monitor

The space environment monitor (SEM) measures three kinds of solar particles (protons, alpha particles, and electrons) using the energy absorbed in five silicon detectors. Energetic particles entering the detector chips deposit their energy, creating charge pulses proportional to the energy absorbed. Charge sensitive amplifiers convert the charge pulses to voltage pulses, which are then analyzed and discriminated for counting. The categorized energy pulses are then counted and sent to the telemetry sub-system.

The SEM characteristics are tabulated in Table 5.

Communication Subsystem

The GMS-3 communication subsystem consists of satellite antennas; rotary joint; primary and redundant S-band, UHF, and unified S-band (USB) receivers and transmitters. Either the primary or redundant units can be activated USB by ground command except for the USB receivers, which are always on. The communication subsystem is divided into three groups: S-band transponder, UHF transponder, and USB

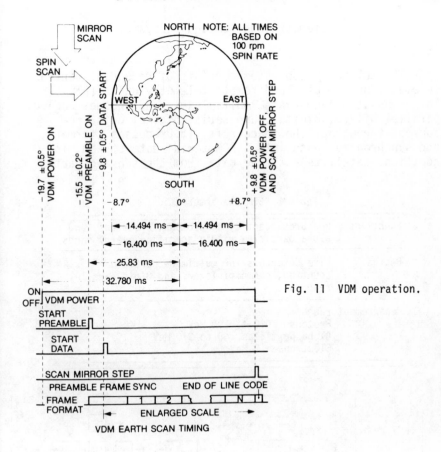

Fig. 11 VDM operation.

transponder. They provide the following functions:

1) S-band transmission of VISSR signals to CDAS.

2) S-band relay of facsimile signals from CDAS to MDUS and SDUS.

3) S-band relay of trilateration ranging signals from/ to CDAS and two TARSs.

4) S-band transmission of telemetry signals to and S-band command reception from CDAS and TACS.

5) S-band to UHF relay of DCP signals from CDAS (at S band) to the DCPs (at UHF).

6) UHF to S-band relay of DCP report signals from DCP (at UHF) to CDAS (at S band).

7) USB tracking, telemetry, and command capability acts as the primary link during orbit transfer and as a backup during synchronous orbit.

The block diagram of communication subsystem is shown in Fig. 12 and communication subsystem performance summary is tabulated in Table 6.

Telemetry and Command Subsystem

Telemetry

The telemetry subsystem consists of redundant central telemetry units (CTU) and remote telemetry units (RTU). This subsystem conditions, multiplexes, and encodes analog, parallel bilevel digital, and serial digital data from sources throughout the spacecraft. It processes, formats, and synchronizes data into a PCM serial data stream. In addition, satellite attitude data from the sun and Earth

Table 5 SEM characteristics

Functions	Measures quantity of protons, electrons, and alpha particles within specified energy bands
Design	Five detectors for multimode particle counting, submultiplexer, and 8 bit parallel readout
Measurement range	Protons 0.8 to 100 MeV Alpha particles 8 to 370 MeV Electrons ≥ 2 MeV

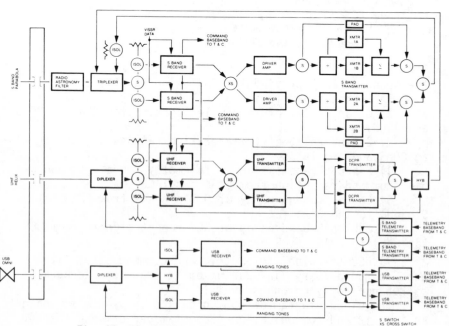

Fig. 12 Block diagram of communication subsystem.

sensors, nutation data from the sun and Earth sensors, nutation data from the accelerometers, command execute verification signals, and thruster and AKM firing signals are sensed. Also, subcarriers are modulated for simultaneous real-time transmission with the PCM data. The telemetry multiplex baseband signal consists of the sun for the real-time subcarriers and the PCM data stream. This signal is

Table 6 Communication subsystem performance summary

S-band transponder

Design	All solid state hybrid circuitry; channelized and fully redundant; dual conversion with limiting signal multiplexing/demultiplexing, and interface with UHF at IF
RF power	20 W at transmitter output for VISSR and multifunction (Low power 2 W) 200 mW at transmitter output for DCPR 1.25 W at transmitter output for S-band telemetry
Noise figure	3.8 dB at receiver input
EIRP	57 ± 1.5 dBm for VISSR and multifunction (Low power 47 ± 1.5 dBm) 34 ± 1.5 dBm for DCPR
G/T	40 ± 1.5 dBm S-band telemetry -22 dB/°K
Antenna	Vertically polarized Earth coverage parabola, mechanically despun and pointed at Earth

UHF transponder

Design	All solid state hybrid circuitry; fully redundant; dual conversion; interfaces with S band through UHF IF processor and AGC at IF
RF power	4 W at transmitter output
Noise figure	2.5 dB at receiver input
EIRP	$46^{+2}_{-1.5}$ dBm
G/T	-23 dB/°K
Antenna	Right-hand circular polarized bifilar helix, mechanically despun and pointed at Earth

USB transponder

Design	All solid state hybrid circuitry; fully redundant
RF power	4.o W at transmitter output
Noise figure	3.1 dB at receiver input
EIRP	27.5±1.5 dBm
G/T	-40 dB/°K
Antenna	Vertical linear polarized ±50° coverage bicone, mounted coincident with spin axis on despun section

transferred to the communication subsystem for transmission
to the ground by either the S-band telemetry or USB transmitters.

Command

Redundant command demodulator-decoders demodulate and
decode PCM (NRZ)/FSK-AM baseband signals received from the
S-band or USB receivers of the communication subsystem.

Table 7 Telemetry and command subsystem characteristics

Functions	
Processes discrete, analog, digital, and real-time data for telemetry; demodulates and decodes 3 tone command signals; provides high level drive signals to activate squibs, valves, relays, and heaters	
Design	
All solid state, programmable read-only memory processing control, full redundant remote and central telemetry units, central demodulator/decoders	
Telemetry	
Channel capacity	256×2 (combination of analog and digital)
Digital format	Biphase level (Biφ-L) PCM
Bit rate	250 b/sec
Minor frame length	64 words (8 bits per word)
Major frame length	64 minor frames
Subcommutation	3 housekeeping (one 64-word, one 32-word and one 16-word), 2 SEM (8 words each)
Analog accuracy and resolution	±0.6%, 8 bits
Real time	Sun pulses, Earth pulse, index pulses, accelerometer, thruster valve actuation and AKM fire verification and command execute with priority gating of IRIG channel 12 and B SCOs and gating of a 64 KHz tone
Commands	
Number of commands	254 (pulse)+1 (serial)
Format	NRZ PCM/FSK-AM/PM
Bit rate	128 b/sec ±0.2%
Command tones	Logic 1: 8600 Hz ±0.2%
	Logic 0: 7400 Hz ±0.2%
	Execute: 5790 Hz ±0.2%
Drivers	Heater, solenoid, valve, relay, squib (68 total)

The two command channels are actively redundant (both simultaneously in operation). Satellite-received command messages are verified by telemetry prior to command execution. Command outputs to the various spacecraft subsystems consist of discrete pulse and serial magnitude commands.

The command driver unit amplifies pulse commands for driving relays, pyrotechnic devices, valves, thrusters, and thermal control heaters.

The characteristics are tabulated in Table 7.

Control Subsystem

The control subsystem consists of a despin bearing assembly (DBA); redundant despin control electronics (DCE); redundant precision sun sensors, Earth sensors, and accelerometers; a nutation damper; and two dynamic balance mechanisms (DBM).

DBA provides the mechanical interface between the spinning section, which give gyroscopic stability, and a despun antenna assembly pointed at the Earth. Pointing control is accomplished in DCE by comparing spin-to-despun orientation information from the DBA with spin-to-sun orientation information from the precision sun sensor. When the sun is in eclipse, the Earth sensor is used in place of the precision sun sensor.

The sensor outputs are also used by DCE to generate the timing signals required by VISSR and VDM for stepping the mirror, resetting the infrared channel, starting the scan line, etc. Similar reference signals are sent to the ground station for attitude determination and to time attitude correction maneuvers.

The accelerometer is used for active nutation control (ANC). During orbit transfer, the satellite with the AKM

Table 8 Attitude and orbit control salient performance

Spin speed (on station)	100 ± 1 rpm
Stationkeeping	1° N-S, 0.5° E-W
Attitude maintenance	0.5°
Attitude determination	±0.07°
Attitude stability (N-S)	
spin axis	2.0μ rad over 0.6 sec
	24.6μ rad over 25 min
spin phase	2.81μ rad over 0.6 sec
	20.4μ rad over 25 min
VISSR timing accuracy	0.15°
Antenna E-W pointing accuracy	0.39° (sun reference)
	0.56° (Earth reference)

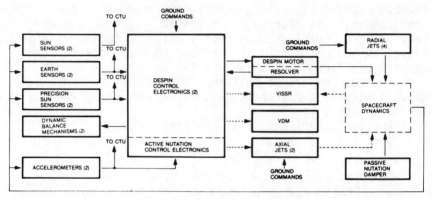

Fig. 13 Block diagram of control subsystem.

attached is unstable about its spin axis. Therefore, the
spin axis tends to cone, or nutate, at a slowly increasing
angle. This nutation angle is sensed by the accelerometer
and ANC electronics in DCE. When the angle becomes approximately 0.3 deg, the ANC electronics commands the thrusters
to fire a short pulse to decrease the nutation angle.

In geostationary orbit after the AKM and its adapter
separate, the satellite is stable. Any nutation that occurs
naturally decreases. However, a passive damper is included
to ensure the rapid decrease of such nutation. The damper
is a hoop partially filled with alcohol and is offset
approximately 60 cm from the satellite center of gravity
(c.g.). This offset position causes the damper fluid to
effectively counteract nutation. Also, the damper position
is so designed that the hoop plane-to-c.g. offset is zero
during orbit transfer. This damper does not affect satellite stability during the transfer.

Two DBMs are used to correct deviations in the dynamic
balance of the satellite in order to prevent spin axis
tilt.

The attitude and orbit control salient performance is
tabulated in Table 8 and a block diagram is shown in Fig.
13.

Bibliography

"GMS-3," National Space Development Agency of Japan, Tokyo, Japan.

"Introduction to Meteorological Satellite Center of Japan Meteorological Agency," Japan Meteorological Agency.

Marine Observation Satellite MOS-1

M. Kusanagi,* Y. Ishizawa,† T, Masuda,‡ and Y. Fujimori§
National Space Development Agency of Japan, Ibaraki-Ken, Japan

ABSTRACT

The Marine Observation Satellite MOS-1 is Japan's first in a planned series of marine and land observation satellites and is scheduled to be launched by a N-II launch vehicle from the Tanegashima Space Center in the summer of 1986. The main missions for the MOS-1 are 1) to establish the fundamental technologies of Earth observation satellites, 2) to carry out the observation of the earth and atmosphere using three different radiometers (a multispectral electronic self-scanning radiometer, a visible and thermal infrared radiometer, and a microwave scanning radiometer), and 3) to performe basic experiments for a data collection system. The MOS-1 will be placed in a sun-synchronous orbit at an altitude of about 909 km with an inclination of 99.1 deg. The window for the local time of descending node passage is 10:00-11:00. The MOS-1 circles the Earth about every 103 min. completing 14 orbits/day and provides systematic coverage of the entire Earth every 17 days. The MOS-1 has a rectangular structure with a three-segment deployable solar array attached to one side of the satellite and three radiometers attached to the Earth pointing side of the main body. The main body of satellite consists of two aluminum honeycomb sandwich boxes. One at the top is used mainly for mission equipments and the other at the bottom is for spacecraft bus equipment. The total weight of the satellite is 740 kg. The attitude control is accomplished by a biased momentum three-axis stabilization system. The design includes both passive and active thermal control devices. Further detailed information about the satellite and its mission equipment is given in this paper with some results of an analysis and developments tests. Also the expected benefits and future plans will be briefly described.

Introduction

Effective use of limited land and natural resources and preservation of land and the environment are very important and a prime concern of Japan, as the country is now facing the dual problems of high industrialization and overpopulation. The feasibility

*Senior Engineer, Tracking and Control Center.
†Director, Earth Observation Satellite Group.
‡Senior Engineer, Earth Observation Satellite Group.
§Head of Structure Laboratory, 2nd Airframe Division National Aerospace Laboratory.

study for Marine Observation Satellite 1 (MOS-1) program was started in 1978 in hopes of finding a new approach in this field.

Since Japan is surrounded by water the Pacific Ocean on the east and the Sea of Japan on the west, our life strongly relies on natural resources from the ocean. It is very desirable to know such ocean phenomena as water temperature, changes in ocean currents, fog distribution near the islands, and abnormal growth of plankton or red tide, which has strong influence on the fishing industry. Although it is difficult to see the schools of fish directly, it might be possible to find them by mapping water temperatures or plankton swarms. With this information, fisheries will benefit from both greater efficiency and fuel savings. Monitoring of the Kurile and Japan currents, cold water fronts, and the drift of ice will help to forecast unusual or abnormal weather in Japan. Also data taken by MOS-1 will be analyzed and used to prevent the ship wrecks and will help safety of ocean-going traffic.

By observing snow distribution and water in reservoirs, ponds, lakes, and rivers, i.e., preserved in land, one can forecast the water reserves for agriculture and forestry and also predict the possible shortages of urban water supplies. It is also possible to monitor the polution of environment by observing the mouths of rivers, bays, and water fronts. Both volcanic activity and earthquakes are common phenomena in Japan; hence, the steady monitoring of them from orbit is important for davance warning and damage estimate. It might be also used to investigate the portion of land used for habitation, farming, etc. Meteorlogical information about clouds, water vapor over the oceans, snow, and rainfall are observed by using the microwave radiometer. The data collection system will be used to collect remotely sensed data such as wind direction and speed, temperature of air and water, and weather from data platforms. By monitoring the drift of platforms or buoys, the precise course of local ocean currents will be determined.

Ground Support for MOS-1

For the development phase, Tsukuba Space Center's test facilities are used to check the system validation, especially for the expected spacecraft environment. Mechanical tests for static load, sinusoidal vibration, accoustios, separation and pyro shock, are being made, as well as thermal vacuum, EMI, and RF tests. Final checkout will take place at the Tenegashima Space Center, a launch site, where MOS-1 will be launched by the NLV-II.

The tracking and control network during the operational phase is composed of tracking and control center (TACC) at Tsukuba Space Center and three tracking and control stations (TACS) at Katsuura, Masuda, and Okinawa. TACC is the focal point of the MOS-1 tracking and control network and manages all network operations. The major tasks performed at TACC are network facilities asignment, direction of spacecraft operation at TACS, processing of the received TT&C data, and orbit determination.

TACC communicates with MOS-1 directly under the direction of TACC and routes the received TT&C data to TACC. The major tasks are command transmission to MOS-1, telemetry data acquisition, tracking data acquisition, and acquired data transmission to TACC. The facilities at each station are standarized as shown in Fig. 1. Katsuura is asigned to be the major station for daily operations and Masuda and Okinawa standby stations.

The operation control system is the central body of all MOS-1 mission operations. The special experimental and foreign stations are to contact the mission management organization (MMO) of this system. MMO sends ephemeris data, satellite status data, etc., to foreign stations. The data acquisition and processing system is responsible for reception, processing, inspection, archiving, retrieval and distribution of image and data from the data collection system (DCS). The main facilities of this system will be installed at the Earth Observation Center at Hatoyama now serving as a Landsat ground station.

Overview of MOS-1

Mission and Orbit Requirements

Development of MOS-1 started in April 1980, with a planned launch by NLV-II from Tanegashima Space Center in the summer of 1986. The total weight of MOS-1 is 740 kg with three radiometers and a data collection transponder as payloads. A schematic of MOS-1 is shown in Fig. 2. Major mission objectives of MOS-1 are

1) Establishment of fundamental technologies common to both marine and land observation satellites.

2) Observation of the state of the sea surface and atmosphere using visible, infrared, and microwave radiometers and verification of the performance of these radiometers. Among the additional mission objectives of MOS-1 are basic testing of the data collection subsystem, achievement of a sun-synchronous recurrent orbit, extension of the ground support system for tracking and house keeping data handling to a sun-synchronous recurrent satellite, and establishment of operational system for an Earth observation satellite.

A sun-synchronous recurrent orbit was selected for effective observation by radiometers. The merit of recurrent orbit is the fact that the same site can be seen at the same time of a day and, therefore, planning of the ground operation becomes straightforward and search and access to the stored data becomes simple. Considering the operational condition and the quality of picture, a local time for the descending node passage of

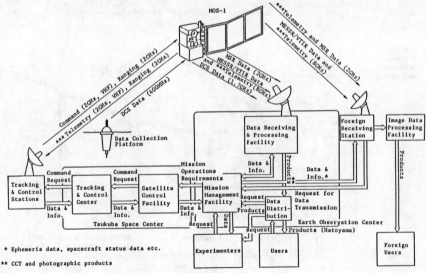

* Ephemeris data, spacecraft status data etc.

** CCT and photographic products

*** Attitude data is obtained from Telemetry (2GHz & 8GHz).

Fig. 1　MOS-1 ground support system.

10:00–11:00 was selected. To keep the sun-synchronous orbit, inclination and altitude of 99 deg and 909 km are selected; thus, the satellite circles the Earth every 103 min. completing 14 rev/day and viewing the entire Earth every 17 days with 237 orbits. The major orbital parameters are shown in Table 1. Ground traces based on these orbital paramenters are shown in Fig. 3 and 4. Figure 3 shows the ground trace for a day and Fig. 4 for a week in the vicinity of Japan.

Several perturbing forces (atmospheric drag, the gravitational attraction of the sun and the moon, radiation pressure of the sun, etc.) act upon the satellite after the desired orbit has been attained. These forces cause changes in the orbit that deteriorate the coverage and repeatability. If an orbit correction is not made the ground trace deviation from initial orbit during a period of 2 years accumulate to 1500 km. Thus, orbit correction is necessary to keep the ground trace deviation within 20 km.

Figure 5 shows the estimated ground trace deviation during the 2 years of mission life when orbit control with respect to altitude is put into practice every eight recurrent

Table 1 Orbital parameters

Altitude	908.7 km
Semimajor axis	7286.9 km
Inclination	99.1 deg
Eccentricity	< 0.004 deg
Nodal period	6190.5 s
Repeat cycle	17 days
Orbits/cycle	237 rev/s
Orbital periods/day	$14 - \frac{1}{17}$ rev/s
Ground trace spacing at equator	167.0 km
Ground trace accuracy	20 km
Sidelap at equator (MESSR)	7.7 km
Decending node time	10:00–11:00

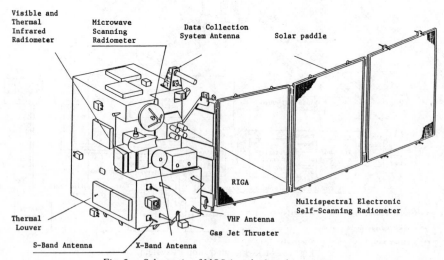

Fig. 2   Schematic of MOS-1 as deployed in space.

cycles (136 days). The altitude rises about 95 m on each orbit control and the maximum ground trace deviation is estimated to be 13.4 km. The attitude drift error on each axis causes image distortion. The allowable drift error of each axis during one scan time was assumed to be less than 4% of one pixel (instand field of view, IFOV) of each payload sensor. The drift rate requirement for the satellite (which is based on the allowable drift error of each payload sensor) is summarized in Table 2. The allowable pointing error of the sensors was assumed to be less than 7% of one scene or 1 FOV of the multispectral electronic self-scanning radiometer (MESSR), because image resolution of the MESSR is the highest of the three radiometers. The pointing error around each axis is summarized in Table 2.

The flight path of the NLV-II launch vehicle is selected so as not to let the payload sensors see the sun directly and to avoid the extreme local heat gradient of the satellite. The satellite will be separated from the second stage at the eclipse zone with 10 deg and 0.4 deg/s injection allowance. Two minutes after separation, when the rate integrating gyro is fully warmed up, rate damping will start to settle the satellite motion to the low constant yaw rate. See Fig. 6, steps 1 and 2.

As soon as the satellite comes out of the eclipse zone, the sun sensors are ready to work and hence sun aquisition starts. Through three steps the -Z axis (anti-Earth pointing side) will capture the sun, maintaining a 0.7 deg/s yaw rate aroung the Z axis. About 30 min after sun acquisition starts, paddle deployment takes place (Fig. 6, step 3), assuring the event occurs near the tracking station in Japan. The Earth acquisition sequence is initiated by ground command (Fig. 6, step 4). Earth acquisition is completed when the

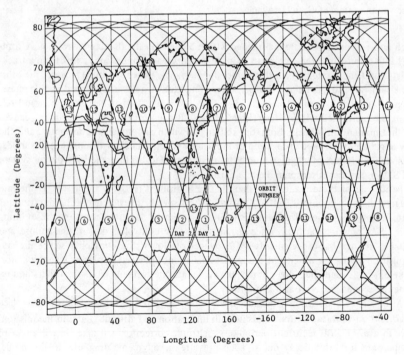

Fig. 3   One-day orbit ground trace of MOS-1.

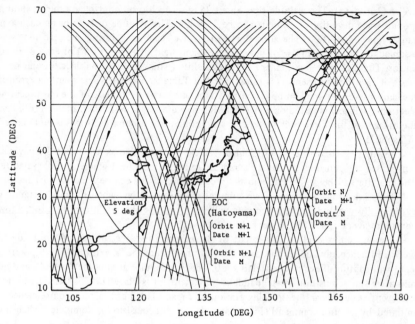

Fig. 4   Seven-day orbit ground trace of MOS-1 and area covered by the anthenna of the Earth
observation center (EOC) in Hatoyama.

pitch and roll deviations are maintained within 5 deg with the 0.7 deg/s yaw rate. Affirm-
ing Earth acquisition, the command to initiate coarse yaw acquisition is sent from a tracking station (Fig. 6, step 5). In this phase, the yaw angle is kept within 15 deg of the orbit
plane with the aid of the sun sensors. The momentum wheels are engaged in this phase.
Coarse yaw acquisition is followed by a fine yaw correction, where the pitch and roll
errors are controlled within 4 deg (Fig. 6, step 6). Because of the roll-yaw coupling caused
by the momentum wheels, both the roll angle, which is controlled constantly, and the
yaw angle are controlled. The speed of the wheels is kept constant throughout this mode;
thus, the deviation of angular momentum is controlled by the reaction control system
(RCS) using an Earth sensor and a rate gyro.

Besides all of these maneuvers, there is one additional recovery maneuver. If the rate
integration gyro assembly (RIGA) output, wheel speed, thruster operating duration, or
attitude and orbit control electronics (AOCE) converter output exceeds the preset limits
or if ESA loses its Earth presence signal, the safety controller detects the failure and
switches to the backup elements. After wheel rundown, the controller select the sun
acquisition status, at which a thorough trouble shooting will take place. Once the abnormal element is identified, the controller will isolate the element from the others and re-
sume the sequence from Earth acquisition.

After all the acquisition sequences have been completed, orbit control will take place
to correct any orbit injection errors in both inclination and altitude. Later in the mission,
once in every eighth recurrent period or so, altitude correction will take place in order to
compensate for orbit decay due to solar pressure, aerodynamic drag, etc. In this mode,
momentum wheels are kept at a constant speed and used only to augment the stability;
active control is done by the RCS.

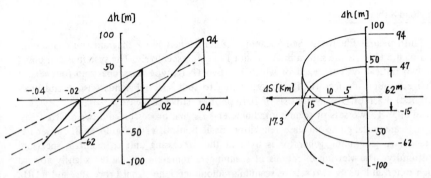

Fig. 5   Drift and orbit correction.

Table 2 Drift rate and pointing error

Parameter	Axis		
	Roll	Pitch	Yaw
Drift rate requirement, deg/s	±0.016	±0.016	±0.05
Apportionment of pointing error, deg			
AOCS Control performance	0.4	0.4	0.9
Structural distortion	0.1	0.1	0.1
Thermal distortion	0.1	0.1	0.1
Alignment error of radiometer	0.11	0.11	0.4
Margin	0.1	0.1	0.1
Total (RSS)	0.45	0.45	1.0

The operational mode or normal mode is controlled by the biased momentum wheel system, which are unloaded by magnetic coils. Unloading by thrusters is also available as a backup system in case of large disturbance torques. The momentum wheels are arranged in a V shape at a 30 deg half-cone angle and the plane is skewed at 20 deg offset angle. About 90 N·m·s nominal bias momentum is available via two wheels around pitch axis. Due to the built-in offset angle effect, the momentum difference between the two wheels creates roll and yaw control torques at the same time.

MOS-1 Subsystems

The payload sybsystems of MOS-1 include the multispectral electronic self-scanning radiometer (MESSR), visible and thermal infrared radiometer (VTIR), mircowave scanning radiometer (MSR), and data collection system (DCS). The spacecraft bus includes the observation data transmitter antenna subsystem (XANT); telemetry, tracking, and command subsystem (TT&C); electrical power subsystem (EPS); solar paddle subsystem (PADL); attitude and orbit control subsystem (AOCS), reaction control subsystem (RCS); structure subsystem (STR); termal control sybsystem (TCS); mechanical integration hardware (MINT); and electrical integration hardware (EINT). A block diagram of these subsystems is shown in Fig. 7. Weight distributions, power consumptions, and reliability allocations are summarized in Table 3. Brief descriptions of the major subsystems follow.

Payload Subsystems

Multispectral Electronic Self-Scanning Radiometer. A block diagram and characteristics of the MESSR are shown in Fig. 8 and Table 4, respectively. The system is composed of two optical systems, each of which has two Gauss-type telescopes and four sets of charged couple devices (CCD) corresponding to four spectral bands (visible and near-infrared). Each CCD array consists of 2048 photosensitive elements.

In MOS-1, two sets of scanning radiometers, a signal processor, and two 8 GHz transmitters are installed to increase reliability. Each transmitter has a different carrier frequency. A scrambling generator is used in the processing unit to maintain spectrum uniformity. The viewing directions of scanning radiometers are canted slightly toward each other and, using two sets of scanning radiometers, the signal processor, and 8 GHz transmitter simultaneously, a swath width of 220 km is achieved. MESSR's resolution is about 50 x 50 m. Since this operation mode cannot be provided routinely, normal operation of one side of MESSR (100 km swath width) will take two repeat cycles for total coverage of the Earth. The systematic scanning pattern of MESSR is shown in Fig. 9.

Visible and Thermal Infrared Radiometer. The VTIR has one visible and three thermal infrared channels with the characteristics shown in Table 4. Si-PIN diodes are used for detecting visible band signals and Hg/Cd/Te for infrared signals. Each channel has two detector elements in order to increase reliability. A bulky radiation cooler is installed facing space to maintain the infrared signal detecter at about 100 K. A block diagram of

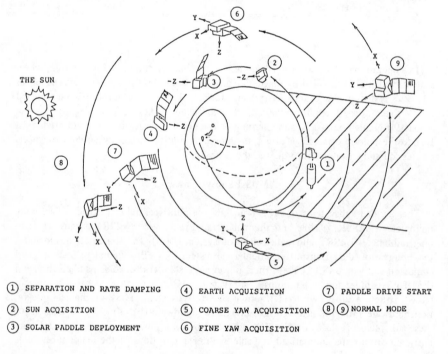

① SEPARATION AND RATE DAMPING	④ EARTH ACQUISITION	⑦ PADDLE DRIVE START
② SUN ACQISITION	⑤ COARSE YAW ACQUISITION	⑧⑨ NORMAL MODE
③ SOLAR PADDLE DEPLOYMENT	⑥ FINE YAW ACQUISITION	

Fig. 6   Orbital sequence.

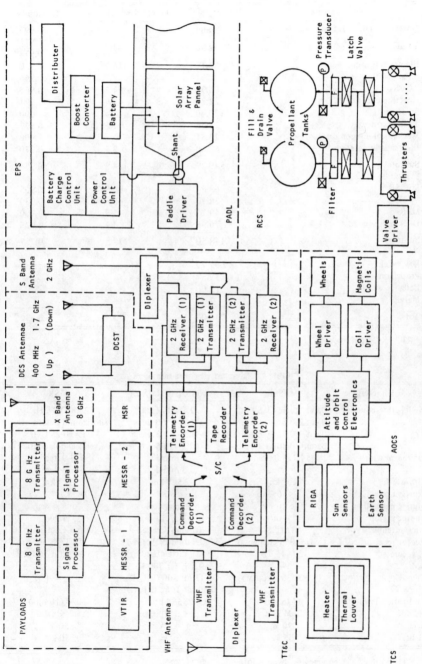

Fig. 7   Functional block diagram of MOS-1.

Table 3 MOS-1 subsystems

Subsystem	Weight, kg	Power consumption	Reliability
Observation data TM antenna	0.84	–	0.999
TT&C	42.96	41.7	0.971[a] 0.974[b]
Electrical power	62.17	16.7	0.950
Solar paddle	92.61	7.5	0.946
AOCS	86.97	61.2	0.965
Reaction control	22.35	47.9	0.971
Structure	130.40	–	1.000
Themal control	24.68	17.5	0.977
Mechanical integration	23.51	–	1.000
Electrical integration	62.80	2.4	0.970
Subtotal	549.29	194.9	0.755
MESSR	63.24	89.8	0.905
VTIR	28.70	40.8	0.930
MSR	49.71	45.8	0.900
DCS transponder	6.85	3.4	0.928
Subtotal	148.50	179.8	0.757
Dry weight	697.79	–	–
Propellant	19.68	–	–
Ballance weight	15.00	–	–
Margin	7.53	–	–
Total	740.00	374.7	0.530

[a] RF.   [b] Digital.

Table 4 Characteristics of radiometers

Characteristic	MESSR	VTIR (visible[a]/i.r.)	MSR
Wave length/frequency[b]	Band 1:0.51–0.59 μm	0.5– 0.7 μm[a]	23.8±0.2 GHz[b]
	Band 2:0.61–0.69 μm	6.0– 7.0 μm	(horizontal polarization)
	Band 3:0.72–0.80 μm	10.5–11.5 μm	31.4±0.25 GHz[b]
	Band 4:0.80–1.10 μm	11.5–12.5 μm	(vertical polarization)
IFOV/beam width[c]	54.7±5.0 μrad	1 m rad[a]	1.9 deg[c]
		3 m rad	1.3 deg[c]
Swath width	100 km	1500 km	317 km
Distortion rate	<16%	<3.3%	<1.7%
Scanning method	Electronic	Mechanical	Conical scan
Scanning period	7.6 m/s	1/7.3 s	3.2 s
Optics/antenna[d] type	GAUSS	Ritchey-Cretien	Offset-Casegrain[d]
Detector/receiver[e]	CCD (2048 elements)	Si-PIN diode[a]/Hg Cd Te	Dicke type[e]
S/N/accuracy[f]	39–15 dB	55dB (alve db 80%)[a]	1.5 DFC (at 300 K)[f]
NEΔT	–	0.5 K (at 300 K)	–
MTF	0.2 (at 36 1ps/mM)	0.42 (at 500 C/RAD)	–
		0.40 (at 166.7C/RAD)	
Quantization level	64 (6 bits)	256 (8 bits)	1024 (10 bits)
Data rate	8 Mbit/s	1.6 Mbit/s	2 Kbit/s
Power	90 W	45 W	50 W
Weight	65 kg	30 kg	50 kg

[a] VTIR visible; [b] frequency; [c] beam width; [d] antenna type;
[e] receiver type; [f] accuracy.

VTIR is shown in Fig. 10. The optical part of the VTIR is a Ritchery-Chretien type. Dichroic beam splitters and optical filters are used to distribute each spectral band signal to the four sensors. The scan is done by mechanically rotating mirror at a speed of 7.3 rps. The calibration signals are made by viewing the blackbody and space when the rotating mirror is not directed toward Earth. The VTIR had 16 gain steps to measure the albedo and surface temperature of the objects in detail.

Microwave Scanning Radiometer. In order to detect the temperature difference of 1–3 K from weak radiation noise, the MSR uses two Dicke-type radiometers at frequencies of 23 and 31 GHz. The scanning is performed conically by rotating an offset Casegrain-type antenna with the speed of about 18 rpm as shown in Fig. 9. The characteristics and the block diagram of MSR are shown in Table 4 and Fig. 11, respectively. Two types of integrating time constants are adopted in order to obtain the precise temperature resolution of 1 K and high surface reslolution. Such components as the receiver, mixer, and broadband low-noise IF amplifier, which are critical to MSR performance, are carefully designed to not be influenced by the ambient temperature variation.

In the front part of the nadir along the track of the satellite's orbit, the radiometer is operated in a caribration mode, using switches, skyhorn, and standard noise source data. In the rear part of the nadir, radiometer is operated in the observation mode.

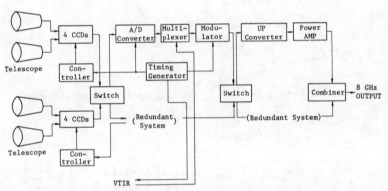

Fig. 8   Functional block diagram of MESSRs, signal processors, and 8 GHz transmitters.

Table 5 AOCS components characteristics

Components		Performance and characteristics
Rate integrating	±2 deg/s	Range
gyro assembly	±12 deg/s	Non g sensitive drift rate
Sun sensor assembly	±20/±45 deg	Linear/operating range
	±70 deg	Off-axis operating range
Earth sensor assembly	±4/±60 deg	Linear/operating range
Momentum	50A/N·m·s ±10%	Angular momentum range
wheel and WDE	(4600 rpm ±10%	rotational speed)
Magnetic coil	0.07 N·m	Maximum output torque
and MCE	50 tm²	Maximum magnetic dipole moment
Reaction control	±0.6 N·m	Roll torque
subsystem and VDE	±1.0 N·m	Pitch and raw torque

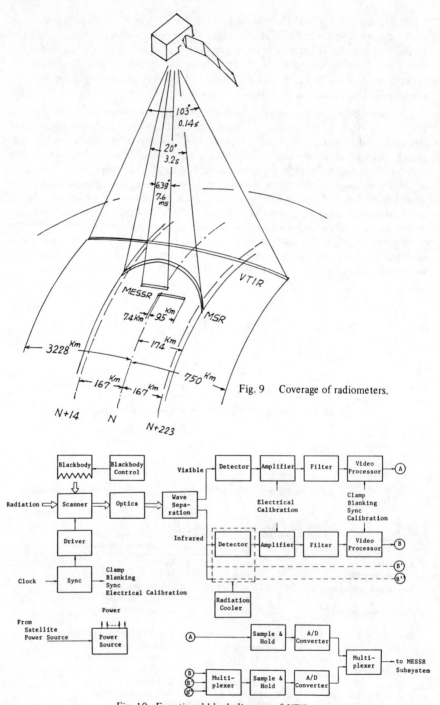

Fig. 9   Coverage of radiometers.

Fig. 10   Functional block diagram of VTIR.

Data Collection System. The block diagram of DCS transponder is shown in Fig. 12. The 400 MHz received signal from the data collection pratform enters the down converter and the waveform of the output intermediate of the frequency (IF) down converter is used to modulate the 1.7 GHz downlink carrier frequency. In order to minimize the deviation of the local oscilator freqnency, the DCS transponder has only one local oscilator and it supplies for both the receiver and transmitter.

Spacecraft Bus Subsystems

Telemetry, Tracking, and Command Subsystem. Telemetry data transmission, real-time and high-speed playback of the stored data, and command could be realized by both VHF and S-band. The VHF is primally used for an attitude acquisition phase and the S-band for a normal mode. The tape recorder is installed to collect the housekeeping data when the RF link from the NASDA ground station is not engaged. Delayed commands are employed to initiate the orbit control, the attitude control of transition phase, and the opeartion of mission equipment when the satellite is out of the visibility range of the NASDA Earth station. A shaped beam antenna pointing to the Earth is adopted for the S-band to compensate for the distance variation of the RF link between the satellite and the Earth station. Also, to ensure the RF link during the attitude acquisition phase, another broadbeam S-band antenna is installed on the rear pannel, i.e., anti-Earth pannel. The S-band equipment is also capable of handling the ranging signal and transmitting the MSR data.

Besides these TT&C subsystems, MOS-1 has an X-band transmitter for the transfer of MESSR and VTIR data. Base-band telemetry data can also be received by the X-band through the MESSR/VTIR signal processor.

RF link analysis based on antenna patterns measured on an engineering model shows that the design for all RF bands has a sufficient margin to ensure the link to the Earth station.

Solar Paddle Subsystem and Electrical Power Subsystem. The main power source of MOS-1 is one-wing solar paddle subsystem. The solar paddle consists of an aluminum yoke and three aluminum core honeycomb sandwich pannels with carbon fiber-reinforced plastic (CFRP) face plates on which are mounted about 9400 solar cells, each 2 x 4 cm. A shunt decipater is mounted on the yoke to take the excess power. The two outer panels are canted so as to face the sun and the yoke and inner panel are arranged as

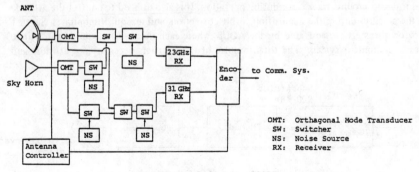

Fig. 11 Block diagram of MSR.

the center of mass lying on the same line as the drive shaft. This paddle can create a minimum of 570 W at the end of life. The paddle has to be controlled to maximize the power supply, i.e., the paddle is rotated to follow the sun by the paddle drive. The electric power thus obtained is controlled to a constant 29 V by the power control unit and is fed to each subsystem.

Transition phase and in the shadow zone the electric power is supplied by three 13 A·h batteries. Each battery consist of 17 series NiCd battery cells. The changing of battery is controlled by a battery charge control unit.

Simulation and analysis for the power supply and consumption for all phases show the sufficient power generation by the solar paddle (570 W end of life) and sufficient augmentation capability of the batteries for the entire mission duration.

Attitude and Orbit Control Subsystem. The main part of the AOCS is a so-called biased momentum-type, three-axis control analog system. During the aquisition phease, it utilizes rate integrating gyros, sun sensors, and Earth sensors successively. Most of these are used during the transient phase in combination with 1 N thrusters that are employed as actuators.

In operational or normal mode, a skewed V-shaped pair of 50 N·m·s momentum wheels (MW), driven by wheel drive electronics (WDE), generates the main driving force. Besides its built-in stabilizing effect due to the 50 N·m/s bias momentum, it can control the pitch and roll angles by changing the speed of each wheel independently. Because it is not actively controlled in the operational mode, yaw angle pointing has the poorest accuracy. However, roll-yaw coupling will in the long run also will help to converge the yaw error to zero. Since they have saturation limits, the momentum wheels are augmented by an unloading system that utilizes the Earth's magnetic field by switching the magnetic coils several times every revolution. Also reaction control subsystem is considered to be used as a back up for the wheel unloading.

Some of the characteristics figures for AOCS components are listed in Table 5.

The design was verified by analyses. The performance of the hardware components at a subsystem level was tested by using the engineering model (EM) in both the transient and normal phases. The validity of the subsystem components design was demonstrated. The AOCS subsystem components of the prototype model (PM) went through the subsystem qualification level environment test successfully. Performance test results of PM AOCS subsystem were almost the same as those of the EM subsystem.

Reaction Control Subsystem. The RCS is utilized to correct the orbit injection error and induced ground trace error during operation. It is also utilized to control the attitude of the satellite during the acquisition, orbit correction, and reacquisition phases. Seven 1 Newton thrusters are activated by the AOCS, where each thruster is clustered as a pair to form a redundant system. The total impulse of the thrusters necessary for attitude and

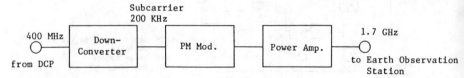

Fig. 12 Block diagram of DCS transponder.

orbit control during the mission life have been estimated and fuel (hydrazine) consumption has been derived in accordance with the characteristics of the RCS, i.e., impulse and Isp. The estimated impulses and fuel comsumption are shown in Table 6. Based on this estimate, the two RCS tanks will carry 18.5 kg of fuel with N_2 as the pressurizing gas.

Structure Subsystem. MOS-1 is composed of two aluminum honeycomb sandwich panel boxes with one wing solar paddle at one side. The box on the top contains primarily the mission equipment and that at the bottom primarily the spacecraft bus equipment. Two panels can be opened at the corner hinge for easy access to the components during installation and testing of the satellite on the ground. The size of MOS-1 is approximately 1.6 × 1.5 m with a height of 2.4 m. The large movable solar paddle and fuel tanks are put on the middle panel to minimize any change in the mass center or burden on the control subsystem. The panels facing Earth are used primarily for mission equipment and antennas. The solar paddle is attached to the panel facing the sun, while the thermal louvers and radiation cooler for the VTIR are installed on the opposite side. Dimensions of the basic members and the strength of each member are determined by analysis and verified by static load testing. Modal and stress analyses by the finite element method are con-

Table 6 Estimated thruster impulses fuel consumption

Parameter	Thruster inpulse, N·s	Fuel consumption, kg
Correction of orbit injection error		
Semimajor axis, Δa	7445	3.6
Inclination, Δi	6700	3.3
Ground trace correction	190	0.1
Attitude control		
Initial acquisition and orbit control	6880	3.9
Reacquisition	3995	3.6
Total	25210	14.5

Table 7 Thermal characteristics

	Hot mode	Cold mode
External heat flux absorption, W	192	220
Internal heat sorce, W	82 / 207	34 / 143
Total, W	482	397
Louver state	Almost open	Almost closed
Heater, W	0	3[a]
Balanced temperature, °C	20 / 25	3 / 8

a   for RCS and batteries.

ducted and the dynamic load for each onboard equipment are assigned. These analytical results are verified by both sinusoidal and accoustic viblation tests of the structural model.

Thermal Control Subsystem. Excpt the limited elements (i.e., mission equipment, the sun and Earth sensors, thruster, antennas, and solar paddle are directly exposed to the space environment) most of MOS-1 body is covered with a thermal blanket and radiation windows. The radiation windows consist of a radiator and passive and active thermal louvers that control the internal heat balance. Active louvers and heaters are attached near the batteries and temperature-sensitive elements and are controlled by the thermal control electronics. The MOS-1 body is so designed as to be thermally isolated from the solar paddle.

The influence of external heat flux, solar and Earth radiation, and Earth albedo are minimized by thermal insulation. These influences are estimated by solar simulation and thermal balance tests. The most critical item was estimation of the thermal characteristics of the blankets, which cover the most of the outer body of MOS-1. To keep the inside temperature uniform, most of the elements attached to each pannel from the inside are painted black. Thermal control must be effective for both the steady-state normal and the transient modes. In the transient phase, heaters attached near heat-sensitive components are turned on automatically or by command to keep temperatures in the proper range. During the normal mode, deviation of the external heat flux is slight due to the sun-synchronous orbit; hence, radiation control by thermal louver seems sufficient.

The validation of the thermal design has been checked by both analysis and tests. A solar simulation test is conducted to specify the thermal characteristics of the external elements. The results of the analysis and the thermal balance tests with a thermal model show good agreement. The results are summarized in Table 7.

Summary

The basic design of MOS-1 started in 1980 with NEC Corporation as the prime contractor. The subcontracters include Mitsubishi Electric Corporation (MELCO) for the AOCS, Toshiba Corporation for PADL, and Ishikawajima-Harima Heavy Industry Company Ltd. for RCS. RCA of the United States supported NEC by reviewing the structure and thermal design and providing some hardware components. The MESSR, MSR and VTIR have been developed by NEC, MELCO, and Fujitsu Limited, respectively. The design review was completed in July 1981. The critical design elements were checked on test models. The most critical element of the thermal design was to estimate the thermal properties of the blankets and outlying components, which were determined through solar simulation testing. The total thermal design was checked by thermal balance testing using the thermal test model. The mechanical test model was used for static, sinusoidal vibration, and acoustic testing, as well as for gas leakage, mass balance, alignment, paddle deployment, and separation. The subsystem engineering model tests included those for the AOCS closed-loop, paddle drive, thruster performance, battery cycle, the performance of mission equipment, etc. At the system level, the engineering model tests included integration, electrical performance, RF characteristics and operational mode. As reliability was not accounted for in the engineering model, redundant elements were not assembled in the EM and high-reliability parts were not required. Reliability and flight environments are taken into account in the prototype model. With all of these tests and analyses, the critical design was completed and a design review was made in May 1983. The design was then finalized and the production phase of the prototype model started. All sub-system PM tests are completed and are now under integration and assembly testing.

MOS-1 will be launched in 1986, but at this moment NASDA does not have a definite follow-on program for marine observation. A feasibility study of the MOS-2 program with improved sensors has just started. The technology and experience obtained thus for with MOS-1 will be utilized in succeeding Earth resource satellite projects (ERS).

Acknowledgments

General contents of this paper are based on material prepared for the working group meeting of International Society of Photogrametry and Remote Sensing, Tokyo, November 1983. Descriptions of the mission analysis and AOCS subsystem are based on a paper by Y. Ishizawa et al. [1] and the description of the ground systems are based on a NASDA document [2].

The authors deeply appreciate the assistance and cooperation of those working to achieve the goals of the MOS-1 project.

References

[1] Ishizawa, Y., Kusanagi, M., Shimamura, T., Shirako, G., and Nakagawa, E., "Marine Observation Satellite-1 System and Control Concepts," Paper presented at Annual Rocky Mountain Guidance and Control Conference, Keystone, Colo., 1984.

[2] "Technical Description for Design of MOS-1 Ground Station," National Space Development Abency of Japan, Tokyo, Sept. 1983.

Studies on Japanese Earth Resources Satellite 1

Yasushi Horikawa*

National Space Development Agency of Japan, Tokyo, Japan

Abstract

This paper deals with the studies of the Earth Resources Satellite, ERS-1, an active microwave sensing satellite using synthetic aperture radar (SAR). The preliminary design of ERS-1 has been completed, the results of which are summarized here. Covered is the design of the overall system, as well as the subsystems including SAR; visible and near-infrared radiometer (VNR); telemetry, tracking, and command; electrical power; reaction control; attitude control; etc. Also included is some system analysis of the mission operations power, etc. The design of ERS-1 is found to be compatible with the Japanese H-1 launch vehicle.

Introduction

Since the early 1970s, a number of remote sensing satellite such as the meteorological satellite and/or Landsat series have been launched.

The remote sensing satellite provides synoptic views and frequent repetitive coverage of the Earth's surface and makes regional and global observation of Earth resources and environments. The Landsat satellites, launched by the Untied States, have demonstrated their great effectiveness for such applications as land use, crop inventory, water resources, surface mine detection, environmental monitoring, and others.

The National Space Development Agency of Japan (NASDA) is carrying out the research and development of the

---

Presented as part of Paper IAF-83-120 at the 34th IAF Congress, Budapest, Hungary, October 1983. Copyright © American Institute of Aeronautics and Astronautics, Inc., 1983. All rights reserved.

*Director, Earth Observation Satellite Program Office, Program Planning and Management Department.

satellite   remote   sensing   technologies,   including
satellites, sensors, and ground facilities.   Marine
Observation Satellite 1, the first of the series, is now
under development, and is scheduled for launch in 1986.

Development of Earth Resources Satellite 1, which will
carry synthetic aperture radar, began in 1980. At that
time, a system design study of ERS-1 was performed with
several types of sensor combinations as the initial
concept.

Three private companies in Japan presented their design
studies in 1980.   From the results of the studies, a
combination of synthetic aperture radar (SAR) and visible
and near-infrared radiometer (VNR) was selected.   In
1982, the design was reviewed from the viewpoint of the
system's manufacture along with the tradeoff studies of
the various design alternatives.   This study and the
research and development of synthetic aperture radar and
visible and near-infrared radiometer are being carried
out by industry under the sponsorship of NASDA.   This
paper presents the summary of the ERS-1 conceptual
design.

The design objectives of ERS-1 are to establish active
microwave sensing techniques and to collect information
of geological features, land use, agriculture, forestry,
fishery,   environment   preservation,   coastal   zone
monitoring, etc. In order to establish these objectives,
global experimental operation aimed at the application of
an Earth resource observation system, development of
Earth observation equipment, and verification of their
functions and performance, as well as development of the
spacecraft bus equipment and its verification, will be
carried out.

The definition phase of ERS-1 will be performed in
1984, targeted toward a launch in 1991. Figure 1 shows a
tentative program schedule.

ERS-1 Design

System Requirements and Configuration

The systems of the ERS-1 program are shown in Fig. 2.

Image data from the SAR and VNR will be transmitted to
data receiving stations in Japan and elsewhere.

ERS-1 will be launched by the NASDA H-1 launch vehicle
(two stages) from the Tanegashima Space Center in Japan.
The launch capability of H-1 is approximately 1400 kg to
about a 570 km altitude circular orbit at about a 98 deg
inclination. (The H-1 fairing size is about 2.2 m in

diam and about 7 m in height.) Tracking of the ERS-1 will be done by NASDA tracking stations and the TDRS network of the United States. A schematic view of ERS-1 is shown in Fig. 3 and a functional block diagram in Fig. 4.

ERS-1 is configured with the following subsystems; 1) synthetic aperture radar; 2) visible and near-infrared radiometer; 3) observation data transmitter; 4) observation data recorder; 5) tracking, telemetering, and command; 6) electrical power; 7) attitude control; 8) reaction control; 9) structural; 10) thermal control; and 11) integration hardware.

ERS-1 system design was conducted with consideration of the design, test, and integration techniques developed in past space programs.

Each subsystem will be developed separately as a module according to the procurement policy, system requirements,

	1984	1985	1986	1987	1988	1989	1990
Mile-Stone			△ PDR	△ CDR1	△ CDR2	△ PQR	△ PSR △ Launch
Preliminary Design							
Basic Design							
Detail Design							
BBM							
EM							
PFM							

Fig. 1 ERS-1 tentative schedule.

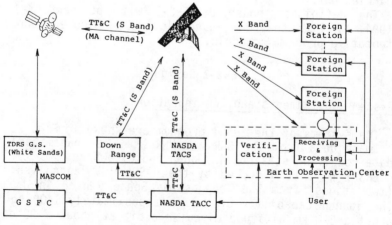

Fig. 2 Total system of ERS-1.

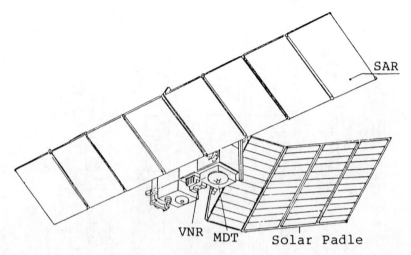

VNR MDT   Solar Padle

SAR

Fig. 3 Schematic view of ERS-1.

and interface conditions.   However, some components will
be imported from foreign suppliers.   Each subsystem will
utilize   existing   technology   as   much   as   possible.
However, if new technology is needed, it must be started
in the early phases of development.   The SAR, VNR, and
bus equipment will be designed by domestic technology
from this standpoint.   The spacecraft bus equipment will
be designed to achieve high reliability, weight
reduction, and low power consumption.   System and
subsystem design of ERS-1 will take into account the
future expansion toward an operational large-scale
satellite.   The design must also consider the test
facilities and methods.

Design of Mission Equipment

SAR.   Synthetic aperture radar (SAR) will be the
principal earth observation instrument on the active
sensing satellite.   The L-band radar frequency was
selected in order to achieve antenna flatness and high-
power transmission. Off-nadir pointing of the antenna at
33 deg was selected based on an analysis of pulse
repetition frequency, signal-to-noise ratio, signal-to-
ambiguity ratio, and antenna size compatibility with the
faring clearance envelope.   One of the technically
critical items in the SAR is the deployment of the radar
antenna. Various methods of deployment of the paddle and
truss have been studied. Based on the results of such
study, the folded paddle deployment method was selected,

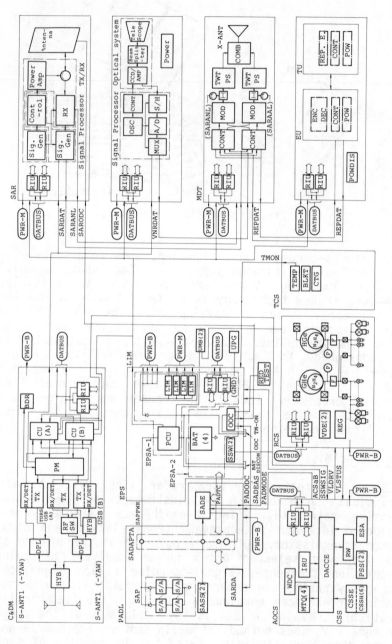

Fig. 4　Functional block diagram of ERS-1.

Table 1   Synthetic aperture radar

Item	Characteristics
Swath width	74 km
Spatial resolution	25 x 25 m
Off-nadir angle	33 deg
Transmitting frequency	1275 MHz
Polarization	H-H linear
RF band width	12 MHz
S/N	7 dB
S/A	20 dB
Data rate	60 MHz
Transmitting power	1 kW peak
Pulse width	35 μs
Pulse compression ratio	450
Pulse repetition frequency	1550-1690 p/s
Antenna size	2.4 x 12 m
Weight antenna	134 kg
Weight electronics	120 kg

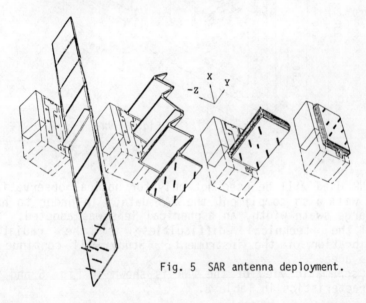

Fig. 5   SAR antenna deployment.

since it required less development time. The deployment sequence is shown in Fig. 5 and the SAR characteristics in Table 1.

VNR. Visible and near-infrared radiometer (VNR) is an improvement over the multispectral electronic self-scanning radiometer (MESSR) with regard to resolution and swath width. The MESSR will be installed on MOS-1, which will be the first remote sensing satellite designed in Japan.

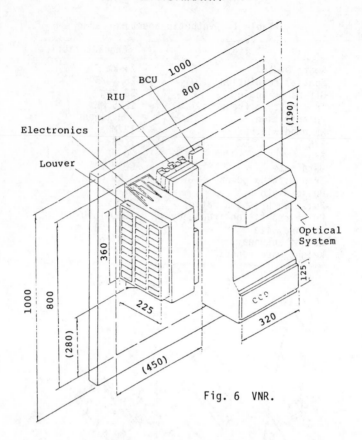

Fig. 6 VNR.

VNR data will be used not only for optical observation, but will also compliment the SAR data. In order to have a large swath width, an aspherical lens was adopted. One of the technical difficulties is the radiation calibration of the instrument. Study will continue in this area.

A schematic view of the VNR is shown in Fig. 6 and the characteristics in Table 2.

MDR. Observation of ERS-1 will be done mainly by existing Landsat stations. However, as a backup and for areas where a Landsat station is not available, a high-density data recorder, called the mission data recorder (MDR), is installed in ERS-1. It will be procured from the United States. The characteristics of the MDR are shown Table 3.

MDT. Observation data will be transmitted through the mission data transmitter (MDT). In order to receive the

Table 2 Visible and near-infrared radiometer

Item	Characteristics
Swath width	150 km
Spatial resolution	25 x 25 m
Wavelength (1)	0.45-0.52 μm
(2)	0.52-0.60 μm
(3)	0.63-0.69 μm
(4)	0.76-0.95 μm
IFOV	44 μrad
FOV	15.4 deg
Image acquisition time	3.6 ms
Weight	40 kg

Table 3 Mission data recorder

Item	Characteristics
Capacity	272 Gbit
Data rate (input/output)	30 Mbps x 2
Recording/reproducing time	20 min
Weight	Approx. 80 kg

ERS-1 data at the Landsat stations, a 20 W TWTA transmitter will be used. A difficult problem for this transmitter is the on/off cycle, the reliability of which will be studied further.

The characteristics and link calculation of the MDT are shown in Tables 4 and 5, respectively.

Subsystem Design

TT&C. The tracking, telemetering, and command (TT&C) subsystem is compatible with existing NASDA tracking stations and the TDRS system. The base band system is configured with the data bus system. The telemetry data rate is 8 kbit/s for the S-band and 128 bit/s for TDRS, while the command data rate is 512 and 125 bit/s, respectively. A maximum of an 8 day delay command capability is also being considered. Ranging is via the tone/PM method for the S-band and via PN code method for TDRS.

EPS. The electrical power system (EPS) will employ a series regulator for design flexibility with the 28±7 V bus voltage. The solar panel will produce 1500 W (EOL).

Four 20 A·H NiCd batteries will support the mission load
during eclipse operation. The first candidate for the
solar cell is a thin 50 mil Si cell. If further weight
and size reduction is needed, an efficient GaAs cell may
be adopted.

ACS. The attitude control system (ACS) will stabilize
ERS-1 with 0.3 deg pointing accuracy and 0.003 deg/sec
stability (3 σ). This will be achieved by a three-axis
zero-momentum stabilization method that will use four
skewed momentum wheels.
The sequence of the initial acquisition phase includes
contingency plans.

RCS. The reaction control system will use a hydrazine
liquid propellant. The liquid tank is configured by two
50 cm, diam tanks. Four 18 N thrusters and twenty 1 N

Table 4 Mission data transmitter

Item	Characteristics
Frequency	8025-8400 (2 frequencies)
Data rate	60 Mbps (1 frequency)
Modulation	QPSK
EIRP	El 90° 2 dB·W
	El 5° 17 dB·W
Radiation pattern	Shaped broad beam
Polarization	RHCL
RF band width	60 MHz (1 frequency)
Weight	40 kg

Table 5 Link calculation

Item	Elevation 90 deg	5 deg
Transmitted power, dBW	13	
Feeder loss, dB	2.0	
Antenna gain, dB	-9	+6
EIRP, dBW	2	17
Free space loss, dB	166	178
Atmospheric loss, dB	0.3	1.1
Rain loss, dB	1.2	3.9
Ground G/T, dB/K	31.0	
C/No, dBHz	94.1	93.6
E/No, dB	16.3	15.8
Required E/No, dB	12.8	
Margin, dB	3.5	3.0

thrusters with complete redundancy will be incorporated for attitude and orbit control.

System Analysis

Orbit Selection. The orbit altitude selected for ERS-1 will be around 570 km for a 1400 kg spacecraft. The parameters selected for a synchronous quasirecurrent orbit are shown in Table 6. An orbital Earth trace is shown in Fig. 7.

Power Analysis. If all the land area data are taken through the MDR, the data coverage is conditioned by the recording capacity. One Japanese station and another high-latitude station will cover three or four times each for SAR and VNR. If the data from ERS-1 are received by a Landsat station, power generated by the solar panel and battery is an important factor. Figure 8 shows a sample observation.

Assuming 5 min SAR recording and 7 min SAR real-time operation during an eclipse and 5 min recording, 10 min

Table 6 Orbital parameter

Recurrent day	44 days
Recurrent number	15 rev/day
Node move direction	West
Attitude	568.01 km
Inclination	97.68 deg
Period	96.15 min
Descending local time	10:30 $\pm$ 30 min
Orbital duration at equator	60.8 km

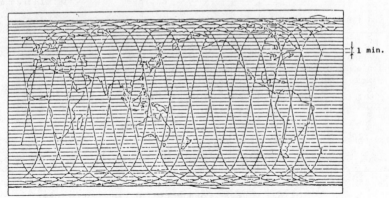

1 min.

Fig. 7 Orbital Earth trace.

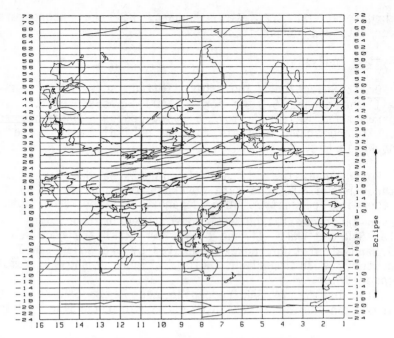

Fig. 8 Observation at Landsat station.

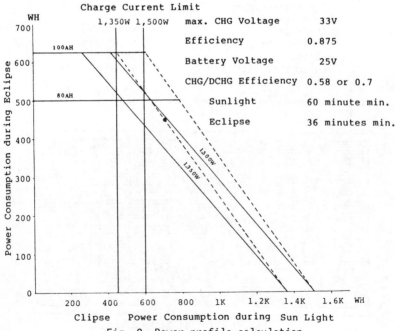

Fig. 9 Power profile calculation.

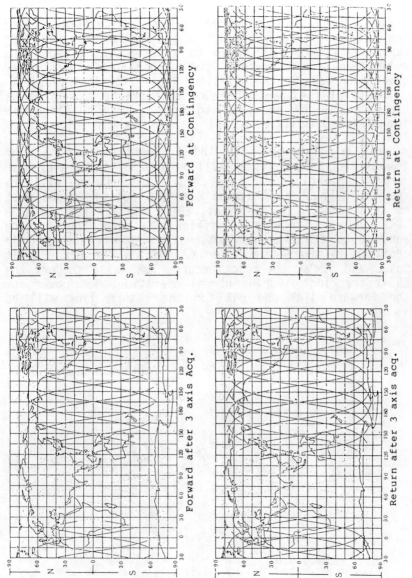

Fig. 10 TDRS link visibility.

SAR real time, and 10 min VNR real-time operation during
sunlight, a reasonable operational scheme would use an 80
A·H battery and 1500 W (EOL) solar power as shown in Fig.
9.

Fuel Budget.   The required fuel was calculated.   Since
the ERS-1 altitude is relatively low, atmospheric drag
cannot be ignored. In order to reduce this effect, the
solar panel was canted, giving more effective power
generation because the satellite local time is 10:30.
The total fuel weight needed to maintain the orbit is
estimated to be about 70 kg for a 2 yr mission life
including acquisition.

Link Calculation.   For the telemetry, tracking, and
command, an S-band system will be used. In cases of both
normal operation and emergency, the links will be
insured.   However, tracking stations outside Japan must
be considered.   In any event, ERS-1 may utilize the NASA
TDRS system. Since it is difficult to point the steering
antenna to TDRS, an omniantenna system will be used in
addition to the S-band antenna.   During the early orbit
phase and if an emergency occurs, TDRS will support the
ERS-1 tracking.   During normal operation, 45% power for
the forward link and 64% for the return link will be

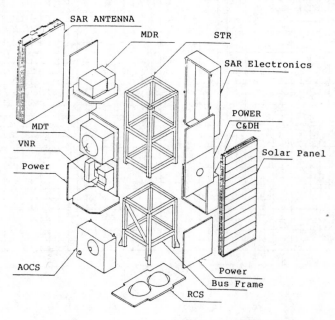

Fig. 11 Structural configuration of ERS-1.

Table 7 Weight summary, kg

AOCS	110.9
C&DH	59.9
EPS	223.2
RCS	134.4
STR	204.0
INTG	52.3
Subtotal	785.6
SAR	283.9
VNR	48.9
MDR	90.4
MDT	42.9
Subtotal	466.1
Attach fitting	55.0
Margin	93.3
Total	1400.0

established. If an emergency occurs, more than 90% for both links will be established. An example of the TRDS link is shown in Fig. 10.

Other Areas of Analysis. Other areas of the ERS-1 operation were investigated, such as mission analysis, launch window and orbital perturbation, operations, attitude, reliability, structural considerations, thermal conditions, mass property, etc. A weight summary of ERS-1 is shown in Table 7.

There were no difficulties in developing ERS-1 to this point. The structural configuration divides ERS-1 into two modules: an upper mission equipment area and a lower bus equipment area could be feasible. However, to save weight, it may be better to have a mixed configuration rather than such a separation. This will be studied further. Figure 11 shows the ERS-1 structure.

Conclusion

One of the principal users of the ERS-1 data will be the Ministry of International Trade and Industry (MITI) for Earth resource exploration. Therefore, ERS-1 will be jointly developed by MITI and NASDA (the former will handle the observation instruments). Other users of data on geological features, land use, agriculture, forestry, fishery, environmental preservation, etc., will be

coordinated under the Science and Technology Agency
(STA). STA controls NASDA for the ERS-1 development.

STA and other ministries and agencies have met to
define the ERS-1 user requirements. These requirements
will also be refined during the definition phase. The
conceptual design of ERS-1 has been reviewed here.

To proceed to next design phase --definition-- more
coordination with the user community will be needed to
establish specifications for the spacecraft. It is
concluded that the presented conceptual design study is
feasible.

Remote Sensing Activities in India—Past, Present, and Future

Y.S. Rajan*

Indian Space Research Organization, Bangalore, India

Abstract

India has planned a comprehensive end-to-end program in remote sensing covering major aspects, such as, sensor development, aircraft surveys, space segment development, establishment of various interpretation facilities including hardware/software systems and application activities. The activities of Indian Space Research Organization (ISRO) beginning early 1970's with experimental satellites are described.

Indian experience in the applications of remote sensing for various end uses is summarized. A brief description of data acquisition facilities and aircraft systems is given. The paper also includes a brief description of the earth station complex near Hyderabad.

The status of data interpretation facilities in India is given including the plans for immediate future. The status of training in remote sensing is described. The paper includes salient specifications of the sensors developed indigenously for the Indian space programs. A brief overview of the space segment is given including the salient details of the Indian remote sensing satellite - IRS-1A - scheduled for launch in 1986. The paper also lists salient details of the very high resolution radiometer of the Indian National Satellite (INSAT) system, a satellite of which is currently operational. It also describes a monocular electro-optical stereo scanner mission which is under approval cycles.

The paper also briefly describes the Indian plans for microwave remote sensing.

*Director, Earth Observation System.

The paper describes, in some length, the National Natural Resources Management System (NNRMS) that is under evolution to make remote sensing applications a part of the operational Indian user systems.

Background

India has planned a comprehensive end-to-end program in remote sensing that spans such aspects as sensor development, aircraft surveys, space segment development, and establishment of various interpretation facilities (i.e., hardware/software systems and application activities). During the period 1972-82, the Indian Space Research Organization built a number of experimental satellites (Aryabhata, Bhaskara I & II, Rohini series (RS-1) and Apple) with the objective of gaining experience in basic spacecraft design, in the conduct of application studies using remote sensing and communications and in scientific and technological experiments. Bhaskara satellites I & II carried two primary payloads (two-band TV cameras and three-frequency microwave radiometers). The TV visible and near-infrared data have been used in developing the methodologies of resources mapping (land cover, forest, snow, flood plains, geology, and vegetation). The passive 19, 22, and 31 GHz microwave data have been used for preliminary investigations of the sea state and the atmosphere over the oceans and have demonstrated the possibility of deriving many ocean-related parameters, viz., sea surface temperature, water vapor and liquid water content, rainfall rates, etc. A miniature payload (3 kg) with a photodiode array (called the "smart sensor") was flown in the Rohini satellite launched in 1983 by the indigenously developed Indian launch vehicle SLV-3.

The Indian remote sensing satellite (IRS-1) is the first of a series of semioperational satellites scheduled for launch in early 1986; the IRS payload will be capable of imaging the earth in four spectral bands in the visible and near-infrared regions at spatial resolutions of 36.5 and 73 m. The spectral bands have been identified after many experiments conducted jointly with user agencies. An IRS Utilization Program has been approved to demonstrate and systematize some typical applications of IRS-1. IRS-1 will form a unique and important component of a National Natural Resources Management System (NNRMS) that is under development. This is a hybrid system of remote sensing combined with conventional techniques for resources and environmental-studies. A major national seminar on NNRMS in 1983 presented 50 end-to-end experiments demonstrating the status of remote sensing *used to monitor natural resources. The resolution passed at the seminar provides the basis for future action.*

User organizations in India are actively cooperating with national agencies on remote sensing. Utilization of remote sensing data is on the increase. Indian scientists have extensively used such data from aircraft as well as the Landsat series. The Indian station receiving Landsat data has been operational since 1979 and has been upgraded to receive thematic mapping data. Different states in the country are planning the formation of remote sensing centers or cells. Besides major facilities available in the Indian Space Research Organization (ISRO) and National Remote Sensing Agency (NRSA), there are many other training facilities being established in the country.

One important addition to India's operational Earth observation system is the very-high-resolution radiometer (VHRR) of the geostationary Indian National Satellite (INSAT) system. INSAT-1B is currently operational. The paper will describe some salient features of the INSAT-VHRR system. India also has facilities to receive data from the National Oceanic Atmospheric Administration (NOAA) satellites.

The improved version of the Indian satellite launch vehicle (ASLV) will be able to carry the 150 kg satellites of the stretched Rohini satellite series (SROSS). One of these satellites is expected to carry a multispectral charge coupled device (CCD) camera payload monocular electro-optical scanning system (MEOSS) for imaging the Earth.

India has used data from the modular optoelectronics multispectral scanner (MOMS) data about India from the Space Shuttle pallet satellite (SPAS) as part of its cooperation with DFVLR. India has also obtained MKF-6 camera imagery from a recent joint Indo-Soviet flight.

In addition to these and other operational applications, India also has definite plans to increase its experimental participation in future systems such as active microwave remote sensing and synthetic aperture radar.

Introduction

India has a long tradition in the use of science and technology for scientific applications. Scientific survey organizations such as the Survey of India and Geological

Survey of India and observational institutions such as the India Meteorological Department have been in existence for more than 150 years. The first aerial photographs were taken in 1920. Realizing the potentials of modern remote sensing, multispectral remote sensing was introduced in 1970 through a joint aerial experiment between the Indian Council of Agricultural Research (ICAR) and the Indian Space Research Organization (ISRO). It has since grown considerably leading to the Indian remote sensing satellite (IRS) series, the first of which is under development for launch in 1986.

There are many publications detailing the use of remote sensing in India. A brief history of remote sensing activities in India and details about the organizations involved and their work in sensor development, aerial[1] surveys, and image interpretation were outlined by Bhavsar[1] at the first Asian Conference on Remote Sensing in November 1980. Annual updates have been presented at subsequent conferences. ISRO published the papers presented at the 1981 conference along with brief reports from various user agencies.

A series of selected papers on remote sensing have appeared[3] in the Proceedings of the Indian Academy of Sciences[3]. This publication contains a program overview by Navalgund and Kasturirangan on the Indian remote sensing satellite. This paper discusses in some detail the scope of the IRS mission, choice of key mission parameters, payload parameters, reasons for selecting spectral bands, radiometric resolution of the IRS sensors, the orbit selection criteria, IRS platform stability, IRS data handling system on the ground, and the spacecraft main frame. The paper also addresses the compatibility of the IRS with other remote sensing satellites such as Landsat and SPOT. The paper includes a brief description of IRS utilization program and a glimpse of the IRS-1 follow-on program.

Selected papers describing the Indian remote sensing activities will appear in the International Journal of Remote Sensing in 1985[4].

In view of such publications, this paper attempts mainly to describe certain overall features of the Indian program, trends, and some vital statistics. For the sake of completeness, certain specifications of the satellites will be given in tabular form. For convenience, the presentation is divided into following sections: applications, data acquisition systems, data interpretation facilities, training, sensors, space segment, IRS, INSAT, miscellaneous experiments, microwave remote sensing, and the National Natural Resources Management System (NNRMS).

Applications

Indian experience in the application of remote sensing to various end uses such as soil mapping, agriculture, geology, marine and coastal studies, forestry, etc., is widespread and comprehensive. More than 50 institutions have some minimal remote sensing data interpretation facilities, albeit rudimentary. About 1000 scientists in various user departments in the country have adequate experience in the use of multispectral aerial imagery and spaceborne remote sensing data from Landsat, NOAA, etc. Visual interpretation still dominates, although some major users outside the space organization began to use computer-based analysis about six years ago. The extensive use of remote sensing data is creating a demand for interactive computer-based systems. It is such widespread use by many agencies (with near-operational use by some agencies) that has led to the approval of the Indian remote sensing satellite (IRS) project and in principle the approval of a series of satellites. A brief overview of the decade of Indian experience was given in a paper[5]. Those interested are directed to the extensive bibliography in that paper.

Data Acquisition Facilities

This section will briefly describe the aircraft remote sensing facilities and satellite data acquisition facilities.

Aircraft System

The main agency in India conducting aerial multispectral remote sensing is the National Remote Sensing Agency (NRSA). It has one HS-748 and two Dakota (DC-3) aircraft that are modified to carry multiple sensors and equipped with modern navigational (day and night) systems. These planes can be deployed for cartographic and remote sensing surveys up to 12,121 m (40,000 ft) altitude. One of the Dakota aircraft has been modified for geophysical survey work with facilities for automatically recording data compatible with fast computer processing on the ground.

A few private aircraft operators are capable of conducting multispectral surveys, provided the sensors are fitted

by the users.   The Space Applications Center (SAC) of
ISRO had earlier conducted a few surveys using indigenously
developed sensors on such privately owned aircraft.   National
Geophysical Research Institute (NGRI) has an instrumented
aircraft for airborne geophysical surveying.   With the
increased use of remote sensing in the country, it is likely
that the demand for aerial surveys to supplement satellite
data as well as to test new sensor systems will increase.

NRSA is planning to acquire a few Dornier 228 aircraft
suitably modified for remote sensing.

Earth Stations

A major Earth station complex to receive data from
remote sensing spacecraft is situated at Shadnagar, near
Hyderabad.   This Earth station complex is the major national
facility operated by NRSA.   It is capable of receiving data
from Landsat satellites including Landsat 5; it also receives
data from the U.S. NOAA meteorological satellites.   With
marginal modifications, the station is capable of receiving
data from other satellites such as SPOT operating in the
X and S bands.   Presently, the complex is being augmented
to receive data from IRS.   The first receiving antenna system
was established in 1979 and NRSA Data Center (NDC) has
since archived the Landsat data.   Data from the NOAA
satellites are presently received only when requested by
a user.   Since a separate antenna system is being built,
it is likely that by 1985 data reception from NOAA satellites
will be on a continuous basis.   India Meteorological Department (IMD) has a system established at Delhi to receive
data regularly from NOAA satellites and also   operates
a number of automatic picture transmission (APT) receiving
stations throughout the country.   IMD has an operational
system to receive and disseminate data from the very-high-
resolution radiometer (VHRR) of INSAT, which will be
described below.

The antenna diameter of the reception terminals is
10.06 m. G/T for the S band (at 5° El) is 20.2 dB/K, for
L band (at 5° El) NOAA frequencies 13.2 dB/K, and for
the X band G/T above 30 dB/K.

Satellite Data Products

The following standard output products are available:
1) Landsat multispectral scanner (MSS) data: Computer
compatible tapes (CCTs), 240 mm film in 1 m scale, 70 mm

film in 4 m scale; return beam vidicon (RBV) data: 70 mm film in 2 m scale. Black and white prints and color composites of MSS and RBV data in 1 m scale can also be supplied.

2) NOAA satellites: CCTs, 70 mm film output   in 60 m scale and enlarged black and white prints in 10 m scale; special products involving enlargements, special signal processing, etc. A data center with microfiche and browse facilities for examining the Landsat data has been established.

A complete set of computer compatible tapes, 70 mm imagery, 9 x 9 in. positive and negative transparencies for India for the period 1973-75 is available for historical studies. Data since 1980 is acquired from the NRSA Earth station.

Data Interpretation Facilities

More than 50 institutions in India (in various state and central government user agencies) have some minimal facilities for the visual interpretation of remotely sensed data. These are mostly simple equipment such as light tables and magnifiers. Some agencies are in the process of augmenting these with more complex instruments such as additive color viewers, optical reflecting projectors, zoom transferscopes, etc.

As of now, comprehensive facilities with computer-based interpretation facilities are available only at the Space Applications Center (SAC) of ISRO in Ahmedabad and NRSA at Hyderabad. SAC has a fully operational VAX 11/780 based interactive system. ISRO scientists have developed many software packages for interpretation. Some user scientists involved in joint projects use SAC and NRSA facilities. Some agencies such as the All India Soil and Land Use Survey (AIS & LUS) of the Ministry of Agriculture at Delhi, the Indian Institute of Technology at Bombay, and the Anna University at Madras are in the process of establishing computer-based interpretation facilities.

Considering the significant use of remote sensing by many users and their demand for computer-based interpretation facilities, the Planning Committee of National Natural Resources Management System (PC-NNRMS), in which the major user ministries participate, has decided to establish five major regional remote sensing data processing service centers (RRSSC) in different parts of the country. Each of these will have a core super-minicomputer with multiple user terminals.   The locations are Dehra Dun (Northern Center), Kharagpur (Eastern Center), Bangalore (Southern Center), Nagpur (Central Center), and Jodhpur (Western Center).   There is an in-principle decision to locate sixth and seventh centers in the northeastern region and Jammu and Kashmir State respectively.

Some institutions, including the Uttar Pradesh Remote Sensing Applications Center at Lucknow, are also in the process of acquiring interpretation facilities based on powerful super-minicomputers.   By the time IRS is launched in 1986, it is expected that many users will have a reasonable amount of access time for sophisticated interpretation facilities.   ISRO and NRSA will provide most of the software required for the RRSSCs, while many other agencies will also be encouraged to develop the required software.   To

Table 1   Remote sensing sensor development

Platform	Sensor	Spectral channels	Applications
Aircraft	Thermal Scanner	10.5-12.5 μm	SST, emissivity studies in conjunction with microwave sensors
Aircraft	Multi spectral scanner	Five bands over 0.5-3.0 μm and thermal channel in 8.0-12.0 μm	Different remote sensing applications, signature studies, crop cover classification, land use, thermal inertia maps
Bhaskara I and II	Slow scan Vidicon	0.54-0.65 μm 0.75-0.85 μm	Land use, snow cover, coastal processes, forestry
Aircraft	Push broom solid state camera	0.5-0.7 μm	Test flights
Ground	Ground truth radiometer	Visible and near infrared regions	Spectral signature studies
Bhaskara I and II	Passive microwave radiometers	19,22,31 GHz	Sea surface phenomena, atmospheric water vapour and liquid water content
Aircraft/ ground	SLAR	9.4 GHz (real aperture	Experiments to discriminate crops, water bodies, roads, etc.
Ground	Microwave radiometers and scatter ometers	9.4, 1.5,10.5 GHz	Signature studies and dielectric constant determination

a limited extent, certain specialized standard software may be imported.

Training

A brief paper describing the training opportunities in India in remote sensing was presented at COSPAR[6]. The Indian Photointerpretation Institution (IPI) at Dehra Dun (presently called the Indian Institute of Remote Sensing - IIRS) began such training in 1966. So far over 1400 scientists have been trained (of which about 70 were from developing countries). The annual number of trainees is about 150. Because of the varied requirements of the Indian system, the training is given under three broad categories: 1) for decision makers, planners, managers, and/or administrators (for a few days); 2) for middle-level supervisory officers or scientist-managers (a few weeks); and 3) for working level scientists and technicians (a few months).

IIRS is a part of the National Remote Sensing Agency (NRSA), which is an operational agency for remote sensing in India. In addition, NRSA organizes specialized advanced courses at Hyderabad. The Space Applications Center, Ahmedabad, also has recently established specialized training program for the IRS utilization activities. The Center of Studies for Resources Engineering (CSRE) of the Indian Institute of Technology (IIT), Bombay, also conducts varied types of short-term workshops of a few weeks' duration. Many other academic institutions are planning to introduce remote sensing courses as electives or postgraduate courses. They are also planning to conduct short-term workshops to retrain many scientists. There are a number of universities providing opportunities for Ph.D work in subjects related to remote sensing.

A recent paper[7] outlines the training of remote sensing users in India.

Sensors

Indian space program, consistent with its stated goal of self-reliance and also to conduct many experiments for different uses, has a comprehensive program in the field of sensor development. The major indigenous sensors developed are listed in Table 1.

Presently, such activities are concentrated on developing the onboard imaging system for IRS, some microwave sensors, and, to a limited extent, the optoelectronic imaging systems for future IRS series (visible infrared systems).

Table 2 Indian remote sensing (IRS) satellite series

Mission objectives	To acquire images over India for Earth resources applications on an operational basis
	To operate ground systems for data reception, processing, and generation of data products
	To use the data from IRS and other sources for the national natural resources management system (NNRMS)
Instruments	One low-resolution LISS-1 (linear imaging, self-scanning) camera with a resolution of 72 m and a swath of 148 km
	Two high-resolution LISS-2 cameras with a resolution of 36 m and a combined swath of 145 km
	Four spectral channels in each camera, viz., 0.45-0.52, 0.52-0.59, 0.62-0.68, and 0.77-0.86 m
Spacecraft	Three-axis stabilized operation, sun synchronous orbit at 904 km, orbits repeating every 22 days, time of equator crossing 10 a.m. data transmission in X and S bands
Design life	3 years
Carrier	USSR launch vehicle
Centers	Indian Space Research Organization Satellite Center, Bangalore
	Space Applications Center, Ahmedabad (payload)
	National Remote Sensing Agency, Secunderabad (data reception, data products)
Schedule	June 1986 launch
Status	Engineering model subsystems under development and testing

Space Segment

A brief overview of the Indian space program and the satellite main frame development in India is given in a paper by Dhawan and Rao[8]. While the Bhaskara and Rohini satellites were relatively rudimentary in terms of the onboard *sensors, the IRS-1 satellite is nearly state-of-the-art.   A good overview of the IRS program in terms of selection of payloads, satellite characteristics, and utilization is given in a recent paper by Navalgund and Kasturirangan. The paper also gives a brief scenario of the   IRS series up to the early 1990s. Salient aspects of IRS-1A satellite is given in Table 2.*

Besides the IRS series, the Indian space program has a 150 kg class stretched Rohini satellite series (SROSS) to be launched by an indigenous launch vehicle called augmented satellite launch vehicle (ASLV). Some of the SROSS may carry Earth observation payloads to test new techniques, concepts, etc, as the 50 kg Rohini satellites did earlier. One such mission is due for launch in 1986. Salient aspects are given in Table 3.

Indian National Satellite System (INSAT)

This is a multipurpose geosynchronous satellite uniquely tuned to India's need for telecommunications, TV services, and meteorological services.   It carries a VHRR having visible and thermal infrared bands.   Present INSAT-1B is positioned at 74° E. It will be followed by INSAT-1C to be launched in 1986.   Some important aspects of INSAT VHRR system is given in Table 4.

Miscellaneous Experiments

Besides concentrating on providing users with remotely sensed data from Landsat, IRS, NOAA, INSAT, etc., satellites, India selectively uses other opportunities as available. For example, when the Indian cosmonaut went on the joint Indo-Soviet mission in April 1984 in Soyuz-Salyut, a number of photographs over India were taken with multispectral MKF-6 and hand-held cameras.   The imagery received are being analyzed and used for resource applications. Similarly, as a part of ISRO's cooperation with the West German Agency for Aerospace Research (DFVLR), Indian scientists have received some imagery over India from the modular optoelectronic multispectral scanner (MOMS) that flew on Space Shuttle missions.   There are Indian scientific investigators in the metric camera experiment through cooperation with European Space Agency (ESA).   Indian scientists also use data from Seasat, Shuttle imaging radar, coastal zone color scanner (CZCS), and other NOAA/Nimbus sensors.

Microwave Remote Sensing

Since most of India is cloud covered, especially during the crucial agricultural months, it has been realized from the beginning that while visible infrared remote sensing applications are very useful, India would need cloud-penetrating sensors in its resource management system. With this in view, a small beginning was made in 1975 in microwave tremote sensing with the passive microwave sensors on the Bhaskara I and II, which were launched in 1979 and 1981, respectively.

In addition, ground scatterometers were also developed and one side-looking airborne radar (SLAR) instrument was flown. There were also a few joint experiments conducted with DFVLR scientists on a 9.6 GHz SLAR and 90 GHz radiometer. Presently, one sophisticated scatterometer on a cherry picker (swept frequency in the band of 1 -

Table 3   Monocular electro-optical stereo scanner (MEOSS)

Mission objectives	Experimental production of monoscopic and stereoscopic photomaps in the scale of 1:250000-1:500000
	Systematic tests of different methods for geometric image correction
Instrument	MEOSS camera with three parallel and rigidly connected CCD linear arrays using common optics for push broom scanning at three angles, resolution 70 m, spectral band 0.57-0.70 m
Spacecraft	Stretched Rohini Satellite Series-2 (SROSS-2), three-axis stabilized at 450 km, 45.5 deg inclination, multimission platform
Design life	6-12 months
Carrier	Indian augmented satellite launch vehicle (ASLV)
Centers	ISRO Satellite Center (SROSS satellite) DFVLR, FRG (MEOSS payload)
Schedule	Launch 1986
Status	Phase-B studies over; approvals awaited for further phases

18 GHz) is ready for use. There is also a swept frequency airborne passive radiometer under development. There are plans to have a dynamic active microwave sensing program including development of a spaceborne synthetic aperture radar during the seventh plan period (1985-1990). Active discussions are underway with ESA for possible reception of ERS-1 data over India. The prime thrust of microwave remote sensing program in India during the seventh plan period is to generate sufficient SAR imagery over India to obtain a large amount of scatterometer data and put it to use jointly with the users. This will provide the data base leading to one of the IRS series in the early 1990s that will carry active microwave sensors in addition to visible infrared.

National Natural Resources Management System (NNRMS)

This is possibly a unique concept, at least organizationally, that is under evolution in the wake of demonstrated and accepted use of remote sensing in various areas of agriculture, geology, etc. Since the Indian program is application oriented and sharply tuned to national development tasks, from the very beginning many experiments were conducted by ISRO jointly with the user agencies. This was the philosophy adopted in Bhaskara data utilization. In 1976, these efforts led to the conceptualization of IRS series, the first two of which were finalized after many presentations and discussions with the users. Along with the approval of IRS project, it was also realized that it was necessary to equip the user agencies with necessary near-operational wherewithal to maximize the benefits from IRS.

Although remote sensing data may be in a single source, namely, ISRO, its applications are widespread in the country. Many agencies in the state and central governments are responsible for agriculture, forestry, soil survey, etc. The NNRMS system envisages the establishment of the necessary technical and managerial links between various agencies to ensure that remotely sensed data are integrated beneficially with the existing conventional resource management systems to qualitatively improve them. A selected set of papers presented in an NNRMS seminar held in May 1983, is to appear in International Journal of Remote Sensing in 1985. This seminar, which was attended by many scientists, managers, and administrators from different parts of the country, resulted in a 16 point resolution giving very

Table 4   Indian national satellite (INSAT) system

Mission objectives	Long-distance telecommunication Round-the-clock Earth imaging for meteorology Round-the-clock meteorological data collection Direct TV broadcast National radio and TV network
Meteorological instruments on INSAT-1B	Very-high-resolution radiometer (VHRR) imaging the full Earth disk, visible band (0.55-0.75 μm) with 2.75 km resolution, infrared band (10.5-12.5 μm) with 11.5 km resolution. Data relay transponder for data collection platforms (DCP).
Spacecraft parameters	Three-axis stabilized, geostationary orbit at 74° E
Design life	7 years
Carrier	U.S. STS
Schedule	INSAT-1B launched on Aug. 30, 1983 INSAT-1C scheduled launch 1986
Status	INSAT-1B operational INSAT-1C under development

good direction for the growth of the use of remote sensing in the country to the NNRMS system.

Subsequent to the recommendations of the national seminar, nine task forces have been constituted to identify the basic elements of the management of the information system for different applications. The task force reports are being finalized. The Task Force on National Resources Information System (NRIS) will use these reports for developing guidelines and making recommendations.

An NNRMS bulletin is published regularly to disseminate information on the developments related to NNRMS and remote sensing activities in the country and abroad.

The planning committee of NNRMS chaired by a member of a Planning Commission and consisting of top administrators/managers of major central departments/ministries oversees, guides, and directs the overall evolution of NNRMS. It has decided to establish five regional centers for generating the necessary trained manpower in the field of machine processing of remotely sensed data. Each center will service its respective region. Subsequent to the decision on locating four centers, it has been decided to locate the Western at Jodhpur in Rajasthan.

The regional center sponsored by the Department of Space (DOS) has been established at Dehra Dun on the premises of the IIRS. The training is currently centered around the multispectral interactive data analysis system (MIDAS) developed by NRSA and installed at IIRS. This center has already conducted seven familiarization courses in digital data processing. Based on the feedback of the first five courses, the duration of subsequent courses have been increased from 2-3 days to 1 week. The courses are also now being organized for groups of scientists, each group in a specialized discipline.

Work on developing the requisite facilities for all the centers is proceeding reasonably well. Civil works have commenced and action is being taken for the procurement of the visual interpretation equipment and the computer system.

Conclusion

A brief review of remote sensing activities in India has been given. It can be seen that remote sensing applications in India are well rooted with the user agencies and active efforts are underway to their use nationally. There is also a defined program to improve upon the space segment/sensor capabilities of IRS series in the near future.

Acknowledgments

The author wishes to thank the many scientists, engineers, and technicians of ISRO, NRSA, numerous user agencies, and some academic institutions, whose tireless efforts have established remote sensing in the country. Author also wishes to thank the heads of many user agencies whose active interest has led to remote sensing becoming operational in the country. It is a pleasant duty to thank Prof. P.R. Pisharoty who founded modern remote sensing in India and Prof.S.Dhawan, Chairman of ISRO in 1972-1984, whose guidance and direction of the Space Program has led to the IRS and INSAT series and the NNRMS concept.

References

[1] Bhavsar P.D., "Remote Sensing Activities in India," Proceedings of the first Asian Conference on Remote Sensing, Bangkok, Nov. 1980.

[2] Rajan, Y.S., "Remote Sensing Activities in India," Proceedings of the second Asian Conference on Remote Sensing, Beijing, Oct. 1981.

[3] Deekshatulu, B.L., and Rajan, Y.S., (eds.), "Remote Sensing," Indian Academy of Sciences, Bangalore, India, 1984.

[4] International Journal of Remote Sensing, special issue, to be published 1985.

[5] Rajan, Y.S., and Rao, V.R., "A Decade of Remote Sensing in India - Some Salient Results," Paper presented at COSPAR, Graz, Austria, Jun. 1984.

[6] Natarajan, T., and Rajan, Y.S., "Training Opportunities in Remote Sensing in India," Paper presented at COSPAR, Graz, Austria, Jun. 1984.

[7] Baldev, S., "Training for Remote Users in India," Paper presented at International Conference on Training for Remote Sensing Users, Toulouse, France, Oct. 1984.

[8] Dhawan, S., and Rao, U.R., "The Indian Space Programme," Proceedings of the Thirteenth International Symposium on Space Technology and Science, Tokyo, 1982, p.19.

[9] Navalgund, R.R., and Kasturirangan, K., Proceedings of the Indian Academy of Sciences, Bangalore, India, Dec. 1983.

Chapter VI.   Remote Sensing from the Space Shuttle

Remote Sensing of the Earth with Spaceborne Imaging Radars

Charles Elachi,* JoBea Cimino,† and James Granger‡

*Jet Propulsion Laboratory, California Institute of Technology,
Pasadena, California*

Abstract

Spaceborne imaging sensors in the visible, infrared
and passive microwave have been used to observe and study
the Earth's surface since the early stages of the space
program. More recently, active microwave imaging sensors
(radars) have been developed to extend our capability to
study the Earth surface processes. Imaging radars, flown
on Seasat (1978) and the Shuttle (1981, 1984), acquired
synoptic images of a variety of geologic, biologic, and
oceanographic features and provided new insight in some of
the land and ocean processes. Subsurface synoptic imaging
was achieved for the first time in some of the arid regions
of the world. Soil moisture distribution after a rainstorm
was clearly delineated, opening the possibility of its
monitoring on a global basis. Polar ice distribution and
dynamics over large areas in the Beaufort Sea were monitored
over a three-month period, thus allowing the possibility of
operational observation of ice dynamics in support of polar
navigation. The successful development and flight of these
spaceborne imaging radars was the result of major technological developments in the 1970s. They used some of the
largest spaceborne lightweight planar array antennas (2 x
10 m) with printed radiating elements. The transmitters
were fully solid state and generated a 1 kW peak power signal
at L-band (1.2 Ghz). The processing of the received data
to generate the high-resolution (25 to 40 m) imagery was
done using both optical and digital processors. More
advanced imaging radar systems are under development.

*Principal Investigator, SIR-A and SIR-B Experiments; currently,
Senior Research Scientist.

†Senior Scientist, Science Collaborator, SIR-B Experiment.

‡Cognizant Engineer, SIR-A Experiment.

Multispectral, multipolarization imaging radar systems are
under development for flight in the late 1980s, thus extending our capability of detailed studies of the Earth surface
processes and the nature of its cover. Extremely fast SAR
digital processors are under development using the most
advanced integrated circuits and allowing real-time processing of the data. This corresponds to a computational
capability of 6 x 10^9 operations/s. This chapter consists
of a review of the recent scientific and technological
developments in the field of Earth observation with spaceborne imaging radars and an overview of planned activities
in the 1980s.

I.   Introduction

Over the last 6 years, two space missions allowed the
acquisition of the first high-resolution radar images of
the Earth's surface. In 1978, the Seasat satellite acquired
extensive radar coverage over North America, western Europe,
the North Atlantic, and the Northeast Pacific.[1] In 1981,
the Shuttle Imaging Radar (SIR-A) acquired a limited amount
of data over a wide range of regions around the world.[2]
Both missions were of an experimental nature and operated
for a limited time period. However, the imaging radar data
acquired during these missions have given us the first insight into the use of these data in a wide range of large-
scale geoscientific research and application topics, including structural and lithologic mapping, arid surfaces imaging
through thin alluvium and sand cover, soil moisture mapping,
forest clear-cutting, ocean wave pattern studies and ship
routing. Both sensor systems used the synthetic aperture
radar (SAR) technique to acquire the high-resolution images.
Spaceborne photography became available in the early
1960s with the advent of the space age. This was followed
in the late 1960s and 1970s with the acquisition of multispectral visible and infrared (i.r.) imagery, thermal imagery, and passive microwave imagery. These sensors allowed
us to acquire information about the surface by studying its
emitted energy in the microwave and i.r. regions of the
spectrum and the reflected energy in the visible and near-
i.r. regions. All of these sensors are passive in nature,
i.e., they detect the energy generated by the surface or
the sun energy reflected by the surface.
The SAR imaging sensor provides information about the
surface by measuring and mapping the reflected energy in
the microwave region, thus extending the capability of

sensing the surface properties into a new dimension. In addition, because it uses its own energy and operates at a relatively long wavelength, it acquires surface imagery at all times, i.e., day or night and through cloud cover. Thus, it has the unique capability required for continuous monitoring of dynamic surface phenomena.

The imaging resolution of passive sensors is equal to their angular resolution (i.e., observing wavelength over aperture size) multiplied by the range between the sensor and the area or object being imaged. Thus, the size of the resolution element increases linearly with the observing wavelength and sensor altitude and is inversely proportional to the aperture size. In the optical and i.r. regions, very high resolution is acheivable from orbit with reasonably sized apertures because of the short operating wavelength. In the microwave region, the operating wavelength is relatively large and apertures of many hundreds of meters to many kilometers are required to achieve high resolution of tens of meters or less. This, of course, is impractical at the present time.

The SAR sensor circumvents this limitation by using the ranging and Doppler tracking capability of coherent radars to acquire high-resolution images of the surface from orbital altitudes. Two neighboring targets are separated by their differential time delay and Doppler history, neither of which is a function of the distance to the sensor. Thus, the resolution for a SAR system is independent of the sensor altitude. This unique advantage does impose some restriction on the sensor imaging swath, antenna size, and power requirements. Because the SAR uses the Doppler history to achieve high resolution in one of the spatial dimensions, each pixel is generated by processing a large number of successive echoes. This leads to a large number of arithmetic operations in order to generate the image. The development of digital processors for spaceborne SAR data is a very active and challenging research field. The basic properties of spaceborne SAR systems are discussed in Sec. II and the technological aspects of the sensor and processor are presented in Sec. VI.

The Seasat imaging radar acquired surface images during the summer of 1978 with a resolution of 25 m, illumination angle of 23 deg from vertical, L-band frequency (23 cm in wavelength) and H-H polarization. The highlights of the corresponding scientific results can be found in a number of scientific articles (e.g., Refs. 3-6). The analysis of the Seasat data clearly indicates that spaceborne radar data are an important tool in a number of applications, including structural mapping, lithologic mapping when used

in conjunction with visible and near-i.r., soil moisture
delineation, vegetation type identification when used in
conjunction with Landsat data, ocean wave pattern studies
and forecasting, internal wave studies, ocean bathymetry in
very shallow regions, and polar ice structure and dynamics.
Unfortunately, the Seasat data were acquired over only one
season. This did not allow the study of dynamic phenomena
over a year's time scale.

In 1981, the SIR-A acquired a limited amount of data
over a number of regions around the world. The SIR-A
characteristics were similar to the Seasat SAR except the
resolution was 40 m and the illumination angle was 50 deg.
The highlights of the SIR-A results are summarized in Refs.
7-9. The SIR-A results confirmed some of the Seasat results, with the following additions:

1) In arid and hyperarid regions, the radar waves will
penetrate through a surface layer of sand or alluvium
several meters deep. This opens a whole new field of near-
subsurface imaging of buried geologic, hydrologic, and
possible archeologic features.

2) In tropical forest regions, a spaceborne radar can
be used to delineate and monitor deforestation.

3) Spaceborne stereo radar images can be used for
topographic contours mapping.

In addition, a comparison of the imagery acquired by SIR-A
and Seasat showed that multiple indidence angle radar images
are required to be able to fully map both small-scale
(roughness) and large-scale (topography) features.

Examples of these different applications are given in
Secs. III and IV. Section V contains a detailed description
of the Seasat and SIR-A sensors as well as of the SIR-B
sensor that was flown in the fall of 1984. Future sensor
systems planned for flights in the late 1980s and early
1990s are briefly dicussed in Sec. VII.

II. Principle of Spaceborne Synthetic
Aperture Imaging Radars

In the synthetic aperture technique, the Doppler information in the returned echo is used simultaneously with
the time delay information to generate a high-resolution
image of the surface being illuminated by the radar. The
radar usually "looks" to one side of the moving platform
(to eliminate right-left ambiguities) and perpendicular to
its line of motion. It transmits a short pulse of coherent
electromagnetic energy toward the surface. Points equidistant from the radar are located on successive concentric
spheres. The intersection of these spheres with the surface

gives a series of concentric circles centered at the nadir point (Fig. 1). The backscatter echoes from objects along a certain circle will have a well-defined time delay.

Points distributed on coaxial cones, with the flight line as the axis and the radar as the apex, provide identical Doppler shifts of the returned echo. The intersection of these cones with the surface gives a family of hyperbolas (Fig. 1). Objects on a specific hyperbola will provide equi-Doppler returns. Thus, if the time delay and Doppler information in the returned echoes are processed simultaneously, the surface can be divided into a coordinate system of concentric circles and coaxial hyperbolas (shown in Fig. 1) and each point on the surface can be uniquely identified by a specific time delay and specific Doppler. The brightness assigned to a specific pixel (picture resolution element) in the radar image is proportional to the echo energy contained in the time delay and Doppler bins that correspond to the equivalent point of the surface being imaged. The resolution capability of the imaging system is thus dependent on the measurement accuracy of the differential time delay and differential Doppler (or phase) between two neighboring points on the surface.

In actuality, the situation is somewhat more complicated. The radar transmits a pulsed signal that is neces-

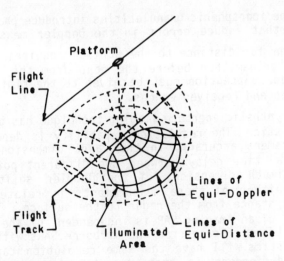

Fig. 1 Synthetic aperture radar geometry. The constant time-delay and constant Doppler lines form the radar imaging coordinate system. The backscatter return from each cell on the surface can be uniquely determined by filtering from the total return the energy in the appropriate time-delay bin and Doppler shift bin.

sary to obtain the time-delay information. To obtain the Doppler information unambiguously, the echoes from many pulses are required to meet the Nyquist sampling criterion. Thus, as the moving platform passes over a certain region, the recorded series of echoes contains a complete Doppler history and range-change history for each point on the surface being illuminated. These complete histories are then processed to identify uniquely each point on the surface and to generate the image.[10-14]. This is why a very large number of operations are required to generate one pixel in the image -- such is not the case in optical sensors. A simplified comparison is that the radar sensor generates the equivalent of a hologram of the surface and further processing is required to obtain the actual image. This processing can be done either optically or digitally.

In the case of spaceborne sensors, there are additional effects[2,14] that are not encountered with airborne sensors:

1) The rotation of the Earth relative to the spacecraft adds a Doppler shift that must be accounted for during processing. This Doppler shift varies as a function of latitude and inclination of the orbit.

2) The orbit eccentricity causes an altitude rate of change that translates into a Doppler shift which must be eliminated.

3) The ionospheric granularities introduce phase scintillations that induce errors in the Doppler measurements.

4) The far distance to the surface requires that many pulses be transmitted before the echo from the first one is received. Attention must be given to the timing of the transmitted and received echoes.

The synthetic aperture imaging technique has one unique characteristic. The resolution capability is dependent on the measurement accuracy, in the range dimension, of the differential time delay between two different points and, in the azimuth dimension, of the Doppler shift from a target. Neither of these measurements is related to the absolute distance from the radar to the surface. Thus, the resolution of an imaging SAR is independent of the altitude of the platform. Spaceborne and airborne SARs with similar characteristics will have the same resolution capability. The main difference is that spaceborne sensors require more transmitted power to be able to obtain the necessary echo signal-to-noise ratio. The size of the antenna aperture is determined mainly by the width of the swath being imaged and the observing geometry, not by the resolution.[7]

Surface Interaction Mechanisms

The brightness of an individual pixel in a radar image is a direct representation of the backscatter cross section of the corresponding area on the surface being imaged. The backscatter cross section is dependent mainly on the physical (e.g., slope, roughness and near-surface inhomogeneities) and electrical (e.g., dielectric constant) properties of the surface, as well as the radar wave characteristics (incidence angle, frequency, and polarization state). A number of interaction mechanisms contribute to the backscattered energy.[5] Bragg scattering is dominant at relatively large incidence angles and for relatively well-organized surfaces. Rayleigh scattering is dominant in the case of discrete objects. Specular reflection is of particular importance at near-vertical incidence and multiple scattering plays a key role in depolarization of the incident wave.

In its simplest form, the behavior of the backscatter cross section as a function of incidence angle is shown in sketch form in Fig. 2. Because of the numerous surface parameters influencing the backscatter cross section, a complete description of the surface properties will most likely require multiple observations with different radar parameters. If the radar system operates at a single

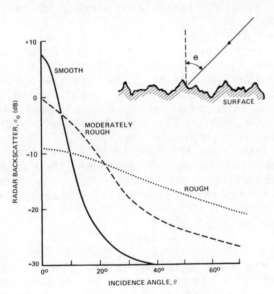

Fig. 2 Illustrative example of backscatter as a function of incidence angle.

frequency, it can be seen from Fig. 2 that large incidence angles are more favorable for observing surface topography because of the resulting shadowing. Small incidence angles are also desirable because of the high sensitivity of back-scatter to variations in the surface slope. Intermediate incidence angles are more favorable for observing surface roughness. Multiple incidence-angle observation will allow the acquisition of information about different surface properties and will allow the use of stereo techniques.

Multiple-frequency observation is of particular interest at intermediate angles in order to acquire a measure of the spectra characteristics of the surface roughness. Multiple-polarization observations provide information about volumetric and multiple scattering and will tend to suppress the effects of the large-scale topography (i.e., slope changes).

Noise in SAR Systems: Thermal and Speckle Noise

Neglecting quantization noise, the two types of noise to be considered in a radar design are the thermal and speckle. The former is an additive noise due to the noise temperature at the input of the receiver. The signal-to-thermal noise ratio can be improved by increasing the transmitted peak power or decreasing the receiver temperature. This is the type of noise encountered in real-aperture radar systems.

Speckle noise is due to the coherent nature of the SAR image-formation process. This noise gives the radar image a fine texture similar to what is observed when a scene is illuminated with laser light. The speckle noise is proportional to the reflected signal power. Thus, it is a multiplicative noise that cannot be reduced by increasing the transmitted power. The speckle noise can be reduced only by averaging independent looks.

Before detection, the speckle noise is assumed to be a zero-mean Gaussian noise on each of the in-phase and quadrature components. After detection, the intensity in an image pixel then has an exponential probability distribution of the form

$$p(I) = (1/I_0)e^{-I/I_0}$$

where I_0 is the average return in the absence of speckle. As multilooks are coherently added, the speckle variance is reduced and becomes chi-squared (χ^2) and distributed with 2N degrees of freedom, where N is the number of independent looks. This gives a probability density function for the intensity of an image pixel as

$$p(I) = \frac{1}{\Gamma(N)} \frac{1}{I_0} \left(\frac{I}{I_0}\right)^{N-1} e^{-I/I_0}$$

This distribution has a mean of $\mu = NI_0$ and a standard deviation $\Sigma = \sqrt{N}\ I_0$.

One measure of an image radiometric resolution, for a stationary scene, is

$$Q = 10\ \log\ \frac{\mu + \Sigma}{\mu - \Sigma} = 10\ \log\frac{\sqrt{N} + 1}{\sqrt{N} - 1}$$

which clearly shows that higher values of N are desirable. However, for $N > 25$ (e.g., $Q = 1.8$ dB), large increases in N give only small improvements in Q. This should be traded off with the fact that increasing N immediately degrades the image resolution in a proportional way.

A detailed theoretical study with experimental verification of the speckle noise property has been made by Bennett and McConnell.[15]

III. Applications in Land Observations

Surface Geology

The response of radar backscatter to changes in the surface topography on both large and small scales make it a powerful tool for geologic structural mapping. Surface details are best observed when the illumination direction is perpendicular to the topographic trend of the surface feature. Unlike visible and infrared systems, which have illumination geometries tied to the sun, the self-illuminating radar has some control over the illumination geometry. Changes in the slope of a few degrees can change the radar backscatter significantly and therefore subtle topographic features can often be detected. On a a smaller scale, changes in the roughness of the surface on the scale of several centimeters can be related to lithology. Rock types that have undergone different erosional processes can be discriminated using the radar. The presence of vegetation associated with different types of soils can be used to delineate underlying geologic structures.

The potential for doing structural geologic mapping using spaceborne imaging radars was clearly demonstrated with the Seasat SAR, even though the imaging geometry was selected for oceanographic studies. Figure 3 depicts the folded Appalachian Mountains in Pennsylvania. Large plunging synclines and anticlines are easily mapped in the radar image. The heavily forested mountain slopes exhibit a smooth image texture due to the uniformity of the forest canopy. The more diverse image tone of the valleys is due to the variety of surface cover, including urban, rural, and agricultural regions. Regional drainage patterns are easily traceable across the older structure of the Appalachians. The most apparent river is the Susquehanna River. A more detailed study of Seasat imagery acquired over the Appalachians by Ford[16] showed that the orientations of short geologically uncorrelated lineaments are easily

N   0   10 km

Fig. 3   Seasat SAR image of the Appalachian Mountains in Pennsylvania.

interpreted. The observed coincidence of some of the uncorrelated lineaments with magnetic and gravitational trends in the basement and alignment with known structural features was the basis of further geologic study in this area.

One of the more well-known geologic features is the San Andreas Fault. This famous fault was imaged by the Seasat SAR and is shown in Fig. 4. To the northeast are the Antelope Valley and the Mojave Desert. These regions are relatively smooth and level, therefore they appear dark on the radar image. To the southwest are the San Gabriel Mountains and the Angeles Forest. Because of the steeper, more rugged terrain, the image tone is much brighter here than northeast of the fault. In the northern portion of the image, the San Andreas Fault is intersected by the

N   0   10 km

Fig. 4 Seasat SAR image of the San Andreas Fault.

Garlock Fault.   The San Andreas Fault is traceable both
because of tis pronounced linear scarp and because of the
diversity in terrain roughness on either side of the fault.
The trace of the Garlock Fault, however, is obscured due to
radar layover, a geometric problem resulting from imaging
steep mountains with a steep incidence angle, and is
traceable only because of the diversity in terrain roughness
on either side of the fault.

A more detailed study of the San Andreas Fault was
done by Sabins et al.[17] A portion of the fault in the
Durmid Hills of southern California imaged by Seasat was
used in the study. Again, the fault was expressed as a
prominant southeast trending tonal lineament that is bright
on the southwest side and dark on the northeast side. The
bright radar return on the southwest side was due to the
rough weathered surface of the Borrego formation. The dark
signature to the northeast was due to the smooth sand and
silt deposits of Lake Cahuilla.

Spaceborne imaging radar data has also been used
extensively to study sand dunes. A detailed assessment of
the ability of orbital SAR systems to provide useful
information about sand dunes was done by Blom and Elachi.[18]
In summary, the backscatter mechanism of sand dunes is
primarily specular.   Observed surface irregularities of
sand dunes are inadequate to cause Bragg or incoherent
scattering at imaging radar wavelengths. This constrains
allowable incidence angles for imaging sand dunes to less
than the angle of repose for dry sand (about 33 deg).
Radar images made without meeting this criterion will show
sand dunes as dark areas and interpretation, and perhaps
even recognition of the existence of sand dunes, is not
possible.

Since dune fields generally contain very directional
elements, the availability of two illumination directions
is highly desirable. Linear features more than about 60
deg from perpendicular to the illumination direction will
not be visible unless they have considerable topographic
variability. In each of the study areas where Seasat data
from both illumination directions were available, a significant contribution was made to the understanding of the dune
structures by the additional illumination direction image.
This information is, in fact, required for inference of
wind regimes responsible for the dune structures. Determination of dune structures such as the Mohawk, Cadiz, and
Sonora dunes using Seasat SAR data would not have been
possible without two illumination directions.

Dune types imaged by Seasat included star, dome,
linear, and crescentic. All of these dune types can be

recognized on the orbital images providing they are favorably oriented to the radar illumination. Identification of star dunes is greatly facilitated by the addition of another illumination direction. Other common types of aeolian features, sand sheets and stringers, do not seem to have a bright radar return unless they are vegetated, as in the Algodones Dunes (Fig. 5). Without the backscatter contribution from the vegetation, they may be imaged as dark areas unless they have considerable topography.

SIR-A also acquired a variety of imagery over many types of terrain including dissected plateaus, volcanic fields, salt pans, drainage features, and sand dunes. Figures 6 and 7 are two examples of the diversity of terrain imaged by SIR-A. The structure shown in Fig. 6 is a linear

N   O   IO km

Fig. 5   The Algodones Dune Field in southeastern California as imaged by Seasat.

extension of the Altyn Tagh Fault.[19] In the eastern portion
of the image, the fault bends southwestward to join the
Gansu Fault.   Both faults are major left-lateral strike
slip faults and are part of a fault system that extends
over 3000 km from the Tarim Basin to the Shanxi Graben.
Along the fault (which extends from the lower left corner
of the image to the right center), evidence of truncation
of ridges and left-lateral drag is apparent. The large
alluvial fans in the upper portion of the image and in the
lower right corner represent a different type of terrain.
Differences in the grain size of the deposits are responsible for variations in image tone brightness along the
fan. Evidence of man is also apparent in the image.
Railroad tracks and roadways extending across the center of
the image and across the large fan are easily discernable.
     Another type of terrain is shown in Fig. 7. This
image, also acquired by SIR-A, is of the Lake Chad Basin in
the intertropical convergence zone. The dunes in the image
are oriented with their long axes transverse to the prevailing southwest and northeast Saharan winds. When Lake Chad
receded, it left behind widespread arrays of large sand
dunes standing above the interdune flats. The identification of the dunes on the radar image is possible because of
the bright response of the vegetated interdune flats, which
are grassy savannas. The overall irregularity of the dunes
is typical of old, vegetated, inactive dunes that have
undergone weathering and erosion.
     The unique capability of radar to image through clouds
makes it an extremely useful tool for mapping in tropical

↑N

Fig. 6   Altyn Tagh Fault in Gansu China as imaged by SIR-A.

regions such as Indonesia. In addition, Indonesia is a very heavily vegetated region. Therefore, although radar waves can only partially penetrate the dense vegetation, the variation in radar backscatter due to large- and small-scale surface roughness provide a means of mapping a variety of terrain types. An extensive study of the lithologic and structural information available in SIR-A images of portions of Kalimantan and Irian Jaya was done by Sabins.[20] The results of this study showed that it was possible to map six major terrain categories including carbonate rocks, clastic rocks, volcanic rocks, alluvial deposits, melange complexes, and metamorphic rocks. Figure 8 shows four of these terrain types in the southeastern Vogelkop region. A variety of structural geologic features were also easily mapped using the radar imagery, including foldbelts, uplifts, basins, and faults. Also visible in Fig. 8 is the Lengguru foldbelt, a doubly plunging syncline with an arcuate axial trace.

Subsurface Imaging

One of the unique properties of radar waves is that they usually sense both the surface and the near subsurface. The depth of penetration is strongly dependent on the absorption and scattering properties of the subsurface layer. It usually ranges from a fraction of a wavelength up to about 10 wavelengths or more, depending primarily on the moisture content of the subsurface layer. Thus, in the case of an L-band (25 cm wavelength) imaging radar, the subsurface penetration can reach many meters. This large

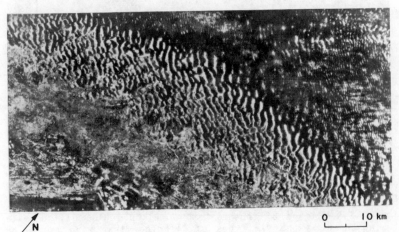

/N   0   10 km

Fig. 7   Sand dunes in the Lake Chad Basin imaged by SIR-A.

penetration occurs in very dry soils, frozen soils, or dry snow cover.

The penetration capability of the imaging radar was most dramatically illustrated with the SIR-A images over southwestern Egypt.[8,21] In a large area of northeast Africa, the surface is covered with a a sand sheet with thickness up to a few meters, thus hiding most of the details of the local morphology. In addition, that area forms the core of one of the most arid regions on Earth. The environmental conditions are such that rain occurs at a rate of once every 40-50 years and the soil moisture is less than 0.5%.

Figures 9 and 10 show the comparison between the Landsat image and the radar image of part of the area. The radar shows a wealth of morphologic details that seem to indicate extensive past fluvial activity over a large region. Field work in the area[8] confirmed that the fluvial activity did occur in the past and its surface signature is covered by a sand sheet with a thickness ranging from about a half a meter to a few meters. Modeling of radar wave interaction with such a covered surface also showed that the subsurface interface should be visible on the radar image.[21] In actuality, the presence of the dry sand layer tends to enhance the radar capability to image the subsurface interface due to wave refraction at the surface.

| **1** Alluvial Deposits | **2** Clastic Terrain | **3** Carbonate Terrain |

Fig. 8 SIR-A image of southeastern Vogelkop region of Indonesia showing three of the six types of lithology that were mapped by Sabins.[20]

Fig. 9 Landsat image over Egypt.

The subsurface imaging capability was also observed on the Seasat radar images of arid areas in southern California where geologic dikes covered by a layer of dry alluvium were clearly imaged.[22]

0 ⊢———————⊣ 50 km

Fig. 10 SIR-A image swath of same region shown in Fig. 9 showing buried river and stream channels.

Vegetation and Soil Moisture Mapping

In vegetated regions, the radar backscatter is controlled primarily by the plant structure, height, wetness, and large-scale geometric properties such as the row direction of fields and orchards. It is not well known to what extent radar actually penetrates the vegetation. The extent of penetration is highly dependent on the radar wavelength, the polarization, and incidence angle, as well as the physical properties of the vegetation canopy.

Radar imagery is very sensitive to the wetness of an area due to large changes in the dielectric constant of soil and vegetation with the addition of water. Soil moisture detection may be an important application of radar once calibrated imagery is available. On Aug. 16, 1978, Seasat acquired the image shown in Fig. 11 in Ames, Iowa. Prior to acquisition of the image, a large convective storm front and several isolated storm cells passed through the areas depositing rain along the paths. The lighter region of the image indicates areas where the rain was deposited and the surface was still moist at the time of acquisition of the image (see Fig. 11 and Ref. 5).

One of the more dramatic images acquired by SIR-A was of the Maranhao Province of Brazil where extensive clearcutting of the Amazon forest is underway. Figure 12 shows the dense Amazon forest, which was a very uniform bright radar return, and the large dark blocks of clearcut regions. The smooth, level clearcut regions, which produce a dark image tone, make the clearcut areas easily mappable.

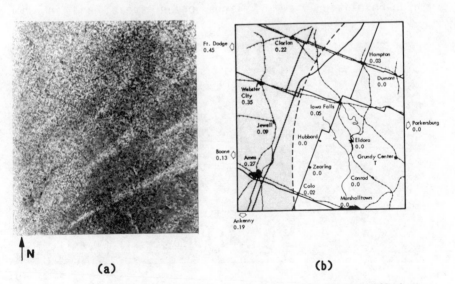

↑N

(a)   (b)

Fig. 11 a) Plains of central Iowa imaged by the Seasat SAR just after a rain storn, Aug. 16, 1978. b) Map of the region in a) showing the location of the wet surface (from Ref. 39).

IV.   Applications in Ocean and Polar
Ice Studies

In oceanographic applications, the imaging radar sensor
has a unique and essential characteristic: the capability
to acquire high-resolution images of the surface regardless
of cloud cover and at any time of the day or night. This
characteristic is essential because of the dynamic nature
of almost all the features on the ocean surface. A review
of spaceborne imaging radar applications in oceanography is
given in Refs. 4 and 23.

The radar sensor provides an image that is representative of the surface backscatter characteristics. In the
case of the ocean, the backscatter is controlled by the
small-scale surface topography: the short gravity and
capillary waves, which scatter the radar energy by the
Bragg scattering mechanism, and the local tilt of the
surface, which is due to the presence of large waves and
swells. Thus, the SAR is capable of imaging surface and
near-surface phenomena that affect the surface roughness
directly or indirectly. These phenomena include surface
waves, internal waves, currents, weather fronts, wind or
oil slicks, and eddies. In this section we discuss examples
of ocean features that have been observed with the Seasat
and SIR-A SAR data.

The Seasat SAR provided for the first time a synoptic
high-resolution view of large ocean areas; and in some

N   0   10 km

Fig. 12   SIR-A image of the Maranhao Province of Brazil showing
extensive clearcutting of the Amazon Forest.

cases, it provided repetitive observations of the same region every 3 days. The SIR-A provided only a very limited ocean coverage.

Surface waves are visible on the radar image as a periodic regular change in the image tone (Fig. 13). The spatially periodic change in the surface-coherent backscatter cross section is a result of three surface effects that are modulated by the presence of a propagating surface wave or swell: local slope; the intensity and bunching of small gravity and capillary waves; and the wave orbital velocity, which affects the phase of the returned echo. The relative importance of these three effects is the topic of current research (see Refs. 4, 24-27).

Figure 13 shows a Seasat image of ocean surface waves acquired over the northeastern Atlantic near the Shetland

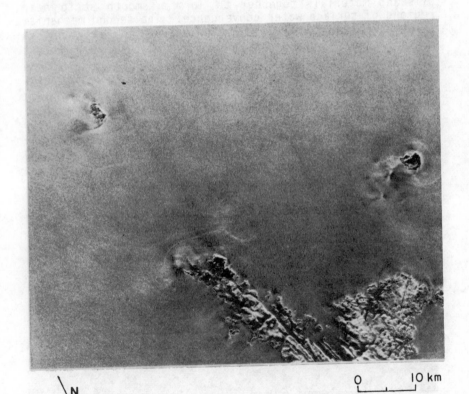

Fig. 13 Seasat image of surface ocean waves near Shetland Island England. The swell had a wavelength of 300 m. The two small islands are Foule and Fair Isle. Observe the refraction and diffraction of the swell near the coast.

Islands. The surface waves had a wavelength of about 300
m, and the refraction patterns near the coast are clearly
visible. This Seasat image was acquired in 14 s. Thus it
represents an almost instantaneous snapshot of the wave
pattern over this 100 x 100 km region.

Figure 14 shows internal waves in the Gulf of California near the island of Angel de la Guardia. These waves
are observed as a result of their surface manifestations
and their effect on the surface roughness. The rather
large currents associated with these waves modify the
capillary ultragravity surface-wave spectrum overlying the
oscillations. The exact mechanisms by which the modifications take place are still the subject of discussion, but
at least two hypotheses have been advanced.[28] According to
the first hypothesis, the high velocity of surface water
arising from the internal wave amplitude can sweep surface
oils and materials together to form a smooth strip near
regions of surface water convergence. The second mechanism
predicts that capillary and ultragravity wave energy is
concentrated in the convergence zone by surface-current
stress, which then becomes a region of enhanced roughness
rather than a smooth area as with the first hypothesis.
When such smooth and rough regions are illuminated away
from normal incidence and then viewed at nonspecular angles,
the smooth region would appear darker and the rough one
brighter than the normal sea surface. This geometry is the
same for both imaging radar and multispectral (including
optical) sensors.

N

0   10 km

Fig. 14   Seasat image of internal waves near the island of San
Nicolas off the coast of California.

Internal waves are usually observed on the radar image as a wave packet that consists of a series of convex strips, with the spatial periodicity becoming shorter toward the center of curvature. The length of the crest may range up to many tens of kilometers. The leading wavelengths are on the order of 1-2 km and decrease monotonically toward the rear. They usually occur in groups or packets and they have been observed in numerous places along the western and eastern coasts of North America. Similar observations have been conducted with aircraft SAR[29] and optical sensors.[30] On some Seasat single swaths, more internal waves could be observed than the total number observed during dozens of aircraft flights over a period of 5 years. This illustrates the new insight that resulted from the Seasat SAR experiment on the extent and rate of occurrence of certain dynamic ocean phenomena.

Fu and Holt[6] conducted a study of the internal waves in the Gulf of California as observed with the Seasat radar. They studied the temporal variability of the internal wave field over a 3-week period. They found that the number of observed wave groups is highly correlated with the strength of the local tides and that the visiblity of the waves on the radar image is somewhat related to the strength of the surface wind. Stronger winds tend to increase the ocean surface roughness over large areas, thus making the rough- ness modulation due to the internal waves harder to detect.

An interesting phenomenon which was observed with the Seasat radar is shown in Fig. 15. The different patterns observed in the shallow waters around Nantucket Island correlate very closely with the bottom bathymetry. The radar waves do not penetrate the ocean surface sufficiently to sense the bottom topography. The most likely interpreta- tion is that the change in the thickness of the water column modulates the velocity of the near-surface current. This in turn modulates the ocean surface roughness that is the main physical parameter that the radar is sensing. Thus, indirectly, the radar image reflects the bottom topography.

Other features observed on radar images include current boundaries, eddies, and vessels.

Polar Ice and Glaciology Applications

Spaceborne imaging of the polar ice cover is of particular interest in two areas: 1) mapping of the ice- cover motion and extent and spatial distribution of the open water channels and 2) determination of ice floes' age.

N   0   10 km

Fig. 15   Seasat image of the Nantucket Island region.   The island
is visible in the upper left corner of the image.   Most of the
other patterns observed on the ocean surface reflect the bottom
topography in this shallow region.

A spaceborne imaging SAR is the ideal sensor for
mapping the spatial distribution, extent, and motion of
ice.   The radar allows repetitive observation all through
the year.   Global coverage every 3-4 days can be easily
achieved at the polar regions.   For this application, the
main observable characteristics are the shape, size, and
distribution (including accurate spatial location) of the
ice features.   Figure 16 shows an example of a Seasat image
of an ice region which was observed over a period of about

October 1, 1978

October 7, 1978 ↑N 0 IO km

Fig. 16 Seasat image of polar ice floes in the Beaufort Sea acquired 6 days apart. The bright section is most likely a stranded iceberg.

2 months in the summer of 1978. Figure 17 shows the motion of that region during that time period.

To be able to determine the ice type and age, a better understanding of the wave/surface interaction mechanisms is required. At the present time, it seems that a multipara-meter radar system might be necessary in order to classify uniquely which ice floes are recently formed, one year old, or many years old.

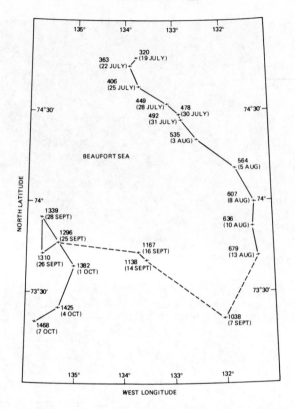

Fig. 17   Trace of the stranded iceberg shown in Fig. 16.

Figure 18 is the Seasat SAR image of the Malaspina Glacier in southeastern Alaska. The ice floe patterns are observed because of the folded moraines, which usually have different roughness characteristics from the surrounding ice.

V.   Technology of Spaceborne Radar Sensors

A spacebonre radar system can be divided into four major elements (Fig. 19). The antenna radiates the electromagnetic signal generated by the rf (radio frequency) electronics toward the surface to be image and it collects the backscattered energy intersecting it. The collected energy is sent to the rf electronics for detection and conversion into a form that can be handled by the data system. The data system formats the data and either records onboard (digital or analog) or transmits to the ground via a data link. On the ground the data are pro-

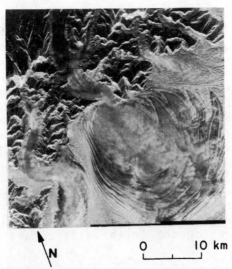

Fig. 18   Seasat image of the Malispina glacier, Alaska. The ice floe pattern is visible as a series of bright and dark curvilinear regions corresponding to the areas of different roughness.

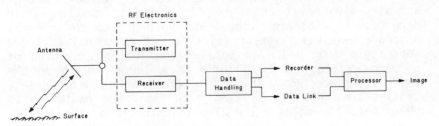

Fig. 19   Basic elements of a spaceborne radar system.

cessed, either optically or digitally, to form the synthetic aperture and generate the radar image. In this section we give a description of the Seasat SAR, SIR-A, and SIR-B. Details of the Seasat SAR are based on the articles by Jordan[31] and Elachi et al.[32]

The Seasat SAR

The first spaceborne imaging radar was launched on June 28, 1978, on Seasat, a free-flying spacecraft carrying a variety of instruments designed for observation of the oceans. The instrument package included a microwave radiometer, a visible/infrared radiometer, and three microwave radars, one of which was a synthetic aperture radar. Seasat's mission ended on Oct. 10, 1978, when a massive

short circuit in its electrical system occurred. During
its 105 days in orbit, however, the Seasat SAR retrieved
imagery of more than 100×10^6 km^2 of the Earth's surface and
provided the first high-resolution SAR images of our Earth.
    The Seasat SAR sensor system, shown in Fig. 20, con-
sists of a planar array antenna, a transmitter/receiver rf
sensor, an analog data link, a data formatter, and a high-
density digital recorder subsystem that outputs the "signal
record". The characteristics of the sensor are summarized
in Table 1. It was designed to provide continuous strips
of radar imagery with a 100 km swath at a resolution of 25
m from an orbital altitude of 795 km. Because the radar
data were directly linked to a limited number of specially
equipped ground stations, the coverage was limited to the
central and northern American hemisphere, western Europe
and North Atlantic, the North Pacific, and the northern
polar regions.

    Antenna. The Seasat SAR antenna system consists of a
10.74 x 2.16 m phased-array system deployed after orbit
insertion. This deployed antenna is configured to fly
with the long dimension along the spacecraft-velocity vector
and bore-sighted at an angle of 20.5 deg from the nadir
direction in elevation (cone) and 90 deg from the nominal
spacecraft-velocity vector (clock). At a nominal 20.5 deg
look angle from nadir, a total beamwidth in elevation of
6.2 deg is required to illuminate a 100 km swath on the
Earth's surface from a 795 km high orbit. Thus, the antenna
cross-track dimension is 2.16 m to limit the radiation to
these sets of angles. The area illuminated on the surface

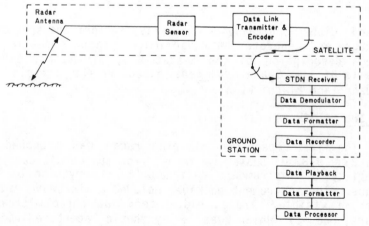

Fig. 20 Basic elements of the Seasat SAR system.

Table 1   Characteristics of Seasat SAR, SIR-A and SIR-B

Parameter	Seasat	SIR-A	SIR-B
Orbital altitude, km	795	259	~ 220
Orbital inclination, deg	108	38	57
Frequency, GHz	1.28	1.28	1.28
Wavelength, cm	23.5	23.5	23.5
Polarization	HH	HH	HH
Look angle(s), deg	20.5	47	15-60
Swath width, km	100	50	20-60
Peak power, kW	1	1	1
Antenna dimensions, m	10.74x2.16	9.4x2.16	10.74x2.16
Bandwidth, MHz	19	6	12
Number of looks	4	6	4
Azimuth resolution, m	25	38	25
Range resolution, m	25	38	58-17
Optical data collection, h	0	8	8
Digital data collection, h	40	0	~ 8
Digital link capability, megabit	110	N/A	46
Coverage, $\times 10^6$ km^2	100	10	~ 10

of the Earth is 240-340 km to the right of the subspacecraft point. The antenna elements in elevation are weighted to limit side lobes in the cross-track direction. The minimum antenna along-track length is limited by a desire to keep azimuth sampling ambiguities to an acceptably low level, while the maximum along-track length is determined by the requirement to illuminate a sufficiently large patch of terrain to allow processing of the data to achieve 25 m resolution in azimuth with four looks.

These two requirements limit the antenna length along the velocity vector to between 10.5 and 14 m. The 10.74 km antenna length was dictated by the available volume within the satellite shroud. The level of integrated abiguities in azimuth was estimated to be between -18 and -24 dB, depending on the selected pulse repetition frequency and processor bandwidth in azimuth.

RF Sensor. The radar rf sensor provides the antenna with a series of high-power coherent pulses of energy at L band (1.275 GHz) and amplifies the weak return echoes collected by the antenna. The bandwidth of the pulses was 19 MHz, which provided a ground range resolution of 25 m. The signal was both transmitted and received horizontally in polarization (HH) with a pulse repetition frequency (PRF) of 1463-1640 pulse/s. The radar sensor consists of

SEASAT-A SAR SYSTEM

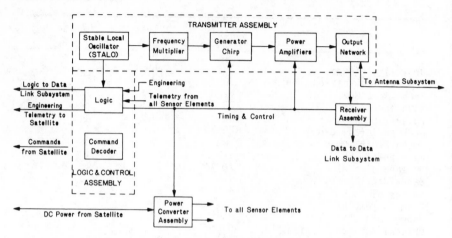

Fig. 21   Block diagram of the Seasat radar rf sensor.

four subassemblies: transmitter, receiver, logic and control, and power converter.   A diagram of the sensor is
shown in Fig. 21 and the principal sensor parameters are
tabulated in Table 2.
     To obtain an adequate signal-to-noise ratio (SNR) from
a system whose range resolution is 25 m on the surface and
that utilizes a solid-state transmitting device, it is
necessary to use a long transmitted pulse and pulse-compres-
sion techniques to reduce the peak-power requirement.   The
output of the transmitter assembly is, as a result, a
linearly swept frequency-modulated pulse (or chirp) having
a 634:1 compression ratio.   It is generated in a surface
acoustic wave (SAW) device located in the chirp generator
subassembly of the transmitter assembly.   The output of the
transmitter is coupled to the antenna subsystem through an
output combiner.   A portion of the output (leakage) is also
impressed on the receive input, where a load is placed in
the circuit each time the transmitter operates.   This
prevents the leakage pulse from burning out the input stage
of the receiver.
     Echo returns are coupled into the receiver assembly
through the output network in the transmitter.   Because the
echo's intensity is expected to vary in proportion to the
variation of antenna gain with angle, a sensitivity time
control (STC) has been incorporated in the receiver.   The
STC action, initiated by satellite stored commands, linearly
decreases the receiver gain by 9 dB during the first half
of the return-echo period and then increases the gain until

Table 2   Sensor electronics subsystem

Parameter	Value
Center frequency	1274.8 ± 0.31 MHz
Bandwidth	19.05 ± 0.05 MHz
STALO frequency	91.059 ± 0.0022 MHz
STALO stability	3 parts/10^{10} in 5 ms
Pulse width	33.9 ± 0.8 s
Peak power	1000 W nominal
Pulse envelope rise time	90 ms
Pulse envelope fall time	90 ms
Pulse repetition frequencies	1464,1540,1580,1647 ± 0.1
Noise temperature	650 K, nominal
Receiver gain control steps	8
Gain control step spacing	3 ± 0.3 dB
Gain control range	77-98 dB
STC gain variation	9
Receiver gain flatness	± 0.33 dB
Receiver gain stability (0-60°C)	± 1.0 dB
Receiver bandwidth (3 dB)	22 ± 0.2 MHz
Receiver phase ripple	4.0 deg dev. from quadratic
Transmitter FM slope	0.5622 MHz/s
Transmitter phase response	3 deg rms

the end of the echo has been received. The application of the STC results in a nearly uniform signal (echo) return for a uniform scattering field and, as a result, the dynamic range required to transmit the resultant data to Earth is reduced by 9 dB.

The sensor/receiver output is sent to the data link along with timing and frequency references derived from the SAR system local oscillator (STALO). The STALO generates a very stable (in frequency) signal at a nominal frequency f_S (91.059 MHz), a portion of which is delivered to the multiplier assembly. Another portion of this signal is used to derive both square-wave clock and sine-wave signals at $f_S/3$, which are used in synchronizing some sensor electronics subsystem functions. The frequency multiplier assembly provides signals at $f_S/3$, which are used in synchronizing other sensor electronics subsystem functions. The frequency multiplier assembly provides signals at 3, 9, and 18 f_S. The 3 and 18 f_S signals are delivered to the chirp generator where, along with a portion of the STALO signal, f_S, they are used to generate the linear FM pulse (chirp) signal at the carrier frequency of 14 f_S. The signal at 9 f_S and a portion of the signal at f_S are delivered directly to the data-link subsystem along with a

signal derived from the PRF event, which divides the
interpulse interval into 4096 sectors.

The remaining two assemblies in the sensor electronics
subsystem are the logic and control as well as the power
converter. They provide the primary electrical interface
with the satellite. The logic and control assembly receives
commands from the satellite, decodes them, and causes the
sensor electronics subsystem to assume one of a number of
operating modes. In addition, the logic and control interfaces between the satellite and the intrasubsystem engineering telemetry. The power converter assembly provides the
stable, isolated power required by all the SAR subsystems.

Data Link Subsystem. The purpose of the data link
subsystem is to transmit the radar echo to the ground for
digitization, storage, and subsequent processing. The link
also maintains the phase and time references necessary to
the processing function, thus providing a unity transfer
function. The chosen implementation technique was a linear
S-band modulator/transmitter/receiver/demodulator combina-
ation. This choice was governed chiefly by the available
frequency spectrum/bandwidth.

In addition to the basic requirement for linearity to
preserve the SAR coherent information, the inclusion of
necessary phase and timing signals placed an additional
burden on the linear property of the link. The data link
subsystem performed the following functions:

1) Translated the L-band echo return to S band.
2) Orthogonally combined the offset video with both
PRF and STALO reference.
3) Amplified the result linearly (with negligible
phase error) for transmission.

On the ground, the data link subsystem:

1) Translated the composite S-band signal to an offset
video frequency centered at 11.25 MHz.
2) Coherently demodulated the signal with the spacecraft local oscillator.
3) Removed the link-induced Doppler from the composite
signal.
4) Reconstructed the PRF and STALO signals from the
video.

Ground Station Subsystem. The Seasat SAR system re-
quired unique equipment at the ground receiving station.
Only three U.S. stations (Fairbanks, Goldstone, and Merritt
Island), one Canadian station (Shoe Cove), and one British

station (Oak Hangar) were equipped to receive the SAR
data. The SAR operations were limited to the time periods
when the satellite was in view of one of those stations.

The ground station subsystem consists of a data formatter and a high-density digital recorder. Upon the
receipt of a trigger signal from the data link subsystem
demodulator assembly, the data formatter accepts and di-
gitizes the analog offset video signal furnished by the
demodulator. Digitization occurs only during the period
(~ 300 μs) when the SAR video return is expected. The
resulting thirteen 680 samples, which are generated at a
rate of 227 megabit/s, are temporarily stored within the
data formatter. Information on the operational status of
the data formatter and the demodulator is also collected
and retained.

The video samples, the status information, and the GMT
time are formatted and sent to the high-density digital
recorder (HDDR) at a rate of about 113 megabits/s. The
HDDR records this high-rate stream on 1 in. width magnetic
tape. Recording uses 40 (of 42) parallel tracks on the
tape at a recording speed of 150 in/s. Parity is included
on each track and timing information is carried on one of
the remaining tracks.

The output "signal" tape is then used in the correlator
element to obtain the final image.

Shuttle Imaging Radar-A (SIR-A)

The Seasat SAR imaged both ocean and land areas and
provided the first spaceborne SAR data set. The success of
the Seasat SAR mission led to the Shuttle imaging radar
series, or SIR series. The first of the Shuttle imaging
radars, SIR-A, flew on the second Shuttle flight as part of
the first scientific payload to be carried into space by
the Shuttle.

The SIR-A was flown on Columbia in November 1981. The
flight lasted for 3 days and the radar acquired data during
a total time period of 8 h. Even with a brief time period,
images were acquired over selected regions in North, Central, and South America, Africa, Asia, and Australia. The
total area covered was about 10×10^6 km^2.

The SIR-A sensor is a modified, but similar, version
of the Seasat sensor, and it used some of the residual
Seasat hardware (Table 1). The main differences in the SIR-
A sensor were the following: a narrower bandwidth (6
vs 19 MHz for Seasat), a larger incidence angle (50 vs
23 deg), a narrower swath (50 vs 100 km), a slightly lower
resolution (38 vs 25 m), but a higher number of looks (6 vs

4). The SIR-A data were optically recorded on an onboard recorder. This allowed acquisition of data at any desired location around the world within the limitation of the orbital coverage (between latitudes of 40°N and 36°S). The "signal film" was retrieved after the Shuttle landing and was processed in an optical correlator to generate the two-dimensional imagery.

Seasat and SIR-A were fixed parameter sensors producing images at constant incidence angles of 23 and 50 deg, respectively.

The data from these two missions were analyzed using photointerpretive methods. A comparison of the two data sets provided the means of examining variable geometric imaging parameters. The most illustrative comparison is shown in Figs. 22 and 23. Figure 22 is the SIR-A image of the Santa Ynez Mountains in California and Fig. 23 a Seasat mosaic of the same area. The California coastline from Ventura westward through Santa Barbara toward Point Concepcion is dominated by the folded sedimentary layers of the Santa Ynez Mountains. The strike of the layered rocks in the mountains is clearly displayed by the bright linear tones along the scarp slope; the bedding is offset by the Santa Ynez Fault in the lower left portion of the image. The dip slopes are indicated by the pattern of flatirons to the north. This pattern is abruptly terminated by the Santa Ynez Fault, which extends the full length of the mountains.

Brightness of the terrain on the SIR-A image varies significantly in response to changes in the local surface roughness. The Little Pine Fault (along the top left of the image), for example, is evidenced by a change from dark

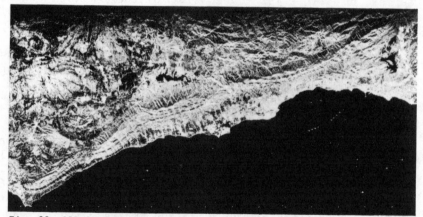

Fig. 22 SIR-A image of the Santa Ynez Range in California acquired with a 50 deg incidence angle.

Fig. 23 Seasat image of the Santa Ynez Range in California acquired
with a 23 deg incidence angle.

on the ocean side of the fault to bright on the mainland
side. This is because the smoother Plio-Pleistocene sedimentary rocks south of the fault reflect the radar energy
away specularly; however, the more rugged Mesozoic ultra-
basic intrusive rocks and the Franciscan Formation to the
north scatter the radar energy diffusely and produce bright
radar returns.

    The Seasat image shows significant differences from
the SIR-A image due to the different incidence angle.
Bedding along the Santa Ynez Range in the Seasat image is
obscured by the dominant returns from the steep slopes of
the drainages; however, on the SIR-A image the bedding is
quite pronounced. The drainage channels normal to coastline
are easily traceable on the SIR-A image, but on the Seasat
image are obscured because of layover. On the other hand,
many of the drainage patterns shown on the Seasat image are
not seen on the SIR-A image. The above differences are due
to differences in local incidence angle of the Seasat and
SIR-A images.

    The effect of variable incidence angle is further
emphasized in the radar returns from the ocean surface.
Small changes in the ocean surface topography are easily
discernible on the Seasat image because small changes in the
local slope result in large changes in the backscatter at
the steep incidence angle of 23 deg.

Shuttle Imaging Radar-B (SIR-B)

    With the launch of SIR-B, NASA took the next step in
an evolutionary radar program toward a final multifrequency,

multiincidence angle, multipolarization imaging radar system.

The SIR-B instrument is an upgraded SIR-A with the additional capability of tilting the antenna mechanically to acquire data at incidence angles of 15-60 deg. Like Seasat and SIR-A, SIR-B will be an L-band, HH polarized radar (Table 1). The variable incidence angle capability will allow several new potential experiments. A specific area may be imaged with a variety of incidence angles on successive days. Images acquired at variable incidence angles can be registered and used to produce curves of backscatter as a function of the incidence angle for various terrain types. These curves can ultimately be used to characterize the terrain. Stereo imaging may also be done in the multiple incidence angle mode. In addition, large areas may be imaged and mosaicked together with only slight variations in the incidence angle with each swath.

In addition to the variable look angle capability, SIR-B has an increased bandwidth, an additional antenna panel, and a digital data processing system. The increased bandwidth will improve the range resolution by a factor of two. At a 47 deg look angle, the resolution will improve from 38 m on SIR-A to 19 m on SIR-B. The additional antenna panel will increase the length of the antenna from 9.4 m, making the overall dimensions of the SIR-B radar antenna 10.7 x 2.1 m. The increased antenna area will improve the SNR slightly, which is important at the larger look angles. The digital data capability will allow data to be sent through a digital data handling system (DDHS) onboard the Shuttle to the ground receiving station at White Sands, NM, via the Tracking and Data Relay Satellite (TDRS). The data rate for SIR-B is 46 megabit/s, which can be handled in real time by the Ku-band 50 megabit/s TDRS link. The digital capability will allow for the first time quantitative and analytical studies of the effects of the varying illumination geometry on the radar image. In addition to acquiring data directly through TDRS, digital data may also be recorded on a digital tape recorder mounted on the aft flight deck of the Shuttle when the TDRS is not in view of the Shuttle and then later transmitted through TDRS or stored on tape onboard the Shuttle. A more detailed description of the DDHS is given below.

The Digital Data Handling Subsystem

The digital data handling system (DDHS) is a new piece of hardware that has been specially constructed for the SIR-B instrument. It adds a digital recording capability to the radar. With the DDHS, the radar's video signal, containing the backscattered echo, is digitized to a resolution of up to 6 bits and recorded on the Shuttle or beamed to a ground station on Earth for recording.

The DDHS is constructed of five main assemblies, as shown in Fig. 24. The ADC (analog-to-digital converter) assembly performs the digitization of the video signal to a fixed 6 bit quantization level. The conversion rate is set by the frequency of the input composite clock-and-synchronous signal. For SIR-B the conversion rate is 30.353 MHz. The output digitized words are fed to six holding registers in the ADC that are then transfered to the buffer assembly at a rate of 30.353/6 = 5.069 MHz during the data latch event. The sync portion of the composite clock-and-sync signal is recovered in the ADC and used to toggle the buffer assembly between its ping-pong memories. The sync signal

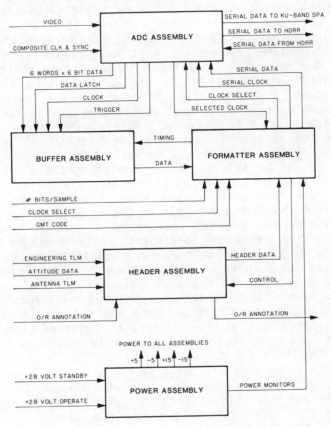

Fig. 24 Functional block diagram of the SIR-B DDHS.

is generated in the SIR-B electronics and begins the digitization window (i.e., the recording window) of the DDHS.

The buffer assembly stores the sampled data for one range line (i.e., one recording window) in one memory while outputting the previous range line's data from another memory. This technique is commonly called "ping-pong" buffering. Each of the two memories in the buffer assembly can store 12,000 six-bit words. Data are continuously read into the memory until it becomes full. Data are read out of the buffer assembly to the formatter assembly as 3, 4, 5, or 6 bit words, depending on the bits/sample control lines from the radar. The number of bits per sample is a variable that may be selected by an investigator. Inasmuch as the total data rate is limited to 45 or 30 megabit/s, it is possible to select fewer bits per sample in order to increase the swath width of an image or, alternatively, to select more bits per sample, which results in a more dynamic range but a reduced swath. The most significant bits are transfered and the least significant bits are ignored.

The formatter assembly takes the parallel-fed data from the buffer, mixes it with housekeeping and header data, and creates a serial bit stream for recording. The serial bit stream is fed to the ADC assembly, which has high-speed, high-power line drivers to drive the long co-axial cables to the Ku-band signal processor assembly and the high data rate recorder (HDRR). The formatter can create the serial bit stream at two rates: 45 megabit/s for the Ku-band link or 30 megabit/s for the HDRR. Only one rate can be selected at a time using the clock select command line from the SIR-B electronics. When the 30 megabit/s rate is chosen, data can be output to the HDRR or read from the HDRR and output to the Ku-band link.

The header assembly generates a pseudo noise code sequence to define the beginning of each range line of data. The pseudo noise code is specially selected and is the same for each range line. It can be easily picked out of the radar data in the ground processing. Following the pseudo noise code is housekeeping and engineering data, including the spacecraft attitude and radar antenna angle. The header assembly also outputs this information to the optical recorder as an annotation to be placed on the film alongside the video data.

The power assembly converts the unregulated spacecraft d.c. power to regulated d.c. power for the DDHS. Both the standby and operational sets of power supplies are used. When digital recording is not required, the DDHS is powerd down to the standby mode to conserve power. In the standby mode, the DDHS will still provide annotation for the optical recorder.

Each of the five assemblies is constructed as a separate module. All five modules are stacked to form the complete assembly. The overall size of the assembly is 18.5 in. wide by 10.0 in. high by 10.5 in. deep. The power supply is the bottom module, followed by the ADC, buffer, formatter, and header assemblies from the power supply up. The buffer, header, and formatter assemblies use wire-wrap techniques for interconnection between the integrated circuits. The ADC assembly, because of its high operating speed, uses multilayer printed-circuit boards with controlled-impedance transmission lines for interconnections between integrated circuits. The DDHS uses 100 K ECL, 10 K ECL, STTL, TTL, LSTTL, NMOS, and CMOS integrated circuits in its design.

The DDHS is mounted on a heat exchanger on the pallet alongside the SIR-B optical recorder. The hottest modules are placed on the bottom of the DDHS for good thermal conduction to the heat exchanger.

The SIR-B experiment was launched on the Space Shuttle Challenger into a nominally circular orbit at an inclination of 57 deg and an average altitude of 360 km for the first 20 orbits, 272 km for the next 13 orbits, and 225 km for the duration of the mission.

SAR Optical Processors

The SAR sensor provides a record of the received echoes forming the signal data. The signal data is processed in either an optical or digital processor to generate the synthetic aperture providing the final high-resolution image Optical techniques for processing SAR data were developed primarily in the 1960s for airborne SAR systems.[33,34] Modifications were then developed to account for additional effects encountered in spaceborne systems.[7]

The phase history generated by a point target is similar to a Fresnel zone plate. This fact makes SAR data natural candidates for optical processing. Since the phase function is quadratic in both dimensions, it diffracts a coherent plane wave, illuminating it into a converging beam that will focus at a point. Unfortunately, the converging wave will come to a focus at different distances from the zone plate for the range and azimuth directions. These distances are referred to as the range and azimuth focal lengths, respectively. Not only is the azimuth focal length different from the range focal length, but it varies linearly with the range dimension. This linear variation can be compensated for by using a conical lens. Manufacturing such lenses is difficult, however, and a cylindrical lens rotated about the horizontal axis leads to the same compensation.

The configuration of the Seasat and SIR-A processors with the tilted-lens mode of operation is shown in Fig. 25. A confocal, spherical lens pair, called the range telescope, images the range and azimuth focal planes. A three-lens cylindrical telescope demagnifies the azimuth dimension. An auxiliary lens pair composed of a tilted azimuth cylinder and a vertical azimuth cylinder are used at the output of the azimuth telescope to bring the azimuth image into coincident focus with the range image. Frequency filtering and range migration correction are done at the back focal plane of the first spherical lens by a combination of cylindrical lenses. A relay lens magnifies an intermediate image onto the output film drive. The spatial filter is composed of a microscope objective lens and a pinhole. The pinhole is located at the back focal point of the objective, blocking out spatial noise in the laser beam. Thus, a "clean" diverging spherical wave emerges from the filter. For the detailed description, the reader is refered to Ref. 7.

SAR Digital Processors

The basic concept of SAR processing is to correlate the signal time-phase history with a reference waveform and to conduct the corrections due to Earth rotation, range

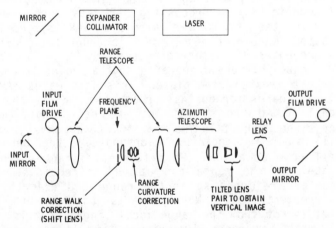

Fig. 25 Elements of Seasat and SIR-A optical processor.

curvature, and range walk. The development of digital SAR processing techniques has two aspects: 1) to define the SAR response of a point target as well as a continuous field of reflecting targets, and 2) to develop algorithms that will allow processing in an efficient and fast thruput fashion. This is important because of the very large number of computations usually associated with the processing of spaceborne radar data. A number of algorithms have been implemented based on time domain convolution or frequency domain correlation (see Refs. 35-38). For an overview of these different techniques the reader is refered to Ref. 7.

VI. Future Development and Conclusions

The Seasat SAR, SIR-A and SIR-B operated at a single frequency band (L) and single polarization (HH). In order to fully utilize the capability of active microwave sensing of the surface, multiparameter imaging radar systems will be required. Such systems are planned for flight in the late 1980s.

When a radar signal interacts with the surface, the returned echo contains both a polarized (same as the incident polarization) and a depolarized component. In order to fully describe the wave/surface interaction, the full polarization matrix is required. A multipolarization radar sensor should be able to transmit both horizontal (H) and vertical (V) polarization quasisimultaneously (i.e., in approximately millisecond time scale) and coherently receive both H and V polarization simultaneously. The polarization information will help in separating returns from the surface interface vs the return from volume scattering in the surface cover (such as vegetation) or subsurface layer (such as sand or alluvium). Plate 16 (see color section of this volume) gives an example of such multipolarization data acquired with an airborne imaging radar. The data were acquired March 1, 1984 using the NASA/JPL airborne L-band SAR system. The swamp area produces bright returns at each polarization due to multiple radar reflections from tree and water surfaces. The dark linear strips are mostly clearcuts in the pine forest. Young pine stands produce strong HH returns that appear red on the image; older, more dense pine canopy provides strong VH returns that appear blue.

The interaction of the radar signal with the surface and near subsurface is also strongly dependent upon the signal frequency. The penetration depth is linearly proportional to the signal wavelength. Thus a multifrequency imaging radar will be able to probe to different depths below the surface interface. In addition, the return is dependent on the physical scale of the scatterer relative to the wavelength. Therefore, a measure of the surface roughness or scatter size distribution spectrum can be obtained, thus providing one mechanism to separate surface units.

The next step in the U.S. spaceborne imaging radar program is the development of a multifrequency (at least L- and C-band) multipolarization sensor, called SIR-C, to fly on the Shuttle in the late 1980s. An X-band channel might be added by concurrently flying the German microwave remote sensing experiment (MRSE). This would be followed by a multiparameter electronically scanning imaging radar system to be developed for the Shuttle and the space station in the early 1990s. In addition, early development is in progress for a Shuttle scanning radar altimeter that would allow the acquisition of global digital topographic data of the land surface with a spatial resolution of about 100-200 m and a height resolution of a few meters.

For long-term global observation, two free-flying imaging radar systems are being planned for the late 1980s, one on the Japanese Earth Resource Satellite and the other on the European Earth Resource Satellite. The Japanese system will emphasize global mapping of the land surface for geologic and land use applications, while the European system will emphasize oceanographic applications. Both systems will have a fixed configuration and a fixed set of parameters. A Canadian system with a very wide accessible swath capability is planned in the 1990s for continuous monitoring of the polar ice cover.

Acknowledgments

A number of sections in this chapter are based on papers and reports written by a number of our colleagues at the Jet Propulsion Laboratory. We would like to particularly acknowledge the work by T. Bicknell, E. Caro, R. Jordan, and C. Wu from JPL who have made major contributions in the development of Seasat, SIR-A, and SIR-B. The authors would like also to acknowledge the support of Ms. M. Fullmer in typing the manuscript and Ms. S. Salas in preparing the artwork.

The research described in this paper was performed at the Jet Propulsion Laboratory, California Institute of Technology, under contract with the National Aeronautics and Space Administration.

References

[1]Born, G.H., Dunne, J.A., and Lame, D.B., "Seasat Mission Overview," Science, Vol. 204, 1979, pp. 1405-1406.

[2]Elachi, C. et al., "Shuttle Imaging Radar Experiment," Science, Vol. 218, 1982, pp. 996-1003.

[3]Elachi, C., "Spaceborne Imaging Radar: Geologic and Oceanographic Applications," Science, Vol. 209, 1980, pp. 1073-1082.

[4]Vesecky, J.F. and Stewart, R.H., "The Observation of the Ocean Surface Phenomena Using Imagery from the Seasat SAR: An Assessment," Journal of Geophysical Research, Vol. 87, 1982, pp. 3397-3430.

[5]Ulaby, F., Razani, M., and Dobson, M., "Effects of Vegetation Cover on the Microwave Radiometric Sensitivity to Soil Moisture," IEEE Transactions on Remote Sensing, Vol. GE-21, 1983, pp. 51-61.

[6]Fu, L. and Holt, B., "Internal Waves in the Gulf of California; Observation from a Spaceborne Radar," Journal of Geophysical Research, Vol. 89, 1984, pp. 2053-2060.

[7]Elachi, C., Bicknell, T., Jordan, R.L., and Wu, C., "Spaceborne Synthetic Aperture Imaging Radar: Applications, Techniques and Technology," Proceedings of IEEE, Vol. 70, 1982, pp. 1174-1209.

[8]McCauley, J. et al., "Subsurface Valleys and Geoarcheology of the Eastern Sahara Revealed by Shuttle Radar," Science, Vol. 218, 1982, pp. 1004-1020.

[9]Cimino, J.B. and Elachi, C., "The Shuttle Imaging Radar-A Experiment," JPL Pub. 82-77, 1982.

[10]Brown, W.M. and Porcello, L.J., IRE Transactions on Military Electronics, MIL-6, 1969, p. 111.

[11]Cutrona, L.J., "Synthetic Aperture Radar," Radar Handbook, edited by M.I. Skolnik, McGraw-Hill Book Co., New York, 1970.

[12]Harger, R.O., Synthetic Aperture Radar Systems, Theory and Design, Academic Press, New York, 1970.

[13]Jensen, H., Graham, L.C., Porcello, L.J., and Leith, E.N., Scientific American, Vol. 237, Oct. 1977, p. 84.

[14]Tomiyasu, K., "Tutorial Review of Synthetic Aperture Radar with Application to Imaging of the Ocean Surface," Proceedings of IEEE, Vol. 66, 1978, p. 563.

[15]Bennett, J.R. and McConnell, P.R., "Considerations in the Design of Optimal Multilook Processors for Imaging Quality," SAR Image Quality Workshop, Paper ESA SP-172, Frascati, Italy, December 1980.

[16]Ford, J.P., "Seasat Orbital Radar Imaging for Geologic Mapping: Tennesseee-Kentucky-Virginia," American Association of Petroleum Geologists Bulletin, Vol. 64, 1980, pp. 2064-2094.

[17]Sabins, F.F., Blom, R., and Elachi, C., "Seasat Radar Image of the San Andreas Fault, California," American Association of Petroleum Geologists Bulletin, Vol. 64, 1980, pp. 614.

[18]Blom R. and Elachi, C., "Spaceborne and Airborne Imaging Radar Observation of Sand Dunes," Journal of Geophysical Research, Vol. 86, 1981, pp. 3061-3070.

[19]Ford, J., Cimino, J.B., and Elachi, C., "Space Shuttle Columbia Views the World with Imaging Radar," Jet Propulsion Laboratory, Pasadena, CA, JPL Pub. 82-95, 1983.

[20]Sabins, F.F., "Geologic Interpretation of Space Shuttle Radar Images of Indonesia," American Association of Petroleum Geologists Bulletin, Vol. 67, 1983, pp. 2076-2099.

[21]Elachi, C., Roth, L., and Schaber, G., "Spaceborne Radar Subsurface Imaging in Hyperarid Regions," IEEE Transactions of Geoscience and Remote Sensing, Vol. GE-22, 1984, pp. 383-388.

[22]Blom, R., Crippen, R., and Elachi, C., "Detection of Subsurface Features in Seasat Radar Images of Means Valley, Mojave Desert, California," Geology, Vol. 12, 1984, pp. 346-349.

[23]Beal, R.C., Deleonibus, P.S., and Katz, I., Spaceborne Synthetic Aperture Radar for Oceanography, Johns Hopkins University Press, Baltimore, MD, 1981.

[24]Elachi, C. and Brown, W.E., "Models of Radar Imaging of the Ocean Surface Waves," IEEE Transactions on Antennas and Propagation, Vol. AP-25, Jan. 1977, pp. 84-95; also IEEE Journal of Oceanic Engineering, Vol. OE-2, Jan. 1977, pp. 84-95.

[25]Alpers, W.R. and Rufenach, C.L., "The Effect of Orbital Motion on Synthetic Aperture Imagery of Ocean Waves," IEEE Transactions on Antennas and Propagation, Vol. AP-27, 1979, pp. 635-690.

[26]Alpers, W.R., Ross, D.B., and Rufenach, C.L., "On the Detectability of Ocean Surface Waves by Real and Synthetic Aperture Radars," Journal of Geophysical Research, Vol. 86, 1981, pp. 6481-6498.

[27]Rufenach, C.L. and Alpers, W.R., "Imaging Ocean Waves by SAR with Long Integration Times," IEEE Transactions on Antennas and Propagation, Vol. AP-29, 1981, pp. 422-428.

[28]Garrett, H.E. and Hughes, B.A., "On the Interaction of Surface and Internal Waves," Journal of Fluid Mechanics, 1972, pp. 179-191.

[29]Elachi, C. and Apel, J., "Internal Wave Observations Made with an Airborne Synthetic Aperture Imaging Radar," Geophysical Research Letters, Vol. 3, 1976, pp. 647-750.

[30]Apel, J.P., Byrne, H.M., Proni, J.R., and Charnell, R.L., "Observations of Oceanic Internal and Surface Waves from the Earth Resources Technology Satellite," Journal of Geophysical Research, Vol. 80, 1975, pp. 865-881.

[31]Jordan, R.L., "The Seasat-A Synthetic Aperture Radar System," IEEE Journal of Oceanic Engineering, Vol. OE-5, 1980, pp. 154-163.

[32]Elachi, C. et al., "Shuttle Imaging Radar (SIR-A) Experiment; Preliminary Results," Science, in press.

[33]Goodman, J.W., Introduction to Fourrier Optics, McGraw-Hill Book Co., New York, 1968.

[34]Kozma, A., Leith, E.M., and Massey, N.G., "Tilted Plane Optical Processor," Applied Optics, Vol. 11, 1972, pp. 1766-1777.

[35]Cumming, I.G. and Bennett, J.R., "Digital Processing of Seasat SAR Data," Proceedings of IEEE International Conference on Acoustic, Speech, Signal Processing, 1979, pp. 710-717.

[36]Vant, M.R., Herring, R.W., and Shaw, E., "Digital Processing Techniques for Satellite Borne Synthetic Aperture Radar," Canadian Journal of Remote Sensing, Vol. 5, No. 1, 1979.

[37]Truong, T.K., Reed, I.S., Lipes, R.G., and Wu, C., "On the Application of a Fast Polinominal Transform and the Chinese Remainder Theorem to Compute a Two-Dimensional Convolution," IEEE Transactions on Acoustic, Speech, Signal Processing, Vol. ASSP-29, No. 1, Feb. 1981, pp. 91-97.

[38]Wu, C., "Electronic SAR Processors for Space Missions," Proceedings of the SAR Technical Conference, Las Cruces, NM, 1978.

[39]Ulaby, F., Moore, R., and Fung, A., "Microwave Remote Sensing," Addison-Wesley Publishing Company, 1982.

The Orbiter Camera Payload System's Large-Format Camera and Attitude Reference System

Bruton B. Schardt*

National Aeronautics and Space Administration, Washington, D.C.

and

Bernard H. Mollberg†

NASA Lyndon B. Johnson Space Center, Houston, Texas

Abstract

The Orbiter camera payload system (OCPS) is an integrated photographic system carried into Earth orbit as a payload in the Space Transportation System (STS) Orbiter vehicle's cargo bay. The major component of the OCPS is a large-format camera (LFC), a precision wide-angle cartographic instrument capable of producing high-resolution stereophotography of great geometric fidelity in multiple base-to-height ratios. A secondary and supporting system to the LFC is the attitude reference system (ARS), a dual-lens stellar camera array (SCA) and camera support structure. The SCA is a 70 mm film system that is rigidly mounted to the LFC lens support structure and, through the simultaneous acquisition of two star fields with each Earth viewing LFC frame, makes it possible to precisely determine the pointing of the LFC optical axis with reference to the Earth nadir point. Other components complete the current OCPS configuration as a high-precision cartographic data acquisition system. The primary design objective for the OCPS was to maximize system performance characteristics while maintaining a high level of reliability compatible with rocket launch conditions and the on-orbit environment. The full OCPS configuration was launched on a highly successful maiden voyage aboard the STS Orbiter vehicle Challenger on Oct. 5, 1984, as a major payload aboard the STS-41G mission.

This paper is declared a work of the U.S. Government and therefore is in the public domain.

*Program Manager, Orbiter Camera Payload System's Large-Format Camera, Office of Space Science and Applications.

†Project Manager/Scientist and Principal Investigator, Orbiter Camera Payload System's Large-Format Camera, Man-Systems Division.

Introduction

The current configuration for the Orbiter camera payload system (OCPS) is shown in Fig. 1. The major component is the large-format camera (LFC), shown mounted on
its maintenance dolly and with its thermal (protective)
door open in the acquisition mode. Supporting the LFC
operations in flight is the attitude reference system
(ARS), which is composed of a dual-lens ballistic camera
called the stellar camera array (SCA) and its flight support structure, an annular ring structure, that rigidly
mounts the SCA to the LFC. The LFC is, of course, used
for making very-high-resolution images of the Earth surfaces with great geometric fidelity and the SCA is used to
make simultaneous photographs of two star fields at the
instance of the midpoint of exposure of each LFC terrain
photograph. By execution of an in-flight stellar calibration sequence, whereby three star fields are photographed
simultaneously, a precise relationship of the LFC optical
axis to the two SCA optical axes is obtained. Such information is later used during postflight data analysis to
determine the precise pointing attitude of the LFC with
reference to the ground nadir point. Other flight items
comprising the OCPS include: electronics assemblies for
both the LFC and the ARS, a high-pressure gas supply
assembly, and pneumatic and electrical lines and cabling.
The ground checkout station is shown in the background of
Fig. 1. Table 1 provides a summary of some of the design
and operational parameters of the LFC and the ARS.

The LFC (Fig. 2) utilizes a roll of film 24.13 cm
(9.5 in.) wide and 1220 m (4000 ft) long, whereas the SCA
uses film 7.0 cm (2.52 in.) wide and 685 m (2250 ft) long.
Both are standard thin-base films 0.05 mm (0.002 in.)
thick, the LFC film roll providing approximately 2500
image frames and weighing 31.75 kg (70 lb) and the SCA
approximately 2500 pairs of stellar images and weighing
5.4 kg (12 lb).

The focal plane of the LFC's cartographic lens assembly (Figs. 2 and 3) is defined by a metal frame with an
opening 22.86 x 45.72 cm (9 x 18 in.). As a key to image
point location and mensuration, two types of fixed references are provided. The first type is provided by a total
of 12 fiducial projectors, 5 on either side of the format
long dimension and 1 each at the center on the fore and
aft edges of the focal frame. The primary fiducials (four
total) are positioned precisely midway on each of the rec-
tangle sides. The four secondary fiducials are used to
define the central 22.9 x 22.9 cm (9 x 9 in.) square of

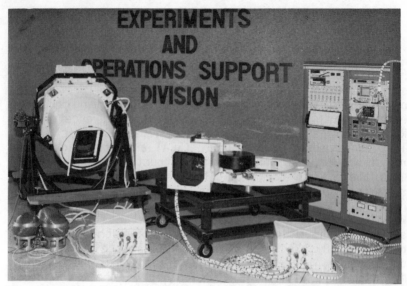

Fig. 1   The Orbiter camera payload system (OCPS) showing the
components (from left to right): gas supply assembly (GSA),
large-format camera (LFC), LFC electronics assembly, stellar
camera array (SCA) shown mounted to the SCA support structure
(ring), ARS electronics assembly, and the electrical test and
checkout console.

the format.   The remaining four fiducials are positioned
at the four corners of the focal frame. All fiducial projectors are flashed for 1 ms at the exact midpoint of the
LFC scene exposure.   In addition to the fiducials,
45 reseau projectors are mounted within the 1 in. thick
machined cast aluminum vacuum film platen.   These projectors are distributed in five rows of nine each, with each
row and member positioned at 5 cm intervals.   They are
flashed through the film base just prior to initiation of
the forward motion compensation (FMC) drive; their sole
purpose is to serve as reference points for the determination of residual errors in the processed imagery (original
or duplicate) due to film shrinkage or stretching.   The
information displayed at the focal plane are fixed data
such as direction-of-flight indicators, system serial
numbers, and mission-related data including day, hour,
minute, second, millisecond, and mission and frame number.
All mission-related data are sampled at the time of the
film exposure midpoint.
        The LFC cartographic lens (Figs. 2 and 4) is a nine-
element aspheric design with an effective focal length of
30.5 cm (12 in.) and a T number of 14. Including a ther-

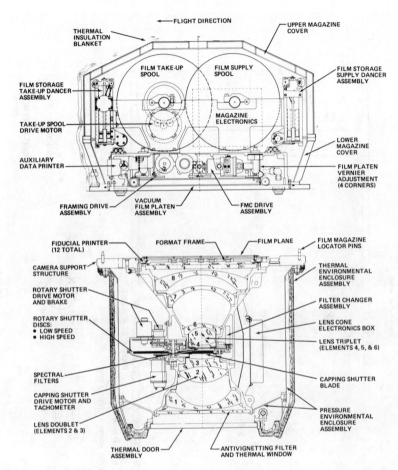

Fig. 2   Schematic of the LFC film magazine assembly (upper) and lens cone assembly (lower). When mated, the two assemblies form a pressure vessel that is pressurized to 2 psig during operation.

mal (glass) window, the total glass weight of the lens is 54.25 kg (119.59 lb). The upper and lower machine lens cell castings (Fig. 4) are of type G30 (GE200) Meehanite, a type of cast iron. The total weight of these two finished castings is 71.44 kg (157.5 lb). The lens element retaining rings are also of machined cast Meehanite. To avoid the prolonged aging process required for normal curing casting, an accelerated thermal cure was employed. The lens design includes a cemented doublet (elements 2 and 3, which has an aspheric surface on the backside of element 3) and a cemented triplet (elements 4-6). The thermal window also serves as the substrate for the anti-

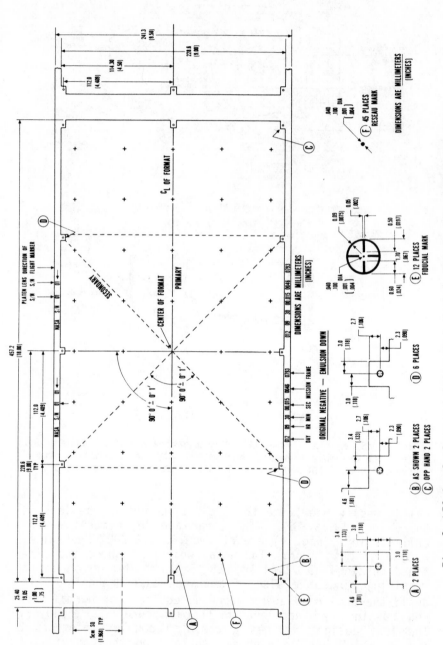

Fig. 3 LFC focal plane and format mask layout with auxiliary data imprints.

Table 1   LFC operational parameters

Parameter	LFC	ARS/SCA
Lens		
Focal length	30.5 cm (12 in.)	15.2 cm (6 in.)
Aperture	f/6.0 (T/16)	f/2.8 (T/3.5)
Spectral range	400-900 nm	400-900 nm
Distortion	< 10 μm (av)	< 5 μm (av)
Shutter		
Type	3 disk rotary intralens with capping blade	Barn doors in front of each lens
Speed range	4-32 ms	200 ms (only)
Setting	External command or AEC	--
Forward motion type	Translation of platen	--
Compensation range	11-41 mrad/s	--
Camera internal pressure	2 psig	Vacuum
Film flattening	Vacuum	Platen press
Image format	22.9x45.7 cm (9x18 in.)	6.48x6.18 cm
Forward overlap modes	10, 60, 70, and 80%	--
Base to height ratios	0.3-1.2	--
Filters		
Antivignetting	Front of lens	--
Minus-haze	Intralens	--
Minus-blue	Intralens	Lens front
Minimum cycle time	7.5 s	7.5 s
Field of view		
Along track	73.7 deg (1.5xH)	24.0 deg
Across track	41.1 deg (0.75xH)	22.9 deg
Film		
Width	24.1 cm (9.5 in.)	7.0 cm (2.75 in.)
Roll length	1220 m (4000 ft)	670 m (2200 ft)
Exposures/roll	2500	2450
Electrical		
Voltage	28 ± 4 V dc	28 ± 4 V dc
Power	273 W (av)	131 W (av)
Total flight weight[a]	435.1 kg (959.2 lb)	186.1 kg (410.3 lb)
Total OCPS LFC/ARS flight weight	618.9 kg (1364.4 lb)	

[a]Fully integrated for flight, including the mission-peculiar equipment support structure (MPESS) and other peripherals, the total flight weight is 1618.3 kg (3567.7 lb).

Table 2 Large-format camera test and flight films

Kodak film type	Description	Test object contrast
3414	High-definition aerial	2:1 1000:1
3412	Panatomic-X Aerocon II	2:1
SO-131	High-definition Aerochrome infrared	2:1
SO-242	Aerial color	2:1

vignetting filter and as the pressure barrier for maintaining the required internal operating pressure within the LFC.

Surrounding the lens cell is a metal cylinder (Fig. 2) that serves as a pressure shell maintaining the internal pressure at 2 psig. Outside of this cylinder is another thermally insulated cylinder made of fiberglass. These two cylinders constitute the environmental enclosure of the LFC lens cone assembly. The LFC was designed to retain internal heat and to reject external heat. Thermal stability of the lens assembly and focal plane is extremely critical in maintaining an exact plane of focus and preserving the calibrated lens distortion characteristics. Should the temperature of the glass and metal of the optical assembly increase or decrease from its desired thermal set point, the focal length of the lens would either increase or decrease, resulting in a shift from critical image focus to varying degrees of defocus. Similarly, the distortion characteristics of the lens internal geometry would change significantly. The focus accuracy of the LFC lens is maintained within a 38 μm (0.0015 in.) degree of uncertainty at the thermal set point.

During an actual mission, and during certain laboratory optical testing, the LFC is stabilized at a thermal set point of 21 ± 1° C (69.8 ± 1.8° F). To accomplish this, passive cooling (thermal dumping) and active heating techniques are employed. A total of 26 strip heaters driven by 11 thermal zone controllers are strategically located throughout the LFC, camera electronics assembly,

Fig. 4 LFC lens components prior to assembly showing the doublet (elements 2 and 3), the triplet (elements 4, 5, and 6), and the machined lens cell castings.

and gas supply assembly that deliver up to 266 W during periods of maximum heating demand. The ARS and its associated SCA, camera electronics, and support structure also have 26 strip heaters and 7 thermal controllers producing only 88 W of active heating during periods of thermal stress.

System Performance Testing

The design objective for the LFC was to produce an instrument capable of superior spatial resolution in the visible (and to some extent the near-infrared spectra) with minimum geometric distortion for precision cartographic applications and, at the same time, providing the photogeologist with wide-area stereoscopic imagery for mineral and fossil fuel exploration. Certain technical performance parameters were established for both optical performance and system dynamic performance. These parameters and their degree of attainment will be described later in a summation of the performance testing. First, it is desirable to highlight certain key test points in the program.

Lens Resolution and Distortion Testing Flight

Lens level testing was performed on the completed lens cone assembly to verify the spatial resolution and radial distortion characteristics. These tests were conducted on a test fixture containing an array of 11 collimators, the focal lengths of which were 61 cm (24 in.) as shown in Fig. 5. It may be noted that this array was not a full array of the 114 collimators that would be required to adequately fill the LFC's defined format. Rather, of the 11 collimators, 7 were positioned orthogonally to the other 4, the lens was rotated to discrete positions, and multiple exposures were made until the proper number of field positions were recorded on film. The minimum number of lens index positions required to accomplish this was 16; thus, 16 film exposures were required.

A special vacuum platen film holder was used rather than the LFC film magazine. In this case, the film platen was an optically flat, glass slab, overcoated with an opaque blocking agent to serve as a light mask, which has along-track and across-track (23 x 47) intersections surrounded by the 12 fiducials within the lens focal frame. These machine-generated intersections were printed by strobing the backside of the glass platen, thus causing them to print through the base of the test film. These intersections were at 1 cm and were used to determine the residual film errors during mensuration of the point images for lens distortion analysis.

Each collimator was supplied with film targets with $12\sqrt{2}$ bars of such contrast that their contrast ratio at the LFC lens entrance pupil was 2:1. Within their formation, these same film targets contained a symmetrical target dot that was used as the reference point for measuring radial image displacement or distortion. At each collimator focal plane, this target dot was subject to precise positioning and alignment through the use of a phototheodolite (see Fig. 6), ensuring that all collimators converged to a point at the LFC lens nodal point. The film images produced by the phototheodolite were used for mensurating the exact radial field position of each target dot.

Once all 11 collimator target positions had been properly aligned and documented, photography was begun. Throughout the development program for the LFC, Kodak type 3414 film was used as the standard for all optical and performance testing and was the only material used for distortion determinations. However, other film types considered to be candidates for Orbiter missions were

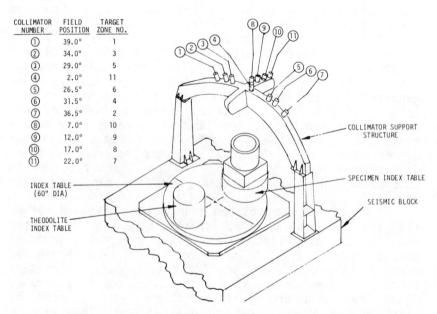

COLLIMATOR NUMBER	FIELD POSITION	TARGET ZONE NO.
①	39.0°	1
②	34.0°	3
③	29.0°	5
④	2.0°	11
⑤	26.5°	6
⑥	31.5°	4
⑦	36.5°	2
⑧	7.0°	10
⑨	12.0°	9
⑩	17.0°	8
⑪	22.0°	7

Fig. 5 LFC image resolution and distortion test fixture.

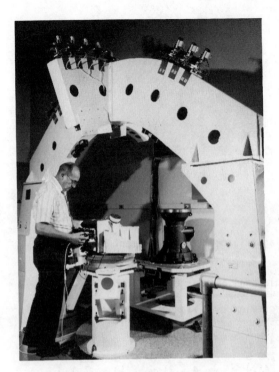

Fig. 6 LFC resolution and
distortion test fixture.

tested for spatial resolution characteristics. These
films are listed in Table 2.

When the task for the phototheodolite had been completed, the large index table was rotated to bring the LFC
lens cone assembly (Fig. 6) into position for photography.
The LFC lens, like the phototheodolite, was on a smaller
index table so that it could be rotated to acquire the
required 16 semidiagonal target arrays illustrated in
Fig. 7. The angular rotation of the semidiagonals originating at the center of the image format and the angular
field position, also originating from the format center,
are summarized in Table 3.

All of the resolution and distortion testing was conducted under ambient laboratory conditions. The temperature was maintained at $21 \pm 0.5°$ C ($70 \pm 1°$ F) and the
pressure at 746 Torr. Under flight conditions, the LFC
internal pressure is maintained through its self-contained
gas pressure control assembly at 2 psig. Thus, in the
vacuum environment of space, the pressure is maintained at
2 psia. All laboratory ambient pressure testing required
defocus of the collimators to compensate for the change in
operating pressure induced by the space environment.

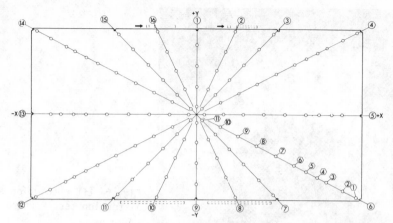

Fig. 7   LFC semidiagonal and target placement reference.

Table 3   Semidiagonal and target placement[a], deg

◯ Semidiagonal rotation		◯ Target field position	
1 = 0.0	9 = 180.0	1 = 39	7 = 22.0
2 = 26.6	10 = 206.6	2 = 36.5	8 = 17.0
3 = 45.0	11 = 225.0	3 = 34.0	9 = 12.0
4 = 63.4	12 = 243.4	4 = 31.5	10 = 7.0
5 = 90.0	13 = 270.0	5 = 29.0	11 = 2.0
6 = 116.6	14 = 296.6	6 = 26.5	
7 = 135.0	15 = 315.0		
8 = 153.4	16 = 333.4		

[a]See Fig. 7.

Lens/Focal Plane Characteristic Testing

Additional knowledge of the lens is normally
required. During the period just after final assembly of
the lens, additional testing was performed to determine
the spectral transmission of the lens (with the permanently installed antivignetting filter in place), relative
illumination at the focal plane, and internal light scatter or veiling glare under conditions of full-field illumination. These tests were conducted using both standard
optical laboratory test equipment and unique test fix-
tures. An example of a unique test fixture is the one
used to determine the principal point of autocollimation
(PPA) and its position relative to the intersections of
both the primary and secondary fiducials (Fig. 3). The
sheer size and weight of the LFC lens cone assembly made
it necessary to customize the test equipment to accomplish

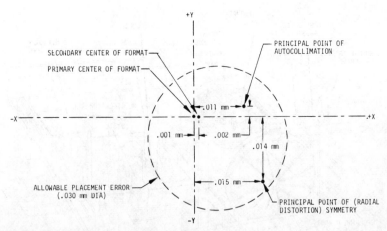

Fig. 8   Coordinates for the geometric centers of the LFC cartographic lens assembly, serial No. 001.

many optical test procedures.   The intersection of the
primary fiducials establishes the primary center of format
and the secondary fiducials represent the secondary center
for format.   The specification for the coincidence of
points of both format centers, the PPA and the principal
point of symmetry (PPS), was a circle of 30 μm diameter
(see Fig. 8).

LFC Flight Simulation Test

As the final and ultimate test of the LFC in the
"full-up" flight configuration, the LFC was "flown" on a
simulated orbital mission in the thermal vacuum test chamber shown in Fig. 9.   During this test sequence, the chamber pressure was maintained at a pressure of 5.6 x -10^{-5}
Torr for a period of several days and the chamber walls
were thermally cycled over the extremes of temperatures
that might be experienced during a typical space flight.
During a series of such tests, the LFC accumulated a total
of 492 h (20.5 days) of vacuum exposure.   Two years later,
when the ARS/SCA was added to the OCPS configuration, both
the LFC and the ARS were subjected to an additional thermal vacuum test during which the LFC accumulated an additional 252 h (10.5 days) of vacuum exposure.
In addition to verifying the environmental stability
and control of the LFC and its operability in the vacuum
environment, the system dynamic resolution performance was
also verified.   To accomplish this, an externally located
and controlled collimator projects images of moving tar-

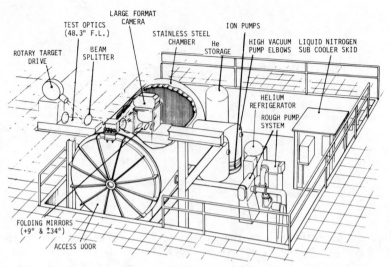

Fig. 9 Thermal vacuum and dynamic resolution test chamber.

gets into the chamber through a viewing port, simulating the orbital velocities that will be encountered during flight.   Three remotely controlled mirrors within the chamber and mounted directly in front of the LFC lens were used to alternately place these targets at -35, +9.5, and +35 deg field positions along the LFC velocity vector. Target drive velocities were adjusted to simulate angular velocities of 0.011, 0.026, and 0.041 rad/s.   These represent the midpoint and high and low FMC capabilities of the LFC which are equivalent to orbital altitudes of 185-700 km (100-375 n.mi.). By keeping the collimator targets stationary and disabling the LFC's FMC drive, the collimator was progressively defocused on either side of the optimum setting to derive a thorough test to verify the proper focus of the LFC.

Large-Format Camera Laboratory Performance Results

The results of the various operational and performance testing conducted during the course of the LFC development program are summarized briefly in this section.
1. Focus setting. During thermal vacuum testing and stationary target photography (as described above), critical focus position for the LFC film magazine vacuum platen was established for the simulated space environment. This was accomplished by using fine adjustment devices that are built into the film platen support structure. Proof of the position recovery was verified many times by resetting

the focus and optically retesting. The accuracy (or repeatability) of position recovery is to approximately 38 μm (0.0015 in.).

2. Veiling glare. The veiling glare, or internal reflections, of both the LFC and SCA lenses was measured as being 7.7%. The specification requirement for veiling glare in both lenses was 8% or less.

3. Relative illumination. In Table 4, the relative illumination at the LFC focal plane is given for three discrete spectral regions. In the specification it was stated that this would vary by no more than 10% across the film format.

4. Lens T number. The LFC lens T numbers were calculated for lenses with various field angles over the 580-720 nm spectral range and other spectral bands generic to the two LFC spectral filters for use with candidate

Table 4   Relative illumination, %

Field angle, deg	Wavelength, nm		
	580	650	720
-35	103	100	101
-25	99	98	100
-10	94	93	94
0	100	100	100
10	97	97	97
25	100	98	100
35	106	102	106

Table 5   Calculated T number

Field angle, deg	Trans- mittance, %	Relative illumination, %	T no.
-35	19.75	1.013	13.5
-25	19.31	0.99	13.7
-10	18.27	0.937	14.0
0	19.5	1.000	13.6
10	18.92	0.97	13.8
25	19.36	0.993	13.6
35	20.42	1.047	13.3
Spectral range, nm			
415-720 nm			13.7
505-720 nm			13.6
515-880 nm			13.6

flight/film combinations. The **specification** stated that the T number be equal to or greater than T-14 (**Table 5**).

   5.   Spectral transmittance. The on-axis spectral transmittance for the LFC lens with antivignetting filter in place is shown in Table 6.

   6.   System resolution (static). Bar targets $(12\sqrt{2})$ that produced a test object contrast (TOC) ratio of 2:1 at the entrance pupil of the LFC optics were used for all resolution determination testing. Area weighted average resolution (AWAR) using 3414 film was specified at not less than 80 line pairs per millimeter (lp/mm) for the full format (9 x 18 in.) and not less than 88 lp/mm for the central (9 x 9 in.) square. Minimum acceptable levels for averages of the four format corners were set at 50 lp/mm for the full format and 79 lp/mm for the central square. Detailed data collection for the four flight films have been plotted in Fig. 10 and the data shown in Table 7.

   7.   System performance (dynamic). Because the LFC employs a mechanism for translating the film platen to correct for image smear due to the forward velocities of the spacecraft, a criteria was established to verify

Table 6   Spectral transmittance

Unfiltered λ, nm	trans., %	Haze filter λ, nm	trans., %
350	9.6		
400	2.1		
500	18.4	580	19.2
600	22.3	620	19.4
700	23.0	660	19.4
800	21.1	700	19.9
900	17.5	720	19.4
1000	17.1		

Table 7   LFC average radial and tangential resolution, lp/mm

Film type	TOC	Corners 9x9	Corners 9x18	AWAR 9x9	AWAR 9x18
3414	2:1	91	62	90	89
	1000:1	114	103	138	125
3412	2:1	66	49	59	57
SO-131	2:1	38	34	41	39
SO-242	2:1	48	48	58	54

adequacy of design over the full range of FMC operation. The specification allows up to 10% degradation for FMC error. The error, as measured in test, was less than 10%.

8.   Geometric distortion.   Radial distortion was specified for the full format (9 x 18) and for the central (9 x 9) square.   For the full format, radial distortion was limited to an envelop of ±25 μm and, for the central square, the specific envelope was ±10 μm.   The radial distortion for the LFC lens with a calibrated focal length of 30.5731 cm (12.037 in.) at ambient laboratory conditions is presented in Fig. 11.

9.   Principal point of autocollimation.   The definition for the primary center of format for the LFC is that point at the intersection of two lines connecting the center forward and center aft fiducials and the two center fiducials on the format sides (Fig. 3).   The secondary center of format is that point of intersection of two lines connecting opposing corner fiducials of the central (9 x 9) square (Fig. 3).   Lines at each intersection must be orthogonal to within ±1 min of arc.   The coordinates for both the primary and secondary centers of format (the PPA and the PPS) were required to fall within a circle

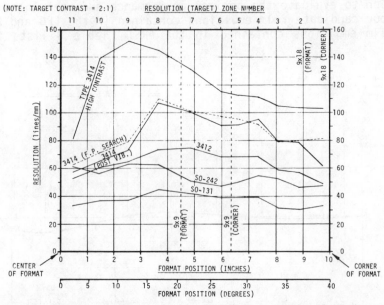

Fig. 10 Static resolution of the LFC lens assembly plotted as a function of field position using the center of the frame format at the point of origin.

with a diameter of 0.030 mm. Actual placement is illustrated in Fig. 8.

Flight Performance Report

On the morning of Oct. 5, 1984, the OCPS configuration was lifted from the launch pad at the Kennedy Space Center (KSC) in Florida and carried into an orbit some 370 km (200 n.mi.) above the Earth by the Orbiter Challenger (mission designation of STS 41-G and known as the OSTA-3/LFC mission). The OSTA-3 payload included the feature identification and location experiment (FILE), measurement of air pollution from space (MAPS) experiment, and Shuttle imaging radar (SIR-B) experiment. In addition to the OSTA-3 and LFC payloads, the STS 41-G mission also carried the Earth Radiation Budget Experiment (ERBE) Satellite, which was deployed in independent orbit early in the mission. The inclination for the STS 41-G mission was 57 deg. This was the maiden voyage of the OCPS payload, lasting 8 days, 5 h, 19 min.

Combined with the laboratory vacuum chamber testing, this brought the total vacuum exposure time of the LFC to 40 days and the ARS to slightly more than 19 days. The Challenger landed at the KSC on Oct. 13, 1984. During this mission, three altitudes were selected for LFC operation to evaluate the optical performance and usefulness of four candidate film emulsions contained in the LFC and two film emulsions contained in the ARS. Table 8 lists the

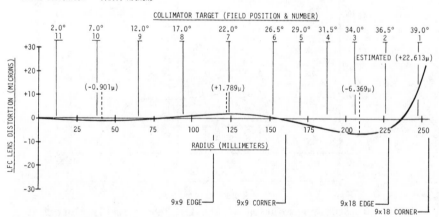

Fig. 11 Geometric distortion characteristics for the LFC.

film emulsions flown. Both rolls were manufactured at the Eastman Kodak facilities in Rochester, N.Y.

Orbital altitudes achieved during the STS 41-G mission and the number of LFC data acquisition passes and frames of photography made at these altitudes are summarized in Table 9.

During the maiden voyage of the OCPS LFC, an inordinant number of broad weather systems were encountered throughout the northern hemisphere, particularly in North America and Europe. The oceanographer aboard the Challenger, P. D. Scully-Powers, commented at crew debriefing, "...look at the total Earth and you would expect about 30% cloud cover....we were looking at more like 60 or 70% cloud cover." The primary LFC test sites for this mission were located in Canada, the U.S., and Europe. It became necessary to abort 80-90% of the planned data passes on these two continents due to

Table 8 Film types flown in the LFC and the SCA on the STS 41-G mission (film types listed in the order of appearance in the film roll)

No.	Type of film (Kodak) Description	Total length m	ft
	Large-format camera (LFC)		
3414	High-definition aerial (B&W neg)	198	650
3411	Plus-X Aerocon[a] (B&W neg)	23	75
3414	High-definition aerial (B&W neg)	62	200
3412	Panatomic-X Aerocon II (B&W neg)	152	500
SO-242	Aerial color (color pos)	152	500
3414	High-definition aerial (B&W neg)	152	500
SO-131	High-definition Aerochrome infrared (color pos)	152	500
3414	High-definition aerial (B&W neg)	152	500
3411	Plus-X Aerocon[a] (B&W neg)	16	50
3414	High-definition aerial (B&W neg)	>43	>140
	Total	1102[b]	3615
	Total LFC frames of photography = 2300		
	Stellar camera array (SCA)		
3411	Plus-X Aerocon (B&W neg)	457	1500
2402	Plus-X Aerographic (B&W neg)	152	500
	Total	609[c]	2000
	Total SCA frame pairs = 2230		

[a]Used for stellar calibration and nighttime photography only.
[b]LFC maximum film capacity with 3414 film is 1220 m (4000 ft) and 2500 frames.
[c]SCA maximum film capacity with 3411 film is 670 m (2200 ft) and 2500 frames.

excessive cloud cover. During the mission, 24 h global weather predictions for upcoming orbital tracks were being provided by the U.S. Air Force Global Weather Central and near-real-time satellite imagery and domestic weather predictions by the National Oceanic and Atmospheric Administration (NOAA) National Weather Service facility at the Johnson Space Center using the U.S. Geostationary Operational Environmental Satellite (GOES) to cover the Americas, the European Meteorological Satellite (Meteosat) to cover Europe and Africa, and Japan's Geostationary Meteorological Satellite (GMS) to cover the Asiatic and Pacific areas.

As a result of cloud cover it became necessary to resort to secondary test sites falling between 28.5° N and S. Of 152 data passes planned premission, 86 passes were aborted and 14 unplanned data passes were added, making a net total of 79 data passes executed, 6 of which were dur-

Table 9   LFC data passes and frames of photography at the three mission altitudes flown by STS 41-G

Orbit no.	Nominal altitude, km (n.mi.)	Total data passes	Total frames
1-22	370 (200)	8	228
23-36	272 (147)	12	333
37-128	239 (129)	59	1675
	Total	79	2236[a]

[a]An additional 54 frames were expended during prelaunch testing at KSC.

Table 10   Summary of the cloud cover content of LFC imagery acquired on the STS 41-G mission during which 2143 frames of photography were made during daylight passes

Acceptable			Marginal			Unacceptable[a]		
% cloud cover	No. of frames	% of total	% cloud cover	No. of frames	% of total	% cloud cover	No. of frames	% of total
0	476	22.2	40	161	7.6	80	125	5.8
5	137	6.4	50	148	6.9	90	83	3.9
10	229	10.7	60	114	5.4	95	11	0.5
20	252	11.7	70	142	6.5	100	71	3.3
30	194	9.1						
	1288	60.1		565	26.4		290	13.5

[a]Many of these are proving to be very useful to the oceanographic and atmospheric science communities.

ing the dark side for stellar calibration of both the LFC and ARS and for experimental applications (lightning, geodesy, etc.).

Premission ground rules were established whereby the scheduled data passes with weather predictions of 35% or less cloud cover would be considered acceptable and executed. Marginal weather conditions, 35-70% cloud cover, would be considered in near real time and decisions based on the need to run film in order to maintain the scheduled rate of film consumption. Unacceptable conditions included any ground tracks with greater than 70% cloud cover. In a few instances, some tracks were run when the conditions were unacceptable in order to reach the scheduled film type changes. A preliminary assessment of the impact of cloud cover experienced during this mission has been made and is summarized in Table 10.

Table 11 Summary of commands issued to the LFC[a]

Command	Parameter	Type	Comments
Power	On/off	Discrete	Activation/deactivation
Mode	Standby	Discrete	Heaters active only
	Operate	"	Data acquisition
	Test	"	Auto 5-frame advance
	Calibrate	"	Single-frame time exposure of 2.4 s
Forward overlap	80%	Discrete	(Percentage of
	70%	"	overlap of imagery
	60%	"	with next frame of
	10%	"	imagery)
Exposure time	4.0 ms (1/250) to	Analog	Minimum exp. time
	32.0 ms (1/32)	"	Maximum exp. time
	AEC	"	Auto exposure control
Exposure bias	+ 1/2 stop	Discrete	
	Normal	"	
	- 1/2 stop	"	
Forward motion	11 mrad/s	Analog	Minimum rate
Compensation	41 mrad/s	"	Maximum rate
Filter select	Minus haze	Discrete	Cutoff at 400 nm
	Minus blue	"	Cutoff at 500 nm
Film select	3-film types	Discrete	Three film speeds
Thermal door		Discrete	Opens or closes door
Capping shutter		Discrete	Opens or closes capping shutter (cal. mode only)
FMC inhibit		Discrete	Inhibits FMC if required

[a]All commands for the ARS/SCA are generated by the LFC logic.

With the exception of the in-flight stellar calibration sequence during orbit 23, which was commanded by the
onboard payload specialist, all OCPS LFC/ ARS commands
were issued from the OCPS team in Mission Control Center
(MCC) at the Johnson Space Center as real-time commands
(RTC) or as stored program commands (SPC). These commands
(Table 11) were uplinked from ground stations direct to
the spacecraft or relayed from ground stations to the
Tracking and Data Relay Satellite System (TDRSS-A) and
thence to the Orbiter vehicle. A reverse of this routing
was employed for the downlink of the OCPS LFC/ARS telemetry (TM). In the event a scheduled data pass was during
a loss of signal (LOS -- out of range of ground stations

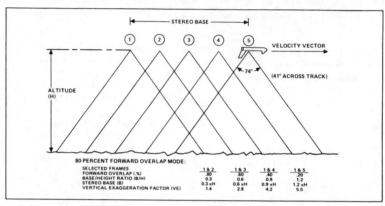

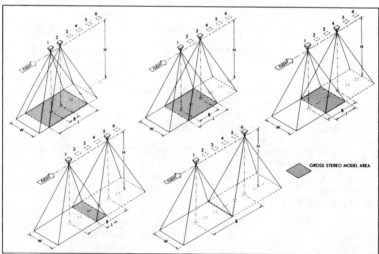

Fig. 12 LFC data acquisition concept for 80% forward overlap
(stereoscopic) photography.

or TDRSS) periods, SPCs were received by the Orbiter during the acquisition of signal (AOS) periods and stored in
buffers within the onboard payload control supervisor
(PCS) or the onboard (general-purpose computer (GPC) and
called up on an automatic time tag schedule for issue to
the payload.   If the scheduled data pass was during a
period of AOS, the RTCs were issued to the OCPS via the
Orbiter the instant they were received.

The acquisition of Earth imagery by the LFC is much
the same as aerial mapping cameras acquire imagery, with
the exception that the STS flies upside down so that the
cargo bay points to the Earth.   Plate 17 (see color section
of this volume) shows the OCPS LFC/ARS as it was mounted in
the aft portion of the Orbiter cargo bay. In this illustration, note that the LFC thermal door is in the open position, indicating that when the crewman took the photo, the
LFC was also in the process of doing photography.   Plate 18
depicts a side view of the same.

The actual acquisition concepts employed by the LFC
is illustrated in Fig. 12.   This graphically demonstrates
how the images are collected as the Orbiter proceeds along
the orbital track.   Determination of the timing between
individual exposures is computed by the LFC electronics
based on calculated values for the velocity-to-altitude
ratio (V/h) uplinked from the MCC at the Johnson Space
Center.   This provides a precise degree of overlap of
adjoining frames (80% forward overlap is shown) and frames
within the five-frame set (and subsequent cascades of
sets).   This provides successive stereo imagery pairs with
an increasing base-to-height ratio (B/H) running from 0.3
to 1.2.   The greater the B/H number, the greater the
stereoscopic vertical exaggeration of the terrain image.

Conclusion

The STS 41-G mission was a very satisfactory maiden
voyage for the OCPS LFC/ARS.   Most of the major test
objectives of this engineering mission were accomplished.
This demonstration of the LFC to the cartographic communities is considered a significant event, perhaps a major
milestone, for cartographic technology.   It is an enormous
stride forward in the utilization of a space platform (the
STS) for worldwide mapping.   For the first time in civil
space applications, this mission combined advanced optics
technology and advanced film technology.   Preliminary
analysis of the imagery strongly indicates that the primary objective of 1:50,000 scale cartographic products has
been achieved.

In summary of the results of this mission, the following items are noteworthy of statement:

1) System thermal stability (21 ± 1° C): excellent.
2) LFC response to uplink commands: excellent.
3) Downlink of telemetry: excellent.
4) Mechanical and electrical functions: excellent.
5) Ground software program: worked exceedingly well.

6) Automatic exposure control: worked quite well.
7) Optical performance: outstanding.
8) Postflight inspection and test: no degradation.

Appendix

Typical examples of the imagery acquired during the STS 41-G mission are included here. They have been selected at random from the various data passes executed by the LFC to illustrate the types of coverage obtained over various parts of the Earth.

LARGE-FORMAT CAMERA PHOTOS FROM THE SPACE SHUTTLE

Fig. A1 Alps; Northern Italy; Po River and Delta; and Adriatic Sea.

Fig. A2 Israel; Jordan; Lebanon; and Saudi Arabia (Dead Sea pictured at lower center).

Fig. A3 Cape Cod, upper right, Massachusetts; Connecticut; Rhode Island; New Hampshire; and Vermont.

Fig. A4 Boston, Massachusetts; altitude=237 km (147 st. mi.).

Fig. A5   China; Nepal (Himalayas); Sikkim; and India.

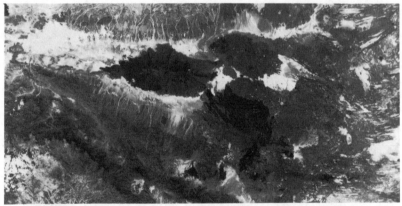

Fig. A6   Afar Depression, Ethiopia; volcanic geology.

Bibliography

Doyle, F. J., "A Large Format Camera for the Shuttle," Photogrammetric Engineering, Vol. 45, 1979, pp. 73-78.

Doyle, F. J., "Film Cameras for Earth Observation from Space," Archives of XV International Congress of Photogrammetry and Remote Sensing, Volumes for Commissions I & IV, Rio de Janeiro, International Society of Photogrammetry, U. S. Geological Survey, Reston, Va., June 1984 (in publication).

Fritz, L. W., "Analytical Instruments to Derive Metric Data from the Large Format Camera," Archives of XV International Congress of Photogrammetry and Remote Sensing, Volumes for Commissions I & IV, Rio de Janeiro, International Society of Photogrammetry, U.S. Geological Survey, Reston, Va., June 1984 (in publication).

Light, D. L. et al., "Satellite Photogrammetry," Manual of Photogrammetry, 4th ed., American Society of Photogrammetry, Falls Church, Va., 1980, pp. 883-977.

Mollberg, B. H., "Performance Characteristics of the Orbiter Payload System's Large Format Camera (LFC)," Proceedings of the Society of Photo-Optical Instrumentation Engineers, Vol. 278, 1981, pp. 66-72.

Mollberg, B. H., "Orbiter Camera Payload System and the Large Format Camera," Archives of XIV International Congress of Photogrammetry and Remote Sensing, Volume Commission I, Hamburg, FRG, International Society of Photogrammetry, U. S. Geological Survey, Reston, Va., June 1980.

Ondrejka, R. J. and El-Baz, F., "Earth Photography by the Large Format Camera," Proceedings of 12th International Symposium of Remote Sensing of Earth, Manila, the Philippines, ERIM, Univ. of Michigan, Ann Arbor, Mich., April 1978, Vol. I., pp. 702-718.

Ondrejka, R. J., "Earth Orbital Photography with the Large Format Camera," Proceedings of Technical Exchange Week, Panama City, Panama, Defense Mapping Agency, Washington, DC, May 1979, pp. 93-107.

Ondrejka, R.J. and Wood, G. A., "Snapshots from a Window of the World," Optical Spectra, Vol. 14, Issue 12, Dec. 1980, pp. 53-56.

Ondrejka, R. J., "Cartographic and Thematic Mapping Potential and Procedures for the Large Format Camera," Archives of XV International Congress of Photogrammetry and Remote Sensing, Volume for Commission I, Rio de Janeiro, International Society of Photogrammetry, U. S. Geological Survey, Reston, Va., June 1984.

Slater, P. N. et al., "Photographic Systems for Remote Sensing," Manual of Remote Sensing, 2nd ed., American Society of Photogrammetry, 1983, pp. 231-291.

Taranik, J. V., "Advanced Aerospace Remote Sensing Systems for Global Resource Applications," Proceedings of XV International Symposium on Remote Sensing of the Environment, ERIM, Univ. of Michigan, Ann Arbor, Mich., May 1981.

Wood, G. A., "Mission Planning Parameters for the Space Shuttle Large Format Camera," Proceedings of 45th Meeting of American Society of Photogrammetry, Vol. II, March 1979, pp. 540-550.

Wood, G. A., "Environmental Factors in the Design of the Large Format Camera," Report of Commission I, Working Group 3, Archives of XIV International Congress of Photogrammetry and Remote Sensing, Volume for Commission I, Hamburg, FRG , International Society of Photogrammetry, U. S. Geological Survey, Reston, Va., June 1980.

Chapter VII.   Future Systems

U.S. Remote Sensing of the Earth from Space—
A Look Ahead

E. Larry Heacock*

National Oceanic and Atmospheric Administration, Washington, D.C.

Abstract

This paper describes the plans for remote sensing of the
Earth and its environment in the decades of the 1980s and 1990s.
With the planned commercialization of land remote sensing, only
the meteorological satellite programs remain as on-going Government responsibilities. Government plans for new or improved
meteorological sensors in the areas of multispectral imaging,
vertical temperature sounding, and data dissemination are described. A short section on some potential areas for exploitation by
a commercial operator in the land remote sensing discipline is
included; this section is, of necessity, highly synoptic in nature
because the commercialization activity for this program is in its
definition phase.

The sections on the National Oceanic and Atmospheric
Administration (NOAA) meteorological satellite programs (Metsats) are more detailed. With the decision to retain the Metsats as
Federal government programs, NOAA, a part of the U.S. Department of Commerce, is moving ahead with plans to develop the next
generation polar and geostationary satellites, with enhanced remote sensing capabilities, by the end of this decade. In addition,
NOAA is planning to upgrade its ground data handling capabilities
by 1987 to permit introduction into the operational system of data
from new sensors such as the visible infrared spin-scan radiometer
(VISSR) atmospheric sounder (VAS) on the current GOES spacecraft
and the new solar backscatter ultraviolet radiometer (SBUV) for
profiling ozone in the Earth's atmoshpere on the NOAA satellites.
In the same time frame, NASA will fly the experimental Earth
radiation budget (ERB) sensor three times (twice on NOAA spacecraft). The VAS has been in orbit since 1980 and the SBUV and

---

This paper is declared a work of the U.S. Government and therefore is in the public domain.

*Director, Office of Satellite Operations, National Environmental
Satellite, Data, and Information Service.

ERB were both carried by the NOAA-9 satellite, launched in December 1984.

Subject, as always to the vagaries of the Federal budget process, NOAA intends to introduce significant improvements into the meteorological satellite systems. Assuming commercialization is successful, the uncertainties of the Federal budget process will be replaced, for Landsat, by those of a private marketing effort. Nevertheless, the potential exists for exciting new capabilities in monitoring both renewable and nonrenewable resources, as well as the other possible missions that can be envisioned for a land remote sensing satellite.

1. Introduction

Today's U.S. remote sensing systems, both the spacecraft and the associated ground systems represent proven but relatively old technology that will require eventual replacement in the next decade. A listing of the present and planned hardware systems, both spaceborne and ground and their nominal lifetimes is given in Table 1. R&D relevant to satellite operations might range from basic science and data utilization in various "client" areas of interest through launch, data handling, and spacecraft technology to advancing the state-of-the-art in observational sensors. For the meteorological satellites (Metsats), the Federal government will continue to play the role of system developer. For land remote sensing, development will depend on the private sector, perhaps aided by some Federal research and development.

1.1 The Atmosphere

1.1.1 Geostationary Satellites. The National Weather Service (NWS) has defined requirements for the next generation of geostationary operational environmental satellites (GOES) which NOAA has labelled GOES-Next. The emphasis in the NWS during the 1990s will be on improving short-term (0-12 h) forecasts of severe weather events such as tornadoes, severe thunderstorms, hail, and flash floods. GOES-Next is expected to provide strong support to improving forecasts of these phenomena and will offer improvements in both imagery and vertical temperature/moisture sounding capabilities. Section 2.2.1 summarizes the expected performance of GOES-Next.

1.1.2 Polar Satellites. Definition studies are currently underway for the NOAA-Next requirements. The primary new instrument candidate is the advanced microwave sounding unit (AMSU). At this time, the requirements are preliminary and are thus subject to change.

The next generation NOAA-Next satellite series should be designed to accommodate the payload instruments required to make measurements of the Earth's atmosphere, its surface and cloud cover, and the proton and electron flux near the Earth. As a part of this mission, the satellite will also have the ability to receive, process, and retransmit data from free-floating balloons and buoys and remote automatic observation stations distributed around the globe and to track those "stations" that are in motion. The satellites will continue the operational use of the search and rescue system.

Provision of direct sounder broadcast (DSB), automatic picture transmission (APT) and high-resolution picture transmission (HRPT) with characteristics similar, if not identical to, the current generation of satellites will also be provided. Sections 2.2.2 and 2.2.3 describe NOAA-Next and the advanced microwave sounding unit (AMSU).

1.2 The Oceans

The need for frequent and accurate measurements of the marine environment has increased dramatically during the past decade. Accurate analysis and prediction of oceanic and coastal conditions are essential for supporting rapidly increasing maritime activities to meet these developing needs.

NASA research and development spacecraft programs (e.g., Nimbus-7, Seasat) have shown that satellite observations can play an important role in providing data for both the operational analysis of, and research on, oceanic conditions. NOAA recognizes

Table 1 Anticipated useful life of
remote sensing satellites and ground stations

Satellite	Satellites Anticipated Service Life	Ground Systems Useful Life
METSAT		
Polar		
NOAA-7	1981-1983	1978-1990
NOAA-8	1983-1985	
NOAA-F	1984-1986	
NOAA-G	1985-1987	
NOAA-H	1986-1988	
NOAA-I	1987-1989	
NOAA-J	1988-1990	
Geostationary		
GOES-5	1981-1985	1983-1993
GOES-6	1983-1988	
GOES-G	1986-1991	
GOES-H	1987-1992	
Landsat		
Landsat-4	1982-1984	1982-1990
Landsat-5	1984-1987	

national requirements for obtaining microwave spectral interval measurements of surface wind velocity, sea surface temperature, significant wave height, sea ice conditions, current measurements, chlorophyll, and other optical characteristics from a polar-orbiting satellite. Because of the ability of microwave sensors to detect surface observations during cloudy conditions, microwave data are expected to improve significantly the efficiency, safety, and effectiveness of marine transportation, off-shore exploration and extraction, platform operations, construction, commercial fishing, and scientific knowledge of ocean surface dynamics. To meet these developing needs, the Federal Government will continue an R&D program. As a first step in this program, the U.S. Navy, with support from NASA and NOAA, is proposing an oceanographic satellite called N-ROSS (Navy Remote Ocean Sensing Satellite). If approved, this program will begin in 1985 with a first launch before the end of the decade.

1.3 The Land

With the launch of Landsat-5 in March 1984, the last of the satellites developed by the U.S. Government is now in orbit. Landsat-5 is expected to be operational until early 1987. The Federal Government is now in the process of evaluating proposals from the private sector for establishing a commercial land remote sensing satellite system. Little can be said until this process is complete, but a few observations can be made with a fair degree of confidence.

1.4 Research and Development

Research and development in the realm of remote sensing, as with all civil space research will continue to be carried out primarily by the NASA. In certain areas of applied research, recent policy decisions by NASA have had the result of transferring some meteorological satellite remote sensing research to NOAA. This policy change is evidenced in the recent decision by NOAA to develop the advanced microwave sounder unit and by various NOAA budget initiatives. Nevertheless, NASA remains the primary agency within the Federal Government for space research on the atmosphere. Section 4 describes the presently planned program of atmospheric research.

2. Atmospheric Remote Sensing

During the last 5 years, the National Oceanic and Atmospheric Administration has matured as one of the United States' three principal space agencies. Given responsibility for all operational civil space remote sensing programs by presidential decision in 1979, NOAA has nevertheless remained preeminent in meteorological remote sensing utilizing the geostationary GOES and the polar-orbiting NOAA satellite series. Thus any description of future atmospheric remote sensing begins, in the near-term, with a description of NOAA's plans for implementation of improvements in the operational weather satellite program. The following sections describe plans for near-term improvement in ground processing of data from current space sensors and for the next generation of geostationary and polar-orbiting operational meteorological satellites.

2.1 The Decade of the 1980s—VAS Implementation

Thousands of weather forecasters rely on the remote sensing capabilities of NOAA's Geostationary Operational Environmental Satellites (GOES). Since the early 1970s, the GOES have provided half-hourly, around-the-clock pictures of the weather systems in the temperate and tropical latitudes over most of the Western Hemisphere. This observational capability has proved extremely useful in detecting the formation of severe weather systems, tracking their course, and monitoring their intensification and decay.

A recent enhancement to the GOES remote sensing instrument greatly expands its observational powers and adds a major new dimension to the role that the GOES system can play in supporting weather forecasting and service programs. The new instrument, visible and infrared spin-scan radiometer atmospheric sounder (VISSR/VAS) can provide new imagery that depicts the distribution of moisture and the temperature patterns in several layers of the atmosphere. It can also be used to derive soundings over space and time scales much smaller than those associated with the current polar-orbiting satellite system or the radiosonde network.

2.1.1 The Challenge of VAS. The present operational observing system, although diverse and extensive, does not provide the kind of information base needed to markedly improve short-term localized forecasts. Balloon-borne instruments (radiosondes and rawinsondes) provide measurements of upper-air conditions only twice a day, only over land, and the stations from which the balloons are released are, on average, about 300 km apart. Measurements over the Earth's oceans and land masses can be obtained from polar-orbiting satellites, but, even with a two-satellite polar-orbiting system, the measurements can be received only once every 6 h. Present land-based (surface observations) stations, although quite numerous, provide no quantitive information of upper-air conditions. Radar observing stations provide valuable information about ongoing precipitation but do not measure a storm's "leading indicators." Since the early 1970s, the GOES have provided near-continuous views of the cloud patterns over most of the Western Hemisphere. The GOES data are used to provide some quantitive measurements: surface temperatures and cloud-top heights are derived from the infrared data, and wind fields are determined by tracking the movements of clouds in a sequence of GOES images. But GOES imagery is, in the main, used by thousands of forecasters in a very subjective manner. That is, the forecasters use photographs or electronic displays to view and interpret the imagery.

However, a remote sensing instrument that greatly expands the observational capabilities of the GOES has now been in orbit since the launch of GOES-4 in 1981. This instrument, called the VAS, is a 13 channel radiometer. Several channels can be used to provide new views (images) that depict small-scale changes in the moisture patterns and temperature variations, as well as the cloud patterns, in several layers of the atmosphere. If all channels are used, vertical temperature profiles of the atmosphere can be derived over a broad area with relatively high-frequency and spatial (horizontal) resolution; e.g., the atmosphere over the 48 coterminous states could be sounded every hour with the distances between soundings in noncloudy areas being as small as 30 km.

2.1.2   Objectives.   The National Environmental Satellite, Data, and Information Service (NESDIS) and the National Weather Service (NWS) have established an overall goal to improve NOAA weather services through more effective use of present GOES remote sensing capabilities by capitalizing on the potential of the VAS.

The major service areas in which improvement is sought include daily numerical forecasts, severe convective storms outlooks and watches, aviation weather support, tropical storm/hurricane analysis and forecasts, flash flood rainfall estimates, and basic weather forecast guidance materials. The VAS potential includes its capabilities for sounding and multispectral imaging, which are inherent in the present space segment of the GOES system but which cannot be exploited operationally until compatible ground systems are established.

The activities called for under this program are aimed at achieving three closely related objectives: A) develop the capability for using VAS data in operational weather forecast and service programs, B) establish reliable satellite data support systems and services, and C) conduct supporting applications research and product development. Objective A is the primary or "end" objective. Objectives B and C, while subordinate to A, require a high level of effort and will be treated as companions to objective A. These objectives are discussed in Section 2.1.5.

2.1.3 Constraints. When introducing a major modification into an operational system, it is essential that there be no disruption of on-going operational products and services. At the same time, given the benefits that have already been shown by experimental use of the VAS data, it is highly desirable to make that data available to operational weather services at the earliest possible date. These (sometimes conflicting) requirements have guided the implementation program definition. Operational VAS assessments will therefore be constrained by the following factors until the second half of this decade:

1) The VAS instruments must be used to support the existing GOES (imaging) mission. That is, they must be used to provide half-hourly visible and infrared imagery in the current format. There is no "stand-by" VAS instrument in space. This dictates the need for conducting a "contingent mode of dual VISSR/VAS satellite operations" to get any VAS data.

2) There exists but one experimental VAS synchronizer/data buffer (SDB). This equipment is vital to any and all VAS data acquisition. When it is not working, VAS data cannot be obtained. The fact that there is only one SDB means that, even in a contingent VAS mode of operations, VAS data can be received from only one of the two GOES/VAS satellites. This situation will be remedied during the scheduled replacement of GOES ground equipment, to be completed about 1986.

3) The Space Science and Engineering Center (SSEC) at the University of Wisconsin is the only place where VAS data, together with other meteorological data, are processed into useful products in a timely way. The SSEC facilities must be used to support the development of VAS products and processing techniques and their evaluation until about 1986.

2.1.4 Approach. The approach to be used in achieving this program's goal is a consequence of the objectives and constraints as set forth in the two preceeding sections.

Developing the capability for using the VAS data in operational weather forecast and service programs will require realistic, i. e., operational, assessments of the products and techniques developed at the R&D centers; definition of detailed functional and performance specifications for operational systems; implementation of these systems; and continued interaction of the R&D and user communities to develop and test new techniques and to determine what enhancements to make to the initial operational systems. The vehicle for doing this was entitled the NOAA operational VAS assessment (NOVA) effort.

The NOVA effort, begun at a low level in 1982, enabled VAS data (multispectral imagery and soundings) to be obtained from an operational GOES/VAS satellite by means of a dual VISSR/VAS mode of operation. The experimental VAS ground equipment runs in parallel with the operational (VISSR) ground equipment. The VISSR equipment at the command and data acquisition (CDA) station extracts the operational (VISSR) data from the VAS data and makes it available to operational VISSR users in the normal manner. At the same time, the VAS equipment at the CDA station is used to make the VAS data available to appropriately equipped R&D centers. This dual VISSR/VAS operation provides a fairly routine flow of VAS data (up to 16 h/day, 6 day/week) to the R&D centers with minimal interference to the on-going VISSR operations.

Under the NOVA effort, the SSEC man-computer interactive data access system (MCIDAS) is used to acquire and process the VAS data in real-time; to produce derived VAS fields; to maintain a VAS data base; to provide data/products to remote user terminals at the National Severe Storms Forecast Center (NSSFC), the National Meteorological Center (NMC), the National Hurricane Center (NHC), and the NOAA Central Computer Facility (NCCF); and to archive all the VAS data.

Thus far, the NOVA effort has provided for the initial testing of VAS data and derived products in the operational environments of the three major centers. Users, scientists, and forecasters have begun to gain experience with the VAS data and experimental processing techniques; and some refinements and changes have been made because of the collaborative efforts of these users and the R&D personnel.

The implementation activities, which are now underway, involve three closely coordinated steps:

1) Replacement of key GOES ground elements. This NESDIS effort, which began in 1983, is aimed at replacing many elements of the existing GOES ground system because of their age, obsolescence, and associated maintenance and reliability problems.

2) Refurbishment of the satellite telemetry and command system. The NESDIS is also in the process of refurbishing its telemetry and command system. One of the objectives of that effort is to develop a new command system that will reliably support both the VISSR and VAS modes of satellite operation.

3) Establishment of a GOES archive and retrieval system (GARS). The NESDIS will establish the GARS in 1985. GARS will have the capability to record all GOES (VISSR or VAS) data at full

resolution in digital format. The GARS will not, however, have the capability to produce computer compatible tapes (CCT) of VAS data from the archive media (video cassettes).

2.1.5 Meeting the Objectives. Recalling the three interrelated objectives stated in Sec 2.1.2, NOAA has embarked upon a plan to enable the use of sounding and multispectral imaging from geostationary satellites by the operational weather services. This use will first be on a quasi-operational basis, with an accepted risk of some data unavailability, but will become fully operational by the end of this decade.

Objective A—Develop the capability for using VAS data in operational weather forecast and service programs:

The first step is evaluation of potential improvements to the national center and field forecast operations. When completed, the output of this step will be a collection of assessment reports to be used in refining decisions on how, when, and where VAS capabilities should be operationally integrated.

The second step is definition of requirements and performance specifications. The output of this step is specification documents that can be used for implementation procurements.

The third and final step under this objective is implementation of initial operational user systems and systems interfaces. The output of this action will be working systems and operating procedures. This end goal is scheduled for completion by the end of the 1980s.

Objective B—Establish reliable satellite data support systems and services:

Step one under this objective is to establish interim "contingent" VAS data acquisition methods and procedures. This was begun in 1983 with the initiation of "contingent VAS operations," which have been providing VAS multispectral imagery and sounding data through R&D channels since that date. These data have been broadcast via a GOES satellite in "standby" status at 91deg W longitude in a format called mode AA.

The second step is providing data and products for both real-time and retrospective (research) users. NOAA has successfully provided VAS data/products to NOAA user terminals located at NSSFC, NMC, and NHC. CCTs of VAS data were also provided to selected retrospective users. Facilities to accommodate VAS data reception and processing have been installed at NSSFC and the

Environmental Research Laboratories (ERL) at Boulder, Colo., and will be installed at NMC and NHC.

The third and most important step is to implement operational data acquisition, distribution, and archiving systems interfaces. As a result of this step, NESDIS and NWS are producing a set of documents that define the steps to be taken to accomplish the operational VAS implementation. Among other things, a new mode, called "mode AAA" will be utilized for broadcast of VAS data via the GOES satellites starting in 1986. This new mode will not only provide the means for distributing VAS multispectral and sounding data, it will also provide some spare capacity for distribution of data products to the same user community in the future. A second output of this task is the definition of a baseline data processing subsystem referred to as the VAS data utilization console (VDUC). This unit will permit preoperational availability of VAS data at the national centers, without the need for passing the data through SSEC, and permit the advanced development of fully operational equipment for general installation in the early 1990s.

Objective C—Conduct supporting applications research and product development:

The first step under this objective is the development of initial products and application techniques. When completed in 1985, the output of this action step will be specific VAS products for introduction when the operational data handling system comes on line.

The second step is to conduct training courses and workshops for operational personnel. Workshops and training courses will be conducted by research personnel for applications development scientists; then courses and workshops will be conducted by the applications development scientists for the operational forecasters.

Finally, the NOAA VAS implementation team expects to investigate new applications and refine present techniques. With the advent of VAS, direct enhancements of existing techniques are possible and entirely new dimensions are added.

2.2 The Post-1990 Period

NOAA and NASA have begun the work necessary to develop the next generation of operational meteorological satellites. The mission requirements for both the GOES-Next and the polar-orbiting meteorological satellites (NOAA-Next) have been established. NASA has released the request for proposals (RFP) for GOES-Next and will release the RFP for NOAA-Next in 1985 or 1986. The

Table 2   GOES-Next comparison

	GOES now	GOES-Next
	System	
Imaging/sounding	Time multiplex or serial	Independent
Reliability	Marginal	Improved
Earth location of sensor data, km		
Absolute	10	2
Picture to picture	5	2 (1 km goal)
Communications		
WEFAX	Time shared	Dedicated Channel
Search and rescue	None	Provision
Other systems		
Data collection system	Included	Same as GOES now
Solar environmental monitor	Included	Same as GOES now
Solar X-ray imager	None	Optional
	Sounding	
No. of channels	12	14 (Min)
Spatial resolution, km	14	8
Sensitivity	Marginal	Improved
Timeliness		
50 deg latitude	5 h	4 h
3000 x 3000 km	2.5 h	40 min
Registration		
Channel to channel	Not specified	10% of an IFOV (2% desired)
Operational mode	Experiment, time-shared with imager	Separate, operational instruments
	Imaging	
No. of channels	2 operational 3 experimental	5 operational
Spectral characteristics, micrometers		
Visible	0.55-0.75	Same
Thermal infrared	9.7-12.8	10.2-11.2
Thermal infrared	12.3-13.0[a]	11.5-12.5
Infrared window	3.8 - 4.0[a]	Same
Infrared water vapor	6.5 - 7.0[b]	Same
Spatial resolution, km		
Visible	1	Same
Thermal infrared	8	4
Thermal infrared window	8	4
Infrared water vapor	8 km	Same
Registration		
Channel to channel	Not specified	10% of the IFOV
Timeliness, min		
Earth disk	20	Same
3000 x 3000 km	5 (3 channels)	5 (5 channels)

[a] Experimental. [b] Four/day.

following sections describe these two spacecraft series, as specified by NOAA to NASA to meet National Weather Service and
other user requirements.

2.2.1 GOES-Next The GOES-Next satellites will be designed
to provide a stable platform for the instruments to be used in
making measurements of the Earth's atmosphere, its surface, cloud
cover and electromagnetic environment. In addition, the satellite
will support data collection and distribution functions which form
the basis for the ongoing operational system. The mission requirements are outlined below. Table 2 summarizes the differences
between GOES-Next and the current series (through GOES-G and
-H).

Mission Performance Requirements: GOES-Next will provide
imaging and sounding services throughout the 24 h day. Indepen-
dence of functions is required so that imaging and sounding may be
accomplished in essentially parallel, simultaneous modes. A capability for dissemination of full resolution imagery to the NOAA
central satellite data processing facility at Suitland, Md., will be
continued.

Imaging: A capability will be provided to obtain high-resolution images from visible and infrared channels. The characteristics
of the imager are shown in Table 3. To minimize conflicts between
synoptic and mesoscale users of the data, it will be possible to
image the Earth (all five channels) within 60 deg (great circle arc)
of the subpoint in 20 min or less. When full-Earth-disk images are
not required, it will be possible to obtain data from limited geographic areas at an equivalent line rate (i.e., 50deg N - 25deg N in
4-5 minutes). The navigation accuracy of the GOES-Next imagery
will provide the capability to measure cloud displacement between
two successive images obtained 30 min apart to an accuracy permiting inference of cloud motion velocity with a precision of 3
m/s. Earth location in an absolute sense for individual images will
be practical to an accuracy of 4 km or less. Channel-to-channel
registration of the infrared channels will be possible to within one-
tenth of a field of view.

Atmospheric sounding: The sounder capability will provide
data that will be used by NOAA to determine the vertical temperature structure of the atmosphere from the Earth's surface to the
stratosphere and water vapor content profiles from the surface to
near the tropopause. Accuracies attainable for these profiles will
be comparable to that attainable from the current VAS instrument.

The GOES-Next temperature/moisture sounder instrument
will have at least 14 channels with characteristics as given in Table
4. The field of view of each channel at nadir will be 8 x 8 km,

Table 3 GOES-Next imaging characteristics

Channel	Simultaneous imaging in five channels Uses (qualitative and quantitative)
Visible	Daytime detection and monitoring of severe storms
Split window infrared	Measure and monitor: Day/night cloud growth Low level moisture Surface temperatures
Infrared window	Detects and tracks: Low level clouds at night Low level moisture (with split-window channels)
Water vapor	Depicts and tracks: Mid/upper level moisture patterns Jet stream locations

Improvements:
1) Combinations of channels provide diagnosis of atmospheric stability for severe weather potential.
2) Clear delineation of low, mid, and jet stream flow patterns conducive to severe weather.
3) Improved infrared resolution (4 vs 8 km) for detection/monitoring of small clouds.
4) Improved Earth location §2 VS 8 km) for accurate storm location/movement.
5) Improved timeliness of observations for longer lead times of warnings.

Channel	Band, micrometers	Resolution, km	Signal-to- noise ratio	Precision, bit
1	0.55-0.75	1	1:1.5 at 0.5% albedo	6
2	3.80-4.00	4	1.4 K @ 300 K scene	10
3	6.50-7.00	8	1.0 K @ 230 K scene	10
4	10.20-11.20	4	0.35 K @ 300 K scene[a]	10
5	11.50-12.50	4	0.35 K @ 300 K scene	10

[a] 1.4 K at 200 K scene.

which is essentially that of the current VAS small detector capability (192 microradian IFOV). It will be possible to obtain data within 60 deg (great circle arc) of the satellite subpoint. Contiguous data from any 3000 x 3000 km area within the latitude range of 60 deg N – 60 deg S and meeting the required signal-to-noise specifications can be obtained in 40 min. Smaller areas will be obtainable in proportionately shorter periods. It is hoped, subject to design verification, to obtain channel-to-channel registration accuracies of 0.2 IFOV.

Space environment monitor: The current GOES capability for monitoring the space environment will be continued with the following three capabilities: a magnetometer for measuring the Earth's magnetic field in three axes; solar x-ray sensing in two energy bands; and three energetic particle sensors for measuring the flux of energetic electrons, protons, and alpha particles in the vicinity of the spacecraft. It is hoped to add a fourth sensor during

Table 4   GOES-Next sounder characteristics[a]

Channel No.	Central Wave number	Bandwidth, Wave numbers	Wavelength, micrometers	Specified NEN, $mW/m^2 \cdot sr \cdot cm^{-1}$
1	679	10	14.73	.87
2	691	12	14.47	.67
3	700	10	14.29	.72
4	710	10	14.08	.70
5	735	13	13.61	.56
6	748	16	13.37	.44
7	787	20	12.71	.38
8	892	50	11.21	.16
9	1365	50	7.33	.18
10	1467	140	6.82	.074
11	2213	35	4.519	.0086
12	2520	100	3.968	.0033
13	2671	100	3.744	.0036
14	14367	1000	.696	.1% Albedo

[a] These parameters are subject to refinement during the design process.

the lifetime of the GOES-Next system with the capability of imaging the sun in the x-ray spectrum.

Data collection from in-situ platforms: The data collection system characteristics for GOES-Next are not expected to be changed from those of the current system at this writing. Changes are planned on the ground, however, to enable expansion to the full capacity permitted by the spacecraft. This includes the capability to support up to 12,500 platforms. The system can support interrogatable platforms, as well as self-timed, threshold triggered, and random-reporting platforms.

Communications: For the first time, a dedicated weather facsimile (WEFAX) capability will be provided. The current system provides WEFAX transmission of imagery and NWS charts only during the periods when imagery is not being acquired by the satellite. The GOES-Next will be capable of providing WEFAX distribution full-time including during the acquisition of imagery data.

System considerations (see Table 2): Frequency allocations will be in the same bands currently allocated to the GOES satellites. The WEFAX transmission frequency, the data collection system (DCS) frequencies, and all other direct services to users will utilize the same frequencies as the current system. Both east-west and north-south stationkeeping will be to a precision of 0.1 deg. Emphasis will be placed on designing for the highest practical reliability.

2.2.2 NOAA-Next. The basic requirements for NOAA-Next, with two or three exceptions, are those of the current generation of satellites. The exceptions involve replacement of the current microwave sounder unit (MSU) and stratospheric sounder unit (SSU) components of the TIROS operational vertical sounder (TOVS) with an advanced microwave sounder unit (AMSU). Minor changes will be made in the Advanced Very -High -Resolution Radiometer (AVHRR) and the High-resolution Infrared Radiation Sounder (HIRS/2). Other changes involve system modifications to accommodate changes in frequency management regulations and to permit launch by the Space Transportation System (STS). Although these requirements will be reviewed again prior to development of the NOAA-Next satellite in the late 1980s, the above requirements (with the exception of launch by STS) will be introduced in the last of the current series, NOAA-K, -L, and -M.

Table 5   NOAA-Next comparison

Function	NOAA Now	NOAA-Next
Space environment monitor	Included	No change
Ozone monitor	SBUV (pm only)	No change
Data collection system	Included	No change
Search and rescue	Included	No change
Equator crossing times, Two satellite system:		
	a.m.: 0730 local	a.m.: No change
	p.m.: 1400 local	p.m.: 1300 local
Communications frequencies, MHz:		
APT	137.50	No change
	137.62	No change
Direct sounding	136.77	S-band
broadcast	137.77	
HRPT	1698.0	No change
	1702.5	"
	1707.0	"
Sounding		
No. of channels:		
Infrared	23	20
Microwave	4	20
Spatial resolution, km:		
Infrared	17.5 (nadir)	Same
Microwave (temperature)	110.0 (nadir)	40.0 (nadir)
Microwave (water vapor)	N/A	15.0 (nadir)
Microwave (ice, rain)	N/A	15.0 (nadir)
Imaging:		
No. of channels	5	6
Spatial resolution, km:		
Visible	1.0	Same
Infrared	1.0	Same
Spectral specifications, micrometers		
Channel 1	0.58-0.68	Same
Channel 2	0.7-1.1	0.82-0.87
Channel 3a	3.55-3.93	1.57-1.78[a]
Channel 3b	N/A	3.55-3.93[a]
Channel 4	10.3-11.3	Same
Channel 5	11.5-12.4	Same

[a] Channels 3a and 3b time-shared.

Table 6 HIRS/2 channels for NOAA-Next[a]

Chan. No.	Channel frequency, wavenumber	Wavelength, micrometer	Half-power bandwidth, wavenumber	Anticipated max. scene temperature	Design goal NEN
1	669	14.95	3	280	0.75
2	680	14.71	10	265	0.25
3	690	14.49	12	240	0.25
4	703	14.22	16	250	0.20
5	716	13.97	16	265	0.20
6	733	13.64	16	280	0.20
7	749	13.35	16	290	0.20
8	900	11.11	35	330	0.10
9	1030	9.71	25	270	0.15
10	1225	8.16	60	290	0.15
11	1365	7.33	40	275	0.20
12	1488	6.72	80	260	0.10
13	2190	4.57	23	300	0.002
14	2210	4.52	23	290	0.002
15	2240	4.46	23	280	0.002
16	2270	4.40	23	260	0.002
17	2360	4.24	23	280	0.002
18	2515	4.00	35	340	0.002
19	2660	3.76	100	340	0.001
20	14,500	0.69	1000	100[b]	--

[a] Tentative, values and channels subject to refinement.

[b] Channel 20 value is 100% albedo.

Table 7 Accuracy of TOVS data

Layer, mb:	Summer set, deg rms	Winter set, deg rms
1000-850	2.3	2.9
850-700	2.1	2.3
700-500	1.7	1.8
500-400	2.0	2.1
400-300	1.9	2.2
300-200	1.9	2.2
200-100	2.1	2.1
100- 70	1.9	2.2

Mission performance requirements: The current performance of the NOAA instruments is described elsewhere. Hence, only the new instrument, the AMSU and the differences in other instruments will be described here. Table 5 summarizes the differences between NOAA-Next and the current system.

HIRS/2: The infrared sounder will be essentially identical to the instrument flown on today's satellites. It will make measurements in 20 channels with the characteristics given in Table 6.

2.2.3 AMSU. The advanced microwave sounding unit (AMSU) provides for the continuation of the sounding program provided by the TIROS series of NOAA satellites. The sounding system currently used on the NOAA satellites consists of the HIRS2, a 20 channel infrared instrument; the MSU, a 4 channel microwave instrument; and the SSU, a 3 channel infrared instrument for stratospheric data. The SSU was furnished by the United Kingdom and is no longer produced. Supplies of this instrument will be exhausted by the late 1980s. The MSU is an instrument designed during the mid-1960s and, as such, contains technology that is obsolete and no longer obtainable. The prime purpose of the AMSU program is to provide for the development of replacement instruments and for enhanced ground processing. Without this replacement, temperature profiles in cloudy areas would no longer be available to operational numerical weather forecasting and the resulting weather predictions would be seriously degraded.

Background: Starting in October 1972 when atmospheric temperature sounding from satellites was instituted operationally by NOAA, the first objective was to provide coverage of the ocean areas of the globe where the small number of conventional radiosonde observations was seriously inadequate for global numerical forecast models. Within 18 months of the introduction of this new system, it had been tuned and refined to the point where most of its data was accepted as input to the numerical models that are run twice daily by the National Meteorological Center of the Weather Service. The importance of satellite data can be illustrated by a simple statistic. Global temperature sounding coverage from two satellites provides 100 times that from the conventional radiosonde network. For the continental United States, at whose latitude the prevailing wind direction is from west to east, the paucity of radiosonde data over the northeastern Pacific Ocean is especially serious. Short range (0-48 h) and fine-scale (a specific city as opposed to an average over a large area) forecasts are especially dependent on the coverage of observations upwind of the area for which the forecast is prepared. The contribution of satellite data to forecasting on the U.S. west coast is evident.

Significant improvements will be provided by the instrument proposed as the successor to the current MSU and SSU on TOVS. The advanced microwave sounding unit (AMSU) is a 20-channel passive microwave radiometer divided into two components—a 15 channel unit to be provided by the United States and a 5 channel unit to be provided by the U.K. Meteorological Office as a continuation of the present, highly successful cooperative program. The U.K. Meteorological Office has already agreed to this continuation of the joint operational system.

Requirements: In recent years, the usefulness of temperature and moisture sounding data from satellites for the meteoro-

logical community has increased dramatically. Indeed, any interruption in the supply of the derived products provokes a swift
reaction from the weather services. Routine use of the data has
provided direct experience that makes it possible to identify those
meteorological parameters for which improvements are most
desirable. At the same time, technological advances make it
possible to propose instruments capable of making improvements in
the measurement.

The four most pressing improvements required for numerical
weather prediction are: improved accuracy of temperature data,
especially in cloud-covered areas; higher horizontal and vertical
resolution; more information concerning water as vapor/liquid in
clouds or rain; and improved timeliness in the delivery of the
observations to the users.

In addition, some special requirements for precipitation
information and stratospheric data for climate monitoring can be
addressed by AMSU, as can some requirements for operational sea
ice monitoring.

Accuracy of Temperature Sounding Data: The present accuracy of the TOVS is presented in the layer temperatures listed in
Table 7. These accuracies are based on comparison of radiosondes
within ±3 h of satellite observation time and within ±3 deg latitude
and longitude of the satellite observation. The rms temperatures
listed include errors based on time, location, and the inherent
radiosonde error.

The AMSU will provide temperature accuracies in nearly all
weather situations comparable to the clear TOVS soundings over
the 1000–500 mb range and superior to the TOVS at higher altitudes. The ability of the AMSU to produce high-quality data in
cloudy as well as clear areas is necessary to supply data to the
models that will improve the forecasts. In the case of severe
storms, the AMSU measurements will be amalgamated with the
higher temporal measurements (but limited to clear areas) obtained
from the geostationary infrared sounder (VAS) to provide timely
observations to forecasters. In addition, the AMSU will serve as a
backup to the HIRS2 instrument in case of failure and conversely
HIRS2 as a backup to the AMSU. In both cases, some degradation
in accuracy will occur, but the satellite would still provide useful
data for the operational product.

Resolution Requirements: Table 8 summarizes the horizontal
resolution requirements for operational systems in the 1990s,
where the horizontal resolution requirements for several applications of the four types of data from the AMSU have been grouped
together.

Table 8 Horizontal resolution requirements[a], km

Parameter	Temperature	Humidity	Clouds and precipitation	Sea ice and snow
Application:				
Global climate studies	250	250	15	50
Operations:				
Global Weather	150	150	15	15
Regional Weather	10-50	10-50	15	15

[a] Measurements at high resolution are useful for statistical parameterization of the effects of small-scale processes on large-scale circulation.

With respect to vertical resolution requirements, the additional microwave channels of AMSU (relative to the MSU) will improve the vertical resolution of temperature soundings in cloudy areas of the lower troposphere. The numerical weather prediction models planned for the 1990s will not achieve their real potential unless they can be fed with higher-resolution data than are available from today's TOVS system. AMSU will provide much of the needed enhancement in resolution.

Technology: Infrared and microwave measurements are complementary and a complete operational system is dependent upon both to satisfy the needs and requirements of the meteorological community. Until microwave measurements became a part of the operational system, certain types of cloud conditions led to systematic errors in temperature profiles. By using the microwave as a control upon the infrared to assure compatibility of the two in the troposphere, the reliability and quality of the results were considerably enhanced. In the process, it also emerged that the use of both in clear and partly cloudy areas has produced soundings whose quality cannot be matched with either system alone.

Clouds are, to varying degrees, opaque to infrared radiation. Therefore, if a thick cloud covers the entire field of view of an instrument, none of the measured radiation arises from the atmosphere below the top of the cloud and nothing can be deduced about that portion of the atmosphere. Microwave radiation, having 100-1000 times the wavelength of the infrared, is largely insensitive to the presence of cloud droplets. Thus, the measured values are the same as they would be if the clouds were not present. An exception to this condition arises from raindrops, snow, and other large ice particles because these particles approach the dimensions of the microwave wavelengths, at which point the radiation interacts with the drops and alters the measurements. This condition has no effect on frequencies up to 90 GHz, minimal effects at 90 GHz, and increasing interaction through the 183 GHz frequencies. This interaction of the large particle size is used to provide an estimate of precipitation rate using the 90 GHz frequency.

Until recently, much of the attention in the microwave area has been focused on the use of channels near the 22.23 GHz water vapor line for deriving the columnar integrated water vapor (precipitable water) over the oceans from satellite measurements. Over land the fact that the surface emissivity is dominated by the amount of moisture in the soil, and hence widely variable, precludes the use of this relatively transparent region of the spectrum for determining accurate precipitable water data. Microwave radiometers on Nimbus-5, -6, and -7 all contained channels around the 22 GHz line for obtaining the global distribution of water vapor under clear and cloudy conditions. The precipitable water data derived from these microwave measurements over the oceans were shown to be within the accuracy of the radiosonde data; hence, they are useful for identifying the circulation of moisture in tropical storms and cyclones at the midlatitudes. However, to be useful in numerical prediction models the integrated quantity must be parameterized to obtain a vertical distribution over both land and sea. A much more accurate technique for obtaining the vertical structure is available by using microwave measurements around the stronger absorption line at 183.31 GHz. By properly selecting a set of three channels in the wings of this line, water vapor profiles can be derived over land and ocean surfaces.

In order to gain the full advantage of the 183 GHz measurements, various improvements in retrieval techniques are undergoing further development. By extending current infrared techniques to the microwave region, one can expect significant improvements in defining the vertical structure of water vapor without the ambiguities resulting from cirrus clouds, etc.

The ability of the 90 GHz channels of the AMSU to detect precipitation is an important feature. In the TOVS, undetected precipitation has caused errors in the retrieved soundings. The ability to remove or correct for precipitation in the sounding retrievals will significantly increase the accuracy. The high-resolution 90 GHz channel (15 km) will provide the capability to map precipitation on the gloval area, a capability that has not existed before and which is important to forecasters.

The electromagnetic properties of the sea ice itself also favor the use of millimeter waves, allowing the ice to be classified into first-year and multiyear ice. This arises because first year ice, with its high brine content, has an emissivity greater than 0.9 at all frequencies, whereas multiyear ice has less brine, is a good scatterer, and has emissivities that decrease with increasing frequency to at least 90 GHz, where it is as low as 0.5.

The 20 channels currently defining the AMSU are given in Tables 9 and 10.

3. Land Remote Sensing

Since 1972, when the Earth Resources Technology Satellite, ERTS-1 (later renamed Landsat-1) was launched, the United States has led in the remote sensing of the Earth's surface for civil purposes. Many potentially lucrative applications have been developed that utilize the high spatial and spectral resolution data gathered by the Landsat series. As the result of a decision by President

Table 9   AMSU-A channel characteristics

Channel Designation	Center Frequency, GHz	No. of Pass Bands	Bandwidth, MHz	Center Frequency Stability, MHz	Temperature Sensitivity, deg K(req'd.)	Calibration Accuracy, deg K	Beam diam, deg
1	23.800	1	380	10	0.3	2.0	3.3
2	31.400	1	180	10	0.3	2.0	3.3
3	50.300	1	200	10	0.35	1.5	3.3
4	52.800	1	400	5	0.25	1.5	3.3
5	53.330	1	400	5	0.25	1.5	3.3
6	54.400	1	400	5	0.25	1.5	3.3
7	54.940	1	400	5	0.25	1.5	3.3
8	55.500	1	400	10	0.25	1.5	3.3
9	57.290[a]	1	330	0.5	0.25	1.5	3.3
10	+217.MHz	2	78	0.5	0.4	1.5	3.3
11	+322.2MHz +48.0MHZ	4	36	0.5	0.4	1.5	3.3
12	+322.2 +22.0MHZ	4	16	0.5	0.6	1.5	3.3
13	+322.2MHZ +10.0MHZ	4	8	0.5	0.80	1.5	3.3
14	+322.2MHZ +4.5MHZ	4	3	0.5	1.2	1.5	3.3
15	89.0	1	6000[b]	50	0.5	2.0	3.3

[a] This frequency forms the basis for channels 9 through 14. Its nominal center frequency is 57,290.344 Megahertz.

[b] Bandwidth specified is maximum and can be adjusted lower if required.

Carter in 1979, it was decided to begin the process of transferring this program to the private sector so that it could be exploited commercially. In 1983, President Reagan decided to take the next logical step in the process, the issuance of a request for proposals for transfer of the U.S. land remote sensing satellite program to the private sector. In early 1984, seven proposals were received from U.S. firms desiring to take over the program as a commercial venture.

3.1 Conditions of Transfer

The Government laid relatively few restrictions on the bidding entities and the legislation passed by the Congress, which took an active role in the commercialization process, was similarly nonrestrictive. The only requirements derived from the desire to protect the national security and international commitments of the United States while getting the government out of the business of land remote sensing as quickly as possible.

3.2 Performance of the Commercial System

As of this writing, few details of the proposals received from industry have not been released. Nevertheless, some characteristics are so highly probable as to be virtual certainties, irrespective of the proposal selected. The RFP required that the commercial system maintain—as a minimum—the capabilities of the multispectral scanner (MSS) that has flown on Landsats-1 through -5. The applications thus far developed using Landsat data depend on data taken in the visible light portion of the spectrum. Since sensors operating in the visible range require sunlight, it is likely that the

Table 10   AMSU-B channel characteristics

Channel Designation	Center Frequency, GHz	No. of Pass Bands	Bandwidth, MHz	Center Frequency Stability, MHz	Temperature Sensitivity, deg K(req'd.)	Calibration Accuracy, deg K	Beam diam, deg
16	89.0[a]	1	6000[b]	50	0.6	2.0	1.0
17	166.0	1	4000	50	0.6	2.0	1.0
18	183.31+1.0	2	1000	30	0.8	2.0	1.0
19	183.31+3.0	2	2000	30	0.8	2.0	1.0
20	183.31+7.0	2	4000	30	0.8	2.0	1.0

[a] 89.0GHz center frequency should be adjusted to avoid interference with channel 15 of AMSU-A.

[b] Bandwidth specified is maximum and can be adjusted lower if required.

orbit will be sun-synchronous. The thematic mapper (TM) flown on Landsats-4 and -5 represented virtually the ultimate in scanning instruments. Because multilinear arrays have now been developed sufficiently to permit their use in space-borne sensors, it is likely that these devices will be used in the commercial system because of their higher inherent reliability. Thus, one can conclude that the commercial system will offer multispectral data with a spatial resolution of 80 m or better, spectral bands that include at least the four MSS bands, flown on a spacecraft in a sun-synchronous orbit. Beyond this, it is also reasonably safe to conclude that the commercial entity that takes over the Landsat system will mount a vigorous marketing campaign to enhance sales of remote sensing data in order to amortize the high capital cost of the system—a feat which the Federal government has never succeeded in doing.

4. Research and Development

A space system typically requires 5 years to manufacture and is expected to last for perhaps 10 years. Thus, much space-related activity is operating on a 15 year time line, with plans for the next 5 to 10 years being largely frozen. Therefore, from the standpoint of system designers, the 1990s are already here and the first opportunity to introduce significant new measurement techniques will be in the 21st century. It is therefore mandatory that a vigorous program of R&D continue to support the needs of the year 2000.

The physical characteristics of the Earth are the result of the interaction between many processes. The absorption of solar radiation and the subsequent transfer of the energy and momentum within the Earth's atmosphere and global oceans produce the terrestrial climate in which we live. The convective flow in the Earth's interior, manifested by slow but unrelenting motions of large masses of the Earth's surface, reshape the Earth continually. The same fluid motions produce a magnetic field in the dense metallic core that shields the Earth's surface from the solar wind streaming outward from the sun. The balance of the physical and chemical processes on the Earth's surface and the near space environment provide the conditions to which living organisms on the land, in the oceans, and in the air owe their continued survival.

The study of Earth sciences can be considered to have begun when man first recorded the phenomena occurring around him. The divison of the Earth sciences into disciplinary areas, such as atmosheric physics, oceanography, geology, and biology, developed because of the necessity to delineate problems that were tractable. However, as the boundaries of each of these disciplines has grown, so has the overlap between the traditional disciplinary areas. At the same time the view of the Earth from space has engendered a growing awareness of the Earth as a planet and the realization that a full understanding of Earth science processes must involve a strong global interdisciplinary research program. The study of the processes governing the solid Earth, its oceans and atmospheres, and its life forms require coordinated global observations and theories that integrate these observations.

It has been speculated that man now has the ability to affect the environment of the globe as a whole and not simply his immediate environment. Examples of global issues consist of the release of carbon dioxide into the atmosphere from the burning of fossil fuels, the release of chlorofluoromethanes and their subsequent impact on stratospheric ozone, deforestation and its impact on weather and climate, and acid rain.

Predictions of the impact of man-made changes on the environment of the globe can differ widely, depending on the choice of data and the disciplinary approach that is used. These differences arise because scientists most frequently think of environmental issues from a single disciplinary point of view—that is, as atmosphere only, or land only, or ocean only. In reality, however, a single-discipline perspecitve is no longer a valid approach to predictions of man-made changes. Changes on Earth of concern to mankind in the next decade or so involve the cycling of energy, water, and essential chemicals through the atmosphere, land, biosphere, and oceans. The issues to be addressed, therefore, involve interactive, interdisciplinary processes and any one process studied in isolation can give only partial and sometimes deceptive answers. What is needed is an interdisciplinary research program whose goal is to provide information based on sound scientific principles that can be used by the policy maker to make cost-effective decisions.

In the past decade, many remote sensing techniques have been developed that can provide the data necessary for such an interdisciplinary Earth sciences program. At the same time, the ability to model some of the complex processes, aided by the rapid improvement in computers, has reached the point of practicality on a global scale. The time has come, therefore, when a program in the Earth sciences coupled with remote sensing technology can be reasonably expected to provide an interdisciplinary understanding of global processes for the first time.

4.1 Program Strategy

The Earth Science and Applications Program led by NASA's Office of Space Science and Applications is a global, integrated, interdisciplinary program with emphasis on understanding those processes that impact the habitability of the Earth, in particular biological productivity and air and water quality. It consists of coordinated observational, theoretical, and experimental investigations and development of future observing technologies. Emphasis is placed upon the physical processes that give rise to observed phenomena and thereby the cause-and-effect relationships characterizing the problems under investigation. Only by this means can realisitic predictive models be developed. The observational investigations typically require collection of data simultaneously and sometimes from several locations in the solarterrestrial system. They involve a variety of instruments making both remote and in situ measurements. Some investigations involve controlled perturbations of the space plasma and the atmosphere, using space as a laboratory. The observational experimental and theoretical programs are complementary and together represent a balanced program of system and process studies. Data from both the advanced remote sensing technologies, as well as the operational Metsat and Landsat systems are essential contributions to such studies.

4.2 Current and Near-Term Programs

4.2.1 Atmospheres. NASA and NOAA are equipped with the experience and facilities to deal with the special problems of understanding the circulation of the atmosphere. This capability includes processing the enormous quantities of data involved and providing interpretations of the results in meteorological issues. The investigation and assessment of the FGGE (first GARP global experiment) data set is proceeding. An effort is underway to develop and fly an advanced microwave (temperature and moisture) sounder unit (AMSU). Studies indicate that the performance expected of such a sensor could approach that of the radiosonde, but with far more complete spatial coverage.

In the area of severe storms and local weather, NASA research emphasis is on the use of remote meteorological observations from space or high-flying aircraft and the consolidation of multiple data sources using high-technology interactive computer techniques for data assimilation and analysis. New measurement techniques are under development utilizing research aircraft flights of the NASA Convair-990 with the doppler laser radar (Lidar) wind velocimeter; the ER-2 for cloud-top physics observations, stereo cloud growth, and ice/water phase meaurements; and the U-2 for spectral and spatial characterization of lightning. Heavy emphasis is being placed upon developing research applications of the visible-infrared spin-scan radiometer atmospheric sounder on the GOES satellites. New algorithms are under development to infer temperature, moisture, and winds at different heights in the atmosphere.

The measurement of winds in the troposhere on a global scale is essential to the verification and improvement of global circulation models of the atmosphere. At present, wind measurements are limited to ground-based stations and to observations of cloud motions from synchronous altitudes. A new concept is being designed to measure wind profiles in the troposphere from the surface to about 15 km altitude using the Doppler shift of a pulsed CO_2 lidar signal backscattered from tropospheric aerosols.

Observations from the Nimbus-6 and -7 Earth radiation budget (ERB) instruments and future operational NOAA satellites are being used as a foundation for developing a continuing series of Earth radiation budget data sets. The data sets formed from these observations will serve as a continuing resource for climate research. These data sets are being continued and augmented by data from the Earth radiation budget experiment (ERBE), launched in 1984.

Recent evidence from the Nimbus-7 and Solar Maximum Mission Satellite observations confirm natural variations in the total solar output of several tenths of a percent for periods of up to about 2 weeks. To determine the impact of such variations on the climate systems, as well as to monitor their long-term trend, several instruments have been designed for Shuttle operations: the active cavity radiometer (ACR), solar ultraviolet spectral irradiance monitor (SUSIM), and solar constant variations (SCV). Research programs have been developed to study cloud formation and cloud interaction with incident or reflected radiation and to study the sources, compositions, and radiative impact of the injection of aerosols into the stratosphere by volcanic explosions. In addition, the development of a global cloud climatology data set is anticipated from the International Satellite Cloud Climatology Project (ISCCP).

Investigations in progress are aimed at developing techniques for measuring the major trace species in the troposhere. Field measurements are being undertaken to test the most promising instrumental techniques, both independently and in groups for intercalibration and/or measursement of chemically related species. Plans are underway to follow this study with an intensive, integrated aircraft measursement program to characterize the chemistry of the troposphere on a global scale, over a 6 yr period.

Research on the upper atmosphere (the stratosphere and mesosphere) continues. In the last few years, the use of more realistic two- and three-dimensional models has increased. NASA is continuing to improve the chemical, radiative, and dynamic computer codes used in these models with the goal of having fully coupled radiative, chemical, and dynamical three–dimensional models that truly simulate the atmosphere. NASA is conducting a series of balloon, rocket, and aircraft measurements utilizing a number of different instrumental techniques to measure trace species in the stratosphere. These measurements will also provide an absolute intercomparison of currently existing experimental techniques.

Data from Nimbus-4, Nimbus-6, Nimbus-7, and the stratospheric aerosol and gas experiment (SAGE) have been validated and are now becoming available for detailed analysis. Results from the solar mesosphere explorer (SME) for ozone, nitric oxide, and water vapor will soon be available for analysis. In addition to these satellite missions, three instruments have been developed for Space Shuttle flights. These are the atmospheric trace molecule spectroscopy (ATMOS) experiment, which measures stratospheric trace species; the imaging spectrometer observatory (ISO), which measures mesospheric trace species; and the solar ultraviolet spectral irradiance monitor (SUSIM).

A new satellite program, the upper atmosphere research satellite (UARS), will provide an extension of the understanding of the chemical and physical processes occurring in the Earth's stratosphere, mesosphere, and lower thermosphere. The UARS mission will utilize remote sensing instruments to measure trace molecular species, temperature, winds, and radiative energy input/losses to the upper atmosphere. Where appropriate, in–situ measurements will be made to determine magnetospheric energy inputs to the upper atmosphere. A high degree of interaction among the experimental and theoretical investigations is anticipated and an interactive central data facility with direct on–line investigator access via remote terminals will be provided as a key element of the program.

4.2.2 Oceans. In the area of oceanic processes, research projects are conducted to develop a solid scientific basis for viewing and understanding the ocean from space. The scientific requirements for viewing the oceans from space fall into three general areas: studying the circulation (both geostrophic and wind driven) and heat content of the oceans, and how these are influenced by the atmosphre; studying the primary productivity of the oceans and how it is influenced by the physical/chemical environment and higher elements in the marine food chain; and studying the growth and movement of sea ice and how it is influenced by the atmosphere and ocean.

Objective techniques are being developed for the removal of the directional ambiguity associated with scatterometer winds (and surface stress), as well as conducting quantitative studies with the Global Weather Program to assess the impact of scatterometer winds on atmospheric forecasts. NASA is working on selected in-situ sensors for the determination of ocean currents; data from such sensors are required both to evaluate the potential of space-borne observations of surface currents, as well as to provide com-plementary subsurface currents. NASA and NOAA are investigat-ing the capabilities and limitations of spaceborne observations of chlorophyll concentration to estimate phytoplankton productivity. NASA is also looking at in-situ techniques for defining the full potential of the Scanning Multichannel Microwave Radiometer (SMMR) aboard Nimbus-7 and Seasat to unambiquously resolve the relative contributions made by first-year and multiyear compo-nents to sea ice concentration images. A technique is also being sought establishing procedures to utilize successive SAR images to quantify the movement and deformation of the sea ice field.

An ocean topography experiment (Topex) is being proposed that would provide a capability to observe the ocean globally such that a vastly improved understanding of the ocean's circulation can be obtained. More specifically, the primary goal of Topex is to measure the surface topography of the ocean over entire ocean basins for several years, to integrate these measurements with subsurface measurements and models of the ocean's density field in order to determine the general circulation of the ocean and its variability. This information will be used to understand the nature of the oceans' dynamics, to calculate the heat transported by the oceans and the interaction of currents with waves, and to test the ability to predict circulation.

Given the success of the coastal zone color scanner (CZCS) that flew on Nimbus in 1978, it has become clear that follow-on flights are required to address the determination of global primary productivity, which forms the base for the various marine food chains. The synoptic, global perspective of a satellite color scan-ner that measures ocean chlorophyll concentration will provide the prime data base to which complementary ship, airplane, and buoy data can be added to improve the accuracy of primary productivity estimates for key oceanic regions. A CZCS derivative, the ocean color imager (OCI), is planned to be the first operational ocean sensor to fly on NOAA's polar-orbiting satellites. The beginning of this service is uncertain and depends on budget uncertainties.

4.2.3 Land and Geodynamics. In the area of geodynamics, research and development activities are being conducted to better understand the solid Earth, including crustal processes, internal structure and composition, rotational dynamics, and geopotential fields. Accurate knowledge of the Earth's gravity and magnetic

Table 11 Earth science and applications
land observing instrument development

Instrument	Objective	Sensor Description	Status
Large format Camera	High-resolution mapping Camera	30.5 cm focal length	STS-14 launch (1984) STS-17 launch (1985)
Shuttle Imaging radar (SIR-B/C)	Fundmental research in microwave remote sensing	L-band SAR tilt and fold antenna, digital data, controllable incidence angle	STS-17 launch (1985)
STS multi-spectral linear array	Biomass, bidirectional reflectance, and atmospheric effects	Off-nadir pointing 10-60 m resolution	Shuttle pay load (CY 1987) 6 bands: (4 visible, 2 shortwave i.r.) focal plane sensor
Shuttle imaging spectrometer (SIS)	Improved spectral discrimination of geology, vegetation and soils	Hi-spectral/spatial resolution spectrometer (0.4-2.5 micrometer)	Shuttle pay-load (CY 1989)

fields is essential to Earth science studies, particularly those involving the solid Earth and oceans, and to studies of energy and mineral resources. Currently, the gravity fields are known to an accuracy of 5-8 mgal for resolutions of 500-800 km and the geoid (mean ocean sea level) to about 50 cm. The magnetic field changes so significantly over a period of 3-5 years that the cumulative erorr renders all models obsolete. The geopotential research mission now being planned by NASA will provide the most accurate global gravity field and geoid models yet available. The resolution will be greatly improved over that presently available and important geological structures, now barely detectable in the magnetic gravity field data, will be revealed in enough detail to permit comprehensive modeling.

In land processing, increasing emphasis is being placed on understanding the structure and processes of the biosphere as these are particularly influenced by land surfaces. The program emphasizes the spatial aspects of biospheric dynamics of both anthropogenic and natural origins, with a focus on the biogeochemical cycles, hydrology, and energy exchange at the land/air interface, land/water interface, and land surface changes as those influence biological productivity.

Landsat-5, second in the series of improved spaceborne land observing systems, was launched on March 1, 1984, and provides a major data source for land processes studies. The instrument complement includes the MSS to provide data continuity with the previous Landsats and the new thematic mapper (TM). The TM has seven spectral bands with an extended spectral range, improved spectral resolution, and higher radiometric accuracy and resolution.

Two major instruments are scheduled for flight on the Shuttle in 1984 as part of the OSTA-3 (an experimental package proposed by the NASA Office of Space Technology and Applications) complement—the large-format camera (LFC) and the shuttle imaging radar-B (SIR-B). The LFC is a high-resolution photogrammatic camera with a 23 x 46 cm format and a resolving power of 15 cm for high-contrast objects from Shuttle altitudes. SIR-B is an upgraded version of the L-band synthetic aperture radar (SIR-A) flown on the second Space Shuttle mission in 1981. SIR-B will have a resolution of approximately 40 m at an incidence angle of 45 deg. In addition, an antenna tilt mechanism will vary the incidence angle between 15 and 65 deg. An analysis of Seasat synthetic aperture radar data and SIR-A data indicates that no single incidence angle for SAR imagery is optimal for all geological terrains and that the incidence angle may be "tuned" to the local topography. The primary objective of the SIR-B mission is to understand radar imaging of the Earth as a function of illumination geometry.

The free-flying imaging radar experiment (Firex) is a multi-parameter radar imaging system for use in both land and oceanic scientific research where seasonal or long-term data are needed. Firex would build on the heritage of SIR-A and SIR-B. Potential additional instruments include a wind-wave scatterometer, multi-band radiometers, and a multiband optical imager. The Firex orbit would provide repeat coverage every 3 days. Table 11 lists the research missions planned in support of Land remote sensing in the next few years.

While the capabilities of the TM represent a significant improvement in our remote sensing capabilities from space, there is a developing need for even higher spectral and spatial resolution in future systems. The technology widely regarded as the best approach for future systems is the push-broom mode sensor utilizing solid-state arrays. NASA's major effort in this rapidly evolving technology is the multispectral linear array (MLA) program. Under this program, technology and instrument developments are in progress with the goal of not only developing the enabling technology base for a potential successor to the TM, but also to develop a basic research instrument for future Shuttle and free flier observation of the Earth's surface cover and topography. The near-term technology emphasis is on the development of an all solid state MLA sensor incorporating a new generation of detector materials, visible and shortwave infrared (SWIR) multispectral linear focal plane arrays, onboard signal processing, and advanced ground data processing concepts. It is this technology that is expected to usher in the transition into a future commercial land remote sensing satellite as described in Sec 3.2.

4.2.4 Future Long-Term Thrusts. One of the future thrusts of NASA's Earth science and applications program in the next decade will be to investigate the long-term physical, chemical,and biological trends and changes in the Earth's environment, including its atmosphere, land masses, and oceans. The program will specifically investigate the effects of natural and human activities on the Earth's environment by measuring and modeling important nutrient chemical cycles and will provide realistic models to estimate the future effects on biological productivity and habitability of the Earth by man and other species. This program will involve space and suborbital observation, land- and sea-based measurements, laboratory research, and supporting data management technologies over a ten year or longer period of time. This thrust will complement the current programs directed toward advancing remote sensing science and applying remote sensing techniques in discipline studies such as hydrology and geology.

The long-term goal of both NASA and NOAA research programs is to expand the boundary conditions of each Earth science discipline until they meet in a global Earth system science.

4.3 Relationship With International Research

4.3.1 R&D Requirements for Foreign Remote Sensing Data. A number of foreign nations/agencies (France, Japan, European Space Agency, Canada, India, Federal Republic of Germany, Brazil) are currently developing or plan to develop remote sensing missions. Some of these are described in other chapters of this publication. Research scientists have already made plans to obtain data from the German-developed modular optoelectronic multispectral scanner (MOMS) instrument flown on an early Shuttle experimental flight and the microwave remote sensing experiment (MRSE) instrument flown on Spacelab-1 in 1983. It is anticipated that research requirements for access to European Space Agency ERS-1 data [in particular ERS-1 synthetic aperture radar (SAR) data] in the 1988 timeframe, Japanese MOS-1 (Marine Observing Satellite-1) data in the 1986 timeframe, and Canadian Radarsat data in the the early 1990s will be developed. Although specific research requirements for French SPOT data have not yet been defined, it is likely that U.S. scientists will have access to these data in the

same manner as will other U.S. users—through purchase of the
data. In the other above-cited instances, it is likely that we will
obtain foreign satellite data for experimental purposes through
cooperative agreement in exchange for U.S. data, in support of
U.S. investigators, or in return for U.S. "ground truth" support.

The U.S. is exploring the possibility of direct readout of
foreign remote sensing satellite data by U.S. ground stations for
experimental purposes.   Such arrangements could be patterned
after similar arrangements whereby U.S. experimental satellite
data have been acquired by direct readout at foreign ground stations on the basis of negotiated agreements.

4.3.2   Foreign Participation in U.S. R&D Programs.   R&D
efforts benefit from the participation of foreign scientists and
investigators.   A number of foreign scientists and counterpart
foreign agency personnel have demonstrated expertise in the area
of Earth sciences. Their own research often complements that of
their U.S. peers. In the Earth sciences area, foreign scientists/in-
vestigators have participated and continue to participate in the
Landsat-4 investigations, SIR-A and -B investigations, and are
associated with the Skylab, Nimbus-7, Magsat, and heat capacity
mapping missions. Foreign involvement is desirable in virtually all
of the future U.S. remote sensing programs.

Foreign scientists and foreign counterpart agencies have
command of resources that are often of value in the context of
cooperative programs.   Foreign instruments have contributed to
the TIROS and follow-on meteorological satellite series (U.K.
instruments, French data collection system) as well as the Nimbus
series of satellites (U.K. instruments). Cooperation is anticipated
in the joint flight of NASA's SIR-C with the German remote sensing experiment (initially flown on Spacelab 1) in the 1986 timeframe.   Another example is the backup tape recorder support at
foreign Landsat ground receiving stations (operated at foreign
agency expense) enabling satisfaction of U.S. data requirements
not otherwise attainable in the period prior to availability of global
data via NASA's tracking and data relay satellite system (TDRSS).

As foreign counterpart agencies develop their own Earth
science missions, we can expect reciprocity in receiving access to
foreign-acquired data and participation by U.S. scientists and
investigators on foreign mission science teams.

5. Conclusion

The United States Remote Sensing Program has undergone
major changes since the start of the 1980s. Fiscal austerity has
forced the NASA to sharply curtail its support for operational

remote sensing activities. This curtailment has been only partially compensated by an increase in other Federally funded programs, although NOAA is undertaking some of the most critical developments and some others (most notably part of the microwave sounding activity) are being undertaken outside the United States. Nevertheless, progress can be expected in remote sensing of the atmosphere and oceans, led by government-sponsored programs. Progress in land remote sensing is more problematic, but is expected to be highly responsive to market forces as a result of commercialization efforts.

Perhaps, the single most significant factor in any forecast of the rate of progress in remote sensing is that, without the long-standing and highly successful program of atmospheric remote sensing in support of the operational system, which was carried out by NASA in the 1960s and 1970s, any future major developments will depend upon the ability of NOAA to convince budget authorities of the immediate benefits to be derived. Even when such convincing arguments can be made, the risk of embarking directly upon operational programs without substantial research in advance cannot be minimized. Users should be prepared to endure periods of difficulties in achieving final objectives.

Having said this, the remainder of the 20th century appears to be a period of healthy growth—both in technology itself and in the benefits to be derived for planet Earth from the still infant discipline of remote sensing from space.

Spaceborne Lidar Sensors: Opportunity and Challenge

David B. Hogan* and Ari Rosenberg†

RCA Astro-Electronics, Princeton, New Jersey

Abstract

The basic principles and limitations of space-based passive remote sensing are discussed. An emphasis is placed on the techniques and systems used to determined three parameters of particular importance to meteorologists: vertical profiles of temperature, water vapor, and wind. A class of active remote sensing instruments, known as lidars, are described which have the potential for overcoming many of the limitations of passive sensors. The lidar techniques used to determine atmospheric temperature, water vapor, and winds are surveyed, and the key technological challenges faced in constructing lidar systems to measure these parameters are highlighted. Finally, the prospects for space-based meteorological lidar are examined by reviewing a variety of proposed projects, ranging from simple experimental missions to full-scale operational systems.

Introduction

While complex atmospheric circulation models and high speed computers are crucial to accurate weather predictions, a weather forecast is no better than the observations on which it is based. To provide the observations required by meteorologists, a diverse and complex worldwide observation and communication network has evolved; meteorological remote sensing satellites are one important component of this system. In the future, as meteorologists strive to improve forecast accuracy and to extend forecasts further into the future, an increasing reliance will be placed on the information obtained from these

*Senior Member of the Technical Staff, Advanced Earth Observation Systems.

†Manager, Advanced Earth Observation Systems.

satellites. Sensors on meteorological satellites must remotely determine atmospheric and surface properties by detecting and measuring electromagnetic radiation that has interacted with the Earth/atmosphere/ocean system. Such remote sensors are classified as either active or passive. Active sensors produce the electromagnetic radiation themselves, while passive sensors merely detect that which occurs naturally.

To date, almost all spaceborne meteorological sensors (and all the operational ones) have been passive. Both the technology and application of satellite passive sensors have been evolving continuously over the past 25 years. The first passive sensors operated in the visible spectral region and provided only qualitative information on weather patterns (revealed principally through clouds). Nevertheless, they offered meteorologists a new perspective and almost revolutionized weather forecasting overnight. Today, passive space-based meteorological sensors have reached a high degree of sophistication. By "seeing" the Earth and its atmosphere in spectral regions ranging from the ultraviolet to the microwave they obtain quantitative information on the state-of-the-atmosphere, information that is routinely incorporated into numerical forecasting models.

The development of passive remote sensors is currently facing the law of diminishing returns. The performance of these sensors is approaching fundamental limitations dictated by the underlying physics of passive sensing and is being outstripped by demands for increasingly accurate weather data at better horizontal and vertical resolutions.

A class of active laser remote sensing instruments, known as lidars (for light detection and ranging), are capable of overcoming these limitations. As the name implies, a lidar is essentially an optical radar. Because of its high power and spectral purity, the laser is the source of electromagnetic energy in most lidars. The lidar systems discussed in this article are used to probe volumes of the atmosphere -- not to track isolated targets -- and as such are similar to weather radars.

As we shall see, the factors limiting the ability of lidars to meet the requirements of meteorologists are primarily technological (relating to the construction of the lidars) and environmental (relating to the abililties of satellites to accommodate the demands of these new sensors). Incorporation of lidars on meteorological satellites will offer many challenges: to instrument designers who must construct the sensors; to spacecraft designers who must integrate them on satellites; to meteorologists who must cope with and understand the new data; and to planners who must formulate a coherent space lidar development program best complementing and enhancing our existing capabilities. Successfully meeting this challenge will mark a significant advance in space-based remote sensing and will be a major opportunity not only to better predict the weather, but also to better understand the Earth and its atmosphere.

In this article we will attempt to answer several questions:

1) What are the basic principles of passive remote sensing and why are passive sensors unable to meet the requirements of weather forecasters?

2) What are lidars and how can they be used to remotely determine the state-of-the-atmosphere?

3) What are the major obstacles to incorporating lidars on spacecraft and what will likely be the role of lidar in the future of satellite meteorology?

In answering these questions we will concentrate on the techniques and systems to determine three parameters of particular importance to meteorologists: vertical profiles of wind, temperature, and water vapor. As a reference point, typical requirements for these parameters are listed in Table 1 for two applications: global weather forecasting[1] and climate monitoring.[2]

Passive Remote Sensing

The Radiative Transfer Equation

A passive remote sensor measures naturally occurring electromagnetic radiation that has interacted with the Earth and its atmosphere in one or more finite spectral bands called channels. The theoretical basis of remote

Table 1   Temperature, water vapor, and wind requirements

			Resolution	
Application	Parameter	Accuracy	Vertical	Horizontal
Global	Temperature	±1 K	2-2.5 km	500 km
forecasting	Wind	±2 m/s	2-2.5 km	500 km
(Ref. 1)	Water vapor	±30%	See note[a]	500 km
Climate	Temperature	±1 K	2-2.5 km	500 km
monitoring	Wind	±3 m/s	2-2.5 km	500 km
(Ref. 2)	Water vapor	±10%	4 km	500 km

[a]Two degrees of freedom in the vertical profile.

sensing is embodied in the radiative transfer equation (RTE), which relates the measured radiation in a given channel to the physical state of the system being probed. The sources and interaction mechanisms of electromagnetic radiation in the Earth/atmosphere system are varied and complex, and consequently the most general form of the RTE is extremely complex.

To characterize the radiant energy detected in a given channel of a remote sensing instrument, one must consider the sources of the energy, the components of the Earth/atmosphere/ocean system with which this energy interacts, and the interaction mechanisms. The sources include solar energy incident on the Earth; thermal emission from atoms, molecules, aerosols, and clouds in the atmosphere, and from the ground, vegetation and water; and even the 3 K "big bang" cosmic background radiation. The relative importance of these various sources depends on the wavelengths of radiation being measured and the observing geometry. Solar radiation is generally important only for wavelengths shorter than about 6 μm -- unless the solar disk itself is being directly viewed. For terrestrial temperatures, thermal emission is of importance for wavelengths longer than 2 μm or so. Even the cosmic background 3 K radiation is occasionally important for measurements in the microwave region.

These sources interact with the Earth and its atmosphere in three basic ways: absorption, scattering, and reflection. These interactions can change the intensity, polarization, wavelength, and/or the directional properties of the electromagnetic radiation. The interacting components (i.e., the interacters) can be atoms and molecules in the atmosphere, clouds, the ground, vegetation, or water.

An important concept in remote sensing is that of sensitivity. A channel of a remote sensing instrument is said to be sensitive to a particular environmental parameter (surface temperature for example) if the radiance measured by that channel changes when the environmental parameter is changed. The complexity of radiative transfer makes it imperative to choose the spectral bands of the channels very carefully to limit the sensitivity of each channel to a small, managable number of variables. It is also important to maximize the sensitivity to the parameters of interest.

To understand the principles and the limitations of passive remote sensing, it is useful to examine the radiative transfer equation for some specific cases. In this paper we shall focus our discussion on the retrieval of temperature profiles, moisture profiles, and winds.

The infrared region is applicable to measurements of temperature and moisture. For a clear sky the radiative transfer equation for an infrared channel centered at wavelength ν_i and of width $\Delta\nu_i$, assuming local thermodynamic equilibrium, can be approximately written as

$$r_i = \epsilon_i B_i[T_0]\,\tau_i(x_0) - \int_{x_0}^{x_t} B_i[T(X)]\,\frac{\partial\tau_i(x)}{\partial x}\,dx \qquad (1)$$

where x is the vertical coordinate; x_0 and x_t the coordinate of the surface and the effective top of the atmosphere respectively; ϵ_i the emissivity of surface at wavelength ν_i; $B_i[T]$ the Planck function at temperature T and wavelength ν_i; T_0 the skin temperature of surface; T(x) the atmospheric temperature at position x; and $\tau_i(x)$ the transmission from the instrument to position x averaged over the wavelength interval $\Delta\nu_i$.

This approximation is a good one for the spectral region of about 6–30 µm. For shorter wavelengths, it is necessary to include the contribution of solar radiation reflected from the Earth and scattered by the atmosphere. For longer wavelengths, the downward atmospheric emission reflected by the Earth must be considered.

The measured radiance is the sum of two terms. The first term (left) in Eq. (1) is the radiation emitted by the Earth and attenuated by the atmosphere. The second term (right) is the atmospheric contribution; it is the sum of the radiance emitted in the various levels of the atmosphere attenuated by intervening layers. The temperature of the surface and the atmosphere influences the radiances principally through the Planck function -- which is contained both in the surface and atmospheric term of Eq. (1). The atmospheric distribution of absorbing gases affects the radiances through the transmission terms.

As revealed in Eq. (1), the state of the entire atmosphere and of the surface affects the radiances measured in any channel. Limited information concerning the vertical structure can be obtained, however, by making measurements in several properly selected channels. This is accomplished by choosing the channels in such a way that the radiance in each channel arises principally from a limited vertical extent of the atmosphere. The radiance contribution from any level is determined by the integrand of Eq. (1): the product of the Planck emission function ($B_i[T]$) and the weighting function ($\partial\tau_i/\partial x$).

The weighting functions for three channels of a hypothetical, but typical, instrument are shown in Fig. 1. Channel 1 is for a spectral region of high absorption and the radiation measured by it comes from levels high in the atmosphere. This is indicated by its weighting function, which peaks high in the atmosphere. Channel 3 of our hypothetical sensor is in a spectral region of low absorption. The radiance measured by it arises primarily from the surface and from layers near the surface. The absorption of channel 2 is intermediate between that of channels 1 and 3 and consequently its weighting function peaks at a level in the middle of the atmosphere.

It is important also to consider the sensitivity of the instrument channels to various desired and undesired geophysical quantities. One can write for the sensitivity function

$$S_i[q(x)] = \frac{\Delta r_i}{\Delta q(x)} \qquad (2)$$

where Δr_i is the change in measured radiance of channel i due to a change Δq in some parameter q in a small layer centered at level x. As presented here, change in q over layers of finite thickness must be considered. A more rigorous formulation can remove this

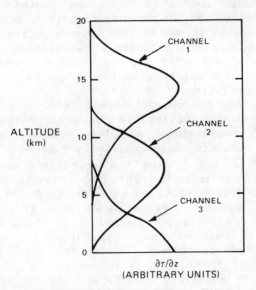

Fig. 1   The weighting function, $\partial \tau / \partial x$, with $x = \ln P$ (P is the pressure) for a hypothetical instrument.

restriction, but the current definition is sufficient for this article.

Like the weighting function, the sensitivity function will in general achieve a maximum at some level. The width and maximum of the sensitivity function is closely related to the ability of a sensor to determine the quantity q at various altitudes. For many applications, the sensitivity function is very similar to the weighting function: temperature sounding is one example. In other applications, however, such as water vapor sounding, the two are quite different.

A key feature of our hypothetical instrument is its broad overlapping weighting and sensitivity functions. In practice, the width of the weighting functions severely limit the ability of an infrared sounder to determine the vertical finestructure of the atmosphere. We will next investigate the radiative transfer properties of a real instrument to explore the techniques used to determine atmospheric temperature profiles.

Temperature Sounding

For temperature sounding channels, it is necessary to select spectral bandpasses in which the main absorber is a molecular species with a constant mixing ratio. A natural candidate is carbon dioxide which has a nearly constant mixing ratio of about 330 ppm and two strong infrared absorption bands, one at 4.3 μm and another at 15 μm. The high resolution infrared radiometric sounder (HIRS) instrument, which is one of the sensors on the NOAA series of polar-orbiting meteorological satellites, contains 20 channels, 10 of which are CO_2 temperature sounding channels The HIRS provides nearly global coverage twice a day at a horizontal resolution of 15 km.[3]

To evaluate the capabilities of HIRS to retrieve vertical temperature profiles, let us examine the properties of the CO_2 temperature sounding channels as revealed through the weighting and sensitivity functions.

Figures 2 and 3 give the normalized weighting and sensitivity functions for the CO_2 channels of the HIRS instruments. Both functions peak at different levels for the various channels. For example, most of the contribution to the radiance of channel 1 is from the stratosphere, while most of the contribution to channel 8 is from the lower troposphere. These two channels are also sensitive to changes in temperature in this region. Channels 3 and 4 exhibit broadly overlapping weighting and sensitivity functions. Consequently, the information contained in these channels is to some extent redundant

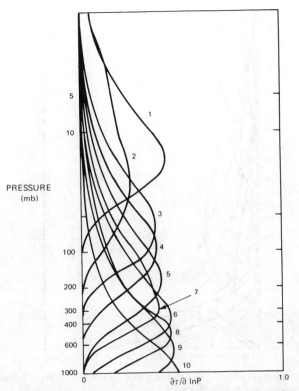

Fig. 2   Weighting functions for the 10 CO_2 temperature sounding channels of the HIRS.

and provides only the average temperature over a large atmospheric layer. It is the widths of the weighting and sensitivity functions that limit the vertical resolution of a passive sounder. The widths of the HIRS weighting functions are partially a result of the broad spectral bandpasses of its channels. However, the widths of any passive sounder's weighting functions has a theoretical limit that is about 50-75% of the scale height of the parameter to be measured. For temperature sounding, this limit is about 4-6 km. The widths of the HIRS weighting functions are close to this theoretical limit.

Any real measurement will unavoidably contain some noise. The measurements in n channels of a temperature sounder can thus be written

$$r_1 = f_1[T(x)] + \sigma_1$$
$$r_2 = f_2[T(x)] + \sigma_2$$
$$\cdot \quad \cdot \quad \cdot$$
$$\cdot \quad \cdot \quad \cdot \quad (3)$$
$$\cdot \quad \cdot \quad \cdot$$
$$r_n = f_n[T(x)] + \sigma_N$$

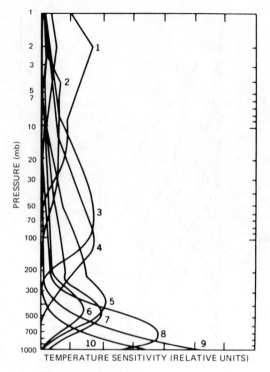

Fig. 3   Sensitivity functions for the 10 CO_2 temperature sounding channels of the HIRS.

where f_i is the right-hand side of the RTE (1) and σ_i the random noise in the measured radiance r_i.

Two mathematically oriented questions arise at this point:

Existence: Is there a solution to Eq. (3)?

Uniqueness: If so, is the solution unique?

As long as the RTE is an accurate representation of the physics of the atmosphere, solutions must exist to the unperturbed Eq. (3) (i.e., with $\sigma_i = 0$). While not guaranteed when $\sigma_i \neq 0$, in practice existence is not a concern. In fact, it can be shown in most cases that if a solution to Eq. (3) exists, then an infinite number of solutions must exist. In other words, solutions to Eq. (3) are not unique. Most problems encountered in solving Eq. (3) for the temperature profile can be traced in one way or another to this fact.

Of the infinite set of solutions some are wildly oscillating profiles which are physically unrealistic. If care is not taken, the retrieval procedure is likely to result in such "unphysical" solutions. Indeed, when investigations began in passive sounding techniques this is exactly what happened. A variety of techniques have evolved to prevent this: solutions that minimize their derivative can be required (thus preventing highly oscillatory solutions); solutions can be constrained to minimize their difference from a first guess "likely" profile; or solutions can be constructed to resemble some real looking profile assembled from atmospheric statistics. Many other approaches are possible.

All attempts must proceed along one or the other or both of the following lines:

1) Additional information -- outside of the radiance measurements themselves -- must be incorporated in the retrieval process.

2) The solution space must be restricted (e.g. by retrieving only a few average temperatures over broad layers).

While retrieval algorithms employing the above strategies can produce physically realistic solutions, there is a more fundamental problem: for each set of observed radiances, there are many meteorologically significant but distinct profiles corresponding to them. Stated another way, there can be two profiles with distinct meteorological consequences that equally well reproduce a given set of observed radiances. Such a situation is sketched in Fig. 4.

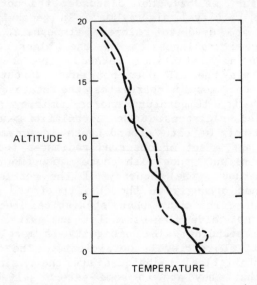

Fig. 4   Two distinct temperature profiles may yield the same radiance measurements.

Twomey[4] has shown that this ambiguity is confined to the high spatial frequency components of the vertical temperature profiles -- sometimes referred to as the vertical finestructure. Because the details of the vertical finestructure cannot be resolved, solutions are necessarily smoothed. This smoothing hides much information of importance to meteorologists.

By adding channels to the instrument, the extent of this ambiguity can be decreased -- but only to a limit. Twomey defines this limit as the point where the radiance of the new channel can be estimated to within its noise level from the radiances of the other channels -- or in other words, when the channel contributes no new information. For the broad weighting functions (and sensitivity functions) of passive temperature sounders this point is reached with only five or so channels. By reducing the noise, this number can theoretically be extended, but the requirements on signal-to-noise ratio rapidly become unrealistic.

For the HIRS instrument the number of independent tropospheric temperature channels is significantly less than 10. Properly handled, the additional channels can add redundancy to the instrument, but they add no new independent information about the temperature profiles. Consequently, many important details of the atmospheric temperature finestructure are lost.

Thus far, we have not discussed the details of the temperature retrieval algorithms. In general, two basic approaches are used to retrieve atmospheric information from observed radiances. In one class of methods, referred to as statistical methods, the physics of the atmosphere via the RTE does not enter directly into the solution. One merely correlates the state-of-the-atmosphere, that is, temperature and/or humidity profiles, to the observed radiances. The correlations are obtained from a set of in situ ground-truth measurements of the atmosphere and a set of observed radiances that are colocated in time and space with these measurements. In statistical methods, the accuracy of the retrieved information depends strongly on the quality of the ground-truth measurements. The fact that statistical techniques are used does not hide the essential ambiguity inherent in temperature sounding; this ambiguity is merely hidden in the statistical retrieval coefficients. The chief advantages of statistical techniques are their simplicity and the fact that they are to some extent self-calibrating. The chief disadvantage is that our knowledge of the physics of radiative transfer is not used in the solution.

In the class of methods, known as physical retrieval methods, Eq. (3), or some approximation to it, is solved simultaneously for all the observed radiances. This method usually requires a first guess of the profile that is being retrieved to initiate the iterative procedure of solving the RTE. The accuracy of retrievals is often dependent on the nature of this first guess. Physical retrieval methods are generally more computationally intensive than statistical methods, but since they use our knowledge of the physics of the atmosphere they can provide better profiles. In practice, the improvement in not always significant. Indeed, if there are instrument calibration problems or inaccuracies in the radiative transfer model the solution may well be worse. Instrument calibration is a serious concern with all physical methods.

Hybrid approaches combining statistical and physical methods are possible. One hybrid technique to retrieve temperatures from the HIRS[5] uses an iterative physically based algorithm. After each iteration, however, the temperature profile estimate is constrained to fit a set of statistically derived vertical eigenfunctions.

Current accuracies for temperature retrievals from the HIRS are about 1.5 to 2.5 K depending on altitude, with a vertical resolution about 5 km.[2,6] Some indication of the potential for improvement in temperature sounding is given by a simulated comparison between a proposed new instrument, the advanced moisture and temperature sounder (AMTS) and the HIRS.[7,8] In the simulation, the AMTS demonstrated a 0.5-1.0 K improvement in root mean square (rms) error in the troposphere compared with the HIRS. The vertical resolution of the AMTS is still severely limited[2] -- about 4 km -- and far short of requirements.

Water Vapor Sounding

For moisture sounding, it is necessary to select a spectral region with water vapor absorption bands. The HIRS instrument, for example, contains three water vapor channels in the 7 and 8 μm regions, and the visible and infrared spin-span radiometer atmospheric sounder (VAS) sounder aboard the geosynchronous weather satellite GOES has two water vapor channels in the 7 μm region. Another infrared water vapor sounder that has flown on a polar orbiting satellite contains seven water vapor channels in the 18-30 μm pure rotational band of water and one channel at 12.5 μm.[9] Table 2 lists these channels and their spectral characteristics. To evaluate the capability of these channels to retrieve water vapor pro-

Table 2   Water vapor sounder characteristics

Channel number	Wavelength μm	Wavenumber cm^{-1}	Halfwidth cm^{-1}	Principal absorbing species
1	13.4	747	12.5	CO_2
2	13.7	731	12.5	CO_2
3	14.1	708	12.5	CO_2
4	14.4	695	12.5	CO_2
5	14.8	676	12.5	CO_2
6	15.0	689	3.0	CO_2
7	12.5	797	12.5	H_2O
8	18.7	535	15.0	H_2O
9	20.1	497	17.0	H_2O
10	24.5	408	14.0	H_2O
11	22.7	441	20.0	H_2O
12	23.9	420	22.0	H_2O
13	25.2	397	12.5	H_2O
14	28.3	353	14.0	H_2O

files, the weighting and the sensitivity functions will be presented.

For temperature sounding channels, the weighting functions depend only slightly on the atmospheric profiles. Water vapor channel weighting functions, however, depend strongly on the atmospheric profile. Figure 5 shows the weighting functions characteristic of three climatological regions for two of the channels.

In water vapor channels, the relative contribution to the radiance from different atmospheric layers depends strongly on the parameter to be retrieved: the water vapor content. Therefore, it is difficult to match, or map, the sounding channels to the different atmospheric layers without some prior knowledge of the atmospheric water vapor profile. As in the case of temperature sounding channels, the weighting functions are very wide and over-lapping.

The sensitivity of the measured radiance to changes in water vapor and temperature is shown in Fig. 6, which shows the change in effective brightness temperature to an 80% increase in water vapor content for a 1 km layer. Figure 6 clearly indicates that none of the channels is sensitive to changes in water vapor near the surface. Even channels 7 and 8 -- considered to be surface sounding channels since most of their contribution to the radiance is from the lower atmospheric layers -- are not sensitive to water vapor changes in this region. This differs from the temperature sounding channels, where the sensitivity functions are very similar in shape to the weighting functions.

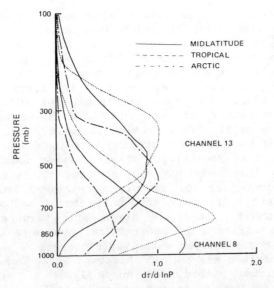

Fig. 5 Water vapor weighting functions for three model
atmospheres. [Note the shift toward lower pressure for the peak
in each weighting function for model atmospheres with larger
amounts of water vapor (tropical) relative to drier models
(arctic).]

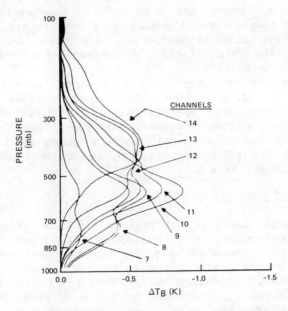

Fig. 6 Water vapor sensitivity functions. (None of the channels
are sensitive to changes in water vapor content near the surface.)

In general, any passive sounder operating in a spectral region for which the surface emissivity is close to unity is insensitive to changes in the concentration of atmospheric constituents near the surface of the Earth. The reason is that when a change occurs in the amount of a constituent near the surface, each of the terms in Eq. (1) change by almost the same magnitude, but with opposite sign. Consequently, the net change in the measured radiance is very small. This problem is faced in all infrared sounding and in microwave sounding over the land.

The lack of sensitivity of water vapor sounding channels means that moisture content near the surface (the lowest kilometer or so) cannot be retrieved from passive sounding data using only physically based methods. Furthermore, small changes in atmospheric temperature near the surface affect the observed radiance more than large changes in surface layer water vapor content.

One possible way out of this bind is to use a statistical retrieval method. In an analysis of water vapor retrieval techniques, it was shown that if radiances from only H_2O channels are incorporated in the statistical retrieval the results are very poor. By incorporating both CO_2 and H_2O channel radiances in statistical retrievals, the results improve markedly. This improvement results primarily because of statistical correlations between water vapor and temperature: on average, the higher the temperature, the more moisture contained in the air. Clearly this situation is less than ideal, since very often the meteorologist is concerned with deviations from average behavior.

Because of the many problems inherent in water vapor sounding, satellite-derived water vapor profiles are not currently being used operationally. There is some hope that proposed microwave sounders (perhaps used in conjuction with advanced infrared sounders, such as the AMTS) might meet the global forecasting and climate monitoring requirements of Table 1.

Passive Wind Measurements

Two basic approaches have been used to passively determine atmospheric winds from space. The first is based on determining the wind by measuring the Doppler shift of a sharp spectral feature, say an emission line. The second approach is to determine the displacement of some observable feature, say a cloud or group of clouds, between two images taken nearby in time. The wind may be determined under the assumption that the feature (e.g., the cloud pattern) is advected by the wind.

Passive Doppler Wind Measurements. The determination of wind from the Doppler shift is perhaps the most straightforward and has been used quite successfully to determine winds in the upper atmosphere (100 km and higher) by measuring the Doppler shift of atmospheric emission lines.[10] Because useful emission lines are limited to regions high in the atmosphere, emission Doppler sensing is not appropriate to tropospheric measurements.

A technique employing Doppler shift measurements of near-infrared O_2 absorption lines has been proposed for stratospheric winds.[11] The technique is not well suited for measurements in the troposphere, however. The principal problem arises from the broadness of spectral features in the troposphere. Throughout most of the troposphere, the Doppler shift caused by winds of several meters per second is a small fraction of the spectral linewidth (0.1% or less); and it is extremely difficult to measure such small displacements of broad spectral features. A second problem concerns the inherently poor vertical resolution of passive radiometric measurements. To be meteorologically useful, vertical resolutions of 2-4 km are required in the troposphere. In the upper atmosphere, the poor vertical resolution can be overcome to some extent by limb scanning and in any event requirements are not quite as stringent. However, limb scanning is not appropriate in the troposphere principally because of the presense of clouds.

Passive Cloud and Water Vapor Tracked Winds. We now turn our attention to wind measurements made by tracking tracers of the wind. To be useful in determining tropospheric winds a tracer must be: prevalant in the troposphere, easy to detect remotely, advected with the winds (at least partially), and inhomgeneously distributed.

Anyone who has watched the sky on a windy day might suggest clouds as an appropriate tracer. The basic approach is to take two images at nearby times. Both visible (day) and infrared window (day or night) channels are appropriate since clouds are readily apparent in such images. Correlations in local regions are calculated and the peak correlation is determined. In practice, this is done by a person matching patterns with the support of a computer. The average wind in this region is simply calculated from the best match (or the peak correlation) and from the time difference between the images. Two types of errors influence the accuracy of winds determined by this technique. First, there are errors in determining the correlation function and locating its peak. These

errors arise from inexact knowledge of Earth location of
the images and noise in the imaged radiances. Careful
instrument design can serve to minimize these errors and
even in current wind measurments these so-called "system
errors" are not believed to be the dominant error source.[12]

The second type of errors are referred to as atmospheric errors and are a consequence of 1) clouds not
tracking the wind, and 2) the inablility to precisely
assign altitudes to cloud-tracked winds. Wind shear, the
changing of wind speed and direction with height, greatly
complicates assigning altitudes to winds determined by
observing only the clouds' tops. Some types of clouds are
not advected with the wind at all and these can be particularly troublesome. Wave clouds are the visible
manifestation of vertically oscillating gravity waves in
the atmosphere. Wave clouds can be recognized by the
regular rows of equally spaced clouds, where the rising
air causes condensation (clouds) and the subsiding motion
results in clear areas. These wave clouds are the result
of topographic forcing by mountains and can often be seen
downwind of the Rocky and Appalachian Mountains. Wind
estimates made by tracking such clouds will be very poor.
There are other types of orographically coupled clouds
that also prevent accurate winds from being estimated.

Despite these difficulties, winds are being routinely
estimated from visible and infrared images obtained from
the GOES satellite. Two visible or 10 μm infrared window images nominally spaced 30 min apart in time are compared. Winds determined from correlating these two images
have an estimated error of 4.7 ms^{-1} at low levels and
8.5 ms^{-1} at upper levels.[12] System errors, which
are the easiest to correct, are a secondary contributor to
the total error.

The atmospheric errors are a more fundamental problem
and are estimated to limit accuracies to 3.5 ms^{-1} at low
levels and 6 ms^{-1} at upper levels. These values probably represent about the best performance that can be
achieved with the current GOES sensors. Improved resolution and a shorter time between images can potentially
result in better performance. The infrared/visible imaging sensor planned for next generation GOES spacecraft
will incorporate these features, allowing shorter
correlation times that will hopefully reduce the wind
errors.

Correctly assigning heights to winds measured by this
technique is a difficult problem. Even when winds are
assigned to the correct altitude, one has a wind vector at
only a single altitude. Another obvious drawback of using
cloud motions to estimate the wind is that winds cannot be

determined in cloud-free areas. Despite these problems, the need for wind data is so great that the winds determined from the current system are finding wide use operationally.

Another tracer that satisfies our basic requirements is water vapor. It is prevalent throughout the troposphere and may be detected in any of a number of infrared bands. At some spatial scales, at least, it is advected by the wind and it is to some extent inhomgeneous. The 6.3 μm water vapor channel on METEOSAT, the European geosynchronous meteorological satellite, has been used to estimate winds.[13] Measurement of winds from water vapor has several advantages and disadvantages as compared with using clouds as tracers. Water vapor is often present in detectable quantities in regions with few or no clouds, thus allowing winds to be determined in these areas. Water vapor patterns are usually not as sharp as cloud patterns. In other words, images from water vapor channels are fuzzy -- they do not have much energy in the higher spatial frequency components. One consequence is that the correlations are more sensitive to noise present in the image.

The estimation of winds by tracking water vapor images is still developing and it has its own problems associated with correctly assigning heights. The next generation U.S. geosynchronous weather satellite will have the capability to simultaneously derive cloud and water vapor tracked winds -- a feature not now present. While the quality of this wind data will certainly fall well short of the 1 ms^{-1} accuracy and 2 km vertical resolution requested by weather forecasters, it will be quite valuable, particularly in oceanic regions where few or no other wind measurements are available.

Active Lidar Remote Sensing

The limitations of atmospheric passive remote sensing has prompted researchers to consider alternatives. Active remote sensing using lidar is one particularly promising approach.

A lidar system consists of a pulsed laser or lasers, transmitting optics, and a receiving system combining a telescope, detector(s), and time-gated electronics. The transmitter and receiver may use separate optics, known as a biaxial system. Other arrangements are possible. For example, by appropriate coupling one could employ a coaxial system in which the transmitter and receiver share the same optics. As with conventional radar, systems such an

approach requires careful isolation of the transmitter and
receiver to prevent damage to sensitive components in the
receiver.

Figure 7 diagrams the principle of lidar atmospheric
measurements. The transmitted laser pulse from a lidar is
propagated through the atmosphere and scattered, absorbed,
or reflected by the various components of the atmosphere
and surface (e.g., clouds, air molecules, aerosols, or the
surface). Some of the scattered or reflected signal is
directed back toward the lidar where it is detected. By
measuring the intensity, polarization, and/or spectral
properties of the return signal as a function of time t,
one can obtain information on the properties of the atmosphere at a distance $ct/2$.

The theoretical vertical resolution is determined by
the lidar pulse duration $\Delta t'$. At any instant the returned signal, assuming the photons are scattered only
once, arises from an atmospheric layer of thickness
$c\Delta t'/2$. It is this capability of a lidar sensor to
probe the atmosphere directly, in a well-defined layer,
that provides the opportunity to remotely sense geo-

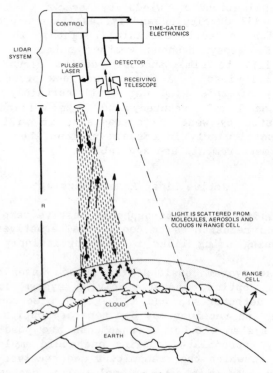

Fig. 7   Principle of lidar measurements.

physical parameters with a vertical resolution unachiev-
able by passive sounders. For example, with a typical
pulse of 50 ns, it is possible to perform measurements
with a vertical resolution of 7.5 m. In practice, it is
usually necessary to integrate the signal over a longer
period of time $\Delta t > \Delta t'$ to obtain an adequate signal-
to-noise ratio. For space applications, the resulting
vertical resolution is typically in the range 100–2000 m
-- still far superior to the vertical resolution
obtainable with most passive sensors.

The Lidar Equation

The theoretical basis of remote sensing with lidar is
embodied in the lidar equation -- the analog of the radiative transfer equation of passive sensing. An analysis of
a simplified form of the lidar equation will provide insight into the measurement opportunities as well as into
the technological challenges of active spaceborne laser
sensors. Assuming that the divergence of the laser beam
is equal to or smaller than the field of view of the receiver and that a detected photon is scattered only once
by the atmosphere, the lidar equation can be written as

$$N_r(\nu',R) = N_t(\nu) \left[\beta(\nu,\nu',R) \ \Delta R \right] (A/R^2) \cdot$$
$$\tau(\nu,R) \ \tau(\nu',R) \ G \tag{4}$$
$$\beta(\nu,\nu',R) = \beta_a(\nu,\nu',R) + \sum_{i=1}^{N} \rho_i(R)\sigma_i(\nu,\nu'R)$$

where $N_t(\nu)$ is the number of photons transmitted by
the laser at frequency ν; $N_r(\nu',R)$ the number of
photons detected by the lidar at frequency ν' from a
layer centered at range R of thickness ΔR;
$\beta_a(\nu,\nu',R)$ the aerosol backscatter coefficient at
range R for photons incident at frequency ν and scattered at ν'; $\rho_i(R)$ the density of gas i;
$\sigma_i(\nu,\nu'R)$ the scattering cross-section of gas i
(incident frequency ν, scattered frequency ν'); the
sum is over the i=1..N gaseous constituents of the atmosphere; A the receiving telescope area; $\tau(\nu,R)$ and
$\tau(\nu',R)$ the transmission from the lidar to range R at
wavelengths ν and ν', respectively; and G a system
calibration term that includes optical losses, detector
efficiencies, field of view mismatches, and other such
factors.

While this equation may seem complex it essentially describes the following process:

The photons of frequency ν produced by the laser $[N_t(\nu)]$ are propagated through the atmosphere and attenuated by it $[\tau(\nu,R)]$ to a layer at range R where they are backscattered by aerosols and molecules with efficiency $[\beta(\nu,\nu',R) \bullet \Delta R]$ at some frequency ν' (ν' may, but does not have to equal ν). These scattered photons are attenuated by the atmosphere on their way back toward the lidar $[\tau(\nu',R)]$ and some fraction is incident on the receiving telescope (A/R^2) where they are detected with efficiency G.

With the exception of the terms G and (A/R^2), atmospheric information is embedded in each of the terms of the lidar equation; this presents the opportunity to determine atmospheric properties.

As may have occurred to the reader, the fact that we find it convenient to measure our signal in terms of photons suggests that our detected signals are quite small. Indeed, of the over 10^{18} photons transmitted in the 1 J pulse of a typical space-based lidar that are scattered by a 1 km layer in the middle atmosphere less than 100 would be detected. This quickly drives many lidar applications to the highest pulse energies, the largest receivers, the highest efficiencies, and the lowest orbits practical. For most space-based lidar applications, what is currently practical falls well short of what is desired. In the future as our capabilities grow, it will be possible to implement lidars with far superior performance to current passive sensors.

A host of techniques have been proposed in the literature to derive atmospheric properties from lidar measurements. Most of these can be understood by a direct examination of Eq. (4). Some of the most significant are described below.

Aerosol Measurements and Visibility. By solving for the aerosol backscatter at one or more frequencies, information on the aerosol content and atmospheric visibility can be obtained. This requires correction for molecular backscatter and for atmospheric transmission.

Doppler Wind Measurements. Movement of aerosols with the wind introduce small Doppler frequency shifts $\Delta\nu = \nu-\nu'$, on the order of 10^{-5} nm in the visible. Hence, from measurements of $\Delta\nu$ along two different directions, the horizontal wind vector can be determined. This assumes that the vertical velocity is negligible -- a good assumption for most situations.

Raman Scattering Measurements. Larger changes in the frequency of the return signal on the order of molecular vibrational and rotational transitions ν_m occur due to the Raman effect. By measuring the returned signal at $\nu' = \nu - \nu_m$ (where ν_m is a vibrational transition of water or a rotational transition of nitrogen or oxygen), it is possible to obtain water vapor densities from $\rho_i(R)$ or temperature profiles from the Raman cross section $\sigma_i(\nu', \nu, R)$. Since the Raman cross section is very small, this method is probably not applicable for space.

Differential Absorption Measurements of Temperature and Constituents. By measuring the returned signal at $\nu' = \nu$, one can obtain information on the transmission properties of the atmosphere $\tau(\nu, R)$. From measurements of the transmission or absorption at a frequency ν that coincides with an atmospheric absorption line, it is possible to retrieve either the mixing ratio of the absorbing species or the temperature. This techinque known as differential absorption lidar (DIAL) is very promising for space application. DIAL variants can also be used to measure pressure.

Flouresence Lidar. Laser-excited flourescence of constituents of the sea surface, land surface, or atmosphere can yield information on composition.

Differential Delay Lidar. The difference in time of flight of a pulse for two wavelengths reflected from the surface can be used to estimate surface pressure. Extremely short pulses and temporal resolution of several nanoseconds are required.

Elastic Scattering Density Lidar. Determination of the total elastic molecular scattered return

$$\sum \rho_i(R)\sigma_i(\nu, \nu', R) \text{ for } \nu = \nu'$$

can yield information on total density, $\sum \rho_i$. Several wavelengths are usually used to eliminate the effects of atmospheric transmission and aerosol scattering.

Other Techniques. This brief list has mentioned only a few of many lidar techniques. For a more complete survey, the reader is referred to the book by Measures.[14] Undoubtedly, the future will see many new approaches put forth and perhaps they will prove superior to the ones we have discovered so far.

In keeping with our theme of temperature, water vapor, and wind retrievals the next two sections will examine in more detail the techniques of Doppler wind sensing and DIAL temperature and water vapor measurements.

Doppler Wind Sensing

Light returned from scatterers in the atmosphere will have a slight wavelength shift caused by the relative velocity (along the incident beam direction) between the scatterers and the lidar. As long as the scatterers are advected by the wind and their random velocities are not so large as to obsure this mean motion, they can be used as tracers. Gas molecules, aerosols (most of which have diameters <1 µm), and cloud water droplets/ice (several µm diameters) are all advected by the wind. The relatively large thermal motions of gas molecules precludes their use in most lidar applications, and so aerosol and cloud backscattering are usually relied on.

The relative motion between the lidar platform and the atmospheric scattering volume can be determined by measuring the wavelength change between the transmitted laser pulse and the backscattered light detected from the atmosphere. The Doppler shifted wavelength is given by

$$\Delta\lambda = 2 \ \lambda_o \ V/c \tag{5}$$

where λ_o is the transmitter wavelength, $\Delta\nu$ the wavelength shift between the received and transmitted wavelength, and V the relative velocity (along the beam path) between the lidar and the scattering medium.

In practice, measuring winds by this method is a difficult task because of several facts:

1) The Doppler shift is extremely small -- a 1 ms^{-1} wind (line-of-sight) results in about 3 x10^{-6} nm shift for a wavelength of 0.5 µm.

2) The spacecraft velocity and Earth rotation also contribute to the Doppler shift. This velocity must be determined to a high accuracy which places stringent requirements on instrument pointing knowledge.

3) The aerosol backscattered signal is often quite small (particularly in the altitude range of 5-12 km where winds are very important) and at some wavelengths is dwarfed by the much stronger molecular backscattered signal.

Two basic approaches have evolved to cope with these problems. The first approach uses heterodyne detection to measure the frequency shift between the received signal and a reference (local) oscillator. The second approach uses a high resolution interferometer to measure the frequencies of the transmitted and received signals.

In the remainder of this section we will focus two systems currently being developed using the above approaches:

1) A 10 μm wind sensor using a transverse excited atmospheric (TEA) CO_2 laser and heterodyne detection.

2) A 0.5 μm wind sensor using a Fabry-Perot interferometer (FPI), multichannel ring detector, and a frequency-doubled single longitudinal mode (SLM) neodymium:YAG (ytrium aluminum garnet) laser.

10 μm Heterodyne Lidar Wind Sensor. Probably the most well-developed lidar wind sensors are those based on pulsed CO_2 TEA lasers that determine the Doppler shift by heterodyne detection. The basic idea is to superpose the Doppler shifted backscattered return with a reference or local-oscillator beam on a square-law detector. Optically mixing the two beams in this way causes a detector output signal with frequency equal to the difference between the return and reference frequencies. By determining this beat frequency, the Doppler shift can be found.

CO_2 TEA lasers are a good choice for this application for several reasons. First, CO_2 TEA lasers are capable of producing high pulse energies (several joules) at good efficiencies (5-10%). Second, several techniques have been developed to produce the extremely narrow-band and stable pulses required for Doppler wind sensing. Third, CO_2 TEA lasers can be discretely tuned in the range 9-11 μm, which falls inside the atmospheric infrared "window" of 8-12 μm. Finally, high bandwidth detectors of reasonable quantum efficiencies are available for the heterodyne detection of the return signal.

The transmitting laser and the local oscillator lasers must both be stable to better than the frequency shift corresponding to the desired wind accuracy: a 1 m/s wind results in a 200 kHz Doppler shift at 10 μm. Such a requirement is stringent, but has been demonstrated in both ground-based[15] and airborne systems.[16]

The principal components of a typical CO_2 Doppler lidar are shown in Fig. 8. A low-pressure CO_2 laser cell is incorporated in the same resonator cavity as the atmospheric pressure CO_2 TEA laser cell. By running the laser (with only the low-pressure cell pumped) in continuous wave (CW) mode, one can control precisely the frequency of operation when the TEA cell is pumped and the high energy pulse is produced. Local servoloops are used to stabilize and offset the transmitter laser and the

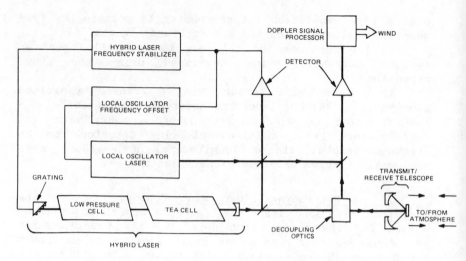

Fig. 8   Schematic of a CO_2 lidar Doppler wind sensor.

local oscillator (also a CW low-pressure CO_2 laser) relative to each other. The high-energy pulse is transmitted through special decoupling optics designed to isolate the received and transmitted pulses, and then out through the transmitting optics. The same telescope is also used to receive the return signal. The return signal is then optically mixed with the local oscillator beam on the primary detector. A signal processor determines the Doppler shift.

While 10 μm heterodyne lidar wind sensor has reached a high level of technological development, a key question concerns the atmospheric scattering efficiency at this wavelength. "Clear" atmospheric scattering at 10 μm is due almost exclusively to aerosols. While a comprehensive climatology of 10 μm backscatter has yet to be developed, measurements made to date indicate a large range of variability. Indications are that a space-based CO_2 wind sensor might not be able to measure winds over extensive regions due to insufficient atmospheric backscattering.

Because of the questions concerning atmospheric backscatter at 10 μm, Doppler lidars operating at shorter wavelengths are being considered -- wavelengths where the backscatter is better documented, larger in magnitude, and less variable than at 10 μm. One such system, now being developed at Stanford University, is based on a 1.06 μm Nd:YAG laser (referred to as the 1 μm wind sensor) that also determines winds using heterodyne detection.[17] Another system operating near 0.5 μm using a frequency-

doubled Nd:YAG laser and employing direct detection will
be discussed in the next section.

0.5 µm FPI Lidar Wind Sensor. The Fabry-Perot interferometer (FPI) based wind lidar system[18] is a natural
evolution of the passive Doppler wind sensor mentioned
previously. The heart of the detection system for this
sensor is a FPI.

A FPI consists of two parallel, partially reflecting
plates separated by a distance d. Multiple reflections of
the incident light between the two reflecting surfaces
produce constructive interference for wavelengths satisfying the condition

$$ndcos\theta = \frac{m\lambda}{2} \qquad \text{for } m = \pm1, \pm2, \ldots \qquad (6)$$

where n is the refractive index of the FPI cavity, d the
separation between the plates, and θ the incident angle
of the light. While the wavelength of incident light could
be determined by varying the index of refraction n or
spacer distance d, these methods require moving parts. For
Doppler wind sensors, the preferred approach is to determine the angle θ of peak transmission with an image plane
detector. This approach has the advantage of not requiring
any moving parts.

The basic principle of the FPI detector system is
shown in Fig. 9. The Doppler shifted backscatter radiation is collected by a telescope and relayed to the FPI.
The light incident on the FPI is of wavelength $\lambda = \lambda_0 + \Delta\lambda$
and is distributed over a range of angles $0 \leq \theta \leq \theta_{max}$,
where θ_{max} is determined by the properties of the telescope and relay optics. Only those angles satisfying the
Eq. (5) will be transmitted by the FPI (see Fig. 9a).
Ring-shaped detectors corresponding to several angles
$\theta_1 \ldots \theta_n$ are used to determine the incident wavelength by determining the channel (i.e., angle) with the
maximum signal. This detection function is performed by a
microchannel plate detector with a 12 ring segmented anode.
The detector is essentially an imaging photomultiplier.
Figure 9b shows the measured signal in each of the twelve
channels of the FPI for the outgoing pulse and returned
signal. From the shift in the distribution of the measured signal over the 12 channels, one can determine the
wavelength shift, and hence the line-of-sight velocity.

The transmitter of such a wind sensor uses a pulsed
narrow-band frequency doubled Nd:YAG laser transmitting
0.53 µm. It is required that the spectral width of the

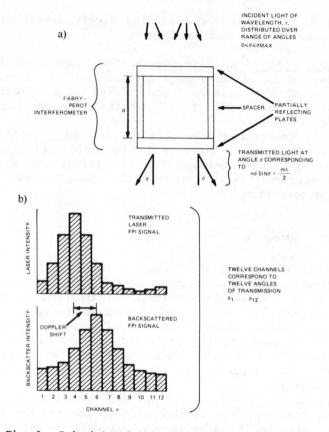

Fig. 9   Principle of lidar wind measurements with a FPI.

laser line be comparable to the FPI resolution and the aerosol scattering width. Construction of such a laser, while possible, is a difficult undertaking, particularly for the high pulse energies required in most lidar applications. Special techniques must be employed to insure that the laser will transmit a single mode only. In practice, these techniques complicate the system and reduce its efficiency.

Comparison of Lidar Wind Sensing Alternatives. Table 3 compares some of the 0.5 and 10 μm lidar wind-sensing approaches. From an overall system technological development standpoint, the 10 μm wind sensor is more advanced. Ground-based[15] and airborne demonstrations[16] have been made of the 10 μm wind sensor, while the 0.5 μm system is currently undergoing laboratory test and evaluation.[18]   A very similar detector to the one proposed

Table 3 Comparison of lidar wind sensor approaches

Feature	10 μm wind sensor	0.5 μm wind sensor
Overall technological development	Ground and air demonstrations	Ground-based system under development, similar FPI detection sytem flown in space
Laser efficiency	5-10%	0.1-1% (could increase to 5-10% with diode pumping)
Atmospheric backscatter	Low, variable, and uncertain	Higher, less variable, and better documented
Daytime operation	Same performance as at night -- no special designs needed	Rejection of scattered solar light requires addition of two narrow-band etalons
Eye safety	Eye safety requirements easily met	Transmit beam may have to be expanded larger than ideal in some applications
Ancillary measurements	10 μm aerosol backscatter coefficient	0.5 μm aerosol backscatter coefficient, atmospheric density (5-15+ km)

for the 0.5 μm sensor, however, has been flown in space on the Dynamics Explorer Spacecraft.[10]

The tradeoff between laser efficiency and atmospheric scattering efficiency has already been mentioned and must await further study. Daytime operation and eye safety are somewhat more easily accommodated with the 10 μm system, but they are not a major concern for the alternative system either. One advantage of the 0.5 μm system is that without major modification it could also be used to determine atmospheric density in the altitude region of 5-15 km or more.

A comparison between the 1 and 10 μm heterodyne wind sensor approaches is given in Ref. 17. It is shown that for a fixed signal-to-noise ratio, the wind error for a heterodyne system operating at 1 μm is 3 to 10 times smaller than for a 10 μm system. The 1 μm system development has so far concentrated on the laser transmitter, a long-pulse SLM slab-geometry Nd:YAG laser.

Which of these approaches will prove itself best for space application is uncertain. More technological development is needed, particularly for the 0.5 and 1 μm systems, before a thorough, in-depth comparison based on experimentally proven performance can be made.

Differential Absorption Lidar

In Doppler wind sensing the geophysical information is obtained from the spectral distribution of the aerosol backscatter term, $\beta_a(\nu,\nu',R)$ in Eq. (4). The technique of differential absoprtion lidar,[19] on the other hand, obtains its information via the atmospheric transmission terms $\tau(\nu,R)$ and $\tau(\nu',R)$. Elastic scattering (from aerosols and molecules) or surface reflections (diffuse or specular) can be used; the condition $\nu \simeq \nu'$ generally holds for these processes.

The basic goal of DIAL is to determine the absorption in an atmospheric layer due to a single spectral line. The DIAL applications discussed here transmit a pulse corresponding to the center of an absorption line. The absorption due to a single line at line center depends on three quantities: the mixing ratio of the absorber, the temperature, and the total pressure. Throughout most of the troposphere, where spectral line broadening is dominated by molecular collisions, the dependence on pressure can be neglected. Two possible DIAL strategies can now be seen:

1)   By selecting a spectral line where the dependence on temperature is small, the mixing ratio of the absorbing gas can be determined.[20]

2)   Temperature can be measured by selecting a spectral line of absorbing gas with a constant mixing ratio and a high sensivity to temperature.[21]

To determine the absorption due to a single spectral line, the effects of all other lines and gases, as well as the dependence of the return signal on the total scattering, must be eliminated. This is accomplished by transmitting laser pulses at two frequencies. The first frequency corresponds to the center of an absorption line. The second is in a nearby spectral region of only background absorption.

These two frequencies are referred to as the on-line and off-line pulses, respectively. Let N_{ri} and N_{ro} be the detected signals at the on-line and off-line frequencies respectively. Under the assumption that the background absorption (i.e., the absorption due to all causes except the single spectral line of interest) and the backscatter are equal at the two frequencies, one may write

$$\tau'(R,R+\Delta R') = \left(\frac{N_{ri}(R) \cdot N_{ro}(R+\Delta R')}{N_{ro}(R) \cdot N_{ri}(R+\Delta R')}\right)^{1/2} \qquad (7)$$

where $\tau'(R,R+\Delta R')$ is the one-way transmission through the layer R to $R+\Delta R'$ due only to the absorption line. A knowledge of the physics of the spectral line absorption can be used to obtain properties of the layer R to $R+\Delta R'$.

Figure 10 illustrates the principle of these measurement strategies. The normalized absorption for three selected lines in the 720 nm region is shown. The line on the left has a negative dependence of absorption on temperature, while the one in the center has a positive dependence. It can be seen that the effect of temperature extends throughout the line, but that it is strongest at the center. The residual absorption shown in the line wings is due to the sum of the wing absorption arising from all of the lines in the band. The spectral line shown on the right has a temperature dependence near zero. Such a line would be selected for the determination of absorber mixing ratio.

A third strategy consists of simultaneously determining both the temperature and absorber amounts. Use of two on-line/off-line pairs permits the simultaneous measurement of both these parameters. Actually, only three frequencies are needed since the same off-line frequency can be used for the calibration of both on-line signals.

Consideration of the error sensitivity of the three-frequency approach lead to the following criteria for the

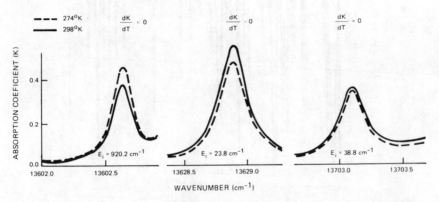

Fig. 10   Temperature variation of absorption for three water vapor lines.

selection of the two spectral lines:[22],[23]

1) There should be reasonable absorption within the layer, but not so much as to highly attenuate the signal (and hence decrease the signal-to-noise ratio).

2) The absorption at the two lines should be roughly equal.

3) The difference in rotational ground-state energy of the two absorption lines should be high.

Figure 11 shows the transmission for a region of water vapor absorption around 10770 cm^{-1} (about 930 nm). Two lines that roughly satisfy the previous criteria are denoted and a spectral region suitable for an off-line pulse is also shown. Figure 12 shows a simulated measured return at each of these frequencies for a space-based three-frequency DIAL system with characteristics as shown in Table 4. The off-line pulse does not undergo significant absorption and consequently the return signal increases nearer the surface where both molecular and aerosol backscatter increase. The return at the two on-line frequencies is attenuated as the ground is approached. Ideally, the absorption of the two on-line pulses would be identical. The lines selected represent a compromise between the previously discussed line selection criteria.

Below 6 km, the proposed system would do quite well, meeting or exceeding the requirements for both water vapor

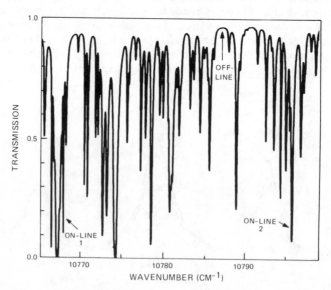

Fig. 11   Transmission through a 2 km layer (midlatitude profile) for spectral region near 10770 cm^{-1}.

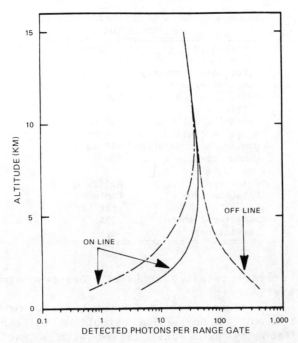

Fig. 12   Simulated return for the two on-line and one off-line frequencies noted in Fig. 14.

and temperature for global forecasting and climate. At altitudes above 6 km, there is insufficient water vapor (and hence insufficient absorption) to permit accurate measurements. The temperature in this region could be obtained by selecting a stronger pair of absorption lines or by using a two-frequency DIAL system based on O_2 lines.[21]

DIAL systems require laser lines almost as narrow and stable as those for wind sensing. In addition, they must be precisely tunable; that is, one must be able to select the transmission frequencies to precisely match the desired spectral lines.

Most current DIAL systems in this spectral region use tunable dye lasers. Such dye lasers are not well suited for space applications. Their overall efficiency is quite low, less then 0.1%. The liquid dye is the most serious problem, because of its volatility and the requirement that it flow at a high rate to ensure continued laser operation. An additional complication is the requirement for another laser source to pump the dye, usually a doubled neodymium-based solid-state laser.

For this reason other tunable lasers suitable for space application are being actively developed at govern-

Table 4   DIAL system characteristics
           for simulation

Parameter	Value
Pulse energy (for each frequency)	100 mJ
Receiver area	1 m^2
Optical system efficiency	50%
Operating altitude	300 km
Range resolution	2 km
Horizontal resolution	250 km
Number of pulses averaged	350
Pointing	Nadir, fixed
Detector type	Photomultiplier
Detector quantum efficiency	7.5%

ment and private research centers. Two promising possibilities are:

1) A frequency-doubled Nd:glass laser (with tunability of about 20 nm) whose output is shifted to the desired frequency by a cell filled with a gas at high pressure[24] (the frequency shifting occurs due to the stimulated Raman effect). Through various combinations of gases and harmonic generators, a number of spectral regions can be reached. Figure 13 shows how several gases and two types of Nd:glass lasers can be used to reach different parts of the spectral region 13000-14000 cm^{-1} -- a region appropriate for DIAL measurements of temperature, water vapor, and pressure.

2) A system based on a relatively new solid-state laser material, Alexandrite.[25] Alexandrite is continuously tunable in the 0.7-0.8 μm spectral region and has the potential of providing an all solid-state source that is both compact and long lived. Several issues concerning efficiency and damage thresholds must be resolved for this potential to be realized.

Much more research and development is needed to determine if one of these approaches, or other more recent developments (such a new solid-state laser based on the material titanium sapphire), or other yet to be discovered systems prove themselves superior for space-based DIAL measurements.

Opportunities for Spaceborne Lidar

System Concept Considerations

From a theoretical point of view, spaceborne active laser sensors provide the opportunity to measure geophys-

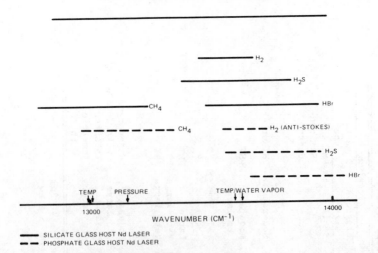

Fig. 13   Tunability region for a Raman laser system based on Nd:glass lasers incorporating two types of glass hosts (silicate and phosphate) and several Raman-active gases.

ical parameters with an accuracy and spatial resolution that cannot be obtained with passive systems. However, implementing space-based operational laser systems for atmospheric probing presents an enormous challenge to instrument builders, spacecraft designers, and cost-orientated program planners. The sophisticated systems that are being proposed for measuring winds, humidity, pressure, and temperature, or even simple laser systems for aerosol probing are heavier, larger, require more power, and are more expensive than the current passive sounders. For example: the TIROS/HIRS infrared temperature sounder requires 25 W power, weighs 34 kg, and has 20 cm diameter optics. An active DIAL system for temperature measurements will require more than 5 kW of power, 100 cm diameter optics, and the weight of the system will be greater than 100 kg (even with lightweighted optics). The cost of a HIRS-type instrument is about $2M, while the cost of an operational DIAL system is estimated to be about 20 times greater.

Table 5 lists the general lidar/spacecraft system requirements to measure a variety of atmospheric parameters with space-based lidar. With the exception of measurements from hard targets and clouds, most measurements require powers of several kilowatts and scanning telescopes of 1 m or larger in diameter to obtain global data with the required accuracy and resolution.

Some of the challenges of Doppler lidars for wind measurements have already been mentioned. These systems

Table 5　Lidar system requirements to measure various parameters

Measurement type	Laser frequencies				Power required[b]	Receiver	
	#	Spectral region	Tunability	Stability/ linewidth[a]		Telescope size[c]	Detector type[d]
Hard target returns (e.g. cloud-top height, sea state, extinction)	1	UV to IR	No	Not critical	Low	Small	PMT and Semiconductor
Aerosol scattering	1+	UV to IR	No	Not critical	Moderate	Moderate	PMT or APD
Density (upper atmos. density/ temperature)	2	UV and near-IR	No	Not critical	Moderate to high	Moderate to large	PMT
DIAL							
Water vapor	2	near IR	Yes	Critical	High	Large	PMT
Temperature	2	near IR	Yes	Critical	Very high	Very large	PMT
Temp./H_2O	3	near IR	Yes	Critical	Very high	Very large	PMT
Doppler wind							
coherent	1	Infrared	No	Very critical	Moderate[e] to high	Moderate[e] to large	Heterodyne with HgCdTe
Direct	1	Visible	No	Very critical	Moderate[f] to high	Moderate[f] to large	Interferometric with FPI

(a) Not critical $> 10^{-3}$ nm; critical 10^{-3} to 10^{-4} nm; very critical $< 10^{-4}$ nm.
(b) Low < 0.2 kW; moderate 0.2 to 1 kW; high 1 to 5 kW; very high > 5 kW.
(c) Moderate < 0.5 m diameter; large 0.5 to 1 m; very large > 1 m.
(d) PMT = photomultiplier tube; APD = avalanche photodiode.
(e) Wind measurements from cloud-top returns.
(f) Wind measurements from "clear" mid-troposphere to lower statosphere.

require stable, narrow spectral bandwidth lasers, operating at 1 J/pulse in the visible or 10 J/pulse in the infrared. The systems must operate at 10 Hz for 10^8 shots or more. Developing lasers with these specifications, qualifying them for space application, integrating them with receiving telescopes, and maintaining a bore sight alignment of several microradians for the duration of the mission is an enormous task for instrument designers.

From a spacecraft point of view, three of the major issues to be addressed are 1) the large power consumption of lidar systems; 2) the high heat dissipation (85-95% or even more of the lidar input power goes to waste heat); and 3) the alignment and stability of large scanning optics greater than 1 m in diameter.

Clearly, the current remote sensing satellites were not designed to fly large lidar sensors. At best they can accommodate small lidar systems for technological evaluation and proof-of-concept demonstration. The implementation of operational spaceborne lidar sensors will probably be done in an evolutionary manner. Simple lidar systems that do not require lasers of high spectral purity and high stability can be flown on the current operational meteorological satellites, in addition to their currently planned sensor payloads. The measurement capabilities of such systems is limited to cloud-top heights, aerosol backscatter coefficients, extinction, and surface albedo. Larger and more sophisticated lidars for humidity and wind measurements require dedicated satellites with modified power systems. Technological developments in the lidar systems themselves are also required. Temperature profiling on an operational basis with the required accuracy of about 1 K is probably the most difficult measurement. Such systems require large amounts of power (greater than 5 kW) which will be available on the polar platform of the space station.

Several feasibility studies of spaceborne lidar systems have been performed and they will be summarized in this section, together with a brief review of the current plans to fly laser sensors.

Shuttle Lidar Studies

The Space Shuttle integrated with the Spacelab can be considered as an ideal platform on which to demonstrate the atmospheric probing capabilities of lidar sensors. It has the capability to accommodate relatively heavy, large, and power-consuming instruments. The moderate orbit altitude (200-300 km) results in a returned signal power 7 to

16 times that from an identical system at the 800 km altitude typical of most polar-orbiting meteorological satellites. The instruments are reusable and mission specialists aboard the Shuttle can assist in operating the system.

Shuttle Atmospheric Lidar Multi-User Instrument System. With these factors in mind, in 1977 NASA convened an international study group of scientists and engineers to develop concepts for an atmospheric Shuttle lidar system and related experiments.[26] The study group suggested developing a Shuttle atmospheric lidar multi-user instrument system (sometimes referred to as the Shuttle lidar facility) and recommended performing 26 experiments. A list of these experiments is given in Table 6. A system definition study of this instrument was performed by General Electric for NASA.[27] The study recommended developing a modular facility capable of performing the entire set of 26 candidate experiments. The baseline system occupies a complete Spacelab pallet, weighs 1300 kg, and uses up to 3000 W of power. The instruments consist of two 1.25 m diameter telescopes and can accommodate a 2 J frequency-doubled Nd:YAG laser, tunable dye lasers pumped by the Nd:YAG lasers, and CW and pulsed CO_2 lasers. This ambitious program met with serious budgetary and technological obstacles and did not proceed towards hardware development.

Laser In Space Technology Experiment. A scaled-down version of the Shuttle lidar facility is now being contemplated by NASA's Office of Advanced Space Technology.[28] The program known by the acronym LITE (for laser in space technology experiement) will be managed by NASA's Langley Research Center.

The envisioned lidar system transmitter is composed of a frequency-doubled and -tripled Nd:YAG laser producing pulses of 0.4 J at 0.53 μm and 0.15 J at 0.353 μm with a 10 Hz repetition rate. The receiver is a 0.5 m diameter nadir viewing telescope. The main objectives of this program are to demonstrate operation of an automated lidar system in space and to perform limited measurements of cloud-top heights and aerosols. This lidar will be able to perform the first six experiments of Table 6. This low-cost system employs available technology and could be flown on the Space Shuttle as early as 1988.

Lidar Sensors on Operational Meteorological Spacecraft

Recognizing the limited time a lidar can operate on a Shuttle mission, researchers have started to explore the

Table 6 Proposed experiments for the Shuttle
lidar facility

Experiment	Wavelength region
Cloud-top heights	530/1060 nm
Profiles of tropospheric Clouds and aerosols	530/1060 nm
Cirrus ice/water discrimination	530 nm
Profiles of nocluticent and circumpolar particulte layers	530 nm
Earth surface albedo	530/1060 nm
Stratospheric aerosol backscatter profiles	530/1060 nm
Alkalai atom density profiles	589/671/770 nm
Ionospheric metal ion distributions	280 nm and other resonance Lines
Water vapor profiles	Two, near 720 or 940 nm
Atmospheric gas species content -- IR ground and cloud returns	Two, in the 9-11 μm range
Chemical release diagnostics	Several in the 400-600 nm range
Stratospheric ozone profiles	Two in the 265-400 nm range
Upper atmospheric trace species content using two satellite occultation	Two, in the 9-11 μm range
Sodium temperature and winds	589 nm
Surface and cloud-top pressure	Two near 760 nm
Tropospheric pressure profiles	Two near 760 nm
Temperature profiles (troposphere to tropopause)	Two near 760 nm
Range-resolved constituent profiles (IR DIAL)	Two in the 9-11 μm range
Cloud-top winds	250-1100 nm or 9-11 μm
Aerosol winds (ground to 30 km)	350-1100 nm or 9-11 μm
OH-density profiles (35-100 km)	~300 nm
Metallic atom, ion, and oxide profiles	280, 285, and 500 nm
Tropospheric NO_2	442 and 448 nm
Stratospheric aerosol composition	9-11 μm
NO density profiles (70 to 150 km)	215-227 nm
Atomic oxygen profiles (florescence lidar)	225 nm transmit, 844.9 nm receive

possibility of flying lidar sensors on operational meteorological spacecraft -- sometimes known as free-flyers. A
detailed study on the feasibility of flying a CO_2 Doppler wind sensor on a dedicated Advanced TIROS-N satellite
has been performed by RCA Astro-Electronics[29] for the
NOAA's Wave Propagation Laboratory. This concept of a
spaceborne global wind monitoring system is known in the
remote sensing community as WINDSAT and was conceived at
NOAA's Wave Propogation Laboratory.[30] The basic
results of the RCA study were that a slightly modified
TIROS-N satellite bus can carry a wind sensor and perform
wind measurements for a period of 2 years. Unfortunately,
budget reductions forced NOAA to stop all WINDSAT activities in fiscal year 1985.

Two studies of space-based lidar systems with reduced
capabilities are now underway. One study is focusing on
accommodating a Nd:YAG-laser based lidar system on a meteorological satellite. The lidar would fly as an add-on
experimental sensor in addition to the planned operational
payload of the host satellite. The proposed lidar is a
nadir-viewing, low-power system capable of cloud and aerosol measurements. In addition, it will provide both
essential atmospheric statistics and engineering experience to aid in the design of the next generation of fully
operational lidars.

The other study,[31] sponsored by the European
Space Agency (ESA) and conducted by the Battelle Institute
in Frankfurt, FRG, considered flying a scanning cloud/
aerosol lidar based on an Alexandrite laser. A host
vehicle for this medium power lidar has not been assigned
at this time.

Long range NASA planning envisions a large intergated
spacebased Earth Observing System,[32] known as EOS,
that will likely be flown on the polar-orbiting platforms
of the space station complex. The current strawman payload of EOS includes two lidar sensors: a Doppler wind
sensing lidar and a lidar atmospheric sounder and altimeter.

WINDSAT - A Global Wind Monitoring System. Simulation
studies employing state-of-the-art atmospheric circulation
models have indicated that more accurate wind data can
improve substantially the skill of mediumand long-range
weather forecasts. Ground-based[15] and airborne[16]
Doppler wind sensors using CO_2 lasers and heterodyne
detection techniques have been developed by NOAA's Wave
Propogation Laboratory and NASA's Marshall Space Flight
Center. NOAA has also initiated studies on the feasibility of flying a spaceborne global wind monitoring

system. A study performed by Lockheed[33] indicated that space-based Doppler lidars imposed very severe demands on the host spacecraft. Lockheed determined that a fully operational CO_2 Doppler wind sensor could only be accommodated on the Space Shuttle or a newly designed dedicated satellite with capabilities similar to those of the Shuttle. However, a recent study by RCA Astro,[29] with the support of Mathematical Sciences North West and the Perkin-Elmer Company, has shown that by relaxing the mission requirements and using lightweighting technologies, the system can be accommodated on a slightly modified version of the Advanced TIROS-N satellite.

The envisioned lidar for WINDSAT consists of a CO_2 laser transmitter, a diffraction-limited scanning telescope, a radiatively cooled HgCdTe detector using heterodyne detection, and an onboard signal processor. The characteristics of the system are summarized in Table 7.

The system can be accommodated on an Advanced Tiros-N satellite with some modifications. The most important changes are: increasing the solar array size by 25%; constructing the key elements of the lidar (including the optical bench and the primary mirror) with honeycombed beryllium; mounting of all attitude sensors on the optical

Table 7   Characteristics of advanced
TIROS-N lidar wind sensor

Parameter	Value
Power:	
Lidar	559 W
Spacecraft bus[a]	229 W
Total	788 W
Weight	1915 kg
Data rate:	
Primary instrument	960 bps
Instrument support	1063 bps
Spacecraft housekeeping	670 bps
Total	2693 bps
Orbit	Sun-synchronous, Polar, 833 km altitude
Telescope aperture	1.25 m
Laser:	
Pulse energy	10 Jolues
Pulse repetition rate	2 Hz
Scanning modes	(1) Continuous conical scan (2) Stop-stare
Signal processing	On-board Doppler processor

[a]For a sun angle of 5 deg.

bench; and strengthening the structure to carry the 470 kg lidar load at the end of the spacecraft. The operational configuration of the spacecraft and the lidar are shown in Fig. 14.

Extensive simulation studies have been performed by NOAA to assess the measurement capability of this system. The major atmospheric parameter that affects the performance of the system is the aerosol backscatter coefficient β_a. Unfortunately, a comprehensive global climatatology of β_a in the 10.6 μm region does not exist. Conservative estimates of β_a indicate that for altitudes between 1 and 20 km under most conditions, the rms errors for the along- and cross-track wind vectors would be 1-2 and 1-5 ms^{-1}, respectively. These results are for a horizontal resolution of 300 x 300 km and a vertical resolution of 1 km.

Although the design has a weight margin of 187 kg, the sensor requires the entire 560 W of available payload power. Thus, a dedicated satellite is required for a wind sensor. This, of course, increased the estimated budget of the project. At this time, NOAA has decided to discontinue the WINDSAT activity.

A Free-flyer Lidar for Atmospheric Scattering Measurements. Recognizing the long-range potential of spaceborne lidar to measure atmospheric propoerties,

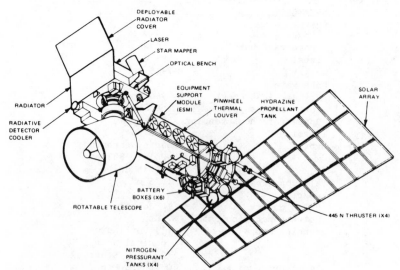

Fig. 14   Operational configuration for CO_2 wind sensor on a modified Advanced TIROS-N satellite. (From Ref. 29, copyright © 1984 Optical Society of America. Used with permission.)

consideration has been given to flying a scaled-down lidar
on a polar orbiting meteorological satellite. An initial
study, performed jointly by RCA, Itek, and Professors J.
Reagan and B. Herman of the University of Arizona, has
developed a conceptual design for this lidar and analyzed
its measurement capabilities. The proposed lidar is a
self-contained, single package that could be mounted on
the Earth-facing panel of a polar orbiting spacecraft.
The structure of the proposed lidar is shown in Fig. 15.

The characteristics of the lidar are summarized in
Table 8. The instrument is based on a Nd:YAG laser that
is frequency-doubled, producing 1 J pulses at 1.064 μm
and 0.532 μm with a repetition rate of 10-20 pulses/min.
The receiving system consists of a fixed nadir-viewing
0.5 m lightweight Dall-Kirkham telescope and two optical
channels: a narrow field-of-view channel for daytime
operation, and a wide field-of-view channel for nighttime
operation. A bifurcated "hole" mirror at the focal plane
of the telescope seperates the two channels. Each optical
channel consists of two photomultipliers (one each for
0.53 and 1.06 μm) and appropriate filters. This two-
channel design avoids the need for moving parts in the
receiving telescope and eliminates single-point failures
in the detector system.

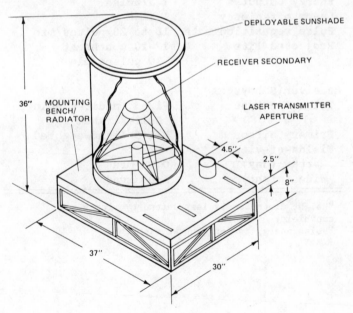

Fig. 15   Structure of a free-flyer lidar.

Table 8   Characteristics of a free-flyer
lidar sounder

Parameter	Value
Overall system	
Input power	120 W
Size[a]	0.75w x 0.951 x 0.22h m
Height	
To secondary	0.65 m
To sunshield	0.91 m (deployed)
Weight	74 kg
Transmitter subsystem	
Laser Type	Solid-state Nd:YAG with frequency doubler
Wavelengths	1064 and 532 nm
Energy output[b]	1 J/pulse
Laser effeciency	1.1%
Pulse repetition rate	10 to 20 pulses/min
Projected life	12-20 months at 10 pulses/min
Receiver Subsystem	
Telescope type	Fixed, nadir-viewing, Dall-Kirkham
Primary Mirror	F/1.5 lightweighted
Fields-of-view	
Narrow (day)	0.05 mrad
Wide (night)	5.0 mrad

[a]Height dimension is less secondary mirror and sunshield.
[b]Pulse energy is for each wavelength.

A variety of parameters can be measured by this lidar, including aerosol and total backscatter, surface spectral reflectivity, cloud-top heights, and atmospheric transmission. One interesting area requiring further study is the possibility of inferring sea state from the reflectivity of the ocean (sea state is closely related to surface winds). Cloud-top heights are of interest by themselves, but they may also be of particular value when used in conjunction with passive temperature sounders. It must be noted that the operational use of these measurements will be somewhat limited by the nonscanning nadir-viewing configuration and low pulse repetition rate of the free-flyer lidar. Nevertheless, the all-season, global measurement of atmospheric scattering at these wavelengths would be an important demonstration of the measurement capabilities of lidars.

The European Orbiting Lidar. A conceptual design study of a simple lidar sytem, to be flown on a future observational satellite (800 km orbit), has been performed by the Battelle Institute in Frankfurt for the European Space Agency (ESA).[31] The general approach calls for a modular design that can be enhanced in several stages, the long-term objective being to develop a DIAL system for humidity and temperature measurements. In the first stage, it is considered to fly a simple lidar system, mainly for cloud-top height and aerosol measurements, with limited coverage capabilities.

The system is based on a tunable solid-state laser, operating in the region between 0.7 to 0.8 μm, with a pulse energy of 1 J at 10 Hz. Candidate lasers are Alexandrite, Emerald, chromium-doped GSGG, or GGG. The receiver consists of a 60 cm diameter, horizontally mounted Newtonian telescope, and a photomultiplier with a GaAs photocathode. One scanning arrangement being considered consists of a flat mirror rotating at 10 rotations/min around an axis 45 deg from the nadir in the along-track direction tilted 8.7 deg to this axis. While not providing complete global coverage, this limited scanning capability is a considerable improvement over nonscanning configurations.

The main reason for selecting a tunable laser in the infrared region is that such a laser could potentially be upgraded for DIAL measurements: a major objective for future lidar missions. To keep the power consumption of the transmitter at a 500 W level the design calls for a tunable laser with 2% wall-plug efficiency. A tunable laser with this efficiency is not available at this time.

The ESA/Battelle study is continuing with the major objectives of selecting a candidate host spacecraft and identifying technology development requirements.

Earth Observing System. NASA is currently developing plans to meet the observational and data system requirements of a wide variety of Earth science research,[32] ranging from plate tectonic studies to investigations of the CO_2 greenhouse effect. In formulating its plans, NASA has recognized the multidisciplinary nature of many, if not most, of these problems. The solution proposed by NASA is an integrated environmental observation and data system named the Earth Observing System (EOS). EOS is meant to complement and enhance currently planned operational and research satellite missions: such as the operational satellites NOAA, GOES, and N-ROSS; and the research satellites UARS, TOPEX, and GRM. While EOS is intended primarily as a research tool, it has great potential for augmenting the capabilities of our operational meteorological satellites.

A strawman payload for EOS has been proposed that, in addition to a variety of passive sensors, includes five active sensors: two lidars and three active microwave sensors. The first lidar sensor, the lidar atmospheric sounder and altimeter (LASA), is part of a comprehensive surface imaging and sounding package. The second lidar, a Doppler wind sensor, is part of an atmospheric physical and chemical monitoring package.

The prime mission of LASA is to measure the distribution of water vapor to aid in understanding the global hydrological cycle. This application requires a horizontal resolution in the range 10-100 km and a vertical resolution of about 1 km. Additionally, LASA will measure aerosol distribution, temperature profiles, and profiles of trace gases and pollutants (e.g., NO_2 and SO_2). With suitable processing it is planned to also use LASA as an altimeter for geologic studies. Constituents and temperature would likely be determined by a DIAL technique. To accomplish its full set of measurement goals, an extremely complex multifrequency tunable laser is required.

The goals of EOS's Doppler lidar is to provide wind profiles twice daily at a horizontal resolution of about 200 km and a vertical resolution of 1 km. The Doppler wind sensing approach for this sensor has yet to be decided. All three Doppler lidar systems mentioned in this paper -- the 0.5 μm FPI system, and the 1.06 and the 10 μm heterodyne systems -- are potential candidates.

EOS would be a valuable tool, not only in Earth science research -- its primary purpose -- but also in operational meteorology. The prospects for EOS are closely tied to the development of satellites with the abilities to meet the needs of its sophisticated sensors. One promising host vehicle is the polar platform of the space station. The first flight for this polar platform is planned for sometime in the 1990's. Given sufficient technological development in lidar systems and adequate funding, EOS may well be the first true demonstration of the potential of full-scale lidar sensors.

Conclusions

Lidar investigations performed to date -- both theoretical analyses and experimental measurements with ground- and air-based systems -- clearly indicate the great potential of lidar to provide high-quality global environmental data. Such data will not only have a profound impact on the skill of weather forecasting, but will also enhance our understanding of chemical and physical processes in the atmosphere. Careful planning is required to minimize the cost and risk in flying operational lidar sensors in space, both in the targeting of research and development efforts and in the selection of lidar missions.

In the sensor area, a key driver of the system is the laser transmitter. The development of single axial mode stable lasers, operating at several joules per pulse, for more than 10^9 shots, with high wall-plug efficiency is crucial for flying a Doppler wind sensor. Accommodating spaceborne DIAL systems for pressure, temperature, and humidity measurements requires the development of solid-state tunable lasers, also with narrow spectral bandwidths, long lifetimes, and high efficiencies. Low-noise detectors with high quantum efficiencies and narrow-band filters are also areas that require further work.

The development of diode pumping holds great promise for improving the efficiency and lifetime of those lidar systems based on neodymium host lasers (which includes many of the proposed wind- and temperature-sensing systems). Current neodymium host lasers are pumped by flashlamps which limits both the efficiency (due to the poor spectral matching between the flashlamp output and the pump bands of the lasing material) and the lifetime (due to the limited life of the flashlamps). Pumping by arrays of injection diode lasers has the potential for alleviating both these problems, with laser efficiencies in the 5-10% range and lifetimes on the order of 10^9 shots. Diode pumping is being developed at a number of industrial research centers including RCA, Spectra Diode, and McDonnell Douglas.

In the spacecraft area, an important driver is the power subsystem. Even with highly efficient lasers, operational wind, temperature, or humidity lidar sensors will require several kilowatts of power. Current meteorological operational satellites provide payload power on the order of 500 W.

Implementing operational lidar sensors on space platforms will require careful planning, taking into account budgetary constraints and technological risks. Past experience indicates that it is desirable to develop such systems in an evolutionary manner, in three major steps.

The first step should be of an experimental nature, with the major objective to obtain experience in operating laser systems in space and probing the measurement capabilities of spaceborne lidars. These objectives can be accomplished with a simple lidar that measures returns from hard targets such as clouds, the surface of the Earth and the oceans, fog, and high-density layers of aerosols. Since the spectral purity and the stability of the transmitter are not critical for these measurements, these systems can use available laser technology. The power requirements of these experimental sensors will be relatively small since they do not have to operate continuously. Consequently, they can be accommodated on current meteorological satellites without disturbing these satellites' operational missions.

The next step should be a proof-of-concept demonstration, measuring meteorological parameters such as wind, pressure, humidity, or temperature profiles. Such systems will require stable lasers with high spectral purity. For some experiments, they must also be tunable. The receiving system will consist of nonscanning, moderate size telescopes. Measurements will be performed along the track of the satellite and they will require moderate amounts of power (a few hundred watts). These systems can still be accommodated on current operational satellites as add-on sensors. However, to increase the measurement capabilities, it is desirable to fly these sensors with only one or two of the operational sensors.

The third stage will be the implementation of operational lidars. This stage will require highly efficient lasers and large scanning telescopes. To accommodate these systems, it will be necessary to design new spacecraft that can provide power of about 5 kW and can carry large and heavy payloads into orbit. The polar platforms of the space station complex are likely host vehicles for these advanced lidar systems.

These operational lidars will be able to meet the requirments of Table 1 for global forecasting and climate monitoring. While it is unlikely that lidars will ever completely replace passive remote sensors, when used in conjunction with advanced passive and active microwave sensors, lidars will be increasingly important tools for observing the Earth and its atmosphere. It is clear that lidar will be one of the key technologies in the next 25 years of satellite meteorology.

Acknowledgments

The authors would like to thank Dr. Andrew Bogdan whose unpublished review of lidar wind sensing techniques formed the backdrop for the relevant sections of this paper. We would also like to express our appreciation to Jerri Lawlor who carefully typed the manuscript and implemented our numerous changes, and to David Buckley who assisted in reviewing the paper.

References

[1] "The First GARP Global Experiment – Objectives and Plans," GARP Publications Series No. 11, WMO-ICSU Joint Organizing Committee, Geneva, 1973, pp. 107.

[2] Atlas, D. and Korb, C. L., "Weather and Climate Needs for Lidar Observations from Space and Concepts for their Realization," Bulletin of the American Meteorological Society, Vol. 62, Sept. 1981, pp. 1270-1285.

[3] Smith, W. L., Woolf, H. M., Hayden, C. M., Wark, D.Q., and McMillin, L. M., "The TIROS-N Operational Vertical Sounder," Bulletin of the American Meteorological Society, Vol. 60, Oct. 1979, pp. 1177-1187.

[4] Twomey, S., Introduction to the Mathematics of Inversion in Remote Sensing and Indirect Measurements, Developments in Geomathematics 3. Elsevier Scientific Publishing Co., Amsterdam, pp. 107-112, 185-212.

[5] Susskind, J., Rosenfield, J., Reuter, D., and Chahine, M. T., "The GLAS Physical Inversion Method for Analysis of HIRS2/MSU Sounding Data," NASA Technical Memorandum 84936, Goddard Space Flight Center, Greenbelt, Md., Nov. 1982, pp. 101.

[6] McMillin, L. D., Gray D. G., Drahos, H. F., Chalfant, M. W., and Novak, C. S., "Improvements in the Accuaracy of Operational

Satellite Soundings," Journal of Climate and Applied Meteorology, Vol. 21, Nov. 1983, pp. 1948-1955.

[7]Susskind, J., Rosenberg, A., and Kaplan, L. P., "Advanced Moisture and Temperature Sounder (AMTS) Simulations," Fourth National Aeronautics and Space Administration Weather and Climate Review, Goddard Space Flight Center, Greenbelt, Md., 24-25 Jan. 1979, pp. 191-196.

[8]Kaplan, L. D., Chahine, M. T., Susskind, J., and Searl, J. E., "Spectral Bandpasses for a High Precision Satellite Sounder," Applied Optics, Vol. 16, Feb. 1977, pp. 322-325.

[9]Rosenberg, A., Hogan, D. B., and Bowman, C. K., "Satellite Moisture Retrieval Techniques. Volume 1: Technique Development and Evaluation," Naval Environmental Prediction Research Facility Contractor Report CR 83-01(a), Monterey, Ca., Jan. 1983, pp. 96.

[10]Killeen, T. L., Kennedy, B. C., Hays, P. B., Symanow, D. A., and Checkowski, D. H., "Image Plane Detector for the Dynamics Explorer Fabry-Perot Interferometer," Applied Optics, Vol. 22, 15 Nov. 1983, pp. 3503-3513.

[11]Hays, P. B., "Remote Sensing of Atmospheric Winds," Optical Remote Sensing of the Atmosphere, Technical Digest, Optical Society of America, 15-18 January 1985, Incline Village, Nv., paper WA-3.

[12]Hubert, L. F. and Tomasell, A., Jr., "Error Characteristics of Satellite Derived Winds," NOAA Technical Report NESS 79, June 1979, pp. 35.

[13]Eigenwillig, N. and Fisher, H., "Determination of Mid-tropospheric Wind Vectors by Tracking Pure Water Vapor Structures in METEOSAT Water Vapor Image Sequences," Bulletin of the American Meteorological Society, Vol. 63, Jan. 1982, pp. 44-58.

[14]Measures, R. M., Laser Remote Sensing: Fundamentals and Applications, John Wiley and Sons, New York, 1984, pp. 510.

[15]Post, M. J., Richter, R. A., Hardesty, R. M., Lawrence, T. R., and Hall, F. F., Jr., "National Oceanic and Atmospheric Administration (NOAA) Pulsed Coherent Infrared Doppler Lidar -- Characteristics and Data," Physics and Technology of Infrared Radar, SPIE, Vol. 300, 1981, pp. 60-65.

[16]Fitzgerald, D. E., "Preliminary Results from 1984 Airborne Lidar Wind Measurements," Optical Remote Sensing of the Atmosphere, Technical Digest, Optical Society of America, 15-18 Jan. 1985, Incline Village, Nv., paper MC30-1.

[17]Kane, T. J., Zhou, B., and Byer, R. L., "Potential for Coherent Doppler Wind Velocity Lidar Using Neodymium Lasers," Applied Optics, Vol. 23, 1 Aug. 1984, pp. 2477-2481.

[18]Sroga, J., Rosenberg, A., O'Hara, L., Hays, P. B., and Kennedy, B. C., "Ground Based 0.53 μm Wind Sensor," Optical

Remote Sensing of the Atmosphere, Technical Digest, Optical Society of America, 15-18 Jan. 1985, Incline Village, Nv., paper WC30-1.

[19]Schotland, R. M., "Errors in Lidar Measurements of Gases by Differential Absorption," Journal of Applied Meteorology, Vol. 13, Feb. 1974, pp. 71-77.

[20]Browell, E. V., Wilkerson, T. D., and McIlrath, T. J., "Water Vapor Differential-Absorption Lidar Development and Evaluation," Applied Optics, Vol. 18, 15 Oct. 1979, pp. 3474-3483.

[21]Korb, C. L. and Weng, C. Y., "A Theoretical Study of a Two-Wavelength Lidar Technique for Measurement of Atmospheric Temperature Profiles," Journal of Applied Meteorology, Vol. 21, Sept. 1982, pp. 1346-1355.

[22]Endemann, M. and Byer, R. L., "Remote Single-Ended Measurements of Atmospheric Temperature and Humidity at 1.77 Micron Using a Continuously Tunable Source," Optics Letters, Vol. 5, 5 Oct. 1980, pp. 452-454.

[23]Rosenberg, A. and Hogan, D. B., "Lidar Technique of Simultaneous Temperature and Humidity Measurements: Analysis of Mason's Method," Applied Optics, Vol. 19, 1 October 1981, pp. 3286-3288.

[24]Pethram, J. C., "A Raman Laser for Temperature/Humidity Profiling," Optical Society of America, Annual Meeting, New Orleans, La., October 1983, pp. 17-20.

[25]Schwemmer, G. K., Korb, C. L., Dombrowski, M., and Kagan, R. H., "Atmospheric Pressure Profiles Measured Using an Alexandrite Differential Absorption Lidar," Optical Remote Sensing of the Atmosphere, Technical Digest, Optical Society of America, Incline Village, Nv., 15-18 Jan. 1985, paper TuC29-1.

[26]"Shuttle Atmospheric Lidar Research Program," Final Report of the Atmospheric Lidar Working Group, NASA SP-433, National Aeronautics and Space Administration, Washington, D. C., 1979, pp. 220.

[27]Greco, R. V., ed., "Atmospheric Lidar Multi-User Instrument System Definition Study," NASA Contractor Report 3303, NASA Langley Research Center, Hampton, Va., pp. 323.

[28]McCormick, M. P., private communication.

[29]Gurk, G. M., Kaskiewicz, P. F., and Altman, W. P., "Windsat Free-Flyer Using the Advanced TIROS-N Satellite," Applied Optics, Vol. 15, 1 Aug. 1984, pp. 2537-2544.

[30]Huffacker, R. M., ed., "Feasibility Study of Satellite-Borne Lidar Global Wind Measuring System," NOAA Tech. Memo., ERL WPL-37, U.S. GPO, Washington D. C., Aug. 1978.

[31]Endemann, M., Grassl, H., Schlussel, P., Labitzke, K., Quenzel, H., Thomalla, E., and Nodop, K., "Orbiting Lidars for Atmospheric Sounding," Final Report, Volume 1, Battelle-Institute E. V., Frankfurt, Federal Republic of Germany, Dec. 1984, pp. 270.

[32]"Earth Observing System," Science and Mission Requirements Working Group Report, Volume 1 (Part 1), NASA Technical Memorandum 86129, Goddard Space Flight Center, Greenbelt Md., Aug. 1984, pp. 51.

[33]"Global Wind Measuring Satellite System - Windsat," Final Report, NOAA contract #NA79RSC00127, Lockheed Missiles and Space Co., Report LMSC-D767868, prepared for National Atmospheric and Oceanic Administration, Wave Propogation Laboratory, Apr. 1981.

The Earth Observing System:
A Multidisciplinary System for the Long-Term
Acquisition of Earth Science Data from Space

Douglas R. Broome Jr.*
National Aeronautics and Space Administration, Washington, D.C.

Abstract

A brief background on the evolution of Earth science satellite-based remote observation missions is presented to set the development of the Earth Observing System (EOS) requirements into perspective. The EOS is then discussed from the perspective of being NASA's major multidisciplinary approach to acquisition of Earth science data in the 1990s. It is noted that this new approach, really no more than the next logical evolutionary step in the scientific remote sensing of the Earth, differs considerably in concept from previous programs. As discussed in this paper, the EOS is envisioned as a total, comprehensive Earth science information system, rather than as just one more experiment- or discipline-dedicated scientific satellite system. Rationale and assumptions for the EOS are presented, together with a discussion of the anticipated operations and use environments. Planned instrumentation concepts are discussed — concepts involving a broad array of multiuse sensors operating across the electromagnetic spectrum from the ultraviolet to the microwave and including both active and passive techniques. Concepts for the near-polar orbiting observatory system, an essentially permanent man-serviced and -tended facility, are presented, as are concepts for information capture, processing, and distribution and for common data base referencing of acquired data. The concluding section discusses future milestones to be accomplished in the examination of the EOS before a

---

This paper is declared a work of the U.S. Government and therefore is in the public domain.

*Earth Observation System Program Manager; presently, Upper Atmosphere Research Satellite Program Manager.

commitment to program execution can be made later in this
decade.

Background

Man's utilization of satellite-borne instruments to
observe the Earth began with the launch of the first TIROS
satellite in 1960. Since that time, remote observation has
increased in complexity from simple cameras and ion probes
mounted on relatively simple spin-stabilized satellites to
complex three-axis stabilized platforms. These platforms,
in turn, have carried a diversity of instrument complements
designed to make a variety of different measurements --
using both active and passive techniques -- across much of
the electromagnetic spectrum.

The measurement approach of the early days, necessarily
constrained by limitations in launch vehicle liftweight,
centered around the flight of one or two instruments
dedicated to a specific experiment goal. As time passed
however, lift capability grew and with it the complexity
and orientation of the payload complements.

Begun in the early 1960s, the Nimbus series of
observatory spacecraft initially served as "platforms of
opportunity" for flights of meteorologically oriented
instruments. The Nimbus missions represented a step forward
for a large part of the Earth sciences community in that
they were discipline oriented in nature, as opposed to the
primarily single-instrument/single-experiment missions
launched up to that time. As technology progressed, Nimbus
observatory instrument complements gradually expanded to
include other science disciplines. The final observatory
of that series, Nimbus-7, was to a limited extent a
multidisciplinary platform. Nimbus-7 carried a diverse
complement of instruments ranging from a solar
backscattered ultraviolet monitor, operating at one end of
the electromagnetic spectrum, to a mechanically scanning
multifrequency multichannel microwave radiometer for ice,
water, and precipitation studies, operating at the other.
Other Nimbus-7 instruments were dedicated to coastal zone
ocean color investigations, study of the characteristics
and levels of emitted and backscattered solar energy,
measurement of atmospheric gaseous constituents and
aerosols, and the global measurement of the Earth's ozone
distribution.

The basic observatory structure and systems developed
for the Nimbus Program were also used as the basic elements

of the Earth Resources Technology Satellite. The latter program -- later renamed the Landsat Program -- was begun in the late 1960s and was somewhat multidisciplinary in nature, being dedicated to the development of technology related to the use of land surface and cover data for a variety of purposes. The primary instruments carried by the earlier Landsat observatories were the multispectral scanner (MSS) and the return beam vidicon cameras. The last two Landsats carried the MSS and a new instrument, the thematic mapper.

Concurrent with the development and flight of the Nimbus-7 observatory, the world's first satellite dedicated to oceanography -- Seasat -- was developed. Seasat's primary instrument complement included a synthetic aperture radar, a scatterometer, and a duplicate of the Nimbus-7 scanning multichannel microwave radiometer.

Other discipline oriented satellites followed Seasat, Landsat, and Nimbus: Dynamics Explorer, Stratospheric/ Mesospheric Explorer, the Solar Maximum Mission, the Heat Capacity Mapping Mission, and so on. In the fall of 1984, the latest satellite system of this discipline oriented class -- the Earth Radiation Budget Satellite (ERBE) -- will be launched. In addition, the operational Advanced TIROS-N satellites (the NOAA series) are carrying Earth science instruments such as the solar backscattered ultraviolet instrument and the ERBE, and there are also plans underway to fly two microwave radiometers, a scatterometer, and a radar altimeter on what will probably be a specially dedicated TIROS-N bus. This latter mission will be under the auspices of the U.S. Navy and is designated NROSS (Naval Remote Ocean Sensing System). NASA will be providing the scatterometer for this mission.

The Upper Atmosphere Research Satellite (UARS), now under development and scheduled for launch in the fall of 1989, will be the largest and most ambitious Earth science satellite development to date. For the future, the Ocean Topgraphy Experiment (TOPEX), International Solar Terrestrial Physics Program (ISTP), and Geopotential Reference Mission (GRM) Program are the next Earth science missions in NASA's program approval queue. These programs all include sophisticated multisensor satellite payloads dedicated to answering specific discipline-oriented questions, but they differ considerably in philosopy and approach from the earlier missions described above. For example, the UARS payload consists of 11 complex instruments. In addition to the 11 hardware-associated

principal investigator teams, the UARS investigator
complement also includes 10 theoretical investigator teams.
All investigators -- hardware and theoretical -- will have
equal access in near-real time to all of the data from all
11 instruments. Although there are thus 21 separate
investigation teams, their activities are quite focussed in
that the UARS mission is, in the broader view, a single
complex integrated experiment designed to answer a specific
set of questions related to the dynamics, composition, and
energy balance of the upper atmosphere.

In this introductory discussion, we have briefly
reviewed the evolution of remote scientific observation of
the Earth. From the simple, single experiment spacecraft
of the early 1960s, we have progressed to the highly
complex, discipline-unique, specific question-oriented
science measurment systems of the 1980s. What, then lies
in the future? What will be the thrust of the 1990s? The
balance of this paper is dedicated to answering these
questions.

The Earth Observing System

The long lead times involved in progressing from
concept formulation to system implementation necessitate
that planning begin today for the Earth science observation
systems that will be required in the 1990s. Toward this
end, NASA has initiated a comprehensive study of the
requirements for Earth science measurements for the
remainder of this century and of the systems concepts that
will satisfy those requirements. To focus the activities
involved in conducting these studies, NASA has established
an Earth Observing System Program office at its Washington,
D.C., headquarters and an EOS Project Office at the Goddard
Space Flight Center in (reenbelt, Md.

Overview

The basic underlying assumption of the Earth Observing
System (EOS) is that optimally addressing the Earth science
issues of the 1990s will require a coordinated
multidisciplinary approach. That is, the synergistic use
of a broad array of sensors, operating across the spectrum
from the ultraviolet to the microwave, together with the
synergistic applications of the products of those sensors
by both disciplinary and multidisciplinary teams of
scientists, is the next logical advancement in the remote
observation of the Earth. In accordance with this
assumption, an EOS Science and Mission Requirements Working

Group (S&MRWG) was established in March 1983. This group has been active since then in developing an overview of the next decade's Earth science measurements requirements. The result of this activity has been the development of sets of science issues to be addressed in the 1990s, together with the development of "strawman" instrument complements necessary to provide the measurement capabilities required to address those issues.

Conceptually, the EOS consists of an integrated, essentially permanent (i.e., decadal) observatory system positioned in near polar orbit, operating in conjunction with an integrated ground-based science information system. This total science data acquisition and delivery system will be utilized to provide investigator-interactive data accessibility for the broad United States and international Earth science communities.

The orbiting platform (or, possibly, platforms) will be a highly adaptable, evolutionary civilian space facility located in low Earth orbit (approximately 700 km). Observatory subsystems, both those of the basic platform bus and those of the instruments, will be modular in design. Expendables will be replenished and equipment, subsystems, and systems will be repaired or serviced during periodic revisits by the Space Transportation System (STS) -- the Shuttle. Also during these revisits, instruments, instrument modules, and other equipments may be added or replaced as the need or desirability arises.

The ground-based EOS science information system will provide a highly interactive data access and manipulation capability for the broad Earth science community, as well as the capability for interaction with other existing and

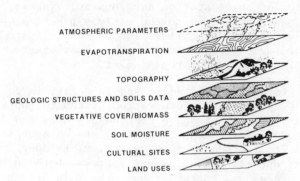

Fig. 1 Geobased information system: examples of data base parameters.

planned science information data base systems. The
architecture of the system will be such that it will
effectively operate as a distributed information network,
with processing centers linked together for mission
management control purposes and for the dissemination of
acquired and processed data. This requirement for timely,
efficient, and interactive data dissemination will, in
turn, require the development of a major program-related
georeferenced data base such as that shown in Fig. 1 and
also the procedural, hardware, and software interfaces
required for utilization of the data from other science
data bases, both ongoing and historical.

Study Ground Rules and Considerations

    The fundamental ground rules for the EOS study are
that:

    1) Science objectives will be both disciplinary and
interdisciplinary.
    2) System design will be driven by the science
requirements, and not vice-versa (within certain rational
limits).
    3) A major goal is the long term collection of global
coverage data sets.
    4) A supporting Remote Data Collection and Location
System location and data relay system will be a key element
of the EOS system (floating buoys, fixed ice and land
probes, etc.).
    5) The EOS science information system will be
interactive with existing and proposed science data bases.
    6) The orbiting platform(s) will be a permanent
facility in space.
    7) The orbiting platform(s) will be characterized by:
evolutionary development; modular systems and equipment
design; utilization of the Space Transportation System;
utilization of space station development, systems,
hardware, and components to the maximum practical extent;
on-orbit servicing and calibration; on-orbit instrument
complement augmentation; and on-orbit instrument
substitution, repair, or replacement.

    Specific areas to be addressed in detail in conducting
the EOS study include: information system concepts;
optimal utilization of space station concepts and
architectures; instrument technology status assessment and
synergism, to include mission as well as hardware
synergism; optimal use of expert systems, both on board the
platform system and on the ground; the role of man vs that

of robotics, considering a spectrum of concepts for
platform assembly, servicing, equipment changeout, etc.;
the potential for major government-industry and
international cooperative activities; relationships between
EOS and existing and potential future "operational" space
data acquisition systems; and EOS mission, technical, and
cost trades.

The EOS study was limited to low Earth orbit systems
due to the state-of-the-art considerations involving
propulsion, sensor development status, synergism with the
space station study activities, and potential system
system.

Organization and Schedule

In early 1983, a program office, consisting of a
program manager and a program scientist, was established at
NASA Headquarters to develop a plan for conducting what was
then called the System-Z study (System-Z has been
subsequently renamed the Earth Observing System). A
project office was established at the Goddard Space Flight
Center and a project manager, a project scientist, and
supporting staff selected. An early decision was made to
elicit the help of the Jet Propulsion Laboratory (JPL) in
Pasadena, Calif., in the conduct of space platform concept
studies. An EOS office was then established at JPL,
serving as an integral part of the EOS Project Office under
the overall guidance of the Goddard project manager.
Immediately following the establishment of the EOS Project
Office, the program and project scientists were charged
with the establishement of the EOS Science and Mission
Requirements Working Group (S&MRWG). Membership was
somewhat constrained in order to keep the size of the group
within workable limits. It was possible, however, within
this constraint, to include respected representatives of
all the pertinent Earth science disciplines -- a major task
considering the broad scope of activities to be addressed.

The first six months of the EOS study activity were
used to develop goals and objectives for the study, to
organize the project and science teams, to establish a
working relationship with the Space Station Task Force, and
to develop an assessment of the activities, funding, and
time requirements for conducting the study. The primary
emphasis during 1983 and into the first quarter of 1984
then shifted to supporting the activities of S&MRWG in
their deliberations in developing the EOS mission science
requirements.

In addition to providing technical support to the
S&MRWG, the Project Office also began an assessment of
instrument, robotics, and expert systems state-of-the-art
technologies and began a series of platform and end-to-end
information system conceptual studies. Activities of the
project team at the present time are geared to completion
of this initial phase of the EOS study by mid-1985. This
schedule, in turn, will provide the information necessary
to support the FY 1987 budget cycle, should the decision
resulting from the study be to go forward with the advanced
definition and mission execution phases of system
development. EOS is currently viewed as a FY 1989 new start
candidate by NASA's Office of Space Science and Applications.

The Science and Mission Requirements Working Group

The charter of the S&MRWG was twofold: 1) develop a
scientific rationale for Earth science missions in the
1990s and 2) determine the requirements for low Earth orbit
observations for Earth science studies. The term "Earth
science" as used in the EOS study was defined to include
those sciences related to studies of the solid Earth; the
whole atmosphere, hydrosphere, cryosphere, and biosphere; and
the climatological, hydrological, and biogeochemical cycles.

The membership of the S&MRWG is shown in Table 1, which
also shows each member's organizational affiliation and
area of science expertise. Note also that the EOS program
scientist served as chairman of the S&MRWG and the EOS
project scientist served as the executive secretary.

A series of working group meetings were held during
1983 and the first half of 1984. The scientific rationale
for the EOS was developed during this period and a foundation
of multidisciplinary cooperative activities was established.
The final S&MRWG report was published on Aug. 10, 1984.

In developing the Earth science goals for the EOS, the
S&MRWG divided the major Earth science disciplines into
four broad groupings: hydrology, biogeochemistry,
climatological processes, and geophysical processes.

For hydrology, the central goals established were to
quantify the processes of precipitation, evaporation,
evapotranspiration, and runoff on a global basis; to
determine the factors controlling the hydrological cycle;
and to quantify the interactions between the components of
the hydrological cycle and the vegetation, soil, and
topographic characteristics of the land surface.

For biogeochemistry, the goals established were to
understand the biogeochemical cycling of carbon, nitrogen,

Table 1   Science and mission requirements working group
===

Atmospheric chemistry	Volker Mohnen (New York State University, Albany)
	John Gille (National Center for Atmospheric Research)
	Dixon Butler(NASA Headquarters)[a]
Atmospheric circulation	Conway Leovy (University of Washington)
Physical oceanography	Robert Chase (Woods Hole Oceanographic Institution)
	Lawrence McGoldrick (Johns Hopkins University)
Biological oceanography	Mark Abbott (University of California, La Jolla)
Cryosphere/sea ice	Steve Ackley (Cold Regions Research and Engineering Lab.)
	Gordon Robin (Scott Polar Research Institute, Cambridge, England)
Geology	Ray Arvidson (Washington University)
	Roger Phillips (Southern Methodist University)
Biogeochemical cycles	Berrien Moore (University of New Hampshire)
	C. C. Delwiche (University of California, Davis)
Climate	Verner Soumi (University of Wisconsin)
Aeronomy	Paul Hays (University of Michigan)
	Richard Hartle (NASA Goddard Space Flight Center)[b]
Land ecosystems	Paul Zinke (University of California, Berkley)
	John Melack (University of California, Santa Barbara)
Hydrology	Albert Rango (U.S. Department of Agriculture)
	Edward Kanemasu (Kansas State University)

===

[a]Chairman. [b]Executive secretary.

phosphorous, sulfur, and trace metals; to determine the
global distribution of biomass and the factors controlling
both its heterogenous distribution in space and its change
over time; and to quantify the global distribution and
transport of tropospheric gases and aerosols, including the
determination of the strengths of their sources and sinks
in the ocean, on the land surface, in coastal and inland
waters, and in the upper atmosphere.

For the climatological processes, the goals were to
predict climate on a probabilistic basis; to determine the
effect on the atmosphere of changes in the ocean
circulation and heat content and in the laid surface and
solar input; and to determine the role of sea and land ice
cover in controlling global climate.

The goals established for the geophysical processes
were further subdivided into three major subsets:
atmospheric, oceanic, and solid Earth. The atmospheric
goals were to understand the coupling of the chemical,
radiative, and dynamic processes of the troposphere,
stratosphere, and mesosphere; to determine the coupling
between the lower and upper atmosphere; and to extend
deterministic weather forecasting toward its theoretical
limit. Oceanic goals were to measure the meso- to
macroscale circulation of the ocean and to develop a better
understanding of the long-term variability in this
circulation; to determine the global heat, mass, and
momentum coupling between the ocean and the atmosphere; and
to understand the processes controlling the dynamics of sea
ice and its interaction with the underlying water. Solid
Earth goals were to determine the global distribution,
geometry, and composition of continental rock units; to
understand how episodic processes such as rainfall, runoff,
dust storms, and volcanism modify the surface of the Earth;
and to determine the relationships between the factors of
climate, topography, vegetation, and the geologic
substrate, and the processes of soil formation and
degradation.

Recommendations of the
Science and Mission Requirements Working Group

The preliminary recommendations of the S&MRWG,
presented in a midterm report by the EOS study team to
NASA's Associate Administrator for Earth Science and
Applications on April 30, 1984, were as follows:

1)   A program must be initiated to ensure that the present time series' of Earth science data are maintained and continued and that the collection of new data sets is begun.

2)   A long-term research effort must be established to study and understand these time series' of Earth observations.

3)   A data system that provides easy but complete access to past, present, and future data bases must be developed as soon as possible.

4)   The EOS should be developed as an Earth science information system to carry out those aspects of the above recommendations which go beyond existing and currently planned activities. This EOS science information system should serve as a focal point for the observation and study of Earth processes, functioning as the lead node or site within a distributed scientific information network.

5)   The scientific direction of the EOS should be established and continued under the guidance of a scientific steering committee having international representation.

In addition to these basic recommendations, the S&MRWG also defined three strawman instrument complements, or packages, for further study and definition as candidate evolutionary payload complements for the initial configurations of the EOS.

Earth Observing System Concepts

As currently envisioned, the EOS is comprised of three major programmatic elements -- a near-polar orbiting platform, multiple complements of scientific instruments, and a ground-based science information acquisition, processing, and distribution system. Each of these elements is discussed in more detail below.

The Instruments

It should be noted that the proposed instruments "selected" by the S&MRWG consist of those instrument types considered suitable for achievement of the science goals developed by the S&MRWG and are described here for planning purposes only. Final instrument selection will be based on a number of science and programmatic resource-related factors and will involve utilization of NASA's Announcement of Opportunity process as well.

Table 2   EOS science and observations for MODIS and HIRIS
==

Discipline	Science	Observation
Geology	Mapping of soil and sediment characteristics	Physical configuration of surface materials; thermo-physical properties (arid and semiarid regions)
	Distribution of rock and soil types on land surface; mine-ralogy where soil or bedrock is exposed	Spectral temperature; thermal emissivity
Terrestrial vegetation	Energy and water balance components	Surface temperature; leaf area; canopy structure
	Plant health, species iden-tification	Spectral reflectance of vegetation
Hydrology	Characterize fluxes in hydro-logic cycle; observe variabil-ity in fluxes; evapotranspiration; snow cover area	Surface temperature; vegetation cover and structure; snow bound-aries and properties; soil moisture
Cryospheric science	Interannual variations	Iceberg discharge; ice motion; boundaries
	Sea ice characteristics; heat fluxes	Floe size distribution; ice boundaries
Inland aquatic	Biological productivity; sediment load-ing; variability	Water color
Atmospheric science	Air/sea interaction	Sea surface temperature
	Effects of cloud structure and distribution	Albedo, temperature
Oceanography	Mapping of phyto-plankton pigment groups	Water color
	Productivity	Chlorophyll fluorescence

==

Three major groupings, or "packages," of instruments were established by the S&MRWG. These were the surface imaging and sounding package (SISP), the sensing with microwaves package (SAM), and the atmospheric physical and chemical monitor package (APACAM).

The SISP consists of four major instruments: moderate/resolution imaging spectrometer (MODIS), high-resolution imaging spectrometer (HIRIS), high-resolution multifrequency microwave radiometer (HMMR), and lidar atmospheric sounder and altimeter (LASA). The SAM consists of three active microwave instruments: synthetic aperture radar, radar altimeter, and scatterometer. The APACAM includes eight instruments: correlation radiometer, interferometer/spectrometer, doppler lidar, infrared radiometer, imaging spectrometer, and Fabry-Perot and Michelson interferometers.

Tables 2 and 3 are examples of the detail to which the S&MRWG assessed the synergistic utilization of instruments to satisfy multidisciplinary science requirements. These Tables relate the science disciplines supported, observational methods, operational considerations, etc. for the MODIS and HIRIS instruments of the SISP package. Similar assessments were conducted for the other candidate instruments.

It should also be noted that certain supporting or complementary Earth science instruments will also be flown on the 28 deg unmanned platform to be developed as part of the overall space station effort.

Further instrument definition activities to be completed during the remainder of the EOS definition study include the identification of instrument development critical path technologies and data system utilization requirements, determination of EOS platform resource requirements (power, propellant, etc.), and identification of areas requiring advanced definition and technology development.

The Orbiting Platform

A key ground rule for the conduct of the Jet Propulsion Laboratory platform concept studies is to maximize the commonality of approach with those of the space station study effort. This is expected to result in a reduction in total space assets cost.

Table 3   Instrument: high-resolution imaging spectrometer (HIRIS)
==
REQUIREMENTS:
  - Biological, geological, forestry, hydrology applications
  - 262 bands, up to 64 selectable
  - 0.4-2.5, 3-5, and 8-12.5 um
  - 30 m spatial resolution
  - Pointable up to 30° either side and fore and aft
  - 10, 50, and 500 nm spectral resolution, respectively
  - 50 km swath width
  - Highly programmable
  - Provide nested coverage with MODIS

COMMENTS:

  SISEX used as modeling instrument (STS flight planned 1988);
   heritage from the AIS and the AVIRIS programs.
  Instrument requires cooled i.r. focal plane
  Considered developmental at present because of focal plane
   technology and study status of optics/instrument design
  High spatial resolution may be carrier driver
  Cryogen system TBD

STRAWMAN PARAMETERS:

  WEIGHT   1200 kg   POWER   700 W
  SIZE   10 m^3 DATA RATE   160 mb/s

ORBIT CONSIDERATIONS: 2 pm orbit

CARRIER CONSIDERATIONS:

  Flies with MODIS for selected mapping
  Pointing requirement 30 deg to nadir
  Momentum compensation of pointing mechanism
  30 m resolution
  Tailored fov for thermal radiator
  Pointing
    co-registration to MODIS $\pm$ 1 HIRIS pixel
    stability 20 urad/14s (1/$\overline{3}$ px/100 km "frametime")
    accuracy 2 mrad (1% fov)
    knowledge - TBD
  Thermal   - TBD

SERVICING CONSIDERATIONS:
  Instrument servicing internal TBD
  Nominal life 3-4 yrs
  Calibration - TBD
  Cryogen consumables - TBD

ATTACHMENT DATA SHEETS:
  SISEX instrument summary and layout
==
ACRONYMS: SISEX   - Shuttle Imaging Spectrometer Experiment
                       (planned 1988)
            AIS   - Airborne Imaging Spectrometer (1983)
            AVIRIS - Airborne Visible and i.r. Imaging
                       Spectrometer (1985)

The orbiting platform conceptually consists of two major pieces of hardware: a space station resource module (sometimes also referred to as a utility module) and an instrument carrier module.

The key elements of the design philosophy for the platform conceptual study are that: design is to be driven by the science requirements; commonality with space station architecture, subsystems, and components will be maximized; modular designs will be used where practical; growth capability for all system elements is required; operational ground support requirements will be minimized; on-orbit operations will be continuous and essentially permanent in duration; and subsystems and equipments will be man servicable (for replenishment of expendables) and man tendable (for pointing, recalibration, repair).

Other major programmatic and design considerations include: the possible science need for two separate observation platforms; implications of the Shuttle bay envelope in driving the payload module configuration and instrument design envelopes; instrument fine pointing and stability requirements; and payload evolution, growth, servicing, and maintenance requirements.

A summary of typical instrument accommodation requirements that must be considered in developing platform concepts is shown in Table 4. As can be seen, the mass, power, data, and volume requirements are very large. To demonstrate the implications of these requirements, the initial on-orbit operating configuration of the EOS may weigh in excess of 32,000 kg, clearly greater than the lift capability of a single Shuttle mission. To accommodate those instruments requiring particularly fine or precise

Table 4 Instrument accommodation requirements

Payload package	Mass, kg	Peak power, W	Raw maximum data rate, mb/s	Raw daily data, volums, bits	Raw ave. data rate, mb/s
SISP[a]	4,396	4,550	194	2.6×10^{12}	30.1
SAM	1,020	13,400	300	2.6×10^{12}	30.1
APACAM[b]	4,040	6,256	2	1.8×10^{11}	2.1
Total	9,456	24,206	496	5.4×10^{12}	62.3

[a]Includes ADCLS but not laser altimeter.
[b]Includes solar/magnetosphere monitors.

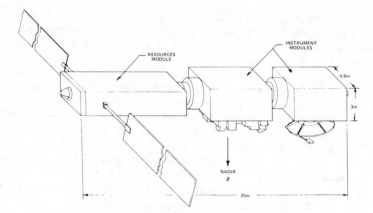

Fig. 2   EOS "railroad train" concept.

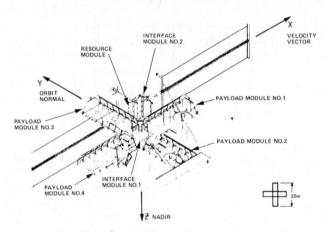

Fig. 3   EOS "cross" concept.

pointing, special stabilization and pointing platforms will
be provided.

Figures 2 and 3 present overviews of two platform
configurations being considered. Figure 2 is a line
drawing of the so-called "railroad train" concept for the
EOS. In this configuration, modules would be added to the
platform in much the same manner that cars are added to a
train. Advantages of this configuration are that
look-angle constraints would be minimized and the
mechanical, thermal, and electrical interfaces could be
simplified and standardized. However, disadvantages are
the problems associated with the long moment arm of the
configuration and resulting disturbance torques, other

control system implications, and the propensity for
single-point failures. On the other hand, the
configuration of Fig. 3, although not as free from
look-angle problems as is the railroad train concept,
avoids or minimizes most of the problems associated with
that concept. Note in Fig. 3 that the resource module
shown is the 37 kW version of the space station system
resource module and that several standard payload modules,
with varying instrument complements, are "plugged" into a
standard EOS interface module. In this concept, each
payload module can be removed and replaced, as can the
individual instruments within a module.

At this time, these configuration studies are
continuing so as to permit the further evaluation and
refinement of these conceptual approaches. These studies
will continue to examine, in detail, questions concerning
mechanical coupling, disturbance isolation, pointing
considerations, control system design, and on-orbit repair
and maintenance. Further detailed coordination with space
station studies and activities is being accomplished.
These studies also include investigation of the
implications of the divergent requirements in those areas
where there are significant differences in approach for
manned vs unmanned space systems. Examples of such
differences are: revisit periods, servicing methods,
reliability considerations, safety implications, etc.

Table 5 Suggested baseline EOS augmentation scenario[a]

==

IOC	Surface Imaging Spectrometer Package (MODIS, HIRIS, HMMR, LASA) Synthetic Aperture Radar Automatic Data Collection and Location System
IOC+1	Altimeter and Scatterometer
IOC+2	Upper atmospheric winds and upper atmospheric composition sensors
IOC+3	Solar monitors and balance of upper atmospheric composition sensors
IOC+4	Schedule margin allowance
IOC+5	Tropospheric compositon and tropospheric wind sensors

==

[a] "+" numbers indicate years from initial operating
capability.

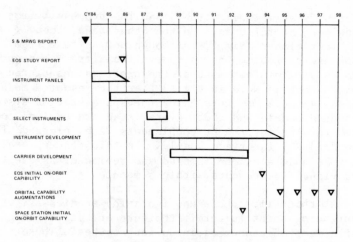

Fig. 4   EOS development schedule.

Mission operations studies are also being conducted as part of this EOS platform concept definitions activity. As a result of these studies, a baseline EOS augmentation deployment scenario has been established as shown in Table 5 and portrayed in Fig. 4, along with the overall EOS Program schedule.

This is obviously an extremely ambitious scenario and will be critically dependent on the level and timing of funding provided for EOS development and augmentation.

EOS Information System

The EOS information system is the heart, and in a manner of speaking, the soul of the Earth Observing System. Although mentioned last in this description of the EOS, it is in fact the primary focus of the system study.

The most fundamental purpose of the EOS as a system is to answer the science questions posed by the S&MRWG; the most fundamental objective of the EOS implementation is to provide to the many investigators involved the data that is necessary to answer those questions, in the formats required by them and on the time scale that they designate.

The point at which most past Earth science missions have historically "broken down" has been in the delivery of processed, Earth coordinate system-located, formated, and time-tagged data to the end "users" -- the science community -- in a timely manner. For the most part, these programs have been directed first and foremost toward the development of the flight hardware, placing significantly less emphasis on the ground data processing and handling system necessary to provide timely delivery of processed science data to the user science community. Budget allocations were such that by far the majority of available resources were utilized for flight systems, while a disproportionately small percentage were allocated to data processing, distribution, and analysis.

In recent years, NASA has begun to reverse this trend. The Dynamics Explorer and Solar Mesospheric Explorer Programs have, from the outset, placed processed data delivery and analysis up front as major programmatic goals. In turn, the UARS Program is carrying this approach a step further, emphasizing from the outset that the investigators -- both instrumental and theoretical -- are the Program's "customers" and that timely, interactive, processed data availability for those customers is the primary program "product." The most fundamental goal of the UARS Program is to provide an end-to-end, interactive, orbital-sensor-to-investigator-remote-terminal data acquisition, processing, and distribution system that will satisfy the requirements of the UARS investigators.

The Earth Observing System implementation will carry the UARS approach one step further. EOS must provide the science information required by an extensive, physically and intellectually diverse and geographically distributed "user" community -- universities, government agencies, industry, commercial "value added" organizations, independent researchers, etc. In addition, the EOS information system must also provide a tie into existing, planned and (at this time) not-yet-identified data bases throughout the user community. No small task, indeed!

In setting about conceptualizing the EOS information system, certain philosophic "requirements" were set down so that practical system boundary conditions could be established. For example, the system must be, as discussed above, fundamentally user oriented and user friendly. Further, the system must provide the capabilities necessary to address the science questions raised by the S&MRWG. Commonality with space station systems architectures must be maximized and the resulting EOS information system architecture must also be compatible with the Tracking and Data Relay Satellite System (TDRSS). Communications uplinks must provide the capability to reconfigure both the

instruments and the platform subsystems, and downlinks must
provide both global and high-data-rate instrument data
sets. The program operations control center must be
primarily a science operational planning and management
center. Data bases shall provide interactive,
well-cataloged browse capabilities, and correlative data
shall be available in the data bases, together with
directories of related data sets. Data preprocessing shall
be centralized and processing decentralized. Distribution
of data shall be keyed to user needs (electromagnetic
disks, data links, etc.). Autonomous platform operations
are highly desirable, and on-orbit preprocessing and
platform and equipment automated reconfiguration capability
must be considered.

   To address these and other related questions, the study
team put together a plan of action to develop the
information system requirements for the EOS. First, the
basic mission and operational requirements would be
established, then various concepts for system
implementation would be developed. Next, system sizing and
loading analyses for candidate mechanization concepts would
be conducted in order to develop the necessary
communications, processing, and data management performance
requirements. And finally, detailed trade studies would be
carried out and the optimum system architecture defined.

   At this time, organization and operations concepts have
been detailed and several candidate architectures have been

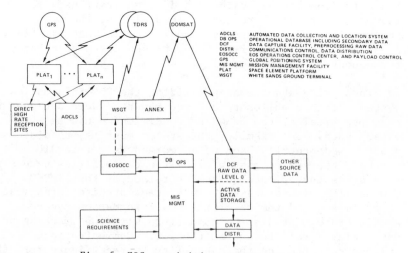

ADCLS	AUTOMATED DATA COLLECTION AND LOCATION SYSTEM
DB OPS	OPERATIONAL DATABASE INCLUDING SECONDARY DATA
DCF	DATA CAPTURE FACILITY, PREPROCESSING RAW DATA
DISTR	COMMUNICATIONS CONTROL, DATA DISTRIBUTION
EOSOCC	EOS OPERATIONS CONTROL CENTER, AND PAYLOAD CONTROL
GPS	GLOBAL POSITIONING SYSTEM
MIS MGMT	MISSION MANAGEMENT FACILITY
PLAT	SPACE ELEMENT PLATFORM
WSGT	WHITE SANDS GROUND TERMINAL

Fig. 5 EOS acquisition system concept.

established. In addition, the EOS informations system requirements have been coordinated with those of the space station activities and are being considered in the funded space station information system studies. Processing algorithms are being identified for each candidate instrument and study activities related to detailed system requirements definition, ground system automation, alternative communications strategies, data base management methodologies, etc., have begun.

The more likely candidate approaches for system implementation, in order of increasing centralized science control are: data control centers -- fully distributed operations; science control centers -- organized around instruments; centers of excellence -- organized by scientific discipline; and science institute -- single focus on Earth science as a whole.

Each of these approaches inherently possesses a myriad of practical implementation problems -- monetary, technical, management, and political, to name the more obvious -- that must be addressed before the final concept

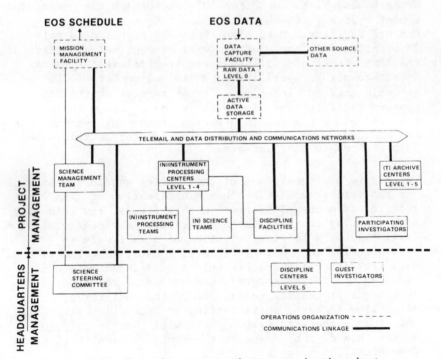

Fig. 6 EOS information system science organization chart.

can be determined. Key features which each candidate
concept must possess include:

1) Assurance of continuity of data by NASA and data
integrity by the scientists.

2) Tri-level participation by scientists under NASA
contract: at the Program level for oversight and
long-range mission planning, at the mission planning level
for scheduling and archival operations, and at the data
acquisition level for processing, and analysis.

3) An integrated, end-to-end information system design
providing centralized mission and data management for the
longer-term planning activites.

4) Distributed data processing and analysis for those
operations and activities planned and executed over the
shorter term (day-to-day).

Figure 5 illustrates the basic concept for the EOS data
acquisition system. Note in this figure that data from the
orbiting platform is transmitted to the TDRSS station at
White Sands, N. M., and then relayed through the commercial
DOMSAT system to the Goddard Space Flight Center Data
Capture Facility. Note also that some higher data rate
information from the platform will exceed the capability of
the TDRSS links and will thus require implementation of
direct downlink capability to a limited number of, but as
yet unidentified, locations. After receipt at the Data
Capture Facility, the raw telemetry data stream is then
transferred to the EOS information processing system. Data
and commands from the EOS ground system follow this same
path back up to the platform.

Figure 6 presents one of the leading candidate concepts
for the further manipulation and utilization of data
received from the platform. In this figure, raw telemetry
data entering the Data Capture Facility is processed into
level 1 data (a brief description of data levels is
presented in Table 6). This level 1 data, together with
data from other sources, is then placed in an active data
storage area for access by system users as required.
Instrument processing teams, discipline facilities,
discipline centers, participating and guest investigators,
and other authorized system users will then be able to
access this data by means of the EOS data distribution and
communications network.

Table 6 Definition of data levels
===

Level 0:
    Raw data
    Reconstructed sensor format
    Time ordered
    Full resolution

Level 1A:
    Reversibly calibrated (physical units)

Level 1B:
    Irreversibly calibrated (physical units)
    resampled

Level 2:
    Expressed in terms of derived physical
    parameters

Level 3:
    Parameter maps on space-time grids concatenated
    and/or interpolated

Level 4:
    Model results analyses

Level 5:
    Special products
===

In order to more clearly understand the allocation of responsibilities, duties, and activities among the several organizational elements comprising the EOS information system, we will now look at the overall system from a hierarchical point of view.

The EOS information system and its operations may be broadly divided into two major categories of activities: those occurring at the program management level and those occurring at the project management level. In turn, each of these categories may be further divided into subcategories. The program management level has three subcategories of activities: the science steering committee, the discipline centers, and the guest investigators. The project management level has two major subcategories of activities: project science activities and project operations activities. Each of these categories and subcategories is described in more detail in the paragraphs that follow.

Starting with the program management level, the membership of the science steering committee will include

both domestic and international scientists, probably
serving on a rotating term basis. The duties of the
steering committee will be to provide advice to the program
manager on long-term program planning; to manage the
establishment and evolution of program scientific
objectives; to develop scientific and operations guidelines
for the science management team; and to perform periodic
reviews and assessments of both overall and detailed
science program status, plans, and results.

The discipline centers will be responsible for
alternate algorithm development (as opposed to primary
algorithm development, which is discussed below),
nonstandard (level 5) data product generation, and for
guest investigator selection and involvement.

Guest investigators will be those investigators not
directly affiliated with the EOS Project, but instead who
have been selected to participate for certain specific
activities not directly related to mainline EOS science
activities. It is envisioned that these investigators will
be funded directly by NASA Headquarters, through NASA
Headquarters by other agencies, or by other national or
international organizations or governments.

Turning now to activities related to the project
management level, and remembering that here there are two
major subcategories, science and operations, we will first
describe the science activities, elements, and
responsibilities.

1) The science management team will be responsible for
day-to-day planning and conduct of the EOS missions.
Specific activities will include:
   a) Science management -- implementation of steering
committee scientific objectives; management of science team
and other related organizational unit activities and
resources -- budgeting, scheduling, investigation planning,
etc.
   b) Payload operations -- planning, scheduling,
integration of interorganizational and international
requirements, and integration of emergency or other
to-be-determined requirements.
   c) Coordination with the mission management facility.
   d) Coordination of the planning, funding, and
scheduling of participating investigator activities.
   e) "Ground" truth program management (rockets,
balloons, buoys, surface investigations, etc.).

2) The instrument processing center will be responsible for processing of instrument data to levels 1-4, distribution of high-volume data, generation of digitized film products, and transfer of master data sets to the archives.

3) The instrument processing team will be responsible for long-term instrument data processing management, operations algorithm developments, primary science algorithm development and maintenance, data product quality control, and archival data integrity.

4) The science support team will be responsible for science algorithm definition, instrument processing center science support, data product definition and validation, "ground" truth requirements definition, and target area definition and coverage planning.

5) The discipline facilities will support science algorithm development and data validation activities, the science support teams, and may also support multiple instrument processing centers.

6) The archive centers will provide permanent storage for level 1-4 standard data products and, as an option, level 5 special data products. It is expected that data from more than one instrument will normally be archived at any particular center.

7) Participating investigators will participate in the program for specific short term science investigations. It is expected that these investigators will be both domestic and international, and will be funded and managed by the EOS Project Office.

This completes the description of activities and elements in the science subcategory. The responsibilities in the operations subcategory are:

1) The mission management facility will be utilized by project operations personnel to manage and schedule longer-term platform activities and payload orbital operations, to coordinate operations and data collection with the appropriate science teams or other organizations, and to perform data quality control and accounting.

2) The data capture facility will ingest raw telemetry data from the TDRSS network and generate level 0 data.

3) The active data storage facility will provide for short-term storage or holding of data prior to further processing or distribution to the network users.

4) The mission control center will provide the capability for day-to-day platform operations management, for the assessment of instrument health and safety, and for data acquisition mangement. In essence, this facility will serve as the day-to-day executor of the longer term planning developed by the project management personnel in the mission management facility.

Summary and Future Plans

The S&MRWG Final Report was issued on Aug. 10, 1984. The translation from science objectives to instrument requirements is essentially complete and instrument definition is well underway. Instrument characteristics and parameters are now being fed into the space station central data base. Platform concepts continue to be evaluated and technology needs are being established. Definition of launch capability constraints has now just begun. A strawman information system concept is being integrated and refined, and information system definition and sizing activities are about to begin. Operational scenarios and pertinent groundrules have yet to be established.

NASA has begun to issue organizational work responsibility packages for the space station definition activities and major funded industry studies will begin in fiscal year 1985.

The next two years will be devoted to completing cost and technology trade studies and to finalizing concepts and definitizing design approaches for the instruments, the EOS platform(s), and ground data system. Activities are being scheduled so that the EOS study team will wind up its activities in the spring of 1986. This, in turn, will result in the availability of the information necessary to support the fiscal year 1988 budget development process and, hopefully, will result in management direction to begin activities leading to implementation of the Earth Observing System.

Author Index for Volume 97

PROGRESS IN ASTRONAUTICS AND AERONAUTICS
SERIES VOLUMES

VOLUME TITLE/EDITORS

*1. Solid Propellant
Rocket Research (1960)
Martin Summerfield
Princeton University

*2. Liquid Rockets and
Propellants (1960)
Loren E. Bollinger
The Ohio State University
Martin Goldsmith
The Rand Corporation
Alexis W. Lemmon Jr.
Battelle Memorial Institute

*3. Energy Conversion
for Space Power (1961)
Nathan W. Snyder
*Institute for Defense
Analyses*

*4. Space Power Systems
(1961)
Nathan W. Snyder
*Institute for Defense
Analyses*

*5. Electrostatic Propul-
sion (1961)
David B. Langmuir
*Space Technology
Laboratories, Inc.*
Ernst Stuhlinger
*NASA George C. Marshall
Space Flight Center*
J.M. Sellen Jr.
*Space Technology
Laboratories, Inc.*

*6. Detonation and Two-
Phase Flow (1962)
S.S. Penner
*California Institute of
Technology*
F.A. Williams
Harvard University

*7. Hypersonic Flow
Research (1962)
Frederick R. Riddell
AVCO Corporation

*8. Guidance and
Control (1962)
Robert E. Roberson
Consultant
James S. Farrior
*Lockheed Missiles and
Space Company*

*9. Electric Propulsion
Development (1963)
Ernst Stuhlinger
*NASA George C. Marshall
Space Flight Center*

*10. Technology of
Lunar Exploration (1963)
Clifford I. Cummings and
Harold R. Lawrence
Jet Propulsion Laboratory

*11. Power Systems for
Space Flight (1963)
Morris A. Zipkin and
Russell N. Edwards
General Electric Company

*12. Ionization in High-
Temperature Gases (1963)
Kurt E. Shuler, Editor
*National Bureau of
Standards*
John B. Fenn, Associate
Editor
Princeton University

*13. Guidance and
Control—II (1964)
Robert C. Langford
General Precision Inc.
Charles J. Mundo
Institute of Naval Studies

*14. Celestial Mechanics
and Astrodynamics (1964)
Victor G. Szebehely
*Yale University
Observatory*

*15. Heterogeneous
Combustion (1964)
Hans G. Wolfhard
*Institute for Defense
Analyses*
Irvin Glassman
Princeton University
Leon Green Jr.
*Air Force Systems
Command*

*16. Space Power
Systems Engineering
(1966)
George C. Szego
*Institute for Defense
Analyses*
J. Edward Taylor
TRW Inc.

*17. Methods in
Astrodynamics and
Celestial Mechanics (1966)
Raynor L. Duncombe
U.S. Naval Observatory
Victor G. Szebehely
*Yale University
Observatory*

*18. Thermophysics and
Temperature Control of
Spacecraft and Entry
Vehicles (1966)
Gerhard B. Heller
*NASA George C. Marshall
Space Flight Center*

*19. Communication
Satellite Systems
Technology (1966)
Richard B. Marsten
*Radio Corporation of
America*

---

*Out of print.

(Other Volumes are planned.)